John Z

TI worldwide sales offices

ALABAMA

Sahara Office Park Bldg., Suite 111
3313 Memorial Parkway, S.W.
Huntsville, Alabama 35801
205-881-4061

ARIZONA

United Bank Bldg., Suite 1702
3550 North Central Avenue
Phoenix, Arizona 85012
602-279-5531

CALIFORNIA

11222 South La Cienega,
Suite 360
Inglewood, California 90304
213-649-2710

Balboa Towers Bldg., Suite 805
5252 Balboa Avenue
San Diego, California 92117
714-279-2622

1505 East 17th St., Suite 201
Santa Ana, California 92701
714-835-9031

753 North Pastoria Avenue
Sunnyvale, California 94086
408-732-1840

COLORADO

2149 South Holly St.
Denver, Colorado 80222
303-758-2151

CONNECTICUT

35 Worth Avenue
Hamden, Connecticut 06518
203-281-0074

FLORIDA

601 W. Oakland Park Blvd.
Fort Lauderdale, Florida 33311
305-566-3294

5400 Diplomat Circle
Diplomat Bldg., Suite 252
Orlando, Florida 32810
305-644-3535

300 Bldg. West, Suite 204
3151 Third Ave., North
St. Petersburg, Florida 33713
813-898-0807

GEORGIA

1720 Old Springhouse Lane, N.E.
Suite 303
Atlanta, Georgia 30341
404-458-7791

ILLINOIS

1701 Lake Street, Suite 300
Glenview, Illinois 60025
312-729-5710

INDIANA

3702 Rupp Drive
Lawrence Bldg., Rm. 106
Fort Wayne, Indiana 46805
219-484-0606

5264 East 73rd Ct.
Indianapolis, Indiana 46250
317-849-7397

MASSACHUSETTS

60 Hickory Drive
Waltham, Mass. 02154
617-890-7400

MICHIGAN

Central Park Plaza
26111 Evergreen, Suite 333
Southfield, Michigan 48075
313-352-5720

MINNESOTA

7615 Metro Blvd.
Suite 202, Analysis Inc., Bldg.
Edina, Minn. 55435
612-835-2900

NEW JERSEY

1245 Westfield Ave.
Clark, New Jersey 07066
201-574-9800

NEW MEXICO

1101 Cardenas Drive, N.E.,
Room 215
Albuquerque, New Mexico 87110
505-265-8491

NEW YORK

7 Adler Drive
East Syracuse, New York 13057
315-463-9291

P.O. Box 618, 112 Nanticoke Ave.
Endicott, New York 13760
607-785-9987

167 Main Street
Fishkill, New York 12524
914-896-6793

102 Lazy Trail
Penfield, New York 14526

245 Newtown Road
Plainview, New York 11803
516-293-2560

NORTH CAROLINA

3631 West Field
High Point, N.C. 27260
919-886-3651

OHIO

23811 Chagrin Blvd., Suite 100
Beachwood, Ohio 44122
216-464-1192

Suite 205, Paul Welch Bldg.
3300 South Dixie Dr.
Dayton, Ohio 45439
513-298-7513

PENNSYLVANIA

275 Commerce Drive
Fort Washington, Pa. 19034
215-643-6450

TEXAS

Headquarters – Gen. Offices
Dallas, Texas 75222
214-238-2011

MS366–P.O. Box 5012
Dallas, Texas 75222
214-238-6805

3939 Ann Arbor
Houston, Texas 77042
713-785-6906

VIRGINIA

8512 Trabue Road
Richmond, Virginia 23235
703-320-3830

WASHINGTON

2737 77th S.E.
Mercer Island, Washington 98040
206-232-2646

WASHINGTON, D.C.

1500 Wilson Blvd., Suite 1100 A.M. Bldg.
Arlington, Virginia 22209
703-525-0336

ARGENTINA

Texas Instruments Argentina S.A.I.C.F.

C.C. Box 2296 · Correo Central
Buenos Aires, Argentina
748-1141

ASIA

Texas Instruments Asia Limited

5F Aoyama Tower Bldg.
24-15 Minami Aoyama Chome
Minato-ku, Tokyo 107, Japan
402-6171

Room 1502, Star House
Harbour Center, Kowloon
Hong Kong
K673139

Texas Instruments Singapore (PTE) Ltd.
27 Kallang Place
Singapore 1, Rep. of Singapore
258-1122

Texas Instruments Taiwan Limited
P.O. Box 3999
Taipei, Chung Ho, Taiwan
921 623

Texas Instruments Malaysia SDN. BHD.
Number 1 Lorong Enggang 33
Kuala Lumpur 15-07, Malaysia
647 911

AUSTRALIA

Texas Instruments Australia Ltd.

P.O. Box 63, 171-175 Philip Highway
Elizabeth, South Australia
55 29 14

Room 5, Rural Bank Bldg.
38 Railway Parade
Burwood, N.S.W., Australia
74-1859

BRAZIL

Texas Instrumentos Electronicos
do Brasil Ltda

Rua Joao Annes, 153-Lapa
Caixa Postal 30.103, CEP 01.000
Sao Paulo, SP, Brasil
260-2956

CANADA

Texas Instruments Incorporated

2750 Pitfield Blvd
St. Laurent 386
Quebec, Canada
514 332-3550

5F Caesar Avenue
Ottawa 12
Ontario, Canada
613-825-3716

280 Centre Str. East
Richmond Hill (Toronto)
Ontario, Canada
416-889-7373

DENMARK

Texas Instruments Denmark

46D, Marielundvej
2730 Herlev, Denmark
(01) 91 74 00

FINLAND

Texas Instruments Finland OY

Fredrikinkatu 75, A7
Helsinki 10, Finland
44 71 71

FRANCE

Texas Instruments France

Boite Postale 5
06 Villeneuve-Loubet, France
31 03 64

379 Av du General de Gaulle
92 Clamart, France
645 07 07

30-31 Quai Rambaud
69 Lyon, France
42 78 50

GERMANY

Texas Instruments Deutschland GmbH

Haggerty Str. 1
8050 Freising, Germany
08161/80-1

Arabellastrasse 4, Sternhaus/V
8000 Munich 81, Germany
0811/91 10 61

Lazarettstrasse, 19
4300 Essen, Germany
02141/20916

Krugerstrasse 24
1000 Berlin 49, Germany
0311/74 44 041

Westendstrasse 52
6000 Frankfurt a.M., Germany
0611/72 64 41

Steimbker Hof 8A
3000 Hannover, Germany
0511/55 60 41

Im Kaisemer 5
7000 Stuttgart 1, Germany
0711/22 50 92

ITALY

Texas Instruments Italia SpA

Via Salaria per l' Aquila Cittaducale
02100 Rieti, Italy
0746-41314

ITALY (Continued)

Texas Instruments Italia SpA

Viale Lungiana 46
20125 Milan, Italy
02-688 31 41

Via Padre Semeria 63
00154 Roma, Italy
06-512 04 37

Via Montebello 2
10124 Torino, Italy
011-83 22 76

MEXICO

Texas Instruments de Mexico S.A.

Poniente 116 #489
Col. Industrial Vallejo
Mexico City, D.F., Mexico
567-92-00

NETHERLANDS

Texas Instruments Holland N.V.

Entrepot Gebouw-Kamer 225
P.O. Box 7603
Schiphol-Centrum
020-17 36 36

NORWAY

Texas Instruments Norway A/S
Sentrumskontorene
Brugaten 1
Oslo 1, Norway
33 18 80

SWEDEN

Texas Instruments Sweden AB

S-104 40 Stockholm 14
Skeppargatan 26
67 98 35

UNITED KINGDOM

Texas Instruments Limited

Manton Lane
Bedford, England
0234-67466

$3 95
(In U.S.A.)

The
Linear and
Interface Circuits
Data Book

for
Design Engineers

First Edition

TEXAS INSTRUMENTS
INCORPORATED

CC-415
71240-113-CSS

Printed in U.S.A.

INTRODUCTION

In this 688-page data book, Texas Instruments is pleased to present important technical information on the industry's broadest and most advanced family of Linear Integrated Circuits.

You'll find complete specifications on TI's 75/55 series of MOS memory interface, data transmission, magnetic memory, peripheral driver, memory sense amplifier, and display interface circuits. Also included is advanced information on some of TI's interface circuits to be introduced shortly.

The book also includes complete data sheets on TI's 72/52 series of control circuits—operational amplifiers, voltage regulators, voltage comparators, video amplifiers, and special functions.

The functional indexes and selection guides are designed for ease of circuit selection. There are margin tabs to guide you quickly to general circuit categories, and the numerical indexes will let you locate specific type numbers quickly.

High-reliability Linear IC's are covered in a section devoted to the MACH IV procurement specification in accordance with MIL-M-38510, a program initiated by TI to ensure that quality and reliability are built into, not tested into, integrated circuits. This section also provides information on Linear JAN IC's.

Although this volume offers design and specification data only for Linear Integrated Circuits, complete technical data for any TI semiconductor/component product is available from your nearest TI field sales office, local authorized TI distributor, or by writing directly to: Marketing and Information Services, Texas Instruments Incorporated, P.O. Box 5012, MS 308, Dallas, Texas 75222.

TEXAS INSTRUMENTS
INCORPORATED
POST OFFICE BOX 5012 • DALLAS, TEXAS 75222

THERMAL INFORMATION

THERMAL RESISTANCE OF LINEAR INTEGRATED CIRCUIT PACKAGES

PACKAGE	PINS	$R_{\theta JC}$ (°C/W) Junction-to-case thermal resistance		$R_{\theta JA}$ (°C/W) Junction-to-ambient thermal resistance	
		50% CONFIDENCE MAX VALUE	90% CONFIDENCE MAX VALUE	50% CONFIDENCE MAX VALUE	90% CONFIDENCE MAX VALUE
FA solder-sealed flat	10	37	42	185	191
	14	38	45	163	171
L plug-in	8, 10	55	61	195	210
LA plug-in, kovar header	3	19	22	202	210
J ceramic dual-in-line	14	24	28	80	92
	16	22	26	73	85
JA glass-header dual-in-line	16	58	65	123	127
JB metal-based header dual-in-line	16	31	33	88	93
JP glass-header dual-in-line	8	29	33	139	150
N plastic dual-in-line	14	35	41	85	97
	16	33	39	80	92
P plastic dual-in-line	8	46	50	120	127
SB solder-sealed flat	16	40	45	159	165
	24	40	45	147	157

Junction-to-case thermal resistance, $R_{\theta JC}$, is measured with the device immersed in a freon bath.
Junction-to-ambient thermal resistance, $R_{\theta JA}$, is measured in still air with the device mounted in either an Augat or a Barnes socket.
Special test chips were used to obtain the above information.

TEXAS INSTRUMENTS
INCORPORATED
POST OFFICE BOX 5012 • DALLAS, TEXAS 75222

Indexes

- **Numerical**
- **Functional**
- **Cross-Reference**

*To be announced

NUMERICAL INDEX

*To be announced.

TEXAS INSTRUMENTS
INCORPORATED
POST OFFICE BOX 5012 • DALLAS, TEXAS 75222

OPERATIONAL AMPLIFIERS

FUNCTION	OPERATING TEMPERATURE RANGE §			PACKAGE TYPES	PAGE
	−55°C to 125°C	−25°C to 85°C	0°C to 70°C		
General-Purpose Operational Amplifiers	SN52702			FA, J, L	4-51
	SN52702A			FA, J, L	
			SN72702	FA, J, L, N	
	SN52709			FA, J, JA, JP, L	4-60
	SN52709A			FA, J, JA, JP, L	
			SN72709	FA, J, L, N	
	SN52741			FA, J, JA, JP, L	4-67
			SN72741	FA, J, L, N, P	
	SN52748			FA, J, JA, JP, L	4-76
			SN72748	FA, J, L, N, P	
Wide-Band Operational Amplifiers	SN52110			FA, JA, JP, L	4-32
			SN72310	FA, JA, L, N, P	
	SN52118*			FA, JA, JP, L	3-2
			SN72318*	FA, JA, L, N, P	
High-Performance Operational Amplifiers	SN52101A			FA, J, JA, JP, L	4-19
			SN72301A	FA, J, L, N, P	
	SN52107			FA, JA, JP, L	4-23
			SN72307	FA, JA, L, N, P	
	SN52108			FA, JA, JP, L	4-27
	SN52108A			FA, JA, JP, L	
			SN72308	FA, JA, L, N, P	
			SN72308A	FA, JA, L, N, P	
	SN52660			FA, JA, JP, L	4-48
			SN72660	FA, JA, L, N, P	
	SN52770			FA, JA, JP, L	4-80
			SN72770	FA, JA, L, N, P	
	SN52771			FA, JA, JP, L	4-86
			SN72771	FA, JA, L, N, P	
	SN52777			FA, JA, JP, L	4-92
			SN72777	FA, JA, L, N, P	
Dual General-Purpose Operational Amplifiers	SN52558			JP, L	4-43
			SN72558	L, P	
	SN52747			FA, J, JA, L	4-72
			SN72747	FA, J, L, N	
Dual Low-Power Operational Amplifiers	SN52L022			JP, L	4-3
			SN72L022	L, P	
Quad Low-Power Operational Amplifiers	SN52L044			JA	4-7
			SN72L044	JA, N	
Chopper-Stabilized Operational Amplifiers		SN62088		N	4-11
			SN72088	N	
FET-Input Operational Amplifiers		SN62004*		JP, L, P	3-1
			SN72004*	L, P	

*To be announced.
§ In free-air.

1

VOLTAGE REGULATORS

FUNCTION		OPERATING TEMPERATURE RANGE§		PACKAGE TYPES	PAGE
		−55°C to 125°C	0°C to 70°C		
Precision Voltage Regulators		SN52723		FA, J, L	5-15
			SN72723	FA, J, L, N	
Negative-Voltage Regulators		SN52104		JA, L	5-2
			SN72304	L, N	
Positive-Voltage Regulators		SN52105		JP, L	5-6
			SN72305	L, P	
			SN72305A	L, P	
			SN72376	L, P	

FUNCTION		OPERATING CASE TEMPERATURE RANGE		PACKAGE TYPES	PAGE
		−55°C to 150°C	0°C to 125°C		
Positive Fixed-Voltage Regulators	5 Volt	SN52109		LA	5-11
			SN72309	LA	
	6 Volt		SN72905*	KC†	3-3
	8 Volt		SN72906*	KC†	3-3
	12 Volt		SN72908*	KC†	3-3
	15 Volt		SN72912*	KC†	3-3
	18 Volt		SN72915*	KC†	3-3
	18 Volt		SN72918*	KC†	3-3
	24 Volt		SN72924*	KC†	3-3

DIFFERENTIAL COMPARATORS

FUNCTION	OPERATING TEMPERATURE RANGE§		PACKAGE TYPES	PAGE
	−55°C to 125°C	0°C to 70°C		
Differential Comparators	SN52710		FA, J, JP, L	6-33
		SN72710	FA, J, L, N, P	
	SN52810		FA, J, JP, L	6-44
		SN72810	FA, J, L, N, P	
Differential Comparators with Strobes	SN52106		FA, J, JP, L	6-2
		SN72306	FA, J, L, N, P	
	SN52111		FA, J, JP, L	6-9
		SN72311	FA, J, L, N, P	
	SN52510		FA, J, JP, L	6-25
		SN72510	FA, J, L, N, P	
Dual-Channel Differential Comparators with Strobes	SN52711		FA, J, L	6-37
		SN72711	FA, J, L, N	
	SN52811		FA, J, L	6-50
		SN72811	FA, J, L, N	
Dual Differential Comparators		SN72720	J, N	6-42
	SN52820		J	6-56
		SN72820	J, N	
Dual Differential Comparators with Strobes	SN52506		FA, J	6-18
		SN72506	FA, J, N	
	SN52514		J	6-31
		SN72514	J, N	

*To be announced.
†Three-lead tab-mounted plastic package (TO-66 mounting).
§In free-air.

TEXAS INSTRUMENTS
INCORPORATED
POST OFFICE BOX 5012 • DALLAS, TEXAS 75222

VIDEO AMPLIFIERS

FUNCTION	OPERATING TEMPERATURE RANGE§		PACKAGE TYPES	PAGE
	−55°C to 125°C	0°C to 70°C		
Differential Video Amplifiers	SN5510		FA, JP, L	7-2
		SN7510	FA, L, P	7-9
	SN5511		FA, L, N	7-16
		SN7511	FA, L, N	
	SN5512		L, N	7-22
		SN7512	L, N	
	SN5514		JP, L	7-22
		SN7514	L, P	
Differential Video Amplifiers with Gain Select	SN52733		FA, J, L	7-28
		SN72733	FA, J, L, N	

SPECIAL FUNCTIONS

FUNCTION	OPERATING TEMPERATURE RANGE§		PACKAGE TYPES	PAGE
	−55°C to 125°C	0°C to 70°C		
Precision Timers	SN52555		JP, L	7-53
		SN72555	L, P	
Precision Level Detector		SN72560	L, P	7-62
Dual Precision Level Detector		SN72D560	L, P	7-62
Zero-Voltage Switch		SN72440	J, N	7-35
Micro-Processor Drive System		SN72595*	N	3-4
Logarithmic Amplifiers	SN56502		J, N	7-40
		SN76502	J, N	
Balanced Mixers	SN56514		J, L, N	7-47
		SN76514	J, L, N	

LINE DRIVERS

FUNCTION	OPERATING TEMPERATURE RANGE§		PACKAGE TYPES	PAGE
	−55°C to 125°C	0°C to 70°C		
Dual Differential Line Drivers	SN55109		J	8-6
		SN75109	J, N	
	SN55110		J	8-6
		SN75110	J, N	
	SN55113		J, SB	8-26
		SN75113	J, N, SB	
	SN55114		J, SB	8-26
		SN75114	J, N, SB	
	SN55183		J	8-84
		SN75183	J, N	
Dual Single-Ended Line Drivers	SN55121		J	8-44
		SN75121	J, N	
		SN75123	J, N	8-50
Dual Line Drivers (Meeting EIA RS-232-C)		SN75150	J, N, P	8-68
		SN75188	J, N	8-95

*To be announced

§In free-air.

TEXAS INSTRUMENTS
INCORPORATED
POST OFFICE BOX 5012 • DALLAS, TEXAS 75222

1

LINE RECEIVERS

FUNCTION	OPERATING TEMPERATURE RANGE§		PACKAGE TYPES	PAGE
	−55°C to 125°C	0°C to 70°C		
Dual Differential Line Receivers	SN55107A		J	8-6
	SN55107B		J	8-25
		SN75107A	J, N	8-6
		SN75107B	J, N	8-25
	SN55108A		J	8-6
	SN55108B		J	8-25
		SN75108A	J, N	8-6
		SN75108B	J, N	8-25
	SN55115		J, SB	8-26
		SN75115	J, N, SB	
	SN55182		J	8-84
		SN75182	J, N	
		SN75207	J, N	9-6
		SN75208	J, N	9-6
Dual Single-Ended Line Receivers		SN75140	P	8-62
	SN55142*		J	3-7
		SN75142*	J, N	
Dual Line Receivers (Meeting EIA RS-232-C/MIL-STD-188)		SN75152	J, N	8-72
Triple Single-Ended Line Receivers	SN55122		J	8-44
		SN75122	J, N	
		SN75124	J, N	8-50
Quad Line Receivers (Meeting EIA RS-232-C)		SN75154	J, N	8-79
		SN75189	J, N	8-99
		SN75189A	J, N	8-99

LINE TRANSCEIVERS

FUNCTIONS	OPERATING TEMPERATURE RANGE§		PACKAGE TYPES	PAGE
	−55°C to 125°C	0°C to 70°C		
Differential Bus Transceivers	SN55116*		J	3-5
		SN75116*	J, N	
	SN55117*		JP	3-6
		SN75117*	P	
Quad Single-Ended Bus Transceivers	SN55138		J	8-56
		SN75138	J, N	

*To be announced.
§ In free-air.

MOS INTERFACE CIRCUITS

FUNCTIONS		OPERATING TEMPERATURE RANGE§		PACKAGE TYPES	PAGE
		−55°C to 125°C	0°C to 70°C		
General-Purpose Level Converters	Dual TTL-to-MOS Level Converter	SN55180		L	9-2
			SN75180	L	
	7-Unit MOS-to-TTL Converter Array		SN75270	J, N	9-12
Memory Interface	Dual TTL-to-MOS Sense Amplifiers		SN75207	J, N	9-6
			SN75208	J, N	9-6
	Dual TTL-to-MOS Drivers		SN75361A	J, N, P	9-15
			SN75362*	P	3-8
	Quad TTL-to-MOS Driver		SN75365	J, N	9-25
	Quad TTL-to-CMOS Drivers (Three-State Outputs)	SN55367*		J, JB, N, SB	3-9
			SN75367*	J, N, SB	
	Dual ECL-to-MOS Driver		SN75368*	J, N	3-10
	Dual MOS Clock Driver		SN75369*	J, N, P	3-11
	Dual TMS4062 Read/Write Amplifier		SN75370	JB, N	9-35
Display Drivers	MOS-TO-VLED Quad Segment Driver		SN75491	N	9-53
	MOS-to-VLED Hex Digit Driver		SN75492	N	9-53

MEMORY DRIVERS

FUNCTIONS	OPERATING TEMPERATURE RANGE§		PACKAGE TYPES	PAGE
	−55°C to 125°C	0°C to 70°C		
2 X 4 Transistor Arrays		SN75303	N	10-3
		SN75308	J, N	10-8
Dual Sink/Source with Decode Inputs		SN75324	J, N	10-13
Dual Sink/Source	SN55325		J, JB, N, SB	10-21
		SN75325	J, N, SB	
Quad Sink	SN55326		J, JB, N, SB	10-36
		SN75326	J, N, SB	
Quad Source	SN55327		J, JB, N, SB	10-36
		SN75327	J, N, SB	
Eight-Channel Core Driver	SN55329*		RA	3-12

*To be announced.
§In free-air.

TEXAS INSTRUMENTS
INCORPORATED
POST OFFICE BOX 5012 • DALLAS, TEXAS 75222

1

PERIPHERAL DRIVERS

FUNCTION	OPERATING TEMPERATURE RANGE§		PACKAGE TYPES	PAGE
	−55°C to 125°C	0°C to 70°C		
Dual Positive-AND†, Uncommitted Transistor	SN55450B		J, JB	10-42
		SN75450B	J, N	
	SN55460		J, JB	10-67
		SN75460	J, N	
	SN55470*		J, JB	3-15
		SN75470*	J, N	
Dual Positive-AND		SN75401*	ND	3-13
		SN75411*	ND	3-14
	SN55451B		JP, L	10-42
		SN75451B	L, P	
	SN55461		JP, L	10-67
		SN75461	L, P	
	SN55471*		JP, L	3-15
		SN75471*	L, P	
Dual Positive-NAND		SN75402*	ND	3-13
		SN75412*	ND	3-14
	SN55452B		JP, L	10-42
		SN75452B	L, P	
	SN55462		JP, L	10-67
		SN75462	L, P	
	SN55472*		JP, L	3-15
		SN75472*	L, P	
Dual Positive-OR		SN75403*	ND	3-13
		SN75413*	ND	3-14
	SN55453B		JP, L	10-42
		SN75453B	L, P	
	SN55463		JP, L	10-67
		SN75463	L, P	
	SN55473*		JP, L	3-15
		SN75473*	L, P	
Dual Positive-NOR		SN75404*	ND	3-13
		SN75414*	ND	3-14
	SN55454B		JP, L	10-42
		SN75454B	L, P	
	SN55464		JP, L	10-67
		SN75464	L, P	
	SN55474*		JP, L	3-15
		SN75474*	L, P	

*To be announced.
†With output transistor base connected externally to output of gate.
§In free-air.

SENSE AMPLIFIERS

FUNCTION	OPERATING TEMPERATURE RANGE§		PACKAGE TYPES	PAGE
	−55°C to 125°C	0°C to 70°C		
Dual-Channel, Open-Collector Output	SN5522		J, JA	11-3
		SN7522	J, N	11-5
	SN5523		J, JA	11-3
		SN7523	J, N	11-5
Dual-Channel, Complementary Outputs	SN5520		J, JA	11-3
		SN7520	J, N	11-5
	SN5521		J, JA	11-3
		SN7521	J, N	11-5
Dual-Channel with Output Register		SN7526	J, N	11-5
		SN7527	J, N	11-5
Dual (Separate Outputs)	SN5524		J, JA	11-3
		SN7524	J, N	11-5
	SN5525		J, JA	11-3
		SN7525	J, N	11-5
	SN55234		J, JA	11-3
		SN75234	J, N	11-5
	SN55235		J, JA	11-3
		SN75235	J, N	11-5
Dual with Open-Collector Outputs	SN55232		J, JA	11-3
		SN75232	J, N	11-5
	SN55233		J, JA	11-3
		SN75233	J, N	11-5
Dual with Test Points	SN5528		J, JA	11-3
		SN7528	J, N	11-5
	SN5529		J, JA	11-3
		SN7529	J, N	11-5
	SN55238		J, JA	11-3
		SN75238	J, N	11-5
	SN55239		J, JA	11-3
		SN75239	J, N	11-5
Dual with Data Register and Buffer Outputs	SN55236		SB	11-59
		SN75236	SB	11-59
	SN55237		SB	11-59
		SN75237	SB	11-59
Four-Channel, A-C Coupled	SN55244		J, JA, N	11-72
		SN75244	J, JA, N	11-72

§In free-air.

TEXAS INSTRUMENTS
INCORPORATED
POST OFFICE BOX 5012 • DALLAS, TEXAS 75222

CROSS-REFERENCE GUIDE

(ALPHABETICALLY BY MANUFACTURERS)

Direct replacements were based on similarity of electrical and mechanical characteristics as shown in currently published data. Interchangeability in particular applications is not guaranteed. Before using a device as a substitute, the user should compare the specifications of the substitute device with the specifications of the original.

Texas Instruments makes no warranty as to the information furnished and buyer assumes all risk in the use thereof. No liability is assumed for damages resulting from the use of the information contained in this list.

FAIRCHILD ORDER INFORMATION

EXAMPLE OF NEW ORDER CODE:

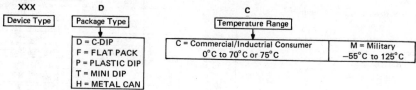

XXX	D		C	
Device Type	Package Type		Temperature Range	

| D = C-DIP |
| F = FLAT PACK |
| P = PLASTIC DIP |
| T = MINI DIP |
| H = METAL CAN |

| C = Commercial/Inductrial Consumer 0°C to 70°C or 75°C | M = Military −55°C to 125°C |

EXAMPLE OF PREVIOUS ORDER CODE:

U	7B	XXXX	59	X
Prefix	Package	Device Type	Temperature Range	Special Sort Code

| 3F, 3I, 3M, 4L = Flat Pack |
| 6A, 6B, 7A, 7B = C-Dip |
| 9A, 9B, 9T = Plastic Dip |

| 59 = 0°C to 70°C or 75°C |
| 51 = −55°C to 125°C |

FAIRCHILD	TEXAS INSTRUMENTS DIRECT REPLACEMENT	TEXAS INSTRUMENTS CLOSEST REPLACEMENT	FAIRCHILD	TEXAS INSTRUMENTS DIRECT REPLACEMENT	TEXAS INSTRUMENTS CLOSEST REPLACEMENT
101A	SN52101A		7806	*SN72906	
107	SN52107		7808	*SN72908	
109	SN52109		7812	*SN72912	
201A		SN52101A	7815	*SN72915	
209		SN52109	7818	*SN72918	
301	SN72301A		7824	*SN72924	
307	SN72307		9614	SN55114	
309	SN72309		9615	SN55115	
702	SN52702				SN75150
709	SN52709		9616		SN75188
709A	SN52709A				SN75189
710	SN52710		9617		SN75189A
711	SN52711				SN75152
715		SN52118			SN75154
723	SN52723		9627		SN75152
733	SN52733		55107	SN55107A	
734		SN52111	55108	SN55108A	
741	SN52741		55109	SN55109	
742		SN72440	55110	SN55110	
747	SN52747		75325	SN75325	
748	SN52748		75450	SN75450B	
776		SN52777	75451	SN75451B	
777	SN52777		75452	SN75452B	
8T13	SN55121		75453	SN75453B	
8T14	SN55122		75454	SN75454B	
8T23	SN75123		75460	SN75460	
8T24	SN75124		75461	SN75461	
1458	SN72558		75462	SN75462	
1558	SN52558		75463	SN75463	
7524	SN7524		75464	SN75464	
7525	SN7525		75491	SN75491	
7805	*SN72905		75492	SN75492	

*To be announced

MOTOROLA ORDER INFORMATION

EXAMPLE OF ORDER CODE:

MC	XXX	P
Prefix	Type Number	Package
	Different Numbers Are Used For Variations In Operating Temperatures	F = Flat Package G = Metal Can L = C-DIP P = Plastic

MOTOROLA	TEXAS INSTRUMENTS DIRECT REPLACEMENT	TEXAS INSTRUMENTS CLOSEST REPLACEMENT	MOTOROLA	TEXAS INSTRUMENTS DIRECT REPLACEMENT	TEXAS INSTRUMENTS CLOSEST REPLACEMENT
MLM301A	SN72301A		MC1709	SN52709	
MC1414	SN72514		MC1710	SN52710	SN52810
MC1420		SN5511	MC1711	SN52711	
MC1430		SN72702	MC1712	SN52702	
MC1431		SN72702	MC1723	SN52723	
MC1433		SN72301A	MC1733	SN52733	
MC1439		SN72101A	MC1741	SN52741	
MC1456	SN72771		MC1748	SN52748	
MC1458	SN72558		MFC4060		SN72723
MC1460		SN72723	MFC6030		SN72723
MC1461		SN72723	MC7520	SN7520	
MC1463		SN72723	MC7521	SN7521	
MC1466		SN72723	MC7522	SN7522	
MC1469		SN72723	MC7523	SN7523	
MC1488	SN75188		MC7524	SN7524	
MC1489	SN75189		MC7525	SN7525	
MC1489A	SN75189A		MC7528	SN7528	
MC1510	SN5510		MC7529	SN7529	
MC1514	SN52514		MC7534	SN75232	
MC1520		SN5511	MC7535	SN75233	
MC1530		SN52702	MC7538	SN75238	
MC1531		SN52702	MC7539	SN75239	
MC1533		SN52101A	MC8070		SN72440
MC1539		SN52101A	MC55107	SN55107A	
MC1556	SN52771		MC55108	SN55108A	
MC1558	SN52558		MC55109	SN55109	
MC1560		SN52723	MC55110	SN55110	
MC1561		SN52723	MC75325	SN75325	
MC1563		SN52723	MC75450	SN75450B	
MC1566		SN52723	MC75451	SN75451B	
MC1569		SN52723	MC75452	SN75452B	
MC1582		SN55110	MC75453	SN74543B	
MC1583		SN55108A	MC75491	SN75491	
MC1584		SN55107A	MC75492	SN75492	
MC1596		SN56514			

NATIONAL ORDER INFORMATION

EXAMPLE OF ORDER CODE:

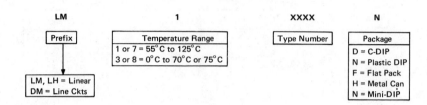

| **LM** | **1** | **XXXX** | **N** |

Prefix	Temperature Range	Type Number	Package
LM, LH = Linear DM = Line Ckts	1 or 7 = 55°C to 125°C 3 or 8 = 0°C to 70°C or 75°C		D = C-DIP N = Plastic DIP F = Flat Pack H = Metal Can N = Mini-DIP

NATIONAL	TEXAS INSTRUMENTS DIRECT REPLACEMENT	TEXAS INSTRUMENTS CLOSEST REPLACEMENT	NATIONAL	TEXAS INSTRUMENTS DIRECT REPLACEMENT	TEXAS INSTRUMENTS CLOSEST REPLACEMENT
LM100		SN52105	LM302	SN72302	
LH101	SN52107		LM304	SN72304	
LM101		SN52107	LM305	SN72305	
LM101A	SN52101A		LM305A	SN72305A	
LM102		SN52110	LM306	SN72306	
LM104	SN52104		LM307	SN72307	
LM105	SN52105		LM308	SN72308	
LM106	SN52106		LM308A	SN72308A	
LM107	SN52107		LM309	SN72309	
LM108	SN52108		LM310	SN72310	
LM108A	SN52108A		LM311	SN72311	
LM109	SN52109		LM318	SN72318	
LM110	SN52110		LM340-5	*SN72905	
LM111	SN52111		LM340-6	*SN72906	
LM112		SN52108	LM340-8	*SN72908	
LM118	SN52118		LM340-12	*SN72912	
LM122		SN52555	LM340-15	*SN72915	
LM123		SN72309	LM340-18	*SN72918	
LM124		SN52L044	LM340-24	*SN72924	
LM200		SN52105	LM350		SN75450
LM201		SN52101A	LM376	SN72376	
LM201A		SN52101A	LM555	SN52555	
LM202		SN52110	LM709	SN52709	
LM204		SN52104	LM710	SN52710	
LM205		SN52105	LM711	SN52711	
LM206		SN52106	LM723	SN52723	
LM207		SN52107	LM725A		SN52108A
LM208		SN52108	LM733	SN52733	
LM208A		SN52108A	LM741	SN52741	
LM209		SN52109	LM747	SN52747	
LM210		SN52110	LM748	SN52748	
LM211		SN52111	LM1414	SN72514	
LM212		SN52108	LM1458	SN72558	
LM218		SN52118	LM1488	SN75188	
LM300		SN72305	LM1489	SN75189	
LM301A	SN72301A		LM1489A	SN75189A	

NATIONAL	TEXAS INSTRUMENTS DIRECT REPLACEMENT	TEXAS INSTRUMENTS CLOSEST REPLACEMENT	NATIONAL	TEXAS INSTRUMENTS DIRECT REPLACEMENT	TEXAS INSTRUMENTS CLOSEST REPLACEMENT
LM1514	SN56514		DM7800	SN55180	
LM1558	SN52558		DM7820A	SN55182	
LM1596		SN56514	DM7830	SN55183	
LM3900		SN72L044	LM7833		SN55138
LM3905		SN72555	LM7834		SN55138
LM4250		SN52108A	LM7835		SN55138
LM5520	SN5520		LM7838		SN55138
LM5521	SN5521		LM7839		SN55138
LM5522	SN5522		DM8820A	SN75182	
LM5523	SN5523		DM8830	SN75183	
LM5524	SN5524		LH24240		SN52L044
LM5525	SN5525		LM55107A	SN55107A	
LM5528	SN5528		LM55108A	SN55108A	
LM5529	SN5529		LM55109	SN55109	
LM5534	SN55232		LM55110	SN55110	
LM5535	SN55233		LM55325	SN55325	
LM5538		SN55238	LM75107A	SN75107A	
LM5539		SN55239	LM75108A	SN75108A	
LM7520	SN7520		LM75109	SN75109	
LM7521	SN7521		LM75110	SN75110	
LM7522	SN7522		LM75207	SN75207	
LM7523	SN7523		LM75208	SN75208	
LM7524	SN7524		LM75324	SN75324	
LM7525	SN7525		LM75450A	SN75450B	
LM7528	SN7528		LM75451A	SN75451B	
LM7529	SN7529		LM75452	SN75452B	
LM7534	SN75232		LM75453	SN75453B	
LM7535	SN75233		LM75454	SN75454B	
LM7538		SN75238	DM75491	SN75491	
LM7539		SN75239	DM75492	SN75492	

RAYTHEON ORDER INFORMATION

EXAMPLE OF ORDER CODE:

R	M	XXX	L
Prefix	Temperature Range	Type Number	Package
	M = Military C = Consumer		DC = C-DIP DP, ND = Plastic DIP Q, J = Flat Pack TO = Metal Can

RAYTHEON	TEXAS INSTRUMENTS DIRECT REPLACEMENT	TEXAS INSTRUMENTS CLOSEST REPLACEMENTS	RAYTHEON	TEXAS INSTRUMENTS DIRECT REPLACEMENT	TEXAS INSTRUMENTS CLOSEST REPLACEMENTS
101A	SN52101A		723	SN52723	
106	SN52106		733	SN52733	
107	SN52107		741	SN52741	
108	SN52108		747	SN52747	
111	SN52111		748	SN52748	
211		SN52111	1488	SN75188	
311	SN72111		1489	SN75189	
702	SN52702		1489A	SN75189A	
709	SN52709		1514	SN52514	
709A	SN52709A		4558	SN52558	
710	SN52710		4741	SN52747	
711	SN52711				

SIGNETICS ORDER INFORMATION

EXAMPLE OF ORDER CODE:

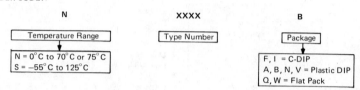

SIGNETICS	TEXAS INSTRUMENTS DIRECT REPLACEMENT	TEXAS INSTRUMENTS CLOSEST REPLACEMENT	SIGNETICS	TEXAS INSTRUMENTS DIRECT REPLACEMENT	TEXAS INSTRUMENTS CLOSEST REPLACEMENT
LM101	SN52101		8T13	SN55121	
LM101A	SN52101A		8T14	SN55122	
LM107	SN52107		8T15		SN75150
LM109	SN52109		8T16		SN75152
LM202		SN52101A	8T23	SN75123	
LM301A	SN72301A		8T24	SN75124	
LM309	SN72309		8T26		SN55138
LM311	SN72311		S5556	SN52771	
SE529		SN55207	S5558	SN52558	
SE537		SN52108	S5596		SN56514
SE550		SN52723	SN7520	SN7520	
SE555	SN52555		SN7521	SN7521	
UA709	SN52709		SN7522	SN7522	
UA710	SN52710		SN7523	SN7523	
UA711	SN52711		SN7524	SN7524	
UA723	SN52723		SN7525	SN7525	
UA733	SN52733		SN75107	SN75107	
UA741	SN52741		SN75108	SN75108	
UA747	SN52747		SN75450	SN75450B	
UA748	SN52748		SN75451	SN75451B	

Ordering Instructions
and
Mechanical Data

ORDERING INSTRUCTIONS

Electrical characteristics presented in this data book, unless otherwise noted, apply for the circuit type(s) listed in the page heading regardless of package. The availability of a circuit function in a particular package is denoted by an alphabetical reference above the pin-connection diagram(s). These alphabetical references refer to mechanical outline drawings shown in this section.

Factory orders for circuits described in this data book should include a four-part type number as explained in the following example.

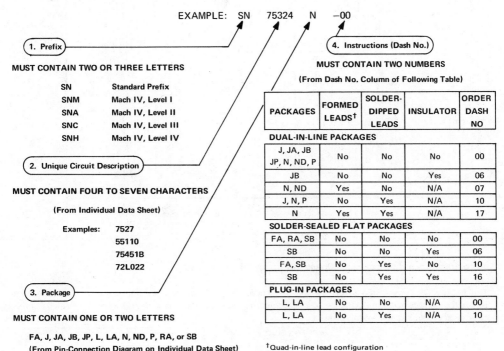

EXAMPLE: SN 75324 N −00

1. Prefix

MUST CONTAIN TWO OR THREE LETTERS

SN	Standard Prefix
SNM	Mach IV, Level I
SNA	Mach IV, Level II
SNC	Mach IV, Level III
SNH	Mach IV, Level IV

2. Unique Circuit Description

MUST CONTAIN FOUR TO SEVEN CHARACTERS

(From Individual Data Sheet)

Examples:	7527
	55110
	75451B
	72L022

3. Package

MUST CONTAIN ONE OR TWO LETTERS

FA, J, JA, JB, JP, L, LA, N, ND, P, RA, or SB
(From Pin-Connection Diagram on Individual Data Sheet)

4. Instructions (Dash No.)

MUST CONTAIN TWO NUMBERS

(From Dash No. Column of Following Table)

PACKAGES	FORMED LEADS†	SOLDER-DIPPED LEADS	INSULATOR	ORDER DASH NO
DUAL-IN-LINE PACKAGES				
J, JA, JB JP, N, ND, P	No	No	No	00
JB	No	No	Yes	06
N, ND	Yes	No	N/A	07
J, N, P	No	Yes	N/A	10
N	Yes	Yes	N/A	17
SOLDER-SEALED FLAT PACKAGES				
FA, RA, SB	No	No	No	00
SB	No	No	Yes	06
FA, SB	No	Yes	No	10
SB	No	Yes	Yes	16
PLUG-IN PACKAGES				
L, LA	No	No	N/A	00
L, LA	No	Yes	N/A	10

†Quad-in-line lead configuration

Circuits are shipped in one of the carriers shown below. Unless a specific method of shipment is specified by the customer (with possible additional costs), circuits will be shipped in the most practical carrier.

Flat (FA, RA, SB)

—Barnes Carrier
—Milton Ross Carrier

Dual-In-Line (J, JA, JB, JP, N, ND, P)

— Slide Magazines
— A-Channel Plastic Tubing
— Barnes Carrier
— Sectioned Cardboard Box
— Individual Plastic Box

Plug-In (L, LA)

— Barnes Carrier
— Sectioned Cardboard Box
— Individual Cardboard Box

INTEGRATED CIRCUITS MECHANICAL DATA

FA flat packages (inch dimensions, see page 2-9 for metric dimensions)

These flat packages each consist of a 10- or 14-lead ceramic-based header and a metal lid. The lid is hermetically sealed to the header at relatively low temperature using a solder preform. The gold-plated leads require no additional cleaning or processing when used in soldered or welded assembly.

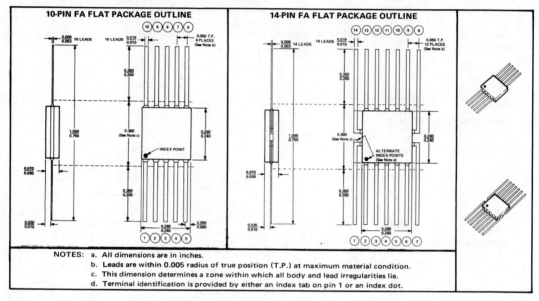

NOTES: a. All dimensions are in inches.
b. Leads are within 0.005 radius of true position (T.P.) at maximum material condition.
c. This dimension determines a zone within which all body and lead irregularities lie.
d. Terminal identification is provided by either an index tab on pin 1 or an index dot.

RA flat package (inch dimensions, see page 2-9 for metric dimensions)

This flat package consists of a 24-lead ceramic-based header and a metal lid. The lid is hermetically sealed to the header at relatively low temperature using a solder preform. The gold-plated leads require no additional cleaning or processing when used in soldered or welded assembly.

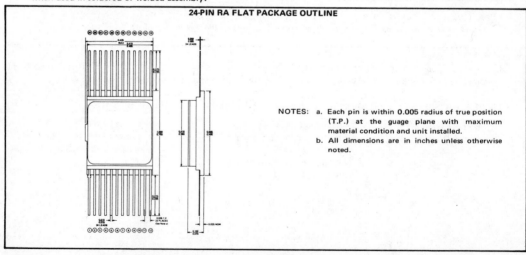

NOTES: a. Each pin is within 0.005 radius of true position (T.P.) at the guage plane with maximum material condition and unit installed.
b. All dimensions are in inches unless otherwise noted.

TEXAS INSTRUMENTS
INCORPORATED
POST OFFICE BOX 5012 • DALLAS, TEXAS 75222

SB flat packages (inch dimensions, see page 2-10 for metric dimensions)

These flat packages each consist of a 16- or 24-lead metal-based header and a metal lid. The lid is hermetically sealed to the header at relatively low temperature using a solder preform. The gold-plated leads require no additional cleaning or processing when used in soldered or welded assembly.

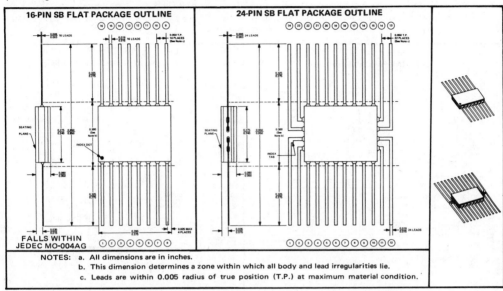

| 16-PIN SB FLAT PACKAGE OUTLINE | 24-PIN SB FLAT PACKAGE OUTLINE |

FALLS WITHIN
JEDEC MO-004AG

NOTES: a. All dimensions are in inches.
b. This dimension determines a zone within which all body and lead irregularities lie.
c. Leads are within 0.005 radius of true position (T.P.) at maximum material condition.

P plastic dual-in-line package (inch dimensions, see page 2-10 for metric dimensions)

This dual-in-line package consists of a circuit mounted on a 8-lead frame and encapsulated within a plastic compound. The compound will withstand soldering temperature with no deformation and circuit performance characteristics remain stable when operated in high-humidity conditions. This package is intended for insertion in mounting-hole rows on 0.300-inch centers. Once the leads are compressed to 0.300-inch separation and inserted, sufficient tension is provided to secure the package in the board during soldering. Silver-plated leads require no additional cleaning or processing when used in soldered assembly.

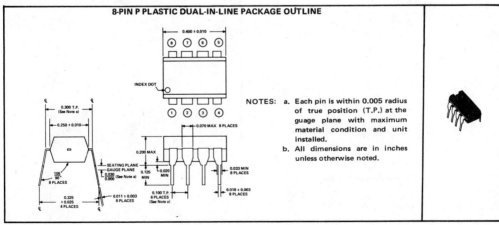

8-PIN P PLASTIC DUAL-IN-LINE PACKAGE OUTLINE

NOTES: a. Each pin is within 0.005 radius of true position (T.P.) at the guage plane with maximum material condition and unit installed.
b. All dimensions are in inches unless otherwise noted.

TEXAS INSTRUMENTS
INCORPORATED
POST OFFICE BOX 5012 • DALLAS, TEXAS 75222

INTEGRATED CIRCUITS MECHANICAL DATA

N plastic dual-in-line packages (inch dimensions, see page 2-11 for metric dimensions)

These dual-in-line packages consist of a circuit mounted on a 14-or 16-lead frame and encapsulated within an electrically nonconductive plastic compound. The compound will withstand soldering temperature with no deformation and circuit performance characteristics remain stable when operated in high-humidity conditions. These packages are intended for insertion in mounting-hole rows on 0.300-inch centers. Once the leads are compressed and inserted, sufficient tension is provided to secure the package in the board during soldering. Silver-plated leads (−00) require no additional cleaning or processing when used in soldered assembly.

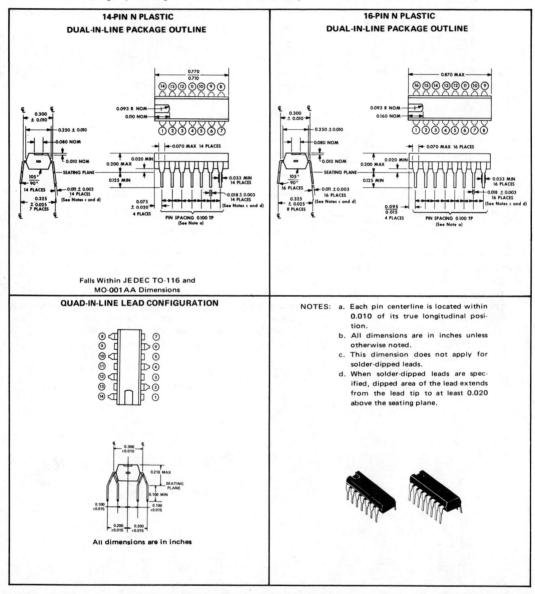

14-PIN N PLASTIC DUAL-IN-LINE PACKAGE OUTLINE

16-PIN N PLASTIC DUAL-IN-LINE PACKAGE OUTLINE

Falls Within JEDEC TO-116 and MO-001 AA Dimensions

QUAD-IN-LINE LEAD CONFIGURATION

All dimensions are in inches

NOTES: a. Each pin centerline is located within 0.010 of its true longitudinal position.
b. All dimensions are in inches unless otherwise noted.
c. This dimension does not apply for solder-dipped leads.
d. When solder-dipped leads are specified, dipped area of the lead extends from the lead tip to at least 0.020 above the seating plane.

TEXAS INSTRUMENTS
INCORPORATED
POST OFFICE BOX 5012 • DALLAS, TEXAS 75222

ND plastic package (inch dimensions, see page 2-12 for metric dimensions)

This dual-in-line package consists of a circuit mounted on a 8-lead, 2-tab frame and encapsulated within a plastic compound. The compound will withstand soldering temperature with no deformation and circuit performance characteristics remain stable when operated in high-humidity conditions. These packages are intended for insertion in mounting rows on 0.300-inch centers. Once the leads are compressed to 0.300-inch separation and inserted, sufficient tension is provided to secure the package in the board during soldering. Pin positions 3, 4, 5, 10, 11, and 12 are occupied by two tabs which facilitate attachment of heat sinks. Silver-plated leads require no additional cleaning or processing when used in soldered assembly.

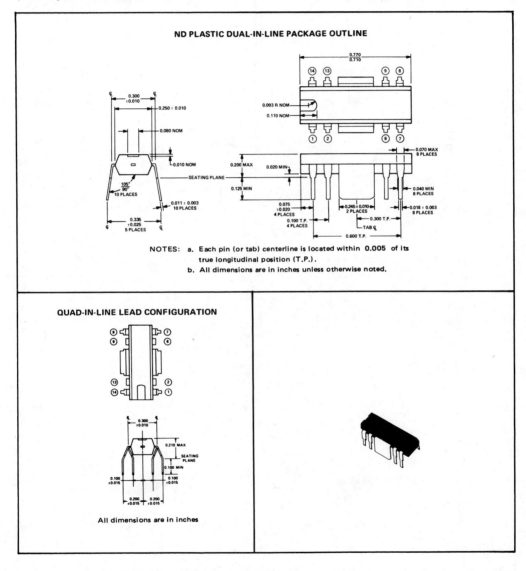

ND PLASTIC DUAL-IN-LINE PACKAGE OUTLINE

NOTES: a. Each pin (or tab) centerline is located within 0.005 of its true longitudinal position (T.P.).
b. All dimensions are in inches unless otherwise noted.

QUAD-IN-LINE LEAD CONFIGURATION

All dimensions are in inches

INTEGRATED CIRCUITS MECHANICAL DATA

J ceramic dual-in-line package (inch dimensions, see page 2-13 for metric dimensions)

These hermetically sealed, dual-in-line packages consist of a ceramic base, ceramic cap, and a 14- or 16-lead frame. The circuit bar is alloy-mounted to the base and hermetic sealing is accomplished with glass. The packages are intended for insertion in mounting-hole rows on 0.300-inch centers. Once the leads are compressed and inserted, sufficient tension is provided to secure the package in the board during soldering. Tin-plated ("bright-dipped") leads (—00) require no additional cleaning or processing when used in soldered assembly.

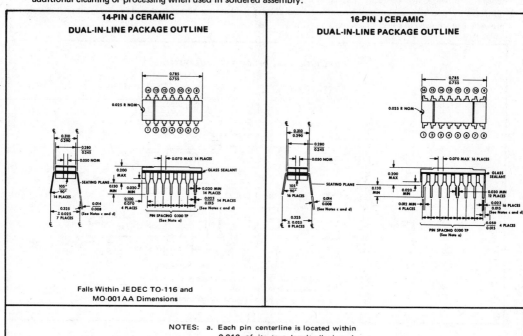

14-PIN J CERAMIC DUAL-IN-LINE PACKAGE OUTLINE

Falls Within JEDEC TO-116 and MO-001AA Dimensions

16-PIN J CERAMIC DUAL-IN-LINE PACKAGE OUTLINE

NOTES:
a. Each pin centerline is located within 0.010 of its true longitudinal position.
b. All dimensions are in inches unless otherwise noted.
c. This dimension does not apply for solder-dipped leads.
d. When solder-dipped leads are specified, dipped area of the lead extends from the lead tip to at least 0.020 above the seating plane.

TEXAS INSTRUMENTS
INCORPORATED
POST OFFICE BOX 5012 • DALLAS, TEXAS 75222

2

JA and JB dual-in-line packages (inch dimensions, see page 2-14 for metric dimensions)

These dual-in-line packages each consist of a 14- or 16-lead header and a metal lid. The JA package has an alumina-filled-glass header while the JB package has a metal-based header. The lid is hermetically sealed to the header at relatively low temperature using a solder preform. The packages are intended for insertion in mounting-hole rows on 0.300-inch centers. Once the leads are compressed and inserted, sufficient tension is provided to secure the package in the board during soldering. The gold-plated leads require no additional cleaning or processing when used in soldered or welded assembly.

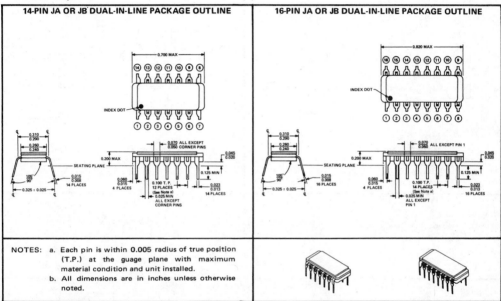

14-PIN JA OR JB DUAL-IN-LINE PACKAGE OUTLINE	16-PIN JA OR JB DUAL-IN-LINE PACKAGE OUTLINE

NOTES: a. Each pin is within 0.005 radius of true position (T.P.) at the guage plane with maximum material condition and unit installed.
b. All dimensions are in inches unless otherwise noted.

JP dual-in-line package (inch dimensions, see page 3-14 for metric dimensions)

This dual-in-line package consists of an 8-lead alumina-filled-glass header having a metalized-ceramic base and a metal lid. The lid is hermetically sealed to the header at relatively low temperature using a solder preform. The package is intended for insertion in mounting-hole rows on 0.300-inch centers. Once the leads are compressed and inserted sufficient tension is provided to secure the package in the board during soldering. The gold-plated leads require no additional cleaning or processing when used in soldered or welded assembly.

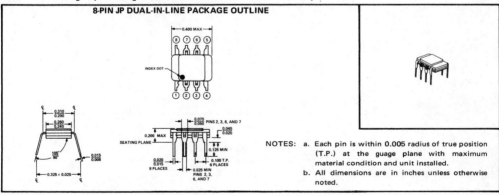

8-PIN JP DUAL-IN-LINE PACKAGE OUTLINE

NOTES: a. Each pin is within 0.005 radius of true position (T.P.) at the guage plane with maximum material condition and unit installed.
b. All dimensions are in inches unless otherwise noted.

INTEGRATED CIRCUITS MECHANICAL DATA

L and LA plug-in packages (inch dimensions, see page 2-15 for metric dimensions)

These hermetically sealed, plug-in packages each consist of a welded metal base and cap with individual leads secured by an insulating glass sealant. The gold-plated leads (−00) require no additional cleaning or processing when used in soldered assembly.

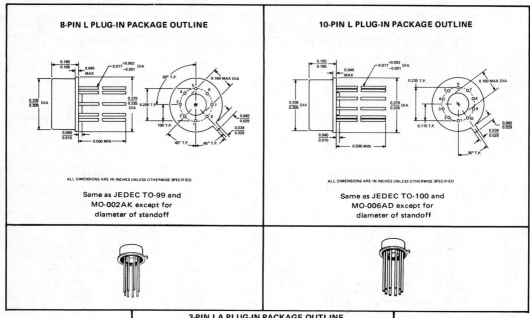

8-PIN L PLUG-IN PACKAGE OUTLINE

ALL DIMENSIONS ARE IN INCHES UNLESS OTHERWISE SPECIFIED.

Same as JEDEC TO-99 and
MO-002AK except for
diameter of standoff

10-PIN L PLUG-IN PACKAGE OUTLINE

ALL DIMENSIONS ARE IN INCHES UNLESS OTHERWISE SPECIFIED

Same as JEDEC TO-100 and
MO-006AD except for
diameter of standoff

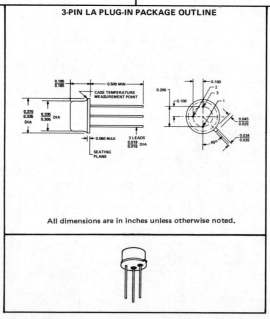

3-PIN LA PLUG-IN PACKAGE OUTLINE

All dimensions are in inches unless otherwise noted.

TEXAS INSTRUMENTS
INCORPORATED
POST OFFICE BOX 5012 • DALLAS, TEXAS 75222

FA flat packages (metric dimensions, see page 2-2 for inch dimensions)

These flat packages each consist of a 10- or 14-lead ceramic-based header and a metal lid. The lid is hermetically sealed to the header at relatively low temperature using a solder preform. The gold-plated leads require no additional cleaning or processing when used in soldered or welded assembly.

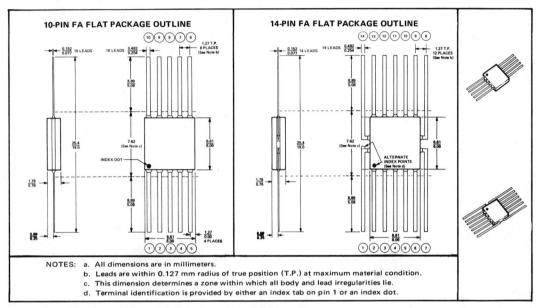

10-PIN FA FLAT PACKAGE OUTLINE

14-PIN FA FLAT PACKAGE OUTLINE

NOTES: a. All dimensions are in millimeters.
      b. Leads are within 0.127 mm radius of true position (T.P.) at maximum material condition.
      c. This dimension determines a zone within which all body and lead irregularities lie.
      d. Terminal identification is provided by either an index tab on pin 1 or an index dot.

RA flat package (metric dimensions, see page 2-2 for inch dimensions)

This flat package consists of a 24-lead ceramic-based header and a metal lid. The lid is hermetically sealed to the header at relatively low temperature using a solder preform. The gold-plated leads require no additional cleaning or processing when used in soldered or welded assembly.

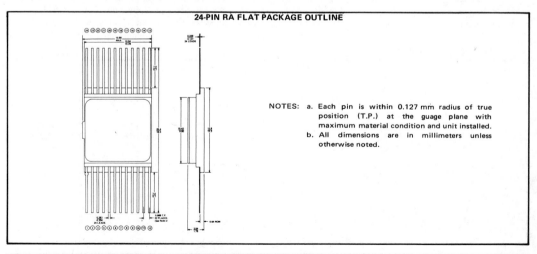

24-PIN RA FLAT PACKAGE OUTLINE

NOTES: a. Each pin is within 0.127 mm radius of true position (T.P.) at the guage plane with maximum material condition and unit installed.
      b. All dimensions are in millimeters unless otherwise noted.

INTEGRATED CIRCUITS MECHANICAL DATA

SB flat packages (metric dimensions, see page 2-3 for inch dimensions)

These flat packages each consist of a 16- or 24-lead metal-based header and a metal lid. The lid is hermetically sealed to the header at relatively low temperature using a solder preform. The gold-plated leads require no additional cleaning or processing when used in soldered or welded assembly.

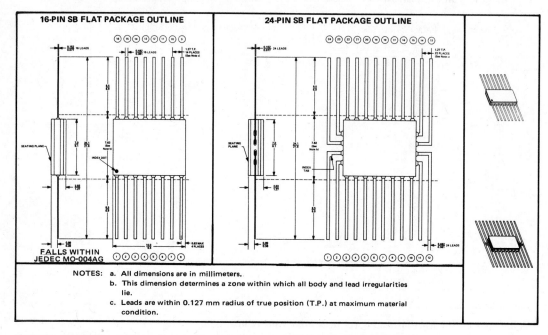

16-PIN SB FLAT PACKAGE OUTLINE

24-PIN SB FLAT PACKAGE OUTLINE

FALLS WITHIN
JEDEC MO-004AG

NOTES:　a. All dimensions are in millimeters.
　　　　b. This dimension determines a zone within which all body and lead irregularities lie.
　　　　c. Leads are within 0.127 mm radius of true position (T.P.) at maximum material condition.

P plastic dual-in-line package (metric dimensions, see page 2-3 for inch dimensions)

This dual-in-line package consists of a circuit mounted on a 8-lead frame and encapsulated within a plastic compound. The compound will withstand soldering temperature with no deformation and circuit performance characteristics remain stable when operated in high-humidity conditions. This package is intended for insertion in mounting-hole rows on 7.62-mm centers. Once the leads are compressed to 7.62-mm separation and inserted, sufficient tension is provided to secure the package in the board during soldering. Silver-plated leads require no additional cleaning or processing when used in soldered assembly.

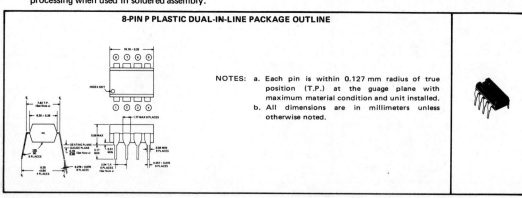

8-PIN P PLASTIC DUAL-IN-LINE PACKAGE OUTLINE

NOTES:　a. Each pin is within 0.127 mm radius of true position (T.P.) at the guage plane with maximum material condition and unit installed.
　　　　b. All dimensions are in millimeters unless otherwise noted.

TEXAS INSTRUMENTS
INCORPORATED
POST OFFICE BOX 5012 • DALLAS, TEXAS 75222

N plastic dual-in-line packages (metric dimensions, see page 2-4 for inch dimensions)

These dual-in-line packages consist of a circuit mounted on a 14- or 16-lead frame and encapsulated within an electrically nonconductive plastic compound. The compound will withstand soldering temperature with no deformation and circuit performance characteristics remain stable when operated in high-humidity conditions. These packages are intended for insertion in mounting-hole rows on 7.62-mm centers. Once the leads are compressed and inserted, sufficient tension is provided to secure the package in the board during soldering. Silver-plated leads (−00) require no additional cleaning or processing when used in soldered assembly.

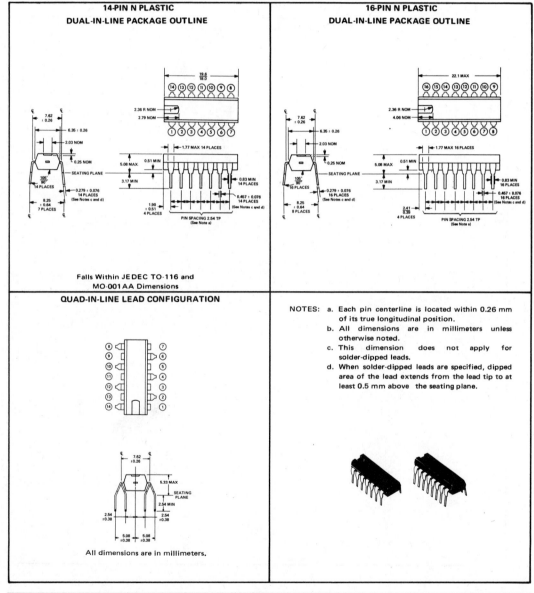

14-PIN N PLASTIC DUAL-IN-LINE PACKAGE OUTLINE

Falls Within JEDEC TO-116 and MO-001AA Dimensions

16-PIN N PLASTIC DUAL-IN-LINE PACKAGE OUTLINE

QUAD-IN-LINE LEAD CONFIGURATION

All dimensions are in millimeters.

NOTES: a. Each pin centerline is located within 0.26 mm of its true longitudinal position.
b. All dimensions are in millimeters unless otherwise noted.
c. This dimension does not apply for solder-dipped leads.
d. When solder-dipped leads are specified, dipped area of the lead extends from the lead tip to at least 0.5 mm above the seating plane.

INTEGRATED CIRCUITS MECHANICAL DATA

ND-package (metric dimensions, see page 2-5 for inch dimensions)

This dual-in-line package consists of a circuit mounted on a 8-lead, 2-tab frame and encapsulated within a plastic compound. The compound will withstand soldering temperature with no deformation and circuit performance characteristics remain stable when operated in high-humidity conditions. These packages are intended for insertion in mounting-hole rows on 7.62-mm centers. Once the leads are compressed to 7.62-mm separation and inserted, sufficient tension is provided to secure the package in the board during soldering. Pin positions 3, 4, 5, 10, 11, and 12 are occupied by two tabs which facilitate attachment of heat sinks. Silver-plated leads require no additional cleaning or processing when used in soldered assembly.

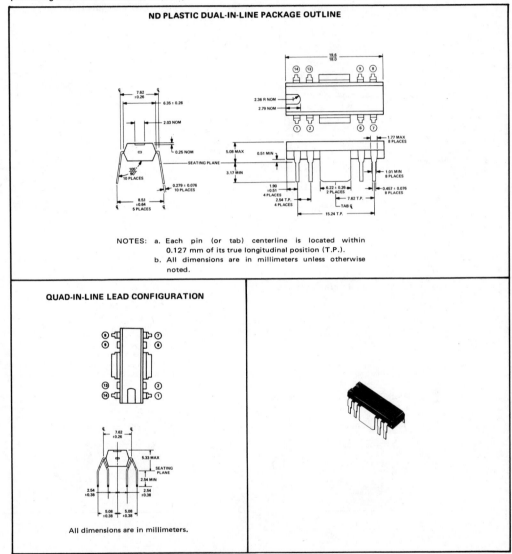

ND PLASTIC DUAL-IN-LINE PACKAGE OUTLINE

NOTES: a. Each pin (or tab) centerline is located within 0.127 mm of its true longitudinal position (T.P.).
   b. All dimensions are in millimeters unless otherwise noted.

QUAD-IN-LINE LEAD CONFIGURATION

All dimensions are in millimeters.

TEXAS INSTRUMENTS
INCORPORATED
POST OFFICE BOX 5012 • DALLAS, TEXAS 75222

J ceramic dual-in-line packages (metric dimensions, see page 2-6 for inch dimensions)

These hermetically sealed, dual-in-line packages consist of a ceramic base, ceramic cap, and a 14-or 16-lead frame. The circuit bar is alloy-mounted to the base and hermetic sealing is accomplished with glass. The packages are intended for insertion in mounting-hole rows on 7.62-mm centers. Once the leads are compressed and inserted, sufficient tension is provided to secure the package in the board during soldering. Tin-plated ("bright-dipped") leads (—00) require no additional cleaning or processing when used in soldered assembly.

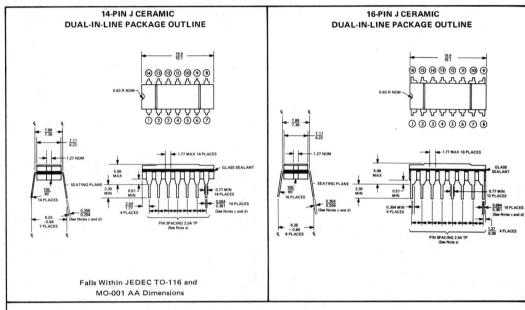

14-PIN J CERAMIC DUAL-IN-LINE PACKAGE OUTLINE

Falls Within JEDEC TO-116 and MO-001 AA Dimensions

16-PIN J CERAMIC DUAL-IN-LINE PACKAGE OUTLINE

NOTES: a. Each pin centerline is located within 0.26 mm of its true longitudinal position.
   b. All dimensions are in millimeters unless otherwise noted.
   c. This dimension does not apply for solder-dipped leads.
   d. When solder-dipped leads are specified, dipped area of the lead extends from the lead tip to at least 0.5 mm above the seating plane.

INTEGRATED CIRCUITS MECHANICAL DATA

JA and JB dual-in-line packages (metric dimensions, see page 2-7 for inch dimensions)

These dual-in-line packages each consist of a 14- or 16-lead header and a metal lid. The JA package has an alumina-filled-glass header while the JB package has a metal-based header. The lid is hermetically sealed to the header at relatively low temperature using a solder preform. The packages are intended for insertion in mounting-hole rows on 7.62-mm centers. Once the leads are compressed and inserted, sufficient tension is provided to secure the package in the board during soldering. The gold-plated leads require no additional cleaning or processing when used in soldered or welded assembly.

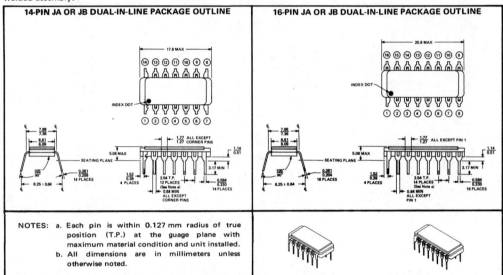

14-PIN JA OR JB DUAL-IN-LINE PACKAGE OUTLINE	16-PIN JA OR JB DUAL-IN-LINE PACKAGE OUTLINE

NOTES: a. Each pin is within 0.127 mm radius of true position (T.P.) at the guage plane with maximum material condition and unit installed.
b. All dimensions are in millimeters unless otherwise noted.

JP dual-in-line package (metric dimensions, see page 2-7 for inch dimensions)

This dual-in-line package consists of an 8-lead alumina-filled-glass header having a metalized-ceramic base and a metal lid. The lid is hermetically sealed to the header at relatively low temperature using a solder preform. The packages are intended for insertion in mounting-hole rows on 7.62-mm centers. Once the leads are compressed and inserted, sufficient tension is provided to secure the package in the board during soldering. The gold-plated leads require no additional cleaning or processing when used in soldered or welded assembly.

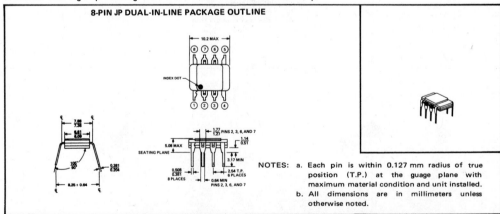

8-PIN JP DUAL-IN-LINE PACKAGE OUTLINE

NOTES: a. Each pin is within 0.127 mm radius of true position (T.P.) at the guage plane with maximum material condition and unit installed.
b. All dimensions are in millimeters unless otherwise noted.

TEXAS INSTRUMENTS
INCORPORATED
POST OFFICE BOX 5012 • DALLAS, TEXAS 75222

INTEGRATED CIRCUITS MECHANICAL DATA

L and LA plug-in packages (metric dimensions, see page 2-8 for inch dimensions)

These hermetically sealed, plug-in packages each consist of a welded metal base and cap with individual leads secured by an insulating glass sealant. The gold-plated leads (—00) require no additional cleaning or processing when used in soldered assembly.

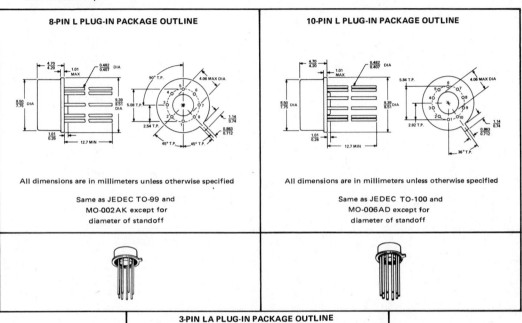

8-PIN L PLUG-IN PACKAGE OUTLINE

All dimensions are in millimeters unless otherwise specified

Same as JEDEC TO-99 and
MO-002AK except for
diameter of standoff

10-PIN L PLUG-IN PACKAGE OUTLINE

All dimensions are in millimeters unless otherwise specified

Same as JEDEC TO-100 and
MO-006AD except for
diameter of standoff

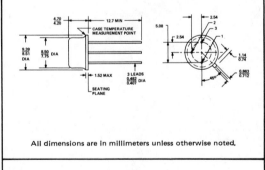

3-PIN LA PLUG-IN PACKAGE OUTLINE

All dimensions are in millimeters unless otherwise noted.

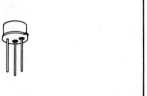

Future Products

SN62004, SN72004 . . . JFET-INPUT OPERATIONAL AMPLIFIERS

key features

- High slew rate . . . 15 V/μs typical
- High input impedance
- Internal frequency compensation
- Short-circuit output current limited
- Offset voltage null capability
- Wide common-mode and differential input voltage ranges

description

The SN62004 and SN72004 are monolithic operational amplifiers with junction-field-effect-transistor inputs intended to satisfy a wide range of high-speed analog applications where high slew rate, high input impedance, and low input bias and offset currents are important.

supply voltage: ±5 V to ±18 V

operating free-air temperature ranges: SN62004 . . . −25°C to 85°C
SN72004 . . . 0°C to 70°C

packages: 8-pin L plug-in and JP and P dual-in-line packages

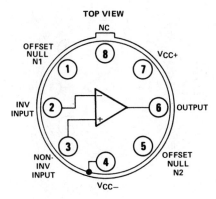

TOP VIEW

SN52118, SN72318 . . . WIDEBAND OPERATIONAL AMPLIFIERS

key features

- Guaranteed 50-V/μs minimum slew rate
- 15-MHz small-signal bandwidth
- Internal frequency compensation for unity gain
- Input and output overload protection

description

The SN52118 and SN72318 are monolithic precision high-speed operational amplifiers designed for applications requiring wide bandwidth and high slew rate, such as analog-to-digital converters, oscillators, active filters, and sample-hold circuits.

supply voltage: ±5 V to ±20 V

operating free-air temperature ranges: SN52118 . . . —55°C to 125°C
SN72318 . . . 0°C to 70°C

packages: JA, JP, N, and P dual-in-line, L plug-in, and FA flat packages

TOP VIEW

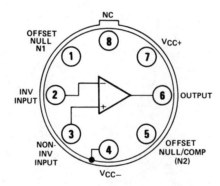

3

TEXAS INSTRUMENTS
INCORPORATED
POST OFFICE BOX 5012 • DALLAS, TEXAS 75222

SN729XX . . . FIXED-VOLTAGE REGULATORS

key features

- Output currents in excess of one ampere
- Thermal overload protected
- Short-circuit current limited
- Fixed output voltages
- No external components

description

The SN729xx series is a family of monolithic three-terminal voltage regulators intended as fixed-voltage regulators in a wide range of applications including local, on-card regulation for elimination and/or reduction of power distribution problems.

TYPE NUMBER	INPUT VOLTAGE RANGE	NOMINAL OUTPUT VOLTAGE	MAXIMUM OUTPUT CURRENT
SN72905	7 to 25 V	5 V	1.5 A
SN72906	8 to 15 V	6 V	1.5 A
SN72908	10.5 to 25 V	8 V	1.5 A
SN72912	14.5 to 30 V	12 V	1.5 A
SN72915	17.5 to 30 V	15 V	1.5 A
SN72918	21 to 33 V	18 V	1.5 A
SN72924	27 to 38 V	24 V	1.5 A

operating case temperature range: 0°C to 125°C

package:

1 . . . INPUT
2 . . . GND
3 . . . OUTPUT

1 2 3

TEXAS INSTRUMENTS
INCORPORATED
POST OFFICE BOX 5012 • DALLAS, TEXAS 75222

3

SN72595 . . . MICRO-PROCESSOR DRIVE SYSTEM

key features

- Dual-frequency, single-phase, self-starting oscillator
- Negative V_{GG} generator, pulsed and static
- Clock driver with high-capacitance drive capability
- Three-input gating circuit for frequency selection
- Low power consumption

description

The SN72595 is a complete drive system for complex MOS arithmetic processors. Designed for compatibility with Texas Instruments Series TMS0100 calculator and processor circuits, the SN72595 provides the complete clock function with the flexibility of operating at one of two selectable frequencies between 20 kHz and 300 kHz while supplying clock drive pulses of essentially constant width and amplitude. The SN72595 generates a negative V_{GG} supply when operating from the positive V_{SS} supply. A three-input OR-logic circuit permits selection of one of the two frequencies while external components are used to adjust the frequencies.

supply voltage: 7.2 V nominal

operating free-air temperature range: 0°C to 70°C

package: 14-pin N dual-in-line package

TOP VIEW

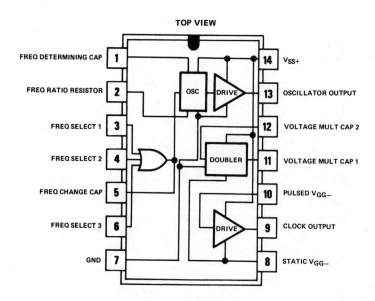

Pin	Name		Pin	Name
1	FREQ DETERMINING CAP		14	V_{SS+}
2	FREQ RATIO RESISTOR		13	OSCILLATOR OUTPUT
3	FREQ SELECT 1		12	VOLTAGE MULT CAP 2
4	FREQ SELECT 2		11	VOLTAGE MULT CAP 1
5	FREQ CHANGE CAP		10	PULSED V_{GG-}
6	FREQ SELECT 3		9	CLOCK OUTPUT
7	GND		8	STATIC V_{GG-}

TEXAS INSTRUMENTS
INCORPORATED
POST OFFICE BOX 5012 • DALLAS, TEXAS 75222

SN55116, SN75116 . . . DIFFERENTIAL PARTY LINE TRANSCEIVER

key features

- Single 5-V supply operation
- Three-state differential driver with open-collector or totem-pole outputs
- Differential receiver has strobe and frequency-response-control inputs
- Driver and receiver are independent

description

The SN55116 and SN75116 are monolithic integrated circuits designed for party-line data communication over differential transmission lines. Each of these devices combines in one package both a differential line driver (similar to types SN55113/SN75113) and a differential line receiver (similar to SN55115/SN75115). Both circuits operate from a single 5-volt power supply. The driver, which is of three-state design, performs the dual input AND and NAND functions. The logic and inhibit inputs are TTL/DTL compatible, and the differential outputs can source or sink 40-milliampere currents or be switched to a high-impedance inhibited state. The outputs also may be used in the open-collector, current-sinking-only configuration. The differential receiver design includes an optional 130-ohm line termination resistor, a TTL/DTL-compatible strobe input, and a frequency response control input. The receiver output is TTL/DTL compatible and is also of split-totem-pole design allowing a choice of either the open-collector or totem-pole output configurations. Except for the power supply and ground pins, the driver and receiver portions of the circuit are totally independent.

supply voltage: 5 V nominal

operating free-air temperature ranges: SN55116 . . . −55°C to 125°C
SN75116 . . . 0°C to 70°C

packages: J and N 16-pin dual-in-line packages

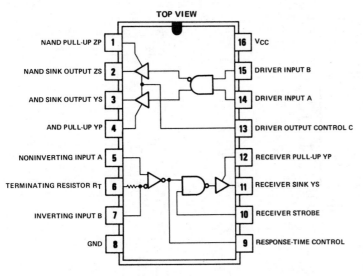

TOP VIEW

1	NAND PULL-UP ZP
2	NAND SINK OUTPUT ZS
3	AND SINK OUTPUT YS
4	AND PULL-UP YP
5	NONINVERTING INPUT A
6	TERMINATING RESISTOR RT
7	INVERTING INPUT B
8	GND
16	Vcc
15	DRIVER INPUT B
14	DRIVER INPUT A
13	DRIVER OUTPUT CONTROL C
12	RECEIVER PULL-UP YP
11	RECEIVER SINK YS
10	RECEIVER STROBE
9	RESPONSE-TIME CONTROL

FUNCTION TABLE OF DRIVER

INPUTS			OUTPUTS	
C	A	B	Y	Z
L	X	X	Z	Z
H	L	X	L	H
H	X	L	L	H
H	H	H	H	L

H = high level
L = low level
X = irrelevant
Z = high impedance (off)

FUNCTION TABLE OF RECEIVER

STROBE	DIFF INPUT	OUTPUT
L	X	H
H	L	H
H	H	L

H = $V_I \geqslant V_{IH}$ min or V_{ID} more positive than V_{TH} max
L = $V_I \leqslant V_{IL}$ max or V_{ID} more negative than V_{TL} max
X = irrelevant

TEXAS INSTRUMENTS
INCORPORATED
POST OFFICE BOX 5012 • DALLAS, TEXAS 75222

3

SN55117, SN75117 . . . DIFFERENTIAL PARTY-LINE TRANSCEIVER

key features

- Single 5-volt supply
- Three-state ±40-mA driver
- High-input-impedance differential receiver
- Independent receiver strobe and driver enable
- All inputs and outputs TTL/DTL compatible

description

The SN55117 and SN75117 are monolithic integrated circuits designed for two-way party-line data communication over differential transmission lines. Each combines in one package both a differential line driver (similar to types SN55113/SN75113) and a differential line receiver (similar to types SN55113/SN75113). The driver is of three-state design and is capable of sourcing and sinking 40-milliampere load currents or of presenting a high impedance to the transmission line terminals when in the inhibited state. Both the driver input and the enable input are TTL/DTL compatible. The differential receiver inputs, which are also connected to the transmission line terminals, have high impedance and present a negligible load to the line. The receiver includes a TTL/DTL-compatible strobe input and has a TTL/DTL-compatible output. Both the driver and receiver operate from the same 5-volt power supply.

supply voltage: 5 V nominal

operating free-air temperature ranges: SN55117 . . . −55°C to 125°C
SN75117 . . . 0°C to 70°C

packages: 8-pin JP and P dual-in-line packages

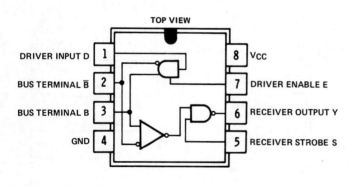

TOP VIEW

DRIVER INPUT D — 1 | 8 — V_CC
BUS TERMINAL B̄ — 2 | 7 — DRIVER ENABLE E
BUS TERMINAL B — 3 | 6 — RECEIVER OUTPUT Y
GND — 4 | 5 — RECEIVER STROBE S

FUNCTION TABLE (TRANSMITTING)

INPUTS			OUTPUTS		
E	S	D	B	B̄	Y
H	H	H	H	L	H
H	H	L	L	H	L
H	L	H	H	L	H
H	L	L	L	H	H
L	H	X	Z	Z	?
L	L	X	Z	Z	H

FUNCTION TABLE (RECEIVING)

INPUTS					OUTPUT
E	S	B	B̄	D	Y
L	H	H	L	X	H
L	H	L	H	X	L
L	L	X	X	X	H

H = high level
L = low level
X = irrelevant
Z = high impedance (off)
? = indeterminate

TEXAS INSTRUMENTS
INCORPORATED
POST OFFICE BOX 5012 • DALLAS, TEXAS 75222

SN55142, SN75142 . . . DUAL LINE RECEIVER

key features

- Individual receiver reference voltage (externally adjustable)
- Fixed internal reference (2.5 V) available at pin 9
- Common and individual strobes
- Single 5-V power supply
- ±100-mV sensitivity
- Low input current

description

The SN55142 and SN75142 are monolithic dual line receivers designed to interface with TTL systems and single-ended transmission lines. These circuits have all the features of the SN75140, but also offer separate strobes for each receiver, separate reference terminals, and a built-in 2.5-volt reference supply. The externally adjustable reference voltage allows noise margin to be optimized for a given system design. Since each receiver has a separate reference pin, it is possible to use the SN55142 or SN75142 with two different reference voltages simultaneously if so desired. Another feature is an internally generated 2.5-volt reference, which is available at pin 9 for systems that require the receiver threshold to be set half-way between 0 and 5 volts. This 2.5-volt reference can be adjusted ±1 volt by means of a single external resistor. The receiver sensitivity is guaranteed at ±100 millivolts over the range of externally applied reference voltage. Outputs are compatible with standard Series 54/74 TTL and can be controlled by a common strobe or by individual strobes.

supply voltage: 5 V nominal

operating free-air temperature ranges: SN55142 . . . −55°C to 125°C
SN75142 . . . 0°C to 70°C

packages: J and N dual-in-line packages

TOP VIEW

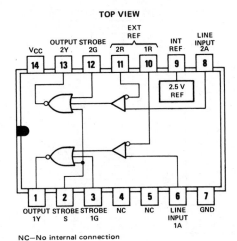

NC—No internal connection

FUNCTION TABLE
(EACH RECEIVER)

LINE INPUT	STROBES		OUTPUT
	G	S	Y
V_{ref}−100 mV	L	L	H
V_{ref}+100 mV	X	X	L
X	H	X	L
X	X	H	L

H = high level, L = low level, X = irrelevant

SN75362 . . . DUAL TTL-TO-MOS DRIVER

key features

- Dual inverting TTL-to-MOS driver
- Versatile interface circuit for use between TTL and high-current, high-voltage systems
- Equivalent to 1/2 of SN75365 device but with single input per channel
- Compatible with many popular MOS RAMs
- TTL and DTL compatible diode-clamped inputs
- V_{CC3} supply pin available, which can be connected to V_{CC2} supply pin in some applications
- High-speed switching
- Low standby power dissipation

description

The SN75362 is a monolithic dual TTL-to-MOS driver and interface circuit. The device accepts standard TTL and DTL input signals and provides high-current and high-voltage output levels suitable for driving MOS circuits. Specifically, it may be used to drive address, control, and timing inputs for several types of MOS RAMs including TMS4062, TMS7001,* and '1103.

supply voltages:

	MIN	NOM	MAX	UNIT
V_{CC1}	4.75	5	5.25	V
V_{CC2}	4.75	20	24	V
$V_{CC3}-V_{CC2}$	0	4	10	V

operating free-air temperature range: 0°C to 70°C

packages: 8-pin P dual-in-line package

TOP VIEW

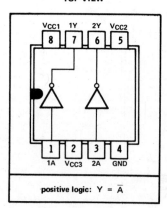

positive logic: Y = $\overline{A}$

*To be announced

TEXAS INSTRUMENTS
INCORPORATED
POST OFFICE BOX 5012 • DALLAS, TEXAS 75222

SN55367, SN75367 . . . QUAD TTL-TO-CMOS DRIVER WITH THREE-STATE OUTPUTS

key features

- Quad inverting TTL-to-CMOS driver
- Versatile interface circuit for use between TTL and high-current, high-voltage systems
- High-speed, three-state outputs
- TTL and DTL compatible inputs
- Separate address and enable/disable inputs per driver
- Output short-circuit protection

description

The SN55367 and SN75367 are monolithic, quadruple, TTL-to-CMOS driver and interface circuits with three-state outputs. The devices accept standard TTL and DTL input signals and create output levels suitable for driving CMOS devices. Each driver output may be disabled to the high-impedance state to allow multiple drivers to be connected to the same bus line for selective enable operation.

supply voltage: V_{CC1} . . . . 5 V nominal
V_{CC2} . . . . 12 V nominal

operating free-air temperature ranges: SN55367 . . . −55°C to 125°C
SN75367 . . . 0°C to 70°C

packages: 16-pin J, JB, and N dual-in-line and SB flat packages

TOP VIEW

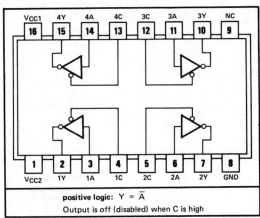

positive logic: $Y = \overline{A}$
Output is off (disabled) when C is high

NC—No internal connection
PIN 8 OF THE JB AND SB PACKAGES IS IN
ELECTRICAL CONTACT WITH THE METAL BASE

SN75368 . . . DUAL ECL-TO-MOS DRIVER

key features

- Dual ECL-to-MOS driver

- Dual ECL-to-TTL driver

- Versatile interface circuit for use between ECL and high-current, high-voltage systems

- Series SN10000 ECL and IBM grounded-reference ECL-compatible inputs

- Single in-phase and dual out-of-phase inputs per driver

- V_{CC3} supply pins available, which can be connected to V_{CC2} supply pin in some applications

- High-speed switching

- Compatible with many popular MOS RAMs

description

The SN75368 is a monolithic dual ECL-to-MOS driver and interface circuit. The device accepts standard SN10000 Series ECL and IBM grounded-reference ECL input signals and creates high-current and high-voltage output levels suitable for driving MOS circuits. Specifically, it may be used to drive address, control, and timing inputs for several types of MOS RAMs including TMS4062, TMS7001*, and 1103. The device may also be used as an ECL-to-TTL converter.

*To be announced.

supply voltages:

	MIN	NOM	MAX	UNIT
V_{CC1} . . .	4.75	5	5.25	V
V_{CC2} . . .	4.75	20	24	V
$V_{CC3} - V_{CC2}$ . . .	0	4	10	V
V_{EE} . . .	-4.68	-5.2	-5.72	V

operating free-air temperature range: 0°C to 70°C

packages: 14-pin J and N dual-in-line packages

TOP VIEW

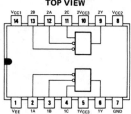

functions

positive-NOR gate

$Y = \overline{A+B}$

FUNCTION TABLE

CONFIGURATION	INPUTS			OUTPUT
	A	B	C	Y
C at V_{BB}	L	L	V_{BB}	H
	H	X	V_{BB}	L
	X	H	V_{BB}	L

noninverting gate

$Y = C$

FUNCTION TABLE

CONFIGURATION	INPUTS			OUTPUT
	A	B	C	Y
A and B at V_{BB}	V_{BB}	V_{BB}	L	L
	V_{BB}	V_{BB}	H	H
A at V_{BB}, B connected low	V_{BB}	L	L	L
	V_{BB}	L	H	H
B at V_{BB}, A connected low	L	V_{BB}	L	L
	L	V_{BB}	H	H

differential ECL line receiver

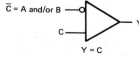

$\overline{C}$ = A and/or B

$Y = C$

FUNCTION TABLE

CONFIGURATION	INPUTS			OUTPUT
	A	B	C	Y
A and B connected together	H	H	L	L
	L	L	H	H
A not used but connected low	L	H	L	L
	L	L	H	H
B not used but connected low	H	L	L	L
	L	L	H	H

H = high level, L = low level, X = irrelevant

V_{BB} = Reference Supply voltage for SN10000 Series ECL.

TEXAS INSTRUMENTS
INCORPORATED

POST OFFICE BOX 5012 • DALLAS, TEXAS 75222

SN75369 . . . DUAL CURRENT-INPUT-TO-MOS DRIVER

key features

- Dual current-input-to-MOS driver
- Versatile high-current, high-voltage interface circuit
- Functional replacement for National MH0026
- Single input per driver driven by current source
- Compatible with TMS6003 clock lines
- Required TTL-to-MOS negative-level shifting may be done with external input p-n-p current source or by a coupling capacitor
- V_{CC} supply voltage variable to 24 V maximum with respect to V_{EE}
- High-speed switching
- Low standby dissipation

description

The SN75369 is a monolithic dual current-input-to-MOS driver and interface circuit. The device accepts appropriate input currents and provides high-current, high-voltage output levels suitable for driving MOS circuits. Specifically, it may be used to drive the clock inputs of the TMS6003 MOS RAM and the address, control, and timing inputs for several other types of MOS RAMs.

supply voltage: $V_{CC} = V_{EE} + 20$ V nominal

operating free-air temperature range: 0°C to 70°C

package: 8-pin P and 14-pin J and N dual-in-line packages

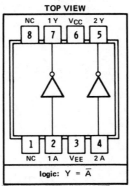

TOP VIEW

logic: $Y = \overline{A}$

NC—No internal connection

SN55329 . . . MSI EIGHT-CHANNEL CORE MEMORY DRIVER

key features

- **Series 54 TTL compatible inputs**
- **±350-mA output current capability**
- **Fast switching times**
- **Internal power control does not require power supply sequencing**

3

description

The SN55329 is an MSI TTL eight-channel memory driver that is ideal for use with military magnetic core memory systems. The circuit contains eight decoded, bipolar, three-state, high-current drivers, a 3-line-to-8-line decoder, power control, source/sink selection, and timing logic. Nominal power supplies are 5 volts and 12 volts with the output core lines returning to 5 volts. Package standby power is typically 30 milliwatts with one-watt nominal operating power. Source and sink output current amplitudes can be controlled as a function of temperature to within ±5.5% by four shared external resistors and two temperature-controlled power supplies.

supply voltage: V_{CC1} = 5 V nominal
V_{CC2} = 12 V nominal
Both TCV(source) and TCV(sink) power supplies can be temperature controlled.

operating case temperature range: −55°C to 110°C

packages: RA 24-pin custom flat package   **functional block diagram**

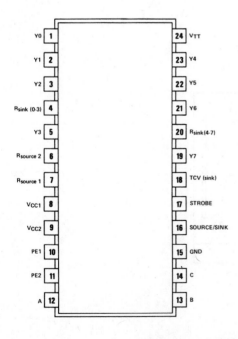

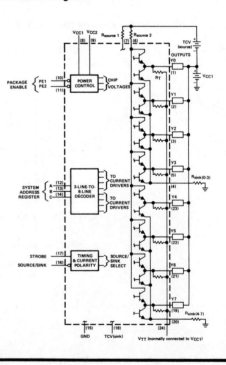

TEXAS INSTRUMENTS
INCORPORATED
POST OFFICE BOX 5012 • DALLAS, TEXAS 75222

SN75401 SERIES . . . DUAL PERIPHERAL DRIVERS

key features

- 500-mA output current capability
- High-voltage outputs
- No output latch-up at 30 V
- Medium-speed switching

description

The SN75401 Series is a group of dual peripheral drivers designed for use in systems that require higher output currents than those of the SN75461 Series drivers at essentially the same switching speeds. The SN75401, SN75402, SN75403, and SN75404 provide (assuming positive logic) AND, NAND, OR, and NOR drivers, respectively, with the output of the logic gates internally connected to the bases of the n-p-n output transistors.

supply voltage: 7 V nominal

operating free-air temperature range: 0°C to 70°C

package: 8-pin ND package with integral heat sink

SN75401 (TOP VIEW)

FUNCTION TABLE
(EACH DRIVER)

INPUTS		OUTPUT
A	B	Y
L	L	L
L	H	L
H	L	L
H	H	H

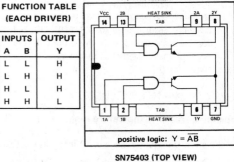

positive logic: Y = AB

SN75402 (TOP VIEW)

FUNCTION TABLE
(EACH DRIVER)

INPUTS		OUTPUT
A	B	Y
L	L	H
L	H	H
H	L	H
H	H	L

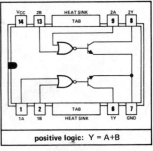

positive logic: $Y = \overline{AB}$

SN75403 (TOP VIEW)

FUNCTION TABLE
(EACH DRIVER)

INPUTS		OUTPUT
A	B	Y
L	L	L
L	H	H
H	L	H
H	H	H

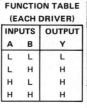

positive logic: Y = A+B

SN75404 (TOP VIEW)

FUNCTION TABLE
(EACH DRIVER)

INPUTS		OUTPUT
A	B	Y
L	L	H
L	H	L
H	L	L
H	H	L

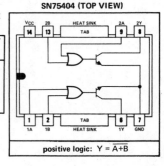

positive logic: $Y = \overline{A+B}$

3

SN75411 SERIES . . . DUAL PERIPHERAL DRIVERS

key features

- 500-mA output current capability
- High-voltage outputs
- No output latch-up at 40 V
- Medium-speed switching

description

The SN75411 Series is a group of dual peripheral drivers designed for use in systems that require higher output voltages than those of the SN75401 Series drivers at essentially the same switching speeds. The SN75411, SN75412, SN75413, and SN75414 provide (assuming positive logic) AND, NAND, OR, and NOR drivers, respectively, with the output of the logic gates internally connected to the bases of the n-p-n output transistors.

supply voltage: 7 V nominal

operating free-air temperature range: 0°C to 70°C

package: 8-pin ND package with integral heat sink

FUNCTION TABLE
(EACH DRIVER)

INPUTS		OUTPUT
A	B	Y
L	L	L
L	H	L
H	L	L
H	H	H

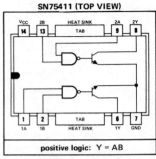

SN75411 (TOP VIEW)

positive logic: Y = AB

FUNCTION TABLE
(EACH DRIVER)

INPUTS		OUTPUT
A	B	Y
L	L	H
L	H	H
H	L	H
H	H	L

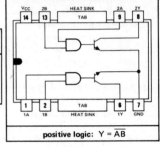

SN75412 (TOP VIEW)

positive logic: Y = $\overline{AB}$

FUNCTION TABLE
(EACH DRIVER)

INPUTS		OUTPUT
A	B	Y
L	L	L
L	H	H
H	L	H
H	H	H

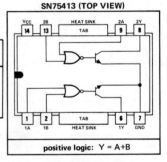

SN75413 (TOP VIEW)

positive logic: Y = A+B

FUNCTION TABLE
(EACH DRIVER)

INPUTS		OUTPUT
A	B	Y
L	L	H
L	H	L
H	L	L
H	H	L

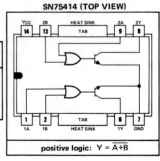

SN75414 (TOP VIEW)

positive logic: Y = $\overline{A+B}$

TEXAS INSTRUMENTS
INCORPORATED
POST OFFICE BOX 5012 • DALLAS, TEXAS 75222

SERIES SN55470/SN75470 . . . DUAL PERIPHERAL DRIVERS

key features

- 300-mA output current capability
- High-voltage outputs
- No output latchup at 40 V
- Medium-speed switching

description

The SN55470/SN75470 series is a group of dual peripheral drivers designed for use in systems that require higher breakdown voltages than the SN75460 Series can provide at the expense of slightly slower switching speeds. Each SN55470 or SN75470 includes two standard Series 54/74 TTL NAND gates and two uncommitted, high-current, high-voltage n-p-n transistors. The SN55471/SN75471, SN55472/SN75472, SN55473/SN75473, and SN55474/SN75474 provide (assuming positive logic) AND, NAND, OR, and NOR drivers, respectively, with the output of the logic gates internally connected to the bases of the n-p-n output transistors.

supply voltage: 7 V nominal

operating free-air temperature ranges: SN55470 . . . −55°C to 125°C
SN75470 . . . 0°C to 70°C

packages: 14-pin J, JB, and N dual-in-line packages
8-pin JP and P dual-in-line and L plug-in packages

SN55470, SN75470

J, JB, OR N
DUAL-IN-LINE PACKAGE (TOP VIEW)

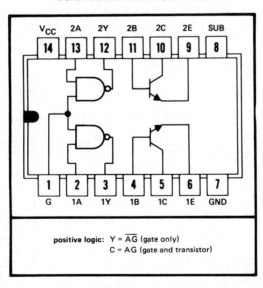

positive logic: Y = $\overline{AG}$ (gate only)
C = AG (gate and transistor)

SN55471, SN75471

FUNCTION TABLE

A	B	Y
L	L	L (on state)
L	H	L (on state)
H	L	L (on state)
H	H	H (off state)

H = high level, L = low level

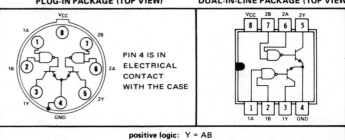

L
PLUG-IN PACKAGE (TOP VIEW)

JP OR P
DUAL-IN-LINE PACKAGE (TOP VIEW)

PIN 4 IS IN ELECTRICAL CONTACT WITH THE CASE

positive logic: Y = AB

SN55472, SN75472

FUNCTION TABLE

A	B	Y
L	L	H (off state)
L	H	H (off state)
H	L	H (off state)
H	H	L (on state)

H = high level, L = low level

L
PLUG-IN PACKAGE (TOP VIEW)

JP OR P
DUAL-IN-LINE PACKAGE (TOP VIEW)

PIN 4 IS IN ELECTRICAL CONTACT WITH THE CASE

positive logic: Y = $\overline{AB}$

SN55473, SN55473

FUNCTION TABLE

A	B	Y
L	L	L (on state)
L	H	H (off state)
H	L	H (off state)
H	H	H (off state)

H = high level, L = low level

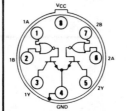
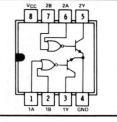

L
PLUG-IN PACKAGE (TOP VIEW)

JP OR P
DUAL-IN-LINE PACKAGE (TOP VIEW)

PIN 4 IS IN ELECTRICAL CONTACT WITH THE CASE

positive logic: Y = A + B

SN55474, SN75474

FUNCTION TABLE

A	B	Y
L	L	H (off state)
L	H	L (on state)
H	L	L (on state)
H	H	L (on state)

H = high level, L = low level

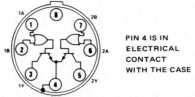

L
PLUG-IN PACKAGE (TOP VIEW)

JP OR P
DUAL-IN-LINE PACKAGE (TOP VIEW)

PIN 4 IS IN ELECTRICAL CONTACT WITH THE CASE

positive logic: Y = $\overline{A + B}$

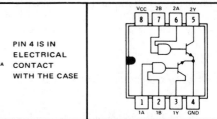

3-16

Operational Amplifiers

Series 52 (−55°C to 125°C operating temperature range)
Series 62 (−25°C to 85°C operating temperature range)

OPERATIONAL AMPLIFIERS, INTERNALLY COMPENSATED

FEATURES	SN52L022	SN52L044	SN52107	SN52110	SN52558	SN52741	SN52747	SN52771	SN62088	UNIT
Input Offset Voltage, Max	6	6	3	6	6	6	6	7	0.1	mV
Temperature Coefficient of Input Offset Voltage, Max	NS	NS	15	12[†]	NS	NS	NS	NS	0.6[†]	μV/°C
Input Offset Current, Max	100	100	20	NS	500	500	500	5	10	nA
Temperature Coefficient of Input Offset Current, Max	NS	NS	200	NS	NS	NS	NS	NS	NS	pA/°C
Input Bias Current, Max	250	250	100	10	1500	1500	1500	35	20	nA
Maximum Output Voltage Swing, Min	20	20	24	20	24	24	24	24	20	V
Voltage Amplification, Min	4	4	25	VF	25	25	25	25	100	V/mV
Input Resistance, Min	NS	NS	1.5[‡]	10 000	0.3[‡]	0.3[‡]	0.3[‡]	100[†]	NS	MΩ
Common-Mode Rejection Ratio, Min	60	60	80	NS	70	70	70	80	80[†]	dB
Supply Voltage Rejection Ratio or Sensitivity¶	150 μV/V	150 μV/V	80 dB	70 dB	150 μV/V	150 μV/V	150 μV/V	150 μV/V	300 μV/V	
Short-Circuit Output Current, Typ	6	6	25	25	25	25	25	22	25	mA
Supply Current, Max	0.2	0.4	2.5	5.5	6.6	3.3	6.6	2	10[†]	mA
Slew Rate at Unity Gain, Typ	0.5	0.5	0.5	30	0.5	0.5	0.5	2.5	25	V/μs
Min Supply Voltage	±5	±5	±5	±5	±5[§]	±5[§]	±5[§]	±5	±12	V
Max Supply Voltage	±22	±22	±20[§]	±18	±18[§]	±18[§]	±18[§]	±22	±18	V
Offset Adjust	No	No	Yes	Yes	No	Yes	Yes	Yes	No	
No. Per Package	2	4	1	1	2	1	2	1	1	

OPERATIONAL AMPLIFIERS, EXTERNALLY COMPENSATED

FEATURES	SN52101A	SN52108A	SN52108	SN52660	SN52702A	SN52702	SN52709A	SN52709	SN52748	SN52770	SN52777	UNIT
Input Offset Voltage, Max	3	1	3	5	3	6	3	6	6	7	3	mV
Temperature Coefficient of Input Offset Voltage, Max	15	5	5	25	10	NS	25	NS	NS	NS	15	μV/°C
Input Offset Current, Max	20	0.4	0.4	5	1500	3000	250	500	500	5	10	nA
Temperature Coefficient of Input Offset Current, Max	200	2.5	2.5	40	16000	NS	2800	NS	NS	NS	150	pA/°C
Input Bias Current, Max	100	3	3	25	10000	20000	600	1500	1500	35	75	nA
Maximum Output Voltage Swing, Min	24	26	26	26	10	10	24	24	24	24	24	V
Voltage Amplification, Min	25	40	25	25	2	1	25	25	25	25	25	V/mV
Input Resistance, Min	1.5[‡]	30[‡]	30[‡]	4	0.006	0.003	0.085	0.04	0.3[‡]	100[†]	2	MΩ
Common-Mode Rejection Ratio, Min	80	96	85	80	70	70[‡]	80	70	70	80	80	dB
Supply Voltage Rejection Ratio or Sensitivity¶	80 dB	96 dB	80 dB	80 dB	200 μV/V	300 μV/V[‡]	100 μV/V	150 μV/V	150 μV/V	150 μV/V	100 μV/V	
Short-Circuit Output Current, Typ	25	15	15	15	NS	NS	NS	NS	25	22	25	mA
Supply Current, Max	2.5	0.6	0.6	1	7.5	6.7[‡]	4.5	5.5[‡]	3.3	2	3.3	mA
Slew Rate at Unity Gain, Typ	0.5	0.2	0.2	0.2	1.7	1.7	0.25	0.25	0.5	2.5	0.5	V/μs
Min Supply Voltage	±5[§]	±5	±5	±5	+6[§] −3[§]	+6[§] −3[§]	±9[§]	±9[§]	±5[§]	±5	±5[§]	V
Max Supply Voltage	±20[§]	±20	±20	±20	+12[§] −6[§]	+12[§] −6[§]	±15[§]	±15[§]	±18[§]	±22	±18	V
Offset Adjust	Yes	No	No	No	No	No	No	No	Yes	Yes	Yes	
No. Per Package	1	1	1	1	1	1	1	1	1	1	1	

NS ≡ Not specified
VF ≡ Voltage follower, minimum gain = 0.999 V/V
[†]Typical value at $T_A = 25°C$
[‡]$T_A = 25°C$

¶Supply voltage rejection ratio is the reciprocal of supply voltage sensitivity. Stated values are minimum in dB or maximum in μV/V, respectively.

Series 72 (0°C to 70°C operating temperature range)

OPERATIONAL AMPLIFIERS, INTERNALLY COMPENSATED

FEATURES	SN72L022	SN72L044	SN72088	SN72307	SN72310	SN72558	SN72741	SN72747	SN72771	UNIT
Input Offset Voltage, Max	7.5	7.5	0.25	10	10	7.5	7.5	7.5	14	mV
Temperature Coefficient of Input Offset Voltage, Max	NS	NS	1†	30	10†	NS	NS	NS	NS	µV/°C
Input Offset Current, Max	200	200	15	70	NS	300	300	300	14	nA
Temperature Coefficient of Input Offset Current, Max	NS	NS	NS	600	NS	NS	NS	NS	NS	pA/°C
Input Bias Current, Max	400	400	30	300	10	800	800	800	40	nA
Maximum Output Voltage Swing, Min	20	20	20	24	20	24	24	24	22	V
Voltage Amplification, Min	2	2	100	15	VF	15	15	25	25	V/mV
Input Resistance, Min	NS	NS	NS	0.5‡	10 000	0.3‡	0.3‡	0.3‡	100†	MΩ
Common-Mode Rejection Ratio, Min	60	60	80†	70	NS	70	70	70	70	dB
Supply Voltage Rejection Ratio or Sensitivity¶	200 µV/V	200 µV/V	300 µV/V†	70 dB	70 dB	150 µV/V	150 µV/V	150 µV/V	200 µV/V	
Short-Circuit Output Current, Typ	6	6	25	25	25	25	25	25	22	mA
Supply Current, Max	0.25	0.5	10†	3‡	5.5	6.6	3.3	6.6	4	mA
Slew Rate at Unity Gain, Typ	0.5	0.5	25	0.5	30	0.5	0.5	0.5	2.5	V/µs
Min Supply Voltage	±5	±5	±5	±5	±5	±5§	±5§	±5§	±5§	V
Max Supply Voltage	±18	±18	±18	±15	±18	±18§	±18§	±18§	±18§	V
Offset Adjust	No	No	No	Yes	Yes	No	Yes	Yes	Yes	
No. Per Package	2	4	1	1	1	2	1	2	1	

OPERATIONAL AMPLIFIERS, EXTERNALLY COMPENSATED

FEATURES	SN72301A	SN72308A	SN72308	SN72660	SN72702	SN72709	SN72748	SN72770	SN72777	UNIT
Input Offset Voltage, Max	10	0.73	10	6	15	10	7.5	14	5	mV
Temperature Coefficient of Input Offset Voltage, Max	30	5	30	30	NS	NS	NS	NS	30	µV/°C
Input Offset Current, Max	70	1.5	1.5	4	7500	750	300	14	40	nA
Temperature Coefficient of Input Offset Current, Max	600	10	10	40	NS	NS	NS	NS	600	pA/°C
Input Bias Current, Max	300	10	10	25	20 000	2000	800	40	200	nA
Maximum Output Voltage Swing, Min	24	26	26	26	10‡	24	24	22	24	V
Voltage Amplification, Min	15	60	15	15	0.8	12	25	25	15	V/mV
Input Resistance, Min	0.5‡	10‡	10‡	4‡	0.0035	0.035	0.3‡	100†	1†	MΩ
Common-Mode Rejection Ratio, Min	70	96	80	80	65‡	65‡	70	70	70	dB
Supply Voltage Rejection Ratio or Sensitivity¶	70 dB	96 dB	80 dB	80 dB	300 µV/V‡	200 µV/V‡	150 µV/V	200 µV/V	150 µV/V	
Short-Circuit Output Current, Typ	25	15	15	15	NS	NS	25	22	25	mA
Supply Current, Max	3‡	0.8	0.8	1	7‡	6.7‡	3.3	4	3.3	mA
Slew Rate at Unity Gain, Typ	0.5	0.2	0.2	0.2	1.7	0.25	0.5	2.5	0.5	V/µs
Min Supply Voltage	±5	±5	±5	±5	+6 −3	±9	±5§	±5	±5§	V
Max Supply Voltage	±15	±18	±18	±18	+12 −6	±15	±18§	±18	±18§	V
Offset Adjust	Yes	No	No	No	No	No	Yes	Yes	Yes	
No. Per Package	1	1	1	1	1	1	1	1	1	

NS ≡ Not specified
VF ≡ Voltage follower, minimum gain = 0.999 V/V
† Typical value at T_A = 25°C
‡ T_A = 25°C
§ Recommended operating voltage range limit

¶ Supply voltage rejection ratio is the reciprocal of supply voltage sensitivity. Stated values are minimum in dB or maximum in µV/V, respectively.

TEXAS INSTRUMENTS
INCORPORATED
POST OFFICE BOX 5012 • DALLAS, TEXAS 75222

- **Very Low Power Consumption**
- **Typical Power Dissipation with ±2-V Supplies . . . 170 μW**
- **Low Input Bias and Offset Currents**
- **Output Short-Circuit Protection**
- **Low Input Offset Voltage**
- **Internal Frequency Compensation**
- **Latch-Up-Free Operation**
- **Popular Dual Op Amp Pin-Out**

description

The SN52L022 and SN72L022 are dual low-power operational amplifiers designed to replace higher-power devices in many applications without sacrificing system performance. High input impedance, low supply currents, and low equivalent input noise voltage over a wide range of operating supply voltages result in extremely versatile operational amplifiers for use in a variety of analog applications including battery-operated circuits. Internal frequency compensation, absence of latch-up, high slew rate, and output short-circuit protection assure ease of use.

The SN52L022 is characterized for operation over the full military temperature range of -55°C to 125°C; the SN72L022 is characterized for operation from 0°C to 70°C.

terminal assignments

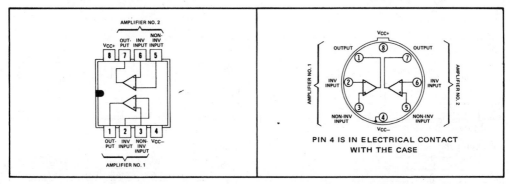

JP OR P
DUAL-IN-LINE PACKAGE (TOP VIEW)

L
PLUG-IN PACKAGE (TOP VIEW)

PIN 4 IS IN ELECTRICAL CONTACT WITH THE CASE

absolute maximum ratings over operating free-air temperature range (unless otherwise noted)

		SN52L022	SN72L022	UNIT
Supply voltage V_{CC+} (see Note 1)		22	18	V
Supply voltage V_{CC-} (see Note 1)		-22	-18	V
Differential input voltage (see Note 2)		±30	±30	V
Input voltage (any input, see Notes 1 and 3)		±15	±15	V
Duration of output short-circuit (see Note 4)		unlimited	unlimited	
Continuous total dissipation at (or below) 25°C	Each amplifier	500	500	mW
free-air temperature range (see Note 5)	Total package	680	680	mW
Operating free-air temperature range		-55 to 125	0 to 70	$^\circ$C
Storage temperature range		-65 to 150	-65 to 150	$^\circ$C
Lead temperature 1/16 inch from case for 60 seconds	L or JP Package	300	300	$^\circ$C
Lead temperature 1/16 inch from case for 10 seconds	P Package	260	260	$^\circ$C

NOTES: 1. All voltage values, unless otherwise noted, are with respect to the zero-reference level (ground) of the supply voltage where the zero-reference level is the midpoint between V_{CC+} and V_{CC-}. If the zero-reference level of the system is not the midpoint of the supply voltages, all voltage values must be changed accordingly.
2. Differential voltages are at the noninverting input terminal with respect to the inverting input terminal.
3. The magnitude of the input voltage must never exceed the magnitude of the supply voltage or 15 volts, whichever is less.
4. The output may be shorted to ground or either power supply. For the SN52L022 only, the unlimited duration of the short-circuit applies at (or below) 125°C case temperature or 75°C free-air temperature.
5. For operation above 25°C free-air temperature, refer to Dissipation Derating Curve, Figure 3.

TYPES SN52L022, SN72L022
DUAL LOW-POWER OPERATIONAL AMPLIFIERS

electrical characteristics at specified free-air temperature, V_{CC+} = 15 V, V_{CC-} = −15 V

PARAMETER		TEST CONDITIONS[†]		SN52L022			SN72L022			UNIT
				MIN	TYP	MAX	MIN	TYP	MAX	
V_{IO}	Input offset voltage	$R_S \leq 10\ k\Omega$	25°C		1	5		1	5	mV
			Full range			6			7.5	
I_{IO}	Input offset current		25°C		5	40		15	80	nA
			Full range			100			200	
I_{IB}	Input bias current		25°C		50	100		100	250	nA
			Full range			250			400	
V_I	Input voltage range		25°C	±12	±13		±12	±13		V
			Full range	±12			±12			
V_{OPP}	Maximum peak-to-peak output voltage swing	$R_L = 10\ k\Omega$	25°C	20	26		20	26		V
		$R_L \geq 10\ k\Omega$	Full range	20			20			
A_{VD}	Large-signal differential voltage amplification	$R_L \geq 10\ k\Omega$, $V_O = \pm10\ V$	25°C	72	86		60	80		dB
			Full range	72			60			
B_1	Unity-gain bandwidth		25°C		0.8			0.8		MHz
CMRR	Common-mode rejection ratio	$R_S \leq 10\ k\Omega$	25°C	60	72		60	72		dB
			Full range	60			60			
$\Delta V_{IO}/\Delta V_{CC}$	Supply voltage sensitivity	$R_S \leq 10\ k\Omega$	25°C		30	150		30	200	μV/V
			Full range			150			200	
V_n	Equivalent input noise voltage	A_{VD} = 20 dB, B = 1 Hz, f = 1 kHz	25°C		50			50		nV/$\sqrt{Hz}$
I_{OS}	Short-circuit output current		25°C		±6			±6		mA
I_{CC}	Supply current (Both amplifiers)	No load, No signal	25°C		130	200		130	250	μA
			Full range			200			250	
P_D	Total dissipation (Both amplifiers)	No load, No signal	25°C		3.9	6		3.9	7.5	mW
			Full range			6			7.5	

[†]All characteristics are specified under open-loop operation, unless otherwise noted. Full range for SN52L022 is −55°C to 125°C and for SN72L022 is 0°C to 70°C.

operating characteristics, V_{CC+} = 15 V, V_{CC-} = −15 V, T_A = 25°C

PARAMETER		TEST CONDITIONS		SN52L022			SN72L022			UNIT
				MIN	TYP	MAX	MIN	TYP	MAX	
t_r	Rise time	V_I = 20 mV, R_L = 10 kΩ, C_L = 100 pF, See Figure 1			0.3			0.3		μs
	Overshoot				5%			5%		
SR	Slew rate at unity gain	V_I = 10 V, R_L = 10 kΩ, C_L = 100 pF, See Figure 1			0.5			0.5		V/μs

schematic

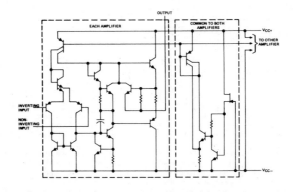

TEXAS INSTRUMENTS
INCORPORATED
POST OFFICE BOX 5012 • DALLAS, TEXAS 75222

DEFINITION OF TERMS

Input Offset Voltage (V_{IO}) The d-c voltage that must be applied between the input terminals to force the quiescent d-c output voltage to zero. The input offset voltage may also be defined for the case where two equal resistances (R_S) are inserted in series with the input leads.

Input Offset Current (I_{IO}) The difference between the currents into the two input terminals with the output at zero volts.

Input Bias Current (I_{IB}) The average of the currents into the two input terminals with the output at zero volts.

Input Voltage Range (V_I) The range of voltage that if exceeded at either input terminal will cause the amplifier to cease functioning properly.

Maximum Peak-to-Peak Output Voltage Swing (V_{OPP}) The maximum peak-to-peak output voltage that can be obtained without waveform clipping when the quiescent d-c output voltage is zero.

Large-Signal Differential Voltage Amplification (A_{VD}) The ratio of the peak-to-peak output voltage swing to the change in differential input voltage required to drive the output.

Unity-Gain Bandwidth (B_1) The range of frequencies within which the voltage amplification is greater than unity.

Common-Mode Rejection Ratio (CMRR) The ratio of differential voltage amplification to common-mode voltage amplification. This is measured by determining the ratio of a change in input common-mode voltage to the resulting change in input offset voltage.

Supply Voltage Sensitivity ($\Delta V_{IO}/\Delta V_{CC}$) The ratio of the change in input offset voltage to the change in supply voltages producing it. For these devices, both supply voltages are varied symmetrically.

Short-Circuit Output Current (I_{OS}) The maximum output current available from the amplifier with the output shorted to ground or to either supply.

Total Dissipation (P_D) The total d-c power supplied to the device less any power delivered from the device to a load. At no load: $P_D = V_{CC+} \cdot I_{CC+} + V_{CC-} \cdot I_{CC-}$.

Rise Time (t_r) The time required for an output voltage step to change from 10% to 90% of its final value.

Overshoot The quotient of: (1) the largest deviation of the output signal value from its steady-state value after a step-function change of the input signal, and (2) the difference between the output signal values in the steady state before and after the step-function change of the input signal.

Slew Rate (SR) The average time rate of change of the closed-loop amplifier output voltage for a step-signal input. Slew rate is measured between specified output levels (0 and 10 volts for this device) with feedback adjusted for unity gain.

TYPES SN52L022, SN72L022
DUAL LOW-POWER OPERATIONAL AMPLIFIERS

PARAMETER MEASUREMENT INFORMATION

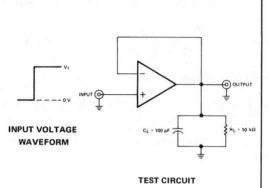

INPUT VOLTAGE WAVEFORM

$C_L = 100$ pF $R_L = 10$ kΩ

TEST CIRCUIT

FIGURE 1—RISE TIME, OVERSHOOT, AND SLEW RATE

TYPICAL CHARACTERISTICS

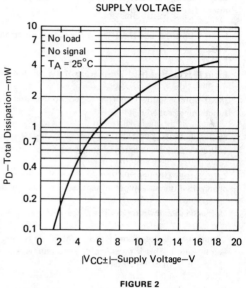

TOTAL DISSIPATION
vs
SUPPLY VOLTAGE

No load
No signal
$T_A = 25°C$

P_D—Total Dissipation—mW

$|V_{CC\pm}|$—Supply Voltage—V

FIGURE 2

THERMAL INFORMATION

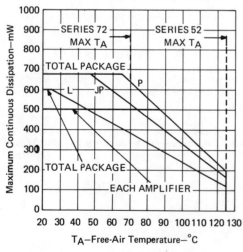

DISSIPATION DERATING CURVE

Maximum Continuous Dissipation—mW

SERIES 72 MAX T_A SERIES 52 MAX T_A

TOTAL PACKAGE

L   JP   P

TOTAL PACKAGE

EACH AMPLIFIER

T_A—Free-Air Temperature—°C

PKG	DERATE	FROM (TOT PKG)	FROM (EACH AMPLIFIER)
L	4.8 mW/°C	25°C	46°C
JP	6.6 mW/°C	47°C	74°C
P	8.0 mW/°C	65°C	87°C

FIGURE 3

TEXAS INSTRUMENTS
INCORPORATED
POST OFFICE BOX 5012 • DALLAS, TEXAS 75222

LINEAR INTEGRATED CIRCUITS

TYPES SN52L044, SN72L044
QUAD LOW-POWER OPERATIONAL AMPLIFIERS

BULLETIN NO. DL-S 7312039, SEPTEMBER 1973

- Very Low Power Consumption
- Typical Power Dissipation with ±2-V Supplies . . . 340 μW
- Low Input Bias and Offset Currents
- Output Short-Circuit Protection
- Low Input Offset Voltage
- Internal Frequency Compensation
- Latch-Up-Free Operation
- Power Applied in Pairs

description

The SN52L044 and SN72L044 are quad low-power operational amplifiers designed to replace higher-power devices in many applications without sacrificing system performance. High input impedance, low supply currents, and low equivalent input noise voltage over a wide range of operating supply voltages result in extremely versatile operational amplifiers for use in a variety of analog applications including battery-operated circuits. Internal frequency compensation, absence of latch-up, high slew rate, and output short-circuit protection assure ease of use. Power may be applied separately to Section A (amplifiers 1 and 4) or Section B (amplifiers 2 and 3) while the other pair remains unpowered.

The SN52L044 is characterized for operation over the full military temperature range of −55°C to 125°C; the SN72L044 is characterized for operation from 0°C to 70°C.

JA OR N
DUAL-IN-LINE PACKAGE (TOP VIEW)

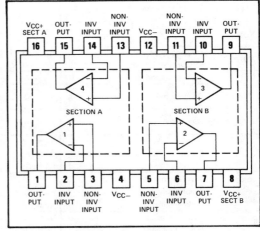

Pins 4 and 12 are internally connected together.

absolute maximum ratings over operating free-air temperature range (unless otherwise noted)

		SN52L044	SN72L044	UNIT
Supply voltage V$_{CC+}$ (see Note 1)		22	18	V
Supply voltage V$_{CC-}$ (see Note 1)		−22	−18	V
Differential input voltage (see Note 2)		±30	±30	V
Input voltage (any input, see Notes 1 and 3)		±15	±15	V
Duration of output short-circuit (see Note 4)		unlimited	unlimited	
Continuous total dissipation at (or below) 25°C	Each amplifier	500	500	mW
free-air temperature range (see Note 5)	Total package	680	680	
Operating free-air temperature range		−55 to 125	0 to 70	°C
Storage temperature range		−65 to 150	−65 to 150	°C
Lead temperature 1/16 inch from case for 60 seconds	JA Package	300	300	°C
Lead temperature 1/16 inch from case for 10 seconds	N Package	260	260	°C

NOTES: 1. All voltage values, unless otherwise noted, are with respect to the zero-reference level (ground) of the supply voltage where the zero-reference level is the midpoint between V$_{CC+}$ and V$_{CC-}$. If the zero-reference level of the system is not the midpoint of the supply voltages, all voltage values must be changed accordingly.
2. Differential voltages are at the noninverting input terminal with respect to the inverting input terminal.
3. The magnitude of the input voltage must never exceed the magnitude of the supply voltage or 15 volts, whichever is less.
4. The output may be shorted to ground or either power supply. For the SN52L044 only, the unlimited duration of the short-circuit applies at (or below) 125°C case temperature or 75°C free-air temperature.
5. For operation above 25°C free-air temperature, refer to Dissipation Derating Curve, Figure 3.

TEXAS INSTRUMENTS
INCORPORATED
POST OFFICE BOX 5012 • DALLAS, TEXAS 75222

electrical characteristics at specified free-air temperature, V_{CC+} = 15 V, V_{CC-} = −15 V

PARAMETER		TEST CONDITIONS†		SN52L044			SN72L044			UNIT
				MIN	TYP	MAX	MIN	TYP	MAX	
V_{IO}	Input offset voltage	$R_S \leqslant$ 10 kΩ	25°C		1	5		1	5	mV
			Full range			6			7.5	
I_{IO}	Input offset current		25°C		5	40		15	80	nA
			Full range			100			200	
I_{IB}	Input bias current		25°C		50	100		100	250	nA
			Full range			250			400	
V_I	Input voltage range		25°C	±12	±13		±12	±13		V
			Full range	±12			±12			
V_{OPP}	Maximum peak-to-peak output voltage swing	R_L = 10 kΩ	25°C	20	26		20	26		V
		$R_L \geqslant$ 10 kΩ	Full range	20			20			
A_{VD}	Large-signal differential voltage amplification	$R_L \geqslant$ 10 kΩ, V_O = ±10 V	25°C	72	86		60	80		dB
			Full range	72			60			
B_1	Unity-gain bandwidth		25°C		0.8			0.8		MHz
CMRR	Common-mode rejection ratio	$R_S \leqslant$ 10 kΩ	25°C	60	72		60	72		dB
			Full range	60			60			
$\Delta V_{IO}/\Delta V_{CC}$	Supply voltage sensitivity	$R_S \leqslant$ 10 kΩ	25°C		30	150		30	200	μV/V
			Full range			150			200	
V_n	Equivalent input noise voltage	A_{VD} = 20 dB, B = 1 Hz, f = 1 kHz	25°C		50			50		nV/$\sqrt{Hz}$
I_{OS}	Short-circuit output current		25°C		±6			±6		mA
I_{CC}	Supply current (Four amplifiers)	No load,	25°C		250	400		250	500	μA
		No signal	Full range			400			500	
P_D	Total dissipation (Four amplifiers)	No load,	25°C		7.5	12		7.5	15	mW
		No signal	Full range			12			15	

†All characteristics are specified under open-loop operation, unless otherwise noted. Full range for SN52L044 is −55°C to 125°C and for SN72L044 is 0°C to 70°C.

operating characteristics, V_{CC+} = 15 V, V_{CC-} = −15 V, T_A = 25°C

PARAMETER		TEST CONDITIONS		SN52L044			SN72L044			UNIT
				MIN	TYP	MAX	MIN	TYP	MAX	
t_r	Rise time	V_I = 20 mV,	R_L = 10 kΩ,		0.3			0.3		μs
	Overshoot	C_L = 100 pF,	See Figure 1		5%			5%		
SR	Slew rate at unity gain	V_I = 10 V, C_L = 100 pF,	R_L = 10 kΩ, See Figure 1		0.5			0.5		V/μs

schematic (each section)

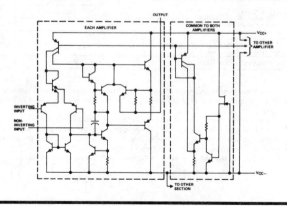

TEXAS INSTRUMENTS
INCORPORATED

POST OFFICE BOX 5012 • DALLAS, TEXAS 75222

DEFINITION OF TERMS

Input Offset Voltage (V_{IO}) The d-c voltage that must be applied between the input terminals to force the quiescent d-c output voltage to zero. The input offset voltage may also be defined for the case where two equal resistances (R_S) are inserted in series with the input leads.

Input Offset Current (I_{IO}) The difference between the currents into the two input terminals with the output at zero volts.

Input Bias Current (I_{IB}) The average of the currents into the two input terminals with the output at zero volts.

Input Voltage Range (V_I) The range of voltage that if exceeded at either input terminal will cause the amplifier to cease functioning properly.

Maximum Peak-to-Peak Output Voltage Swing (V_{OPP}) The maximum peak-to-peak output voltage that can be obtained without waveform clipping when the quiescent d-c output voltage is zero.

Large-Signal Differential Voltage Amplification (A_{VD}) The ratio of the peak-to-peak output voltage swing to the change in differential input voltage required to drive the output.

Unity-Gain Bandwidth (B_1) The range of frequencies within which the voltage amplification is greater than unity.

Common-Mode Rejection Ratio (CMRR) The ratio of differential voltage amplification to common-mode voltage amplification. This is measured by determining the ratio of a change in input common-mode voltage to the resulting change in input offset voltage.

Supply Voltage Sensitivity ($\Delta V_{IO}/\Delta V_{CC}$) The ratio of the change in input offset voltage to the change in supply voltages producing it. For these devices, both supply voltages are varied symmetrically.

Short-Circuit Output Current (I_{OS}) The maximum output current available from the amplifier with the output shorted to ground or to either supply.

Total Dissipation (P_D) The total d-c power supplied to the device less any power delivered from the device to a load. At no load: $P_D = V_{CC+} \cdot I_{CC+} + V_{CC-} \cdot I_{CC-}$.

Rise Time (t_r) The time required for an output voltage step to change from 10% to 90% of its final value.

Overshoot The quotient of: (1) the largest deviation of the output signal value from its steady-state value after a step-function change of the input signal, and (2) the difference between the output signal values in the steady state before and after the step-function change of the input signal.

Slew Rate (SR) The average time rate of change of the closed-loop amplifier output voltage for a step-signal input. Slew rate is measured between specified output levels (0 and 10 volts for this device) with feedback adjusted for unity gain.

TEXAS INSTRUMENTS
INCORPORATED
POST OFFICE BOX 5012 • DALLAS, TEXAS 75222

TYPES SN52L044, SN72L044
QUAD LOW-POWER OPERATIONAL AMPLIFIERS

PARAMETER MEASUREMENT INFORMATION

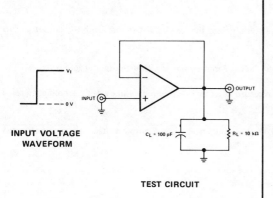

INPUT VOLTAGE WAVEFORM

TEST CIRCUIT

FIGURE 1—RISE TIME, OVERSHOOT, AND SLEW RATE

TYPICAL CHARACTERISTICS

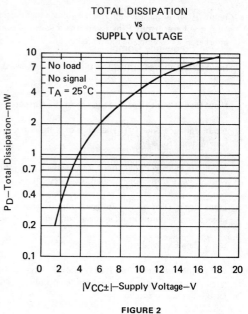

TOTAL DISSIPATION vs SUPPLY VOLTAGE

FIGURE 2

THERMAL INFORMATION

DISSIPATION DERATING CURVE

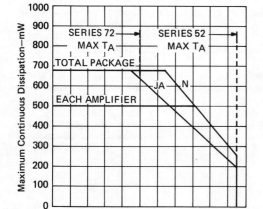

FIGURE 3

PKG	DERATE	FROM (TOT PKG)	FROM (EACH AMP)
JA	8.0 mW/°C	65°C	87°C
N	10.4 mW/°C	84°C	102°C

TEXAS INSTRUMENTS
INCORPORATED
POST OFFICE BOX 5012 • DALLAS, TEXAS 75222

LINEAR INTEGRATED CIRCUITS

TYPES SN62088, SN72088
CHOPPER-STABILIZED OPERATIONAL AMPLIFIERS

BULLETIN NO. DL-S 7312051, SEPTEMBER 1973

- Very Low Input Offset Parameters
- Very Low Input Bias Currents
- No Frequency Compensation Required
- Output Short-Circuit Protection

- High Slew Rates
- High Gain-Bandwidth Product
- Wide Common-Mode and Differential Voltage Ranges

description

The SN62088 and SN72088 are extremely high-performance chopper-stabilized operational amplifiers. High input impedance, very low initial input offset voltage, low input offset voltage temperature coefficient, low input bias and offset currents, and high slew rate are achieved through the combination of state-of-the-art circuit techniques and advanced integrated circuit technologies.

The SN62088 is specified for operation from -25°C to 85°C and the SN72088 for operation from 0°C to 70°C.

N
DUAL-IN-LINE PACKAGE
(TOP VIEW)

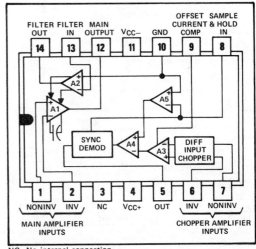

NC—No internal connection

absolute maximum ratings over operating free-air temperature range (unless otherwise noted)

	SN62088	SN72088	UNIT
Supply voltage V_{CC+} (see Note 1)	18	18	V
Supply voltage V_{CC-} (see Note 1)	-18	-18	V
Differential input voltage (see Note 2)	±15	±15	V
Input voltage (any input, see Notes 1 and 3)	±15	±15	V
Duration of output short-circuit (see Note 4)	unlimited	unlimited	
Continuous total dissipation at (or below) 70°C free-air temperature (see Note 5)	800	800	mW
Operating free-air temperature range	-25 to 85	0 to 70	$^\circ$C
Storage temperature range	-65 to 150	-65 to 150	$^\circ$C
Lead temperature 1/16 inch from case for 10 seconds	260	260	$^\circ$C

NOTES: 1. All voltage values, unless otherwise noted, are with respect to the zero-reference level (ground) of the supply voltages where the zero-reference level is the midpoint between V_{CC+} and V_{CC-}. If the zero-reference level of the system is not the midpoint of the supply voltages, all voltage values must be changed accordingly.
      2. Differential voltages are at the noninverting input terminal with respect to the inverting input terminal.
      3. The magnitude of the input voltage must never exceed the magnitude of the supply voltage or 15 volts, whichever is less.
      4. The output may be shorted to ground or either power supply.
      5. For operation of the SN62088 above 70°C free-air temperature, refer to Dissipation Derating Curve, Figure 12.

TEXAS INSTRUMENTS
INCORPORATED
POST OFFICE BOX 5012 • DALLAS, TEXAS 75222

electrical characteristics at specified free-air temperature, V_{CC+} = 15 V, V_{CC-} = -15 V

PARAMETER		TEST CONDITIONS[†]	SN62088 MIN	SN62088 TYP	SN62088 MAX	SN72088 MIN	SN72088 TYP	SN72088 MAX	UNIT
V_{IO}	Input offset voltage	25°C		40	75		70	150	μV
		Full range			100			250	
α_{VIO}	Average temperature coefficient of input offset voltage	Full range		0.6			1		μV/°C
I_{IO}	Input offset current	25°C		0.1	0.3		0.2	0.6	nA
		Full range			10			15	
I_{IB}	Input bias current	25°C		0.4	5		0.6	10	nA
		Full range			20			30	
V_{ICR}	Common-mode input voltage range	25°C	-3 to 10	-5 to 12		-3 to 10	-5 to 12		V
V_{OPP}	Maximum peak-to-peak output voltage swing	R_L = 2 kΩ, 25°C	20	26		20	26		V
		$R_L \geqslant 2$ kΩ, Full range	20			20			
A_{VD}	Large-signal differential voltage amplification	R_L = 2 kΩ, V_O = ±10 V, 25°C	100	140		100	140		dB
		$R_L \geqslant 2$ kΩ, V_O = ±10 V, Full range	100			94			
B_{OM}	Maximum-output-swing bandwidth (closed loop)	R_L = 2 kΩ, $V_O \geqslant \pm 10$ V, A_{VD} = 1, THD ≤ 5%, 25°C		400			400		kHz
B_1	Unity-gain bandwidth	25°C		3			3		MHz
ϕ_m	Phase margin	f = 10 Hz, 25°C		45°			45°		
A_m	Gain margin	25°C		7			7		dB
z_o	Output impedance	f = 10 Hz, 25°C		250			250		Ω
CMRR	Common-mode rejection ratio	$R_S \leqslant 10$ kΩ, 25°C		80			80		dB
$\Delta V_{IO}/\Delta V_{CC}$	Supply voltage sensitivity	$R_S \leqslant 10$ kΩ, 25°C		300			300		μV/V
V_n	Equivalent input noise voltage (closed loop)	A_{VD} = 100, B = 1 Hz, f = 1 kHz, 25°C		110			110		nV/√Hz
I_{OS}	Short circuit output current	To V_{CC+}	25°C		25			25		mA
		To V_{CC-}			-25			-25		
I_{CC}	Supply current	No load, No signal, 25°C		10			10		mA
$V_{O(filter)}$	Quiescent filter output voltage	25°C		13			13		V

[†]Full range for SN62088 is -25°C to 85°C and for SN72088 is 0°C to 70°C. All characteristics are measured in the circuit of Figure 1 with $Z_f = \infty$, unless otherwise noted.

operating characteristics, V_{CC+} = 15 V, V_{CC-} = -15 V, T_A = 25°C

PARAMETER		TEST CONDITIONS	SN62088 MIN	SN62088 TYP	SN62088 MAX	SN72088 MIN	SN72088 TYP	SN72088 MAX	UNIT
t_r	Rise time	V_I = 50 mV, R_L = 2 kΩ, C_L = 100 pF		65			65		ns
SR	Slew rate at unity gain	V_I = 10 V, R_L = 2 kΩ, C_L = 100 pF		25			25		V/μs
$f_{chopper}$	Chopper frequency			1			1		kHz

TEXAS INSTRUMENTS
INCORPORATED

POST OFFICE BOX 5012 • DALLAS, TEXAS 75222

DEFINITION OF TERMS

Input Offset Voltage (V_{IO}) The d-c voltage that must be applied between the input terminals to force the quiescent d-c output voltage to zero.

Average Temperature Coefficient of Input Offset Voltage (α_{VIO}) The ratio of the change in input offset voltage to the change in free-air temperature. This is an average value for the specified temperature range.

$$\alpha_{VIO} = \left| \frac{(V_{IO} @ T_{A(1)}) - (V_{IO} @ T_{A(2)})}{T_{A(1)} - T_{A(2)}} \right| \text{ where } T_{A(1)} \text{ and } T_{A(2)} \text{ are the specified temperature extremes.}$$

Input Offset Current (I_{IO}) The difference between the currents into the two input terminals with the output at zero volts.

Input Bias Current (I_{IB}) The average of the currents into the two input terminals with the output at zero volts.

Common-Mode Input Voltage Range (V_{ICR}) The range of common-mode voltage that if exceeded will cause the amplifier to cease functioning properly.

Maximum Peak-to-Peak Output Voltage Swing (V_{OPP}) The maximum peak-to-peak output voltage that can be obtained without waveform clipping when the quiescent d-c output voltage is zero.

Large-Signal Differential Voltage Amplification (A_{VD}) The ratio of the peak-to-peak output voltage swing to the change in differential input voltage required to drive the output.

Maximum-Output-Swing Bandwidth (B_{OM}) The range of frequencies within which the maximum output voltage swing is above a specified value.

Unity-Gain Bandwidth (B_1) The range of frequencies within which the voltage amplification is greater than unity.

Phase Margin (ϕ_m) $180°$ minus the absolute value of the phase shift between the output and the noninverting input at the frequency at which the open-loop gain is unity.

Gain Margin (A_m) The reciprocal of the differential voltage amplification at the lowest frequency at which the phase shift between the output and the noninverting input is $180°$.

Output Impedance (z_O) The small-signal impedance between the output terminal and ground.

Common-Mode Rejection Ratio (CMRR) The ratio of differential voltage amplification to common-mode voltage amplification. This is measured by determining the ratio of a change in input common-mode voltage to the resulting change in input offset voltage.

Supply Voltage Sensitivity ($\Delta V_{IO}/\Delta V_{CC}$) The ratio of the change in input offset voltage to the change in supply voltage producing it. For these devices, both supply voltages are varied symmetrically.

Short-Circuit Output Current (I_{OS}) The maximum output current available from the amplifier with the output shorted to the specified supply.

Rise Time (t_r) The time required for an output voltage step to change from 10% to 90% of its final value.

Slew Rate (SR) The average time rate of change of the closed-loop amplifier output voltage for a step-signal input. Slew rate is measured between specified output levels (0 and 10 volts for this device) with feedback adjusted for unity gain.

PARAMETER MEASUREMENT INFORMATION

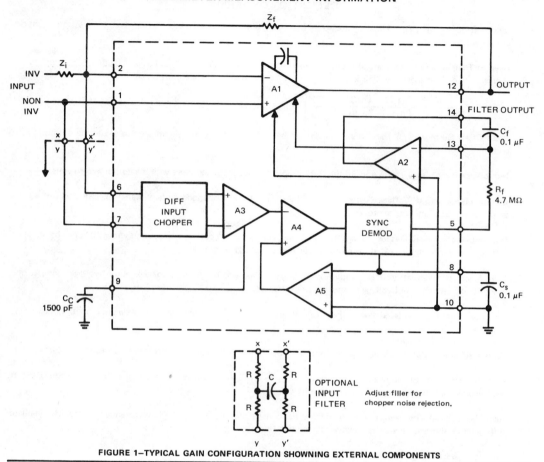

FIGURE 1—TYPICAL GAIN CONFIGURATION SHOWNING EXTERNAL COMPONENTS

PRINCIPLES OF OPERATION

Traditional integrated operational amplifiers have inherent problems that cause inaccuracies in many of the dc and very-low-frequency applications of these devices. The major problems are:

1. Input offset voltage
2. Thermally-induced change of input offset voltage
3. Input offset current
4. Thermally-induced change of input offset current
5. Gain deficiencies
6. Input resistance effects

Chopper stabilization is a technique that is effective in substantially reducing the initial and long-term

input offset voltage, input-offset-voltage drift and gain deficiencies. Other circuit techniques can be utilized to reduce the effects of offset current, offset-current drift, and input resistance effects.

Most chopper-stabilized amplifiers feature single-ended, inverting operation. These are available as bulky modular devices fabricated by discrete or hybrid approaches. For space-critical applications, or for applications requiring the noninverting or common-mode configutation, the traditional chopper-stabilized amplifiers are not suitable.

The SN62088 and SN72088 are effective applications of chopper-stabilization techniques to an integrated

TEXAS INSTRUMENTS
INCORPORATED
POST OFFICE BOX 5012 • DALLAS, TEXAS 75222

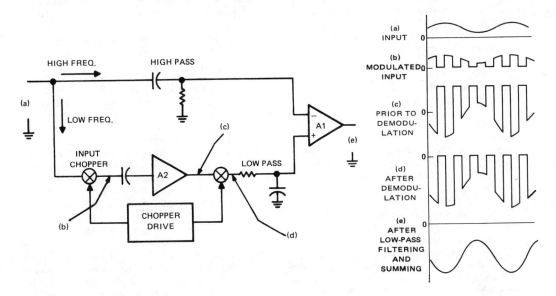

FIGURE 2—SIMPLIFIED BLOCK DIAGRAM OF TYPICAL DISCRETE CHOPPER STABILIZED OPERATIONAL AMPLIFIER

circuit design. They are fabricated in a popular standard dual-in-line package and incorporate a unique differential-input configuration that permits common-mode input voltages and application in inverting or noninverting configurations. Circuit techniques and state-of-the-art technologies have been combined to provide low input bias current, low input offset current, low offset-voltage temperature coefficient and drift, and very high input resistance.

The following discussion is provided to familarize the user with chopper-stabilization techniques. For simplicity, the technique will be described first by reference to a simplified single-ended chopper-stabilized amplifier. Principles will then be extended to the SN62088/SN72088 differential-input integrated-circuit operation amplifiers.

The general approach to chopper stabilization is accomplished by processing low-frequency signal components separately from the higher-frequency components. This is illustrated in Figure 2. The upper signal path passes higher-frequency (>100 hertz, for example) signal components directly. These higher-frequency components are amplified by the wide-band amplifier, A1. The low-frequency components

(<100 hertz in this example) are processed through the lower signal path—the chopper channel. The low-frequency signal is periodically shunted to ground by the action of the input chopper. The resulting waveform at the output of this chopper is amplified by applying it to the ac amplifier, A2. After amplification, the signal is demodulated in synchronism with the input chopper switch to restore the proper dc level. A low-pass filter smooths the demodulated signal and attenuates any noise created by the demodulation switch. The resultant low-frequency signal is finally amplified by the high-frequency amplifier, A1. The chopper path, therefore, processes the low-frequency signal components by converting them to higher-frequency ac signals, amplifying them, and finally converting them back to low-frequency components by demodulation. The chopper channel reduces the offset and drift of amplifier A1 by the gain of the chopper amplifier. Low-frequency gain is a combination of the gain of the higher-frequency and low-frequency channels.

This chopper-stabilization technique results in extremely high low-frequency gains and extremely low voltage offset. Since reduction in offset-voltage change does not depend on cancellation of change due to matched components, the chopper-stabilized amplifier is relatively immune to change due to thermal effects. Long-term-drift stability is also excellent. High-frequency characteristics are primarily a function of the high-frequency amplifier, A1.

The above description is an example of a typical discrete chopper-stabilized operational amplifier with a single-ended input stage.

Operation of the SN62088 and SN72088 may be explained by referring to Figure 1. Amplifier A1 is a high-frequency amplifier featuring a unity-gain bandwidth of 3 MHz and a unity-gain slew rate of 25 volts per microsecond. Frequency compensation is internal.

The low-frequency input signals are "chopped" by the differential input chopper periodically shorting the differential inputs together. During this interval of time, the offsets of amplifiers A3, A4, and other system errors are cancelled out by presenting them as a common-mode signal to the inputs of A4. The sample-hold capacitor, C_S, holds this condition during the next interval of time, while the input chopper couples the offset voltage of A1 to the input of A3. After amplification by A3 and A4, this signal is demodulated by the synchronous demodulator and filtered by the active low-pass-filter amplifier, A2.

Amplifier A2 actually has three outputs: A single-ended output for the filter and two differential current-source outputs that are used to null the initial offset of amplifier A1. This nulling is accomplished at a point in the input stage of A1 that is similar to the

external null-offset terminals of a conventional integrated-circuit operational amplifier. The chopper-stabilization circuit samples and nulls the offset of A1 at a 1-kHz rate, thereby effecting an almost continuous correction of offset.

The connections between the chopper channel and the main amplifier, A1, are made externally to allow flexibility in circuit configuration. For example, an optional low-pass input filter may be inserted (see Figure 1) to further attenuate chopper noise. The chopper-channel input currents are approximately 200 picoamperes. The similar addition of an optional notch filter could be implemented at the output of the synchronous demodulator for further noise cancellation. Performance for most critical applications is acceptable without either of these optional filters.

Using the basic differential-input chopper stabilization technique described above results in input voltage offset and drift much superior to conventional integrated-circuit operational amplifiers. A review and comparison will also reveal input current, input offset current, bandwidth, slew rate, and voltage amplification superior to these amplifiers.

The SN62088 and SN72088 therefore represent dramatic increases in performance and make possible application in critical designs where only discrete or modular designs could be utilized previously. A reduction in cost and increase in reliability make these devices ideal for these applications in addition to applications where periodic or initial calibration can now be eliminated by the SN62088 or SN72088.

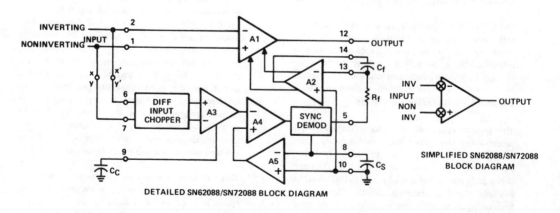

DETAILED SN62088/SN72088 BLOCK DIAGRAM

SIMPLIFIED SN62088/SN72088 BLOCK DIAGRAM

FIGURE 3—SN62088/SN72088 FUNCTIONAL BLOCK DIAGRAMS

TEXAS INSTRUMENTS
INCORPORATED
POST OFFICE BOX 5012 • DALLAS, TEXAS 75222

TYPICAL APPLICATIONS

- Transducer Amplifiers
- Analog Computers
- Sample-Hold Systems
- Peak Detectors
- Instrumentation Systems
- Remote Equipment
- Standard-Cell Amplifiers
- Precision Current Sources

- A-D Converters
- Digital Voltmeters
- High-Accuracy Integrators
- Precision Power Supplies
- Data Acquisition Systems
- Bridge Amplifiers
- Strain-Gauge Amplifiers
- Micro-Voltmeters

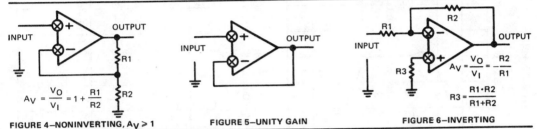

FIGURE 4—NONINVERTING, $A_V \geqslant 1$

$$A_V = \frac{V_O}{V_I} = 1 + \frac{R1}{R2}$$

FIGURE 5—UNITY GAIN

FIGURE 6—INVERTING

$$A_V = \frac{V_O}{V_I} = -\frac{R2}{R1}$$

$$R3 = \frac{R1 \cdot R2}{R1 + R2}$$

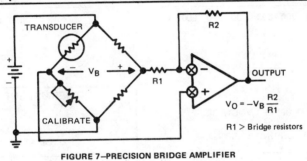

$$V_O = -V_B \frac{R2}{R1}$$

R1 > Bridge resistors

FIGURE 7—PRECISION BRIDGE AMPLIFIER

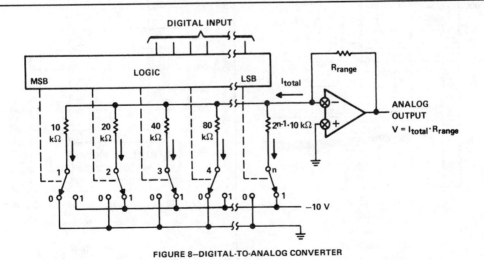

$$V = I_{total} \cdot R_{range}$$

FIGURE 8—DIGITAL-TO-ANALOG CONVERTER

TEXAS INSTRUMENTS
INCORPORATED
POST OFFICE BOX 5012 • DALLAS, TEXAS 75222

TYPES SN62088, SN72088
CHOPPER-STABILIZED OPERATIONAL AMPLIFIERS

TYPICAL CHARACTERISTICS

VOLTAGE-FOLLOWER
TRANSIENT RESPONSE

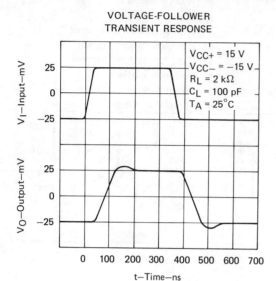

FIGURE 9

VOLTAGE-FOLLOWER
LARGE-SIGNAL PULSE RESPONSE

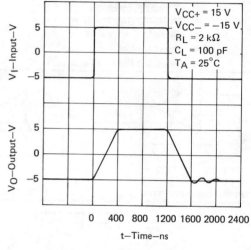

FIGURE 10

INPUT OFFSET VOLTAGE
vs
TIME DURING WARM-UP

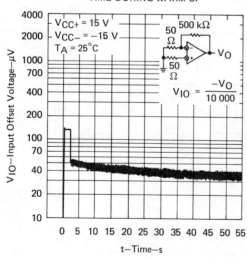

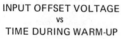

FIGURE 11

THERMAL INFORMATION

SN62088
DISSIPATION DERATING CURVE

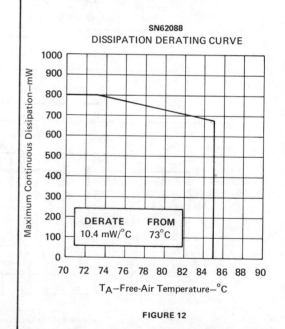

DERATE 10.4 mW/°C FROM 73°C

FIGURE 12

TEXAS INSTRUMENTS
INCORPORATED
POST OFFICE BOX 5012 • DALLAS, TEXAS 75222

LINEAR
INTEGRATED CIRCUITS

TYPES SN52101A, SN72301A
HIGH-PERFORMANCE OPERATIONAL AMPLIFIERS

BULLETIN NO. DL-S 7311432, JANUARY 1971—REVISED SEPTEMBER 1973

- Low Input Currents
- Low Input Offset Parameters
- Frequency and Transient Response Characteristics Adjustable
- Short-Circuit Protection
- Offset-Voltage Null Capability

- Designed to be Interchangeable with National Semiconductor LM101A and LM301A
- No Latch-Up
- Wide Common-Mode and Differential Voltage Ranges
- Same Pin Assignments as SN52709 and SN72709

description

The SN52101A and SN727301A are high-performance operational amplifiers, featuring very low input bias current and input offset voltage and current to improve the accuracy of high-impedance circuits using these devices.

The high common-mode input voltage range and the absence of latch-up make the SN52101A and SN72301A ideal for voltage-follower applications. The devices are protected to withstand short-circuits at the output. The external compensation of the SN52101A and the SN72301A allows the changing of the frequency response (when the closed-loop gain is greater than unity) for applications requiring wider bandwidth or higher slew rate.

A potentiometer may be connected between the offset-null inputs (N1 and N2), as shown in Figure 8, to null out the offset voltage.

The SN52101A is characterized for operation over the full military temperature range of $-55°C$ to $125°C$; the SN72301A is characterized for operation from $0°C$ to $70°C$.

terminal assignments

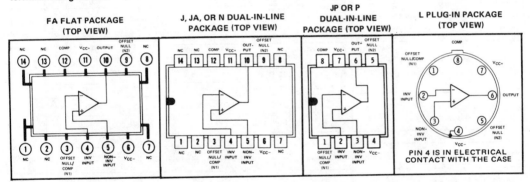

FA FLAT PACKAGE (TOP VIEW)

J, JA, OR N DUAL-IN-LINE PACKAGE (TOP VIEW)

JP OR P DUAL-IN-LINE PACKAGE (TOP VIEW)

L PLUG-IN PACKAGE (TOP VIEW)

PIN 4 IS IN ELECTRICAL CONTACT WITH THE CASE

NC—No internal connection

absolute maximum ratings over operating free-air temperature range (unless otherwise noted)

		SN52101A	SN72301A	UNIT
Supply voltage V_{CC+} (see Note 1)		22	18	V
Supply voltage V_{CC-} (see Note 1)		−22	−18	V
Differential input voltage (see Note 2)		±30	±30	V
Input voltage (either input, see Notes 1 and 3)		±15	±15	V
Voltage between either offset null terminal (N1/N2) and V_{CC-}		−0.5 to 2	−0.5 to 2	V
Duration of output short-circuit (see Note 4)		unlimited	unlimited	
Continuous total power dissipation at (or below) 25°C free-air temperature (see Note 5)		500	500	mW
Operating free-air temperature range		−55 to 125	0 to 70	°C
Storage temperature range		−65 to 150	−65 to 150	°C
Lead temperature 1/16 inch from case for 60 seconds	FA, J, JA, JP, or L package	300	300	°C
Lead temperature 1/16 inch from case for 10 seconds	N or P package	260	260	°C

NOTES: 1. All voltage values, unless otherwise noted, are with respect to the zero reference level (ground) of the supply voltages where the zero reference level is the midpoint between V_{CC+} and V_{CC-}.
2. Differential voltages are at the noninverting input terminal with respect to the inverting input terminal.
3. The magnitude of the input voltage must never exceed the magnitude of the supply voltage or 15 volts, whichever is less.
4. The output may be shorted to ground or either power supply. For the SN52101A only, the unlimited duration of the short-circuit applies at (or below) 125°C case temperature or 75°C free-air temperature.
5. For operation above 25°C free-air temperature, refer to Dissipation Derating Curve, Figure 1.

TEXAS INSTRUMENTS
INCORPORATED
POST OFFICE BOX 5012 • DALLAS, TEXAS 75222

voltages specified

Throughout this data sheet, supply voltages are specified either as a range or as a specific value. A positive voltage within the specified range (or of the specified value) is applied to V_{CC+}, and an equal negative voltage is applied to V_{CC-}.

electrical characteristics at specified free-air temperature, $C_C = 30$ pF (see note 6)

PARAMETER		TEST CONDITIONS†		SN52101A			SN72301A			UNIT
				MIN	TYP	MAX	MIN	TYP	MAX	
V_{IO}	Input offset voltage	$R_S = 50$ kΩ	25°C		0.6	2		2.0	7.5	mV
			Full range			3			10	
α_{VIO}	Average temperature coefficient of input offset voltage		Full range		3	15		6	30	μV/°C
I_{IO}	Input offset current		25°C		1.5	10		3	50	nA
			Full range			20			70	
α_{IIO}	Average temperature coefficient of input offset current	$T_A = -55°C$ to 25°C			0.02	0.2				nA/°C
		$T_A = 25°C$ to 125°C			0.01	0.1				
		$T_A = 0°C$ to 25°C						0.02	0.6	
		$T_A = 25°C$ to 70°C						0.01	0.3	
I_{IB}	Input bias current		25°C		30	75		70	250	nA
			Full range			100			300	
V_I	Input voltage range	See Note 7	Full range	±15			±12			V
V_{OPP}	Maximum peak-to-peak output voltage swing	$V_{CC\pm} = \pm15$ V, $R_L = 10$ kΩ	25°C	24	28		24	28		V
			Full range	24			24			
		$V_{CC\pm} = \pm15$ V, $R_L = 2$ kΩ	25°C	20	26		20	26		
			Full range	20			20			
A_{VD}	Large-signal differential voltage amplification	$V_{CC\pm} = \pm15$ V, $V_O = \pm10$ V, $R_L \geq 2$ kΩ	25°C	50,000	200,000		25,000	200,000		
			Full range	25,000			15,000			
r_i	Input resistance		25°C	1.5	4		0.5	2		MΩ
CMRR	Common-mode rejection ratio	$R_S = 50$ kΩ	25°C	80	98		70	90		dB
			Full range	80			70			
$\Delta V_{CC}/\Delta V_{IO}$	Supply voltage rejection ratio	$R_S = 50$ kΩ	25°C	80	98		70	96		dB
			Full range	80			70			
I_{CC}	Supply current	No load, No signal, See Note 7	25°C		1.8	3		1.8	3	mA
			125°C		1.2	2.5				

†All characteristics are specified under open-loop operation. Full range for SN52101A is −55°C to 125°C and for SN72301A is 0°C to 70°C.

NOTES: 6. Unless otherwise noted, $V_{CC\pm} = \pm5$ V to ±20 V for SN52101A and $V_{CC\pm} = \pm5$ V to ±15 V for SN72301A. All typical values are at $V_{CC\pm} = \pm15$ V.
7. For SN52101A, $V_{CC\pm} = \pm20$ V. For SN72301A, $V_{CC\pm} = \pm15$ V.

TEXAS INSTRUMENTS
INCORPORATED
POST OFFICE BOX 5012 • DALLAS, TEXAS 75222

DEFINITION OF TERMS

Input Offset Voltage (V_{IO}) The d-c voltage which must be applied between the input terminals to force the quiescent d-c output voltage to zero. The input offset voltage may also be defined for the case where two equal resistances (R_S) are inserted in series with the input leads.

Average Temperature Coefficient of Input Offset Voltage (α_{VIO}) The ratio of the change in input offset voltage to the change in free-air temperature. This is an average value for the specified temperature range.

$$\alpha_{VIO} = \left| \frac{(V_{IO} @ T_{A(1)}) - (V_{IO} @ T_{A(2)})}{T_{A(1)} - T_{A(2)}} \right| \quad \text{where } T_{A(1)} \text{ and } T_{A(2)} \text{ are the specified temperature extremes.}$$

Input Offset Current (I_{IO}) The difference between the currents into the two input terminals with the output at zero volts.

Average Temperature Coefficient of Input Offset Current (α_{IIO}) The ratio of the change in input offset current to the change in free-air temperature. This is an average value for the specified temperature range.

$$\alpha_{IIO} = \left| \frac{(I_{IO} @ T_{A(1)}) - (I_{IO} @ T_{A(2)})}{T_{A(1)} - T_{A(2)}} \right| \quad \text{where } T_{A(1)} \text{ and } T_{A(2)} \text{ are the specified temperature extremes.}$$

Input Bias Current (I_{IB}) The average of the currents into the two input terminals with the output at zero volts.

Input Voltage Range (V_I) The range of voltage which if exceeded at either input terminal will cause the amplifier to cease functioning properly.

Maximum Peak-to-Peak Output Voltage Swing (V_{OPP}) The maximum peak-to-peak output voltage which can be obtained without waveform clipping when the quiescent d-c output voltage is zero.

Large-Signal Differential Voltage Amplification (A_{VD}) The ratio of the peak-to-peak output voltage swing to the change in differential input voltage required to drive the output.

Input Resistance (r_i) The resistance between the input terminals with either input grounded.

Common-Mode Rejection Ratio (CMRR) The ratio of differential voltage amplification to common-mode voltage amplification. This is measured by determining the ratio of a change in input common-mode voltage to the resulting change in input offset voltage.

Supply Voltage Rejection Ratio ($\Delta V_{CC}/\Delta V_{IO}$) The ratio of the change in power supply voltages to the change in input offset voltage. For these devices, both supply voltages are varied symmetrically.

THERMAL INFORMATION
DISSIPATION DERATING CURVE

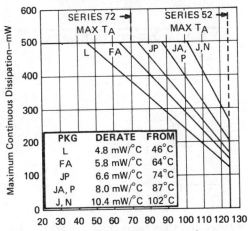

PKG	DERATE	FROM
L	4.8 mW/°C	46°C
FA	5.8 mW/°C	64°C
JP	6.6 mW/°C	74°C
JA, P	8.0 mW/°C	87°C
J, N	10.4 mW/°C	102°C

T_A—Free-Air Temperature—°C

FIGURE 1

TEXAS INSTRUMENTS
INCORPORATED
POST OFFICE BOX 5012 • DALLAS, TEXAS 75222

TYPICAL CHARACTERISTICS

INPUT OFFSET CURRENT
vs
FREE-AIR TEMPERATURE

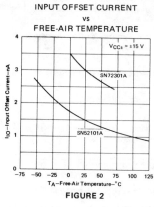

FIGURE 2

INPUT BIAS CURRENT
vs
FREE-AIR TEMPERATURE

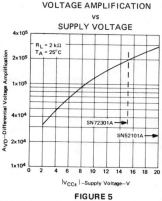

FIGURE 3

MAXIMUM PEAK-TO-PEAK
OUTPUT VOLTAGE (WITH
SINGLE-POLE COMPENSATION)
vs FREQUENCY

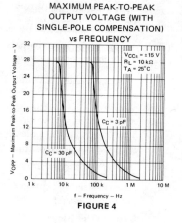

FIGURE 4

OPEN-LOOP LARGE-SIGNAL
DIFFERENTIAL
VOLTAGE AMPLIFICATION
vs
SUPPLY VOLTAGE

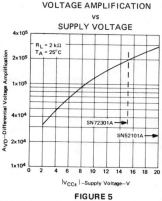

FIGURE 5

OPEN-LOOP LARGE-SIGNAL
DIFFERENTIAL
VOLTAGE AMPLIFICATION
vs
FREQUENCY

FIGURE 6

VOLTAGE-FOLLOWER
LARGE-SIGNAL PULSE RESPONSE

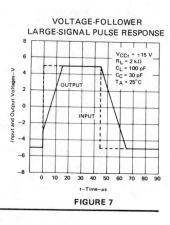

FIGURE 7

TYPICAL APPLICATION DATA

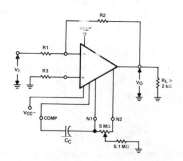

$$\frac{V_O}{V_I} = -\frac{R2}{R1}$$

$$C_C \geqslant \frac{R1 \cdot 30 \text{ pF}}{R1+R2}$$

$$R3 = \frac{R1 \cdot R2}{R1+R2}$$

**FIGURE 8 — INVERTING CIRCUIT WITH ADJUSTABLE GAIN,
SINGLE-POLE COMPENSATION, AND OFFSET ADJUSTMENT**

TEXAS INSTRUMENTS
INCORPORATED
POST OFFICE BOX 5012 • DALLAS, TEXAS 75222

LINEAR INTEGRATED CIRCUITS

- Low Input Currents
- No Frequency Compensation Required
- Offset-Voltage Null Capability
- Low Input Offset Parameters
- Designed to be Interchangeable with National Semiconductor LM107 and LM307

- Short-Circuit Protection
- No Latch-Up
- Wide Common-Mode and Differential Voltage Ranges
- Same Pin Assignments as SN52741 and SN72741

description

The SN52107 and SN72307 are high-performance operational amplifiers, featuring very low input bias current and input offset voltage and current to improve the accuracy of high-impedance circuits using these devices.

The high common-mode input voltage range and the absence of latch-up make the SN52107 and SN72307 ideal for voltage-follower applications. The devices are short-circuit protected and the internal frequency compensation ensures stability without external components. A low-value potentiometer may be connected between the offset-null inputs, as shown in Figure 2, to null out the offset voltage.

The SN52107 is characterized for operation over the full military temperature range of −55°C to 125°C; the SN72307 is characterized for operation from 0°C to 70°C.

terminal assignments

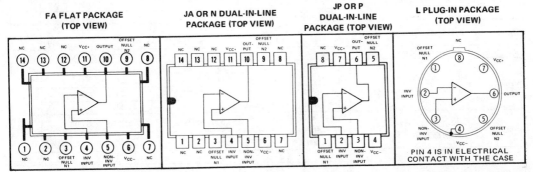

NC—No internal connection

absolute maximum ratings over operating free-air temperature range (unless otherwise noted)

		SN52107	SN72307	UNIT
Supply voltage V_{CC+} (see Note 1)		22	18	V
Supply voltage V_{CC-} (see Note 1)		−22	−18	V
Differential input voltage (see Note 2)		±30	±30	V
Input voltage (either input, see Notes 1 and 3)		±15	±15	V
Voltage between either offset null terminal (N1/N2) and V_{CC-}		±0.5	±0.5	V
Duration of output short-circuit (see Note 4)		unlimited	unlimited	
Continuous total dissipation at (or below) 25°C free-air temperature (see Note 5)		500	500	mW
Operating free-air temperature range		−55 to 125	0 to 70	°C
Storage temperature range		−65 to 150	−65 to 150	°C
Lead temperature 1/16 inch from case for 60 seconds	FA, JA, JP, or L package	300	300	°C
Lead temperature 1/16 inch from case for 10 seconds	N or P package	260	260	°C

NOTES: 1. All voltage values, unless otherwise noted, are with respect to the zero reference level (ground) of the supply voltages where the zero reference level is the midpoint between V_{CC+} and V_{CC-}.
2. Differential voltages are at the noninverting input terminal with respect to the inverting input terminal.
3. The magnitude of the input voltage must never exceed the magnitude of the supply voltage or 15 volts, whichever is less.
4. The output may be shorted to ground or either power supply. For the SN52107 only, the unlimited duration of the short-circuit applies at (or below) 125°C case temperature or 75°C free-air temperature.
5. For operation above 25°C free-air temperature, refer to Dissipation Derating Curve, Figure 1.

voltages specified

Throughout this data sheet, supply voltages are specified either as a range or as a specific value. A positive voltage within the specified range (or of the specified value) is applied to V_{CC+}, and an equal negative voltage is applied to V_{CC-}.

electrical characteristics at specified free-air temperature (see note 6)

PARAMETER		TEST CONDITIONS†		SN52107			SN72307			UNIT
				MIN	TYP	MAX	MIN	TYP	MAX	
V_{IO}	Input offset voltage	$R_S = 50 \text{ k}\Omega$	25°C		0.6	2		2	7.5	mV
			Full range			3			10	
α_{VIO}	Average temperature coefficient of input offset voltage		Full range		3	15		6	30	$\mu V/°C$
I_{IO}	Input offset current		25°C		1.5	10		3	50	nA
			Full range			20			70	
α_{IIO}	Average temperature coefficient of input offset current	$T_A = -55°C$ to 25°C			0.02	0.2				nA/°C
		$T_A = 25°C$ to 125°C			0.01	0.1				
		$T_A = 0°C$ to 25°C						0.02	0.6	
		$T_A = 25°C$ to 70°C						0.01	0.3	
I_{IB}	Input bias current		25°C		30	75		70	250	nA
			Full range			100			300	
V_I	Input voltage range	See Note 7	Full range	±15			±12			V
V_{OPP}	Maximum peak-to-peak output voltage swing	$V_{CC\pm} = \pm15$ V,	25°C	24	28		24	28		V
		$R_L = 10 \text{ k}\Omega$	Full range	24			24			
		$V_{CC\pm} = \pm15$ V,	25°C	20	26		20	26		
		$R_L = 2 \text{ k}\Omega$	Full range	20			20			
A_{VD}	Large-signal differential voltage amplification	$V_{CC\pm} = \pm15$ V, $V_O = \pm10$ V, $R_L \geqslant 2 \text{ k}\Omega$	25°C	50,000	200,000		25,000	200,000		
			Full range	25,000			15,000			
r_i	Input resistance		25°C	1.5	4		0.5	2		$M\Omega$
CMRR	Common-mode rejection ratio	$R_S = 50 \text{ k}\Omega$	25°C	80	98		70	90		dB
			Full range	80			70			
$\Delta V_{CC}/\Delta V_{IO}$	Supply voltage rejection ratio	$R_S = 50 \text{ k}\Omega$	25°C	80	98		70	96		dB
			Full range	80			70			
I_{CC}	Supply current	No load, No signal, See Note 7	25°C		1.8	3		1.8	3	mA
			125°C		1.2	2.5				

†All characteristics are specified under open-loop operation. Full range for SN52107 is −55°C to 125°C and for SN72307 is 0°C to 70°C.

NOTES: 6. Unless otherwise noted $V_{CC\pm} = \pm5$ V to ±20 V for SN52107 and $V_{CC\pm} = \pm5$ V to ±15 V for SN72307. All typical values are at $V_{CC\pm} = \pm15$ V.
   7. For SN52107, $V_{CC\pm} = \pm20$ V. For SN72307, $V_{CC\pm} = \pm15$ V.

TEXAS INSTRUMENTS
INCORPORATED
POST OFFICE BOX 5012 • DALLAS, TEXAS 75222

97:

DEFINITION OF TERMS

Input Offset Voltage (V_{IO}) The d-c voltage which must be applied between the input terminals to force the quiescent d-c output voltage to zero. The input offset voltage may also be defined for the case where two equal resistances (R_S) are inserted in series with the input leads.

Average Temperature Coefficient of Input Offset Voltage (αV_{IO}) The ratio of the change in input offset voltage to the change in free-air temperature. This is an average value for the specified temperature range.

$$\alpha V_{IO} = \left| \frac{(V_{IO} @ T_{A(1)}) - (V_{IO} @ T_{A(2)})}{T_{A(1)} - T_{A(2)}} \right| \quad \text{where } T_{A(1)} \text{ and } T_{A(2)} \text{ are the specified temperature extremes.}$$

Input Offset Current (I_{IO}) The difference between the currents into the two input terminals with the output at zero volts.

Average Temperature Coefficient of Input Offset Current (αI_{IO}) The ratio of the change in input offset current to the change in free-air temperature. This is an average value for the specified temperature range.

$$\alpha I_{IO} = \left| \frac{(I_{IO} @ T_{A(1)}) - (I_{IO} @ T_{A(2)})}{T_{A(1)} - T_{A(2)}} \right| \quad \text{where } T_{A(1)} \text{ and } T_{A(2)} \text{ are the specified temperature extremes.}$$

Input Bias Current (I_{IB}) The average of the currents into the two input terminals with the output at zero volts.

Input Voltage Range (V_I) The range of voltage which if exceeded at either input terminal will cause the amplifier to cease functioning properly.

Maximum Peak-to-Peak Output Voltage Swing (V_{OPP}) The maximum peak-to-peak output voltage that can be obtained without waveform clipping when the quiescent d-c output voltage is zero.

Large-Signal Differential Voltage Amplification (A_{VD}) The ratio of the peak-to-peak output voltage swing to the change in differential input voltage required to drive the output.

Input Resistance (r_i) The resistance between the input terminals with either input grounded.

Common-Mode Rejection Ratio (CMRR) The ratio of differential voltage amplification to common-mode amplification. This is measured by determining the ratio of a change in input common-mode voltage to the resulting change in input offset voltage.

Supply Voltage Rejection Ratio ($\Delta V_{CC}/\Delta V_{IO}$) The ratio of the change in power supply voltages to the change in input offset voltage. For these devices, both supply voltages are varied symmetrically.

THERMAL INFORMATION	TYPICAL APPLICATION DATA
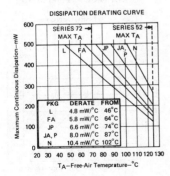	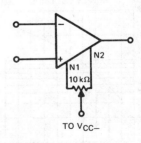
FIGURE 1	**FIGURE 2—INPUT OFFSET VOLTAGE NULL CIRCUIT**

TYPES SN52107, SN72307
HIGH-PERFORMANCE OPERATIONAL AMPLIFIERS

TYPICAL CHARACTERISTICS

INPUT OFFSET CURRENT
vs
FREE-AIR TEMPERATURE

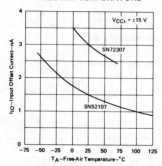

FIGURE 3

INPUT BIAS CURRENT
vs
FREE-AIR TEMPERATURE

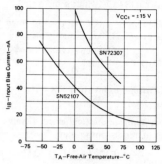

FIGURE 4

MAXIMUM PEAK-TO-PEAK
OUTPUT VOLTAGE
vs
FREQUENCY

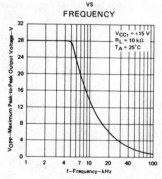

FIGURE 5

VOLTAGE-FOLLOWER
LARGE-SIGNAL PULSE RESPONSE

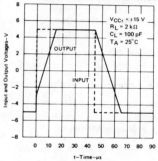

FIGURE 6

OPEN-LOOP LARGE-SIGNAL
DIFFERENTIAL
VOLTAGE AMPLIFICATION
vs
SUPPLY VOLTAGE

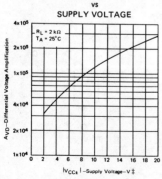

FIGURE 7

OPEN-LOOP LARGE-SIGNAL
DIFFERENTIAL
VOLTAGE AMPLIFICATION
vs
FREQUENCY

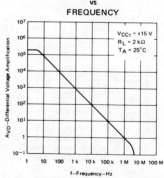

FIGURE 8

‡ Data for supply voltages greater than 15 V is applicable to SN52107 circuits only.

TEXAS INSTRUMENTS
INCORPORATED
POST OFFICE BOX 5012 • DALLAS, TEXAS 75222

- Very Low Input Bias and Offset Parameters
- Low Temperature Coefficients of Input Offset Voltage and Current
- Low Quiescent Power Consumption
- Designed to be Interchangeable with National Semiconductor LM108A, LM108, LM308A, and LM308 Respectively.

description

These operational amplifiers are designed for applications requiring extremely low input bias and offset currents and offset voltages. The SN52108A has a typical input offset voltage of 300 μV and typical input offset current of 50 pA at 25°C. Input bias current is 3 nA maximum over the full military temperature range.

These circuits are guaranteed to operate from supply voltages of ±5 V to ±20 V (SN52108A, SN52108) or ±5 V to ±18 V (SN72308A, SN72308) with a quiescent supply current of typically 300 μA at ±15 V. The supply voltage rejection ratio is sufficient to permit use of unregulated supplies in most applications. The output is protected against damage from shorting to ground or either supply and the input stage is diode-protected against excessive differential input signals. External compensation permits optimization of the frequency response for each application. The compensation circuit shown in Figure 6 can be used to make the amplifier particularly insensitive to supply noise.

The SN52108A and SN52108 are characterized for operation over the full military temperature range of −55°C to 125°C; the SN72308A and SN72308 are characterized for operation from 0°C to 70°C.

terminal assignments

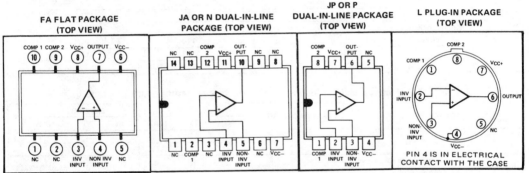

NC—No internal connection

absolute maximum ratings over operating free-air temperature range (unless otherwise noted)

	SN52108A SN52108	SN72308A SN72308	UNIT
Supply voltage V_{CC+} (see Note 1)	20	18	V
Supply voltage V_{CC-} (see Note 1)	−20	−18	V
Input voltage (either input, see Notes 1 and 2)	±15	±15	V
Differential input current (see Note 3)	±10	±10	mA
Duration of output short-circuit (see Note 4)	unlimited	unlimited	
Continuous total power dissipation at (or below) 25°C free-air temperature (see Note 5)	500	500	mW
Operating free-air temperature range	−55 to 125	0 to 70	°C
Storage temperature range	−65 to 150	−65 to 150	°C
Lead temperature 1/16 inch from case for 60 seconds — FA, JA, JP, or L package	300	300	°C
Lead temperature 1/16 inch from case for 10 seconds — N or P package	260	260	°C

NOTES: 1. All voltage values, unless otherwise noted, are with respect to the zero reference level (ground) of the supply voltages where the zero reference level is the midpoint between V_{CC+} and V_{CC-}.
2. The magnitude of the input voltage must never exceed the magnitude of the supply voltage or 15 volts, whichever is less.
3. The inputs are shunted with two opposite-facing base-emitter diodes for over voltage protection. Therefore, excessive current will flow if a differential input voltage in excess of approximately 1 V is applied between the inputs unless some limiting resistance is used.
4. The output may be shorted to ground or either power supply. For the SN52108A and SN52108 only, the unlimited duration of the short-circuit applies at (or below) 125°C case temperature or 75°C free-air temperature.
5. For operation above 25°C free-air temperature, refer to Dissipation Derating Curve, Figure 7.

SN52108A and SN52108 electrical characteristics at specified free-air temperature (see note 6)

PARAMETER		TEST CONDITIONS†		SN52108A			SN52108			UNIT
				MIN	TYP	MAX	MIN	TYP	MAX	
V_{IO}	Input offset voltage		25°C		0.3	0.5		0.7	2	mV
			Full range			1			3	
αV_{IO}	Average temperature coefficient of input offset voltage		Full range		1	5		3	15	µV/°C
I_{IO}	Input offset current		25°C		0.05	0.2		0.05	0.2	nA
			Full range			0.4			0.4	
αI_{IO}	Average temperature coefficient of input offset current		Full range		0.5	2.5		0.5	2.5	pA/°C
I_{IB}	Input bias current		25°C		0.8	2		0.8	2	nA
			Full range			3			3	
V_I	Input voltage range	$V_{CC\pm} = \pm15$ V	Full range	±13.5			±13.5			V
V_{OPP}	Maximum peak-to-peak output voltage swing	$V_{CC\pm} = \pm15$ V, $R_L = 10$ kΩ	Full range	26	28		26	28		V
A_{VD}	Large-signal differential voltage amplification	$V_{CC\pm} = \pm15$ V, $V_O = \pm10$ V, $R_L \geqslant 10$ kΩ	25°C	80,000	300,000		50,000	300,000		
			Full range	40,000			25,000			
r_i	Input resistance		25°C	30	70		30	70		MΩ
CMRR	Common-mode rejection ratio		Full range	96	110		85	100		dB
$\Delta V_{CC}/\Delta V_{IO}$	Supply voltage rejection ratio		Full range	96	110		80	96		dB
I_{CC}	Supply current	No load	25°C		0.3	0.6		0.3	0.6	mA
			125°C		0.15	0.4		0.15	0.4	

SN72308A and SN72308 electrical characteristics at specified free-air temperature (see note 6)

PARAMETER		TEST CONDITIONS†		SN72308A			SN72308			UNIT
				MIN	TYP	MAX	MIN	TYP	MAX	
V_{IO}	Input offset voltage		25°C		0.3	0.5		2	7.5	mV
			Full range			0.73			10	
αV_{IO}	Average temperature coefficient of input offset voltage		Full range		1	5		6	30	µV/°C
I_{IO}	Input offset current		25°C		0.2	1		0.2	1	nA
			Full range			1.5			1.5	
αI_{IO}	Average temperature coefficient of input offset current		Full range		2	10		2	10	pA/°C
I_{IB}	Input bias current		25°C		1.5	7		1.5	7	nA
			Full range			10			10	
V_I	Input voltage range	$V_{CC\pm} = \pm15$ V	Full range	±14			±14			V
V_{OPP}	Maximum peak-to-peak output voltage swing	$V_{CC\pm} = \pm15$ V, $R_L = 10$ kΩ	Full range	26	28		26	28		V
A_{VD}	Large-signal differential voltage amplification	$V_{CC\pm} = \pm15$ V, $V_O = \pm10$ V, $R_L \geqslant 10$ kΩ	25°C	80,000	300,000		25,000	300,000		
			Full range	60,000			15,000			
r_i	Input resistance		25°C	10	40		10	40		MΩ
CMRR	Common-mode rejection ratio		Full range	96	110		80	100		dB
$\Delta V_{CC}/\Delta V_{IO}$	Supply voltage rejection ratio		Full range	96	110		80	96		dB
I_{CC}	Supply current	No load	25°C		0.3	0.8		0.3	0.8	mA

†All characteristics are specified under open-loop operation. Full range for SN52108A and SN52108 is $-55°$C to $125°$C and for SN72308A and SN72308 is $0°$C to $70°$C.

NOTE 6: Unless otherwise noted, $V_{CC\pm} = \pm5$ V to ±20 V for SN52108A and SN52108 and $V_{CC\pm} = \pm5$ V to ±18 V for SN72308A and SN72308. All typical values are at $V_{CC\pm} = \pm15$ V. Throughout this data sheet, supply voltages are specified either as a range or as a specific value. A positive voltage within the specified range (or of the specified value) is applied to V_{CC+}, and an equal negative voltage is applied to V_{CC-}.

TEXAS INSTRUMENTS
INCORPORATED
POST OFFICE BOX 5012 • DALLAS, TEXAS 75222

DEFINITION OF TERMS

Input Offset Voltage (V_{IO}) The d-c voltage which must be applied between the input terminals to force the quiescent d-c output voltage to zero. The input offset voltage may also be defined for the case where two equal resistances (R_S) are inserted in series with the input leads.

Average Temperature Coefficient of Input Offset Voltage (α_{VIO}) The ratio of the change in input offset voltage to the change in free-air temperature. This is an average value for the specified temperature range.

$$\alpha_{VIO} = \left| \frac{(V_{IO} @ T_{A(1)}) - (V_{IO} @ T_{A(2)})}{T_{A(1)} - T_{A(2)}} \right| \quad \text{where } T_{A(1)} \text{ and } T_{A(2)} \text{ are the specified temperature extremes.}$$

Input Offset Current (I_{IO}) The difference between the currents into the two input terminals with the output at zero volts.

Average Temperature Coefficient of Input Offset Current (α_{IIO}) The ratio of the change in input offset current to the change in free-air temperature. This is an average value for the specified temperature range.

$$\alpha_{IIO} = \left| \frac{(I_{IO} @ T_{A(1)}) - (I_{IO} @ T_{A(2)})}{T_{A(1)} - T_{A(2)}} \right| \quad \text{where } T_{A(1)} \text{ and } T_{A(2)} \text{ are the specified temperature extremes.}$$

Input Bias Current (I_{IB}) The average of the currents into the two input terminals with the output at zero volts.

Input Voltage Range (V_I) The range of voltage which, if exceeded at either input terminal, will cause the amplifier to cease functioning properly.

Maximum Peak-to-Peak Output Voltage Swing (V_{OPP}) The maximum peak-to-peak output voltage which can be obtained without waveform clipping when the quiescent d-c output voltage is zero.

Large-Signal Differential Voltage Amplification (A_{VD}) The ratio of the peak-to-peak output voltage swing to the change in differential input voltage required to drive the output.

Input Resistance (r_i) The resistance between the input terminals with either input grounded.

Common-Mode Rejection Ratio (CMRR) The ratio of differential voltage amplification to common-mode voltage amplification. This is measured by determining the ratio of a change in input common-mode voltage to the resulting change in input offset voltage.

Supply Voltage Rejection Ratio ($\Delta V_{CC}/\Delta V_{IO}$) The ratio of the change in power supply voltages to the change in input offset voltage. For these devices, both supply voltages are varied symmetrically.

schematic

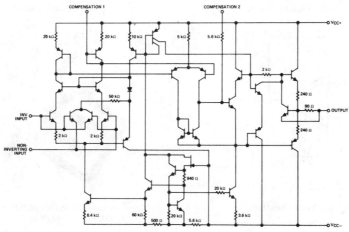

Component values shown are nominal.

TYPES SN52108A, SN52108, SN72308A, SN72308
HIGH-PERFORMANCE OPERATIONAL AMPLIFIERS

TYPICAL APPLICATION DATA

guarding

Extra care must be taken in the assembly of printed circuit boards to take full advantage of the low input currents of these amplifiers.

Even with properly cleaned and coated boards, leakage currents may cause trouble at 125°C, particularly in the L plug-in package (TO-99) where the input pins are adjacent to pins that are at supply potentials. This leakage can be reduced by surrounding the input terminals with a conductive guard ring. The guard ring is connected to a low-impednace point that is at approximately the same voltage as the inputs. As shown in Figure 4, input guarding of the 8-lead L package may be accomplished by using a 10-lead pin circle, with leads of the device formed so that the holes adjacent to the inputs are empty when it is inserted in the board. The conductive guard ring should be used on both sides of the board.

The pin configurations of both the dual-in-line and flat packages are designed to facilitate guarding, since the pins adjacent to the inputs are not internally connected to the chip. Pin connections in these packages are different from the standard pin connections used in other operational amplifiers such as the SN52741/SN72741.

connection of input guard circuit

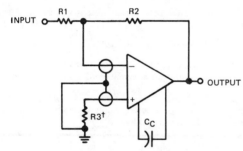

FIGURE 1–INVERTING AMPLIFIER

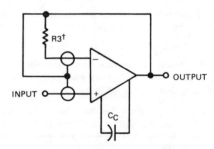

FIGURE 2–VOLTAGE FOLLOWER

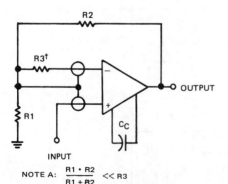

NOTE A: $\dfrac{R1 \cdot R2}{R1 + R2} \ll R3$

FIGURE 3–NON-INVERTING AMPLIFIER

† Resistor R3 is used to compensate for large source resistances.

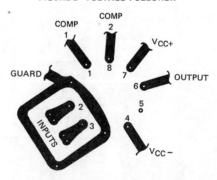

FIGURE 4–BOARD LAYOUT FOR INPUT GUARDING
WITH L PLUG-IN PACKAGE (TOP VIEW)

TEXAS INSTRUMENTS
INCORPORATED
POST OFFICE BOX 5012 • DALLAS, TEXAS 75222

TYPICAL APPLICATION DATA

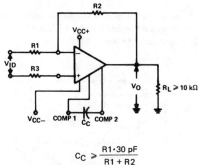

$$C_C \geq \frac{R1 \cdot 30 \text{ pF}}{R1 + R2}$$

$$\frac{V_O}{V_{ID}} = -\frac{R2}{R1}$$

$$R_3 = \frac{R1 \cdot R2}{R1 + R2}$$

FIGURE 5—STANDARD COMPENSATION CIRCUIT

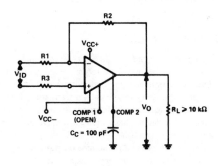

FIGURE 6—ALTERNATE COMPENSATION CIRCUIT

THERMAL INFORMATION

DISSIPATION DERATING CURVE

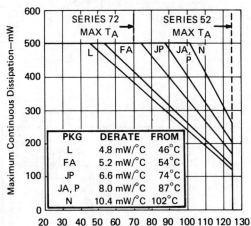

PKG	DERATE	FROM
L	4.8 mW/°C	46°C
FA	5.2 mW/°C	54°C
JP	6.6 mW/°C	74°C
JA, P	8.0 mW/°C	87°C
N	10.4 mW/°C	102°C

FIGURE 7

LINEAR INTEGRATED CIRCUITS

- Maximum Input Bias Current Over Temperature Range . . . 10 nA
- Small-Signal Bandwidth . . . 20 MHz Typ
- Slew Rate . . . 30 V/µs Typ

- Supply Voltage Range . . . ±5 V to ±18 V
- Internally Compensated
- Designed to be Interchangeable with National Semiconductor LM110 and LM310 and to Replace LM102 and LM302

description

The SN52110 and SN72310 are monolithic bipolar operational amplifiers internally connected in a unity-gain non-inverting configuration. A darlington input stage, using very-high-beta transistors, provides extremely low input current without sacrificing speed. The devices have internal frequency compensation and offset-balancing capabilities. The booster terminal can be used to increase output voltage swing under load by connecting an external resistor between the booster terminal and V_{CC-}.

The SN52110 and SN72310 are direct replacements for other operational amplifiers, such as the SN52101, SN52709, and SN52741, in voltage follower applications and provide greater stability and faster slew rates. Applications include fast sample and hold circuits, active filters, and general purpose buffers.

The SN52110 is characterized for operation over the full military temperature range of −55°C to 125°C; the SN72310 is characterized for operation from 0°C to 70°C.

schematic

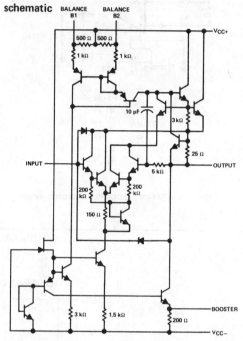

Component values shown are nominal

terminal assignments

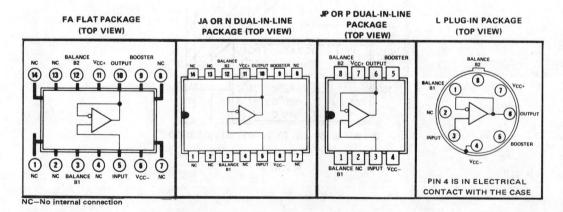

NC—No internal connection

TEXAS INSTRUMENTS
INCORPORATED
POST OFFICE BOX 5012 • DALLAS, TEXAS 75222

absolute maximum ratings over operating free-air temperature range (unless otherwise noted)

		SN52110	SN72310	UNIT
Supply voltage V_{CC+} (see Note 1)		18	18	V
Supply voltage V_{CC-} (see Note 1)		−18	−18	V
Input voltage (see Notes 1 and 2)		±15	±15	V
Duration of output short-circuit (see Note 3)		unlimited	unlimited	
Continuous total dissipation at (or below) 25°C free-air temperature (see Note 4)		500	500	mW
Operating free-air temperature range		−55 to 125	0 to 70	°C
Storage temperature range		−65 to 150	−65 to 150	°C
Lead temperature 1/16 inch from case for 60 seconds	FA or L package	300	300	°C
Lead temperature 1/16 inch from case for 10 seconds	N or P package	260	260	°C

NOTES: 1. All voltage values, unless otherwise noted, are with respect to the zero-reference level (ground) of the supply voltages where the zero-reference level is the midpoint between V_{CC+} and V_{CC-}. If the zero-reference level of the system is not the midpoint of the supply voltages, all voltage values must be changed accordingly.
2. The magnitude of the input voltage must never exceed the magnitude of the supply voltage or 15 volts, whichever is less.
3. The output may be shorted to any voltage between V_{CC+} and V_{CC-}. For the SN52110 only, the unlimited duration of the short-circuit applies at (or below) 125°C case temperature or 75°C free-air temperature. It is necessary to insert a resistor having a value greater than 2 kΩ in series with the input when the amplifier is driven from low-impedance sources to prevent damage when the output is shorted.
4. For operation above 55°C free-air temperature, refer to Dissipation Derating Curve, Figure 14.

voltages specified

Throughout this data sheet, supply voltages are specified either as a range or as a specific value. A positive voltage within the specified range (or of the specified value) is applied to V_{CC+}, and an equal negative voltage is applied to V_{CC-}.

electrical characteristics at specified free-air temperature, $V_{CC\pm}$ = ±5 V to ±18 V (unless otherwise noted)

PARAMETER		TEST CONDITIONS‡		SN52110			SN72310			UNIT
				MIN	TYP†	MAX	MIN	TYP†	MAX	
V_{IO}	Input offset voltage		25°C		1.5	4		2.5	7.5	mV
			Full range			6			10	
α_{VIO}	Average temperature coefficient of input offset voltage		0°C to 70°C					10		µV/°C
			−55°C to 85°C		6					
			25°C to 125°C		12					
I_{IB}	Input bias current		25°C		1	3		2	7	nA
			Full range			10			10	
V_{OM}	Maximum peak output voltage swing (See Note 5)	$V_{CC\pm}$ = ±15 V, R_L = 10 kΩ	Full range	±10			±10			V
A_V	Large-signal voltage amplification	$V_{CC\pm}$ = ±15 V, V_O = ±10 V, R_L = 8 kΩ	25°C	0.999	0.9999		0.999	0.9999		
		V_{CC} = ±15 V, V_O = ±10 V, R_L = 10 kΩ	Full range	0.999			0.999			
r_i	Input resistance	V_O = ±10 V	25°C	10^{10}	10^{12}		10^{10}	10^{12}		Ω
r_o	Output resistance		25°C		0.75	2.5		0.75	2.5	Ω
C_i	Input capacitance		25°C		1.5			1.5		pF
$\Delta V_{CC}/\Delta V_{IO}$	Supply voltage rejection ratio	$R_S \leq 10$ kΩ	Full range	70	75		70	75		dB
I_{CC}	Supply current	No load, No signal	25°C		3.5	5.5		3.5	5.5	mA
			125°C		2	4				

† All typical values are at $V_{CC\pm}$ = ±15 V.

‡ Full range for SN52110 is −55°C to 125°C and for SN72310 is 0°C to 70°C.

NOTE 5: Increased output swing under load can be obtained by connecting an external resistor between the booster terminal and V_{CC-}. See Figure 9.

DEFINITION OF TERMS

Input Offset Voltage (V_{IO}) The d-c voltage that must be applied at the input terminal to force the quiescent d-c output voltage to zero.

Average Temperature Coefficient of Input Offset Voltage (α_{VIO}) The ratio of the change in input offset voltage to the change in free-air temperature. This is an average value for the specified temperature range.

$$\alpha_{VIO} = \left| \frac{(V_{IO} @ T_{A(1)}) - (V_{IO} @ T_{A(2)})}{T_{A(1)} - T_{A(2)}} \right| \quad \text{where } T_{A(1)} \text{ and } T_{A(2)} \text{ are the specified temperature extremes.}$$

Input Bias Current (I_{IB}) The current into the input terminal with the input terminal at zero volts.

Maximum Peak Output Voltage Swing (V_{OM}) The maximum positive or negative peak output voltage that can be obtained without waveform clipping when the quiescent d-c output voltage is zero.

Large Signal Voltage Amplification (A_V) The ratio of the peak-to-peak output voltage swing to the change in input voltage required to drive the output.

Input Resistance (r_i) The ratio of the specified output voltage swing to the corresponding change in input current.

Output Resistance (r_o) The ratio of the change in output voltage to the corresponding change in output current with input voltage remaining constant.

Supply Voltage Rejection Ratio ($\Delta V_{CC}/\Delta V_{IO}$) The absolute value of the ratio of the change in one power supply voltage (with the remaining power supply voltage held constant) to the resulting change in input offset voltage.

TYPICAL CHARACTERISTICS†

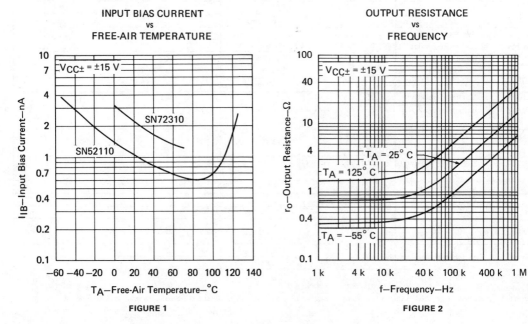

INPUT BIAS CURRENT
vs
FREE-AIR TEMPERATURE

FIGURE 1

OUTPUT RESISTANCE
vs
FREQUENCY

FIGURE 2

†Data for temperatures below 0°C and above 70°C is applicable to SN52110 circuits only.

TEXAS INSTRUMENTS
INCORPORATED
POST OFFICE BOX 5012 • DALLAS, TEXAS 75222

TYPICAL CHARACTERISTICS†

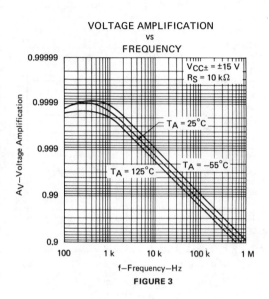

FIGURE 3

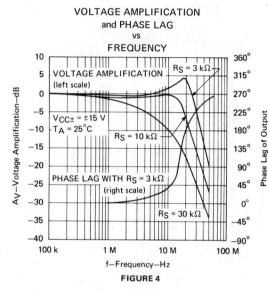

FIGURE 4

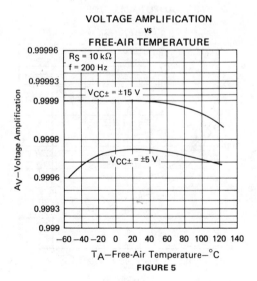

FIGURE 5

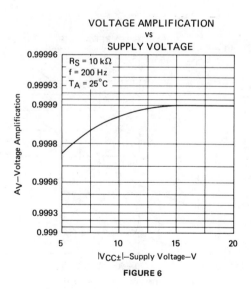

FIGURE 6

†Data for temperatures below 0°C and above 70°C is applicable to SN52110 circuits only.

TYPICAL CHARACTERISTICS[†]

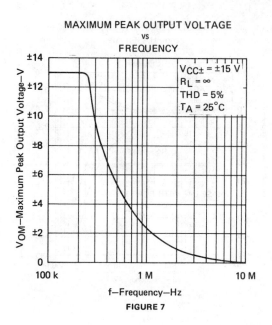

MAXIMUM PEAK OUTPUT VOLTAGE
vs
FREQUENCY

$V_{CC\pm} = \pm15$ V
$R_L = \infty$
THD = 5%
$T_A = 25°C$

V_{OM}—Maximum Peak Output Voltage—V

f—Frequency—Hz

FIGURE 7

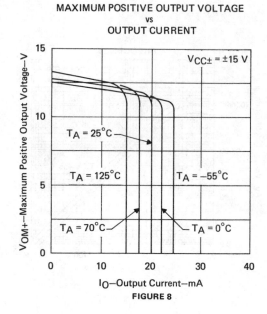

MAXIMUM POSITIVE OUTPUT VOLTAGE
vs
OUTPUT CURRENT

$V_{CC\pm} = \pm15$ V

V_{OM+}—Maximum Positive Output Voltage—V

$T_A = 25°C$
$T_A = 125°C$
$T_A = -55°C$
$T_A = 70°C$
$T_A = 0°C$

I_O—Output Current—mA

FIGURE 8

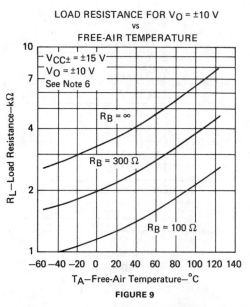

LOAD RESISTANCE FOR $V_O = \pm10$ V
vs
FREE-AIR TEMPERATURE

$V_{CC\pm} = \pm15$ V
$V_O = \pm10$ V
See Note 6

R_L—Load Resistance—kΩ

$R_B = \infty$
$R_B = 300$ Ω
$R_B = 100$ Ω

T_A—Free-Air Temperature—°C

FIGURE 9

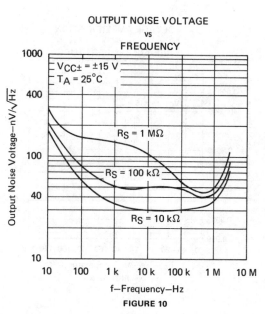

OUTPUT NOISE VOLTAGE
vs
FREQUENCY

$V_{CC\pm} = \pm15$ V
$T_A = 25°C$

Output Noise Voltage—nV/√Hz

$R_S = 1$ MΩ
$R_S = 100$ kΩ
$R_S = 10$ kΩ

f—Frequency—Hz

FIGURE 10

[†] Data for temperatures below 0°C and above 70°C is applicable to SN52110 circuits only.

NOTE 6: R_B is an external resistor connected between the booster terminal and V_{CC-}.

TEXAS INSTRUMENTS
INCORPORATED
POST OFFICE BOX 5012 • DALLAS, TEXAS 75222

TYPICAL CHARACTERISTICS†

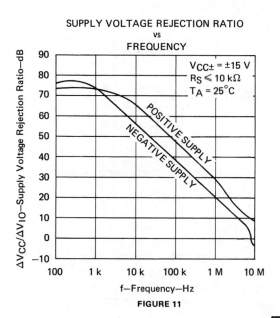

SUPPLY VOLTAGE REJECTION RATIO
vs
FREQUENCY

$V_{CC\pm} = \pm15$ V
$R_S \leqslant 10$ kΩ
$T_A = 25^\circ$C

POSITIVE SUPPLY

NEGATIVE SUPPLY

$\Delta V_{CC}/\Delta V_{IO}$—Supply Voltage Rejection Ratio—dB

f—Frequency—Hz

FIGURE 11

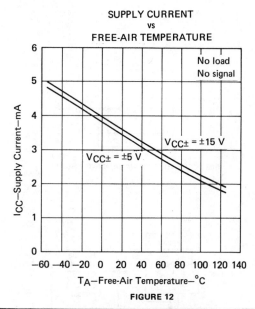

SUPPLY CURRENT
vs
FREE-AIR TEMPERATURE

No load
No signal

$V_{CC\pm} = \pm15$ V
$V_{CC\pm} = \pm5$ V

I_{CC}—Supply Current—mA

T_A—Free-Air Temperature—$^\circ$C

FIGURE 12

4

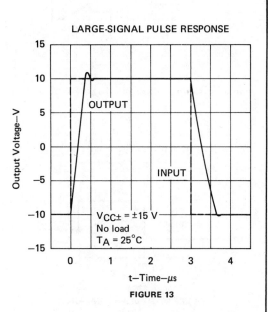

LARGE-SIGNAL PULSE RESPONSE

OUTPUT

INPUT

$V_{CC\pm} = \pm15$ V
No load
$T_A = 25^\circ$C

Output Voltage—V

t—Time—µs

FIGURE 13

THERMAL INFORMATION

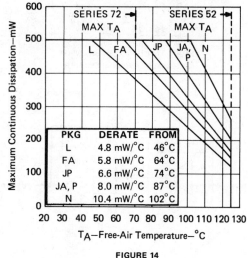

DISSIPATION DERATING CURVE

SERIES 72
MAX T_A

SERIES 52
MAX T_A

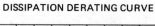

L   FA   JP   JA,   N
                      P

Maximum Continuous Dissipation—mW

PKG	DERATE	FROM
L	4.8 mW/°C	46°C
FA	5.8 mW/°C	64°C
JP	6.6 mW/°C	74°C
JA, P	8.0 mW/°C	87°C
N	10.4 mW/°C	102°C

T_A—Free-Air Temperature—$^\circ$C

FIGURE 14

†Data for temperatures below 0°C and above 70°C is applicable to
SN52110 circuits only.

TEXAS INSTRUMENTS
INCORPORATED
POST OFFICE BOX 5012 • DALLAS, TEXAS 75222

TYPICAL APPLICATION DATA

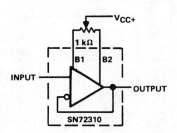

FIGURE 15—OFFSET BALANCING CIRCUIT

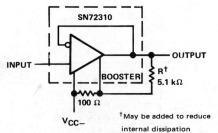

†May be added to reduce internal dissipation

FIGURE 16—INCREASING NEGATIVE SWING UNDER LOAD

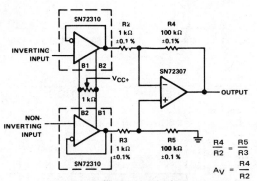

$$\frac{R4}{R2} = \frac{R5}{R3}$$

$$A_V = \frac{R4}{R2}$$

FIGURE 17—DIFFERENTIAL INPUT INSTRUMENTATION AMPLIFIER

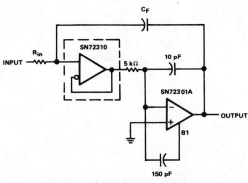

FIGURE 18—FAST INTEGRATOR WITH LOW INPUT CURRENT

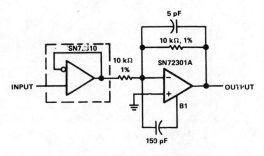

FIGURE 19—FAST INVERTING AMPLIFIER WITH HIGH INPUT IMPEDANCE

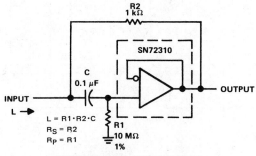

$$L = R1 \cdot R2 \cdot C$$
$$R_S = R2$$
$$R_P = R1$$

FIGURE 20—SIMULATED INDUCTOR

TEXAS INSTRUMENTS
INCORPORATED
POST OFFICE BOX 5012 • DALLAS, TEXAS 75222

TYPICAL APPLICATION DATA

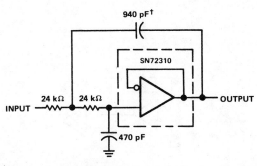

†Values are for 10 kHz cutoff. Use silvered-mica capacitors for good temperature stability.

FIGURE 21—LOW-PASS ACTIVE FILTER

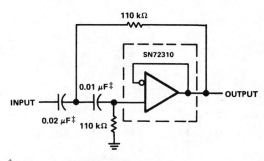

‡Values are for 100 Hz cutoff. Use metalized polycarbonate capacitors for good temperature stability.

FIGURE 22—HIGH-PASS ACTIVE FILTER

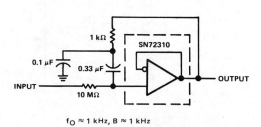

$f_O \approx 1$ kHz, B ≈ 1 kHz

FIGURE 23—BANDPASS FILTER

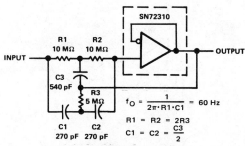

$$f_O = \frac{1}{2\pi \cdot R1 \cdot C1} = 60 \text{ Hz}$$

$$R1 = R2 = 2R3$$

$$C1 = C2 = \frac{C3}{2}$$

FIGURE 24—HIGH-Q NOTCH FILTER

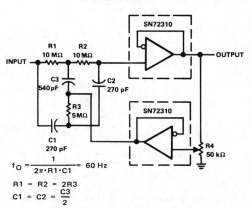

$$f_O = \frac{1}{2\pi \cdot R1 \cdot C1} = 60 \text{ Hz}$$

$$R1 = R2 = 2R3$$

$$C1 = C2 = \frac{C3}{2}$$

FIGURE 25—ADJUSTABLE-Q NOTCH FILTER

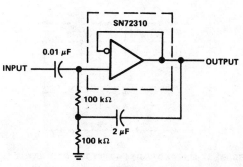

FIGURE 26—HIGH-INPUT-IMPEDANCE AC AMPLIFIER

TYPICAL APPLICATION DATA

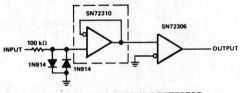

FIGURE 27—ZERO-CROSSING DETECTOR

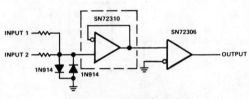

FIGURE 28—COMPARATOR FOR SIGNALS OF OPPOSITE POLARITY

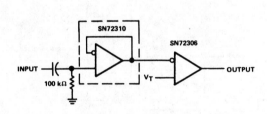

FIGURE 29—COMPARATOR FOR AC-COUPLED SIGNALS

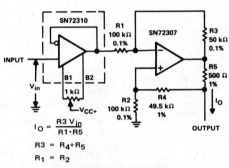

$$I_O = \frac{R3\, V_{in}}{R1 \cdot R5}$$

$$R3 = R_4 + R_5$$

$$R_1 = R_2$$

FIGURE 30—BILATERAL CURRENT SUPPLY

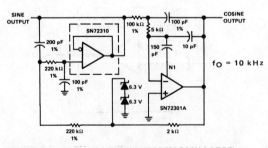

$f_O = 10\ \text{kHz}$

FIGURE 31—SINE AND COSINE WAVEFORM OSCILLATOR

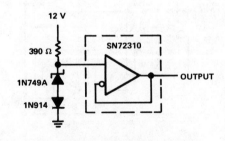

FIGURE 32—BUFFERED, TEMPERATURE-STABLE, 5-V REFERENCE SOURCE

TEXAS INSTRUMENTS
INCORPORATED
POST OFFICE BOX 5012 • DALLAS, TEXAS 75222

TYPICAL APPLICATION DATA

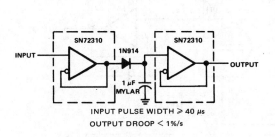

INPUT PULSE WIDTH ⩾ 40 μs
OUTPUT DROOP < 1%/s

FIGURE 33—PEAK DETECTOR

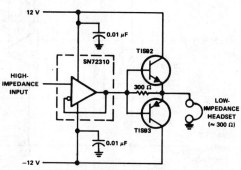

FIGURE 34—AUDIO IMPEDANCE BUFFER

4

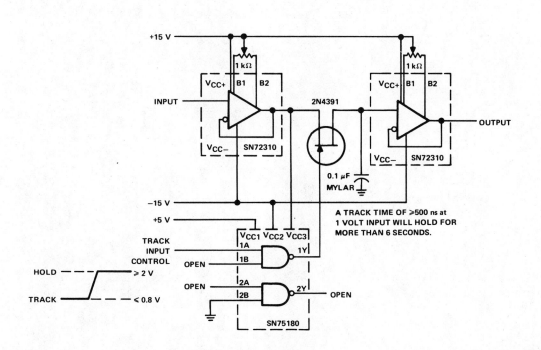

A TRACK TIME OF ⩾500 ns at
1 VOLT INPUT WILL HOLD FOR
MORE THAN 6 SECONDS.

FIGURE 35—TRACK-AND-HOLD CIRCUIT

TYPICAL APPLICATION DATA

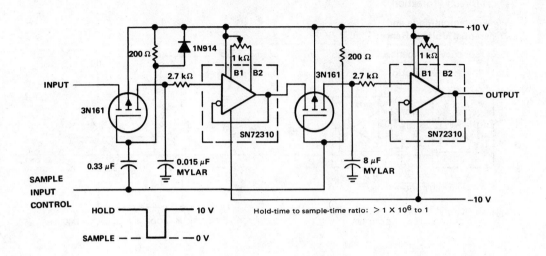

FIGURE 36—SAMPLE-AND-HOLD CIRCUIT

TEXAS INSTRUMENTS
INCORPORATED
POST OFFICE BOX 5012 • DALLAS, TEXAS 75222

LINEAR INTEGRATED CIRCUITS

- Short-Circuit Protection
- Wide Common-Mode and Differential Voltage Ranges
- No Frequency Compensation Required
- Low Power Consumption
- No Latch-up
- Designed to be Interchangeable with Motorola MC1558/MC1458 and Signetics S5558/N5558

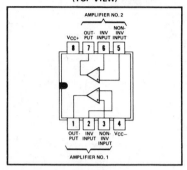

JP OR P
DUAL-IN-LINE
PACKAGE
(TOP VIEW)

description

The SN52558 and SN72558 are dual general-purpose operational amplifiers with each half electrically similar to SN52741/SN72741 except that offset null capability is not provided.

The high common-mode input voltage range and the absence of latch-up make these amplifiers ideal for voltage-follower applications. The devices are short-circuit protected and the internal frequency compensation ensures stability without external components.

The SN52558 is characterized for operation over the full military temperature range of −55°C to 125°C; the SN72558 is characterized for operation from 0°C to 70°C.

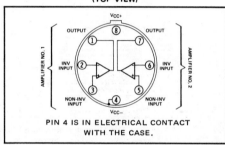

L PLUG-IN PACKAGE
(TOP VIEW)

PIN 4 IS IN ELECTRICAL CONTACT
WITH THE CASE.

absolute maximum ratings over operating free-air temperature range (unless otherwise noted)

		SN52558	SN72558	UNIT
Supply voltage V_{CC+} (see Note 1)		22	18	V
Supply voltage V_{CC-} (see Note 1)		−22	−18	V
Differential input voltage (see Note 2)		±30	±30	V
Input voltage (any input, see Notes 1 and 3)		±15	±15	V
Duration of output short-circuit (see Note 4)		unlimited	unlimited	
Continuous total dissipation at (or below) 25°C	Each amplifier	500	500	mW
free-air temperature range (see Note 5)	Total package	See Figure 1		
Operating free-air temperature range		−55 to 125	0 to 70	°C
Storage temperature range		−65 to 150	−65 to 150	°C
Lead temperature 1/16 inch from case for 60 seconds	JP or L package	300	300	°C
Lead temperature 1/16 inch from case for 10 seconds	P package	260	260	°C

NOTES: 1. All voltage values, unless otherwise noted, are with respect to the zero reference level (ground) of the supply voltages where the zero reference level is the midpoint between V_{CC+} and V_{CC-}.
2. Differential voltages are at the noninverting input terminal with respect to the inverting input terminal.
3. The magnitude of the input voltage must never exceed the magnitude of the supply voltage or 15 volts, whichever is less.
4. The output may be shorted to ground or either power supply. For the SN52558 only, the unlimited duration of the short-circuit applies at (or below) 125°C case temperature or 75°C free-air temperature.
5. For operation above 25°C free-air temperature and for total package ratings, refer to Dissipation Derating Curve, Figure 1.

TEXAS INSTRUMENTS
INCORPORATED
POST OFFICE BOX 5012 • DALLAS, TEXAS 75222

electrical characteristics at specified free-air temperature, V_{CC+} = 15 V, V_{CC-} = −15 V

PARAMETER		TEST CONDITIONS[†]		SN52558			SN72558			UNIT
				MIN	TYP	MAX	MIN	TYP	MAX	
V_{IO}	Input offset voltage	$R_S \leqslant 10\,k\Omega$	25°C		1	5		1	6	mV
			Full range			6			7.5	
I_{IO}	Input offset current		25°C		20	200		20	200	nA
			Full range			500			300	
I_{IB}	Input bias current		25°C		80	500		80	500	nA
			Full range			1500			800	
V_I	Input voltage range		25°C	±12	±13		±12	±13		V
			Full range	±12			±12			
V_{OPP}	Maximum peak-to-peak output voltage swing	$R_L = 10\,k\Omega$	25°C	24	28		24	28		V
		$R_L \geqslant 10\,k\Omega$	Full range	24			24			
		$R_L = 2\,k\Omega$	25°C	20	26		20	26		
		$R_L \geqslant 2\,k\Omega$	Full range	20			20			
A_{VD}	Large-signal differential voltage amplification	$R_L \geqslant 2\,k\Omega$,	25°C	50,000	200,000		20,000	200,000		
		$V_O = \pm 10\,V$	Full range	25,000			15,000			
B_{OM}	Maximum-output-swing bandwidth (closed-loop)	$R_L = 2\,k\Omega$, $V_O \geqslant \pm 10\,V$, $A_{VD} = 1$, $THD \leqslant 5\%$	25°C		14			14		kHz
B_1	Unity-gain bandwidth		25°C		1			1		MHz
ϕ_m	Phase margin	$A_{VD} = 1$	25°C		65°			65°		
A_m	Gain margin		25°C		11			11		dB
r_i	Input resistance		25°C	0.3	2		0.3	2		MΩ
r_o	Output resistance	$V_O = 0$, See Note 5	25°C		75			75		Ω
C_i	Input capacitance		25°C		1.4			1.4		pF
z_{ic}	Common-mode input impedance	$f = 20\,Hz$	25°C		200			200		MΩ
CMRR	Common-mode rejection ratio	$R_S \leqslant 10\,k\Omega$	25°C	70	90		70	90		dB
			Full range	70			70			
$\Delta V_{IO}/\Delta V_{CC}$	Supply voltage sensitivity	$R_S \leqslant 10\,k\Omega$	25°C		30	150		30	150	$\mu V/V$
			Full range			150			150	
V_n	Equivalent input noise voltage (closed-loop)	$A_{VD} = 100$, $R_S = 0$, $f = 1\,kHz$, $BW = 1\,Hz$	25°C		45			45		$nV/\sqrt{Hz}$
I_{OS}	Short-circuit output current		25°C		±25	±40		±25	±40	mA
I_{CC}	Supply current (Both amplifiers)	No load, No signal	25°C		3.4	5.6		3.4	5.6	mA
			Full range			6.6			6.6	
P_D	Total power dissipation (Both amplifiers)	No load, No signal	25°C		100	170		100	170	mW
			Full range			200			200	
V_{o1}/V_{o2}	Channel separation		25°C		120			120		dB

[†]All characteristics are specified under open-loop operation, unless otherwise noted. Full range for SN52558 is −55°C to 125°C and for SN72558 is 0°C to 70°C.

NOTE 5: This typical value applies only at frequencies above a few hundred hertz because of the effects of drift and thermal feedback.

operating characteristics, V_{CC+} = 15 V, V_{CC-} = −15 V, T_A = 25°C

PARAMETER		TEST CONDITIONS	SN52558			SN72558			UNIT
			MIN	TYP	MAX	MIN	TYP	MAX	
t_r	Rise time	$V_I = 20\,mV$, $R_L = 2\,k\Omega$, $C_L = 100\,pF$, See Figure 2		0.3			0.3		μs
	Overshoot			5%			5%		
SR	Slew rate at unity gain	$V_I = 10\,V$, $R_L = 2\,k\Omega$, $C_L = 100\,pF$, See Figure 2		0.5			0.5		$V/\mu s$

TEXAS INSTRUMENTS
INCORPORATED
POST OFFICE BOX 5012 • DALLAS, TEXAS 75222

DEFINITION OF TERMS

Input Offset Voltage (V_{IO}) The d-c voltage which must be applied between the input terminals to force the quiescent d-c output voltage to zero. The input offset voltage may also be defined for the case where two equal resistances (R_S) are inserted in series with the input leads.

Input Offset Current (I_{IO}) The difference between the currents into the two input terminals with the output at zero volts.

Input Bias Current (I_{IB}) The average of the currents into the two input terminals with the output at zero volts.

Input Voltage Range (V_I) The range of voltage which if exceeded at either input terminal will cause the amplifier to cease functioning properly.

Maximum Peak-to-Peak Output Voltage Swing (V_{OPP}) The maximum peak-to-peak output voltage which can be obtained without waveform clipping when the quiescent d-c output voltage is zero.

Large-Signal Differential Voltage Amplification (A_{VD}) The ratio of the peak-to-peak output voltage swing to the change in differential input voltage required to drive the output.

Maximum-Output-Swing Bandwidth (B_{OM}) The range of frequencies within which the maximum output voltage swing is above a specified value.

Unity-Gain Bandwidth (B_1) The range of frequencies within which the voltage amplification is greater than unity.

Phase Margin (ϕ_m) $180°$ minus the absolute value of the phase shift between the output and the noninverting input at the frequency at which the open-loop gain is unity.

Gain Margin (A_m) The reciprocal of the differential voltage amplification at the lowest frequency at which the phase shift between the output and the noninverting input is $180°$.

Input Resistance (r_i) The resistance between the input terminals with either input grounded.

Output Resistance (r_o) The resistance between the output terminal and ground.

Input Capacitance (C_i) The capacitance between the input terminals with either input grounded.

Common-Mode Input Impedance (z_{ic}) The parallel sum of the small-signal impedances between each input terminal and ground.

Common-Mode Rejection Ratio (CMRR) The ratio of differential voltage amplification to common-mode voltage amplification. This is measured by determining the ratio of a change in input common-mode voltage to the resulting change in input offset voltage.

Supply Voltage Sensitivity ($\Delta V_{IO}/\Delta V_{CC}$) The ratio of the change in input offset voltage to the change in supply voltages producing it. For these devices, both supply voltages are varied symmetrically.

Short-Circuit Output Current (I_{OS}) The maximum output current available from the amplifier with the output shorted to ground or to either supply.

Total Power Dissipation (P_D) The total d-c power supplied to the device less any power delivered from the device to a load. At no load: $P_D = V_{CC+} \cdot I_{CC+} + V_{CC-} \cdot I_{CC-}$.

Rise Time (t_r) The time required for an output voltage step to change from 10% to 90% of its final value.

Overshoot The quotient of: (1) the largest deviation of the output signal value from its steady-state value after a step-function change of the input signal, and (2) the difference between the output signal values in the steady state before and after the step-function change of the input signal.

Slew Rate (SR) The average time rate of change of the closed-loop amplifier output voltage for a step-signal input. Slew rate is measured between specified output levels (0 and 10 volts for this device) with feedback adjusted for unity gain.

TEXAS INSTRUMENTS
INCORPORATED
POST OFFICE BOX 5012 • DALLAS, TEXAS 75222

TYPES SN52558, SN72558
DUAL GENERAL-PURPOSE OPERATIONAL AMPLIFIERS

schematic (each amplifier)

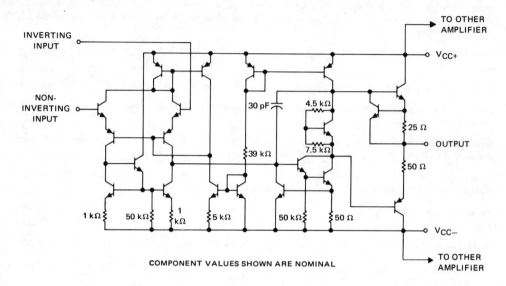

COMPONENT VALUES SHOWN ARE NOMINAL

THERMAL INFORMATION

DISSIPATION DERATING CURVE

PKG	DERATE	FROM (TOT PKG)	FROM (EACH AMP)
L	4.8 mW/°C	25°C	46°C
JP	6.6 mW/°C	47°C	74°C
P	8.0 mW/°C	65°C	87°C

FIGURE 1

PARAMETER MEASUREMENT INFORMATION

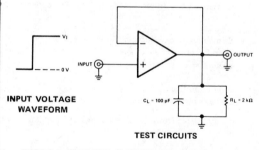

INPUT VOLTAGE WAVEFORM

TEST CIRCUITS

FIGURE 2—RISE TIME, OVERSHOOT, AND SLEW RATE

TEXAS INSTRUMENTS
INCORPORATED
POST OFFICE BOX 5012 • DALLAS, TEXAS 75222

TYPICAL CHARACTERISTICS

INPUT OFFSET CURRENT
vs
FREE-AIR TEMPERATURE

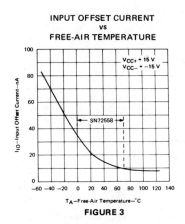

FIGURE 3

INPUT BIAS CURRENT
vs
FREE-AIR TEMPERATURE

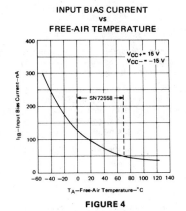

FIGURE 4

MAXIMUM PEAK-TO-PEAK
OUTPUT VOLTAGE
vs
LOAD RESISTANCE

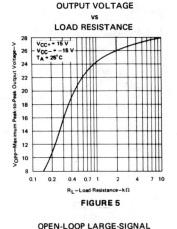

FIGURE 5

MAXIMUM PEAK-TO-PEAK
OUTPUT VOLTAGE
vs
FREQUENCY

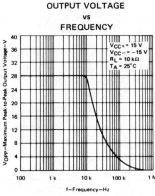

FIGURE 6

OPEN-LOOP LARGE-SIGNAL
DIFFERENTIAL
VOLTAGE AMPLIFICATION
vs
SUPPLY VOLTAGE

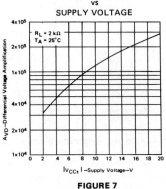

FIGURE 7

OPEN-LOOP LARGE-SIGNAL
DIFFERENTIAL
VOLTAGE AMPLIFICATION
vs
FREQUENCY

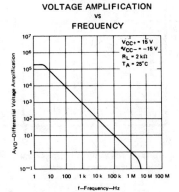

FIGURE 8

COMMON-MODE REJECTION RATIO
vs
FREQUENCY

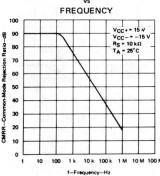
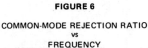

FIGURE 9

OUTPUT VOLTAGE
vs
ELAPSED TIME

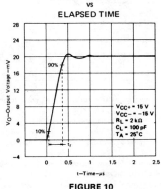
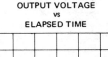
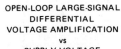

FIGURE 10

VOLTAGE-FOLLOWER
LARGE-SIGNAL PULSE RESPONSE

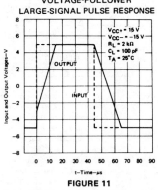
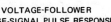

FIGURE 11

TEXAS INSTRUMENTS
INCORPORATED

POST OFFICE BOX 5012 • DALLAS, TEXAS 75222

- **Low Temperature Coefficients of Input Offset Voltage and Current**
- **Low Quiescent Power Consumption**
- **Low Input Bias and Offset Parameters**

description

These operational amplifiers are designed for applications requiring low input bias and offset currents and offset voltages. The SN52660 has a typical input offset voltage of 1 mV and typical input offset current of 0.5 nA at 25°C. Input bias current is 25 nA maximum over the full operating temperature range.

These circuits are guaranteed to operate from supply voltages of ±5 V to ±20 V (SN52660) or ±5 V to ±18 V (SN72660) with a quiescent supply current of typically 300 μA at ±15 V. The supply voltage rejection ratio is sufficient to permit use of unregulated supplies in most applications. The output is protected against damage from shorting to ground or either supply and the input stage is diode-protected against excessive differential input signals. External compensation permits optimization of the frequency response for each application.

The SN52660 is characterized for operation over the full military temperature range of −55°C to 125°C; the SN72660 is characterized for operation from 0°C to 70°C.

terminal assignments

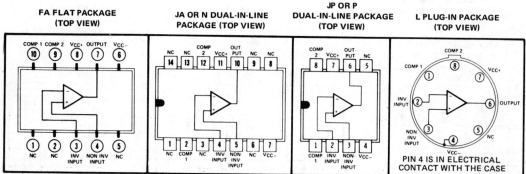

NC—No internal connection

absolute maximum ratings over operating free-air temperature range (unless otherwise noted)

		SN52660	SN72660	UNIT
Supply voltage V_{CC+} (see Note 1)		20	18	V
Supply voltage V_{CC-} (see Note 1)		−20	−18	V
Input voltage (either input, see Notes 1 and 2)		±15	±15	V
Differential input current (see Note 3)		±10	±10	mA
Duration of output short-circuit (see Note 4)		unlimited	unlimited	
Continuous total dissipation at (or below) 25°C free-air temperature (see Note 5)		500	500	mW
Operating free-air temperature range		−55 to 125	0 to 70	°C
Storage temperature range		−65 to 150	−65 to 150	°C
Lead temperature 1/16 inch from case for 60 seconds	FA, JA, JP, or L package	300	300	°C
Lead temperature 1/16 inch from case for 10 seconds	N or P package	260	260	°C

NOTES: 1. All voltage values, unless otherwise noted, are with respect to the zero reference level (ground) of the supply voltages where the zero reference level is the midpoint between V_{CC+} and V_{CC-}.

2. The magnitude of the input voltage must never exceed the magnitude of the supply voltage or 15 volts, whichever is less.

3. The inputs are shunted with two opposite-facing base-emitter diodes for over voltage protection. Therefore, excessive current will flow if a differential input voltage in excess of approximately 1 V is applied between the inputs unless some limiting resistance is used.

4. The output may be shorted to ground or either power supply. For the SN52660 only, the unlimited duration of the short-circuit applies at (or below) 125°C case temperature or 75°C free-air temperature.

5. For operation above 25°C free-air temperature refer to Dissipation Derating Curve, Figure 1.

TEXAS INSTRUMENTS
INCORPORATED
POST OFFICE BOX 5012 • DALLAS, TEXAS 75222

electrical characteristics at specified free-air temperature (see note 6)

PARAMETER		TEST CONDITIONS†		SN52660			SN72660			UNIT
				MIN	TYP	MAX	MIN	TYP	MAX	
V_{IO}	Input offset voltage		25°C		1	3		2	4	mV
			Full range			5			6	
α_{VIO}	Average temperature coefficient of input offset voltage		Full range			25			30	μV/°C
I_{IO}	Input offset current		25°C		0.5	2		0.5	2	nA
			Full range			5			4	
α_{IIO}	Average temperature coefficient of input offset current		Full range			40			40	pA/°C
I_{IB}	Input bias current		25°C		5	15		5	15	nA
			Full range			25			25	
V_I	Input voltage range	$V_{CC\pm} = \pm15$ V	Full range	±13.5			±13.5			V
V_{OPP}	Maximum peak-to-peak output voltage swing	$V_{CC\pm} = \pm15$ V, $R_L = 10$ kΩ	25°C	26	28		26	28		V
			Full range	26			26			
A_{VD}	Large-signal differential voltage amplification	$V_{CC\pm} = \pm15$ V, $V_O = \pm10$ V, $R_L \geqslant 10$ kΩ	25°C	25,000	150,000		25,000	150,000		
			Full range	25,000			15,000			
r_i	Input resistance		25°C	4	12		4	12		MΩ
CMRR	Common-mode rejection ratio		25°C	80	100		80	100		dB
			Full range	80			80			
$\Delta V_{CC}/\Delta V_{IO}$	Supply voltage rejection ratio		25°C	80	96		80	96		dB
			Full range	80			80			
I_{CC}	Supply current	No load, No signal	25°C		0.3	0.75		0.3	0.75	mA
			Full range			1			1	

†All characteristics are specified under open-loop operation. Full range for SN52660 is −55°C to 125°C and for SN72660 is 0°C to 70°C.

NOTE 6: Unless otherwise noted, $V_{CC\pm} = \pm5$ V to ±20 V for SN52660 and $V_{CC\pm} = \pm5$ V to ±18 V for SN72660. All typical values are at $V_{CC\pm} = \pm15$ V. Throughout this data sheet, supply voltages are specified either as a range or as a specific value. A positive voltage within the specified range (or of the specified value) is applied to V_{CC+}, and an equal negative voltage is applied to V_{CC-}.

schematic

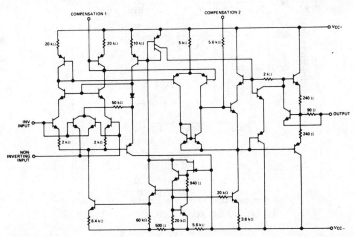

Component values shown are nominal.

TEXAS INSTRUMENTS
INCORPORATED
POST OFFICE BOX 5012 • DALLAS, TEXAS 75222

TYPES SN52660, SN72660
HIGH-PERFORMANCE OPERATIONAL AMPLIFIERS

DEFINITION OF TERMS

Input Offset Voltage (V_{IO}) The d-c voltage which must be applied between the input terminals to force the quiescent d-c output voltage to zero. The input offset voltage may also be defined for the case where two equal resistances (R_S) are inserted in series with the input leads.

Average Temperature Coefficient of Input Offset Voltage (α_{VIO}) The ratio of the change in input offset voltage to the change in free-air temperature. This is an average value for the specified temperature range.

$$\alpha_{VIO} = \left| \frac{(V_{IO} @ T_{A(1)}) - (V_{IO} @ T_{A(2)})}{T_{A(1)} - T_{A(2)}} \right| \quad \text{where } T_{A(1)} \text{ and } T_{A(2)} \text{ are the specified temperature extremes.}$$

Input Offset Current (I_{IO}) The difference between the currents into the two input terminals with the output at zero volts.

Average Temperature Coefficient of Input Offset Current (α_{IIO}) The ratio of the change in input offset current to the change in free-air temperature. This is an average value for the specified temperature range.

$$\alpha_{IIO} = \left| \frac{(I_{IO} @ T_{A(1)}) - (I_{IO} @ T_{A(2)})}{T_{A(1)} - T_{A(2)}} \right| \quad \text{where } T_{A(1)} \text{ and } T_{A(2)} \text{ are the specified temperature extremes.}$$

Input Bias Current (I_{IB}) The average of the currents into the two input terminals with the output at zero volts.

Input Voltage Range (V_I) The range of voltage which, if exceeded at either input terminal, will cause the amplifier to cease functioning properly.

Maximum Peak-to-Peak Output Voltage Swing (V_{OPP}) The maximum peak-to-peak output voltage which can be obtained without waveform clipping when the quiescent d-c output voltage is zero.

Large-Signal Differential Voltage Amplification (A_{VD}) The ratio of the peak-to-peak output voltage swing to the change in differential input voltage required to drive the output.

Input Resistance (r_i) The resistance between the input terminals with either input grounded.

Common-Mode Rejection Ratio (CMRR) The ratio of differential voltage amplification to common-mode voltage amplification. This is measured by determining the ratio of a change in input common-mode voltage to the resulting change in input offset voltage.

Supply Voltage Rejection Ratio ($\Delta V_{CC}/\Delta V_{IO}$) The ratio of the change in power supply voltages to the change in input offset voltage. For these devices, both supply voltages are varied symmetrically.

THERMAL INFORMATION
DISSIPATION DERATING CURVE

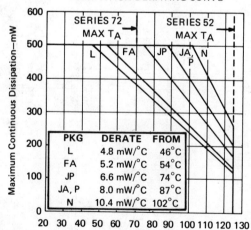

PKG	DERATE	FROM
L	4.8 mW/°C	46°C
FA	5.2 mW/°C	54°C
JP	6.6 mW/°C	74°C
JA, P	8.0 mW/°C	87°C
N	10.4 mW/°C	102°C

FIGURE 1

TEXAS INSTRUMENTS
INCORPORATED

POST OFFICE BOX 5012 • DALLAS, TEXAS 75222

SN52702A features

- **Open-Loop Voltage Amplification . . . 3600 Typ**
- **Designed to be Interchangeable With Fairchild μA702A**
- **CMRR . . . 100 dB Typ**

schematic

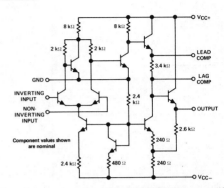

Component values shown are nominal

description

The SN52702A, SN52702 and SN72702 circuits are high-gain, wideband operational amplifiers, each having differential inputs and single-ended emitter-follower outputs. Provisions are incorporated within the circuit whereby external components may be used to compensate the amplifier for stable operation under various feedback or load conditions. Component matching, inherent in silicon monolithic circuit-fabrication techniques, produces an amplifier with low-drift and low-offset characteristics. The SN52702A is an improved version of the SN52702. These amplifiers are particularly useful for applications requiring transfer or generation of linear and non-linear functions up to a frequency of 30 MHz.

The SN52702A and SN52702 circuits are characterized for operation over the full military temperature range of −55°C to 125°C. The SN72702 circuit is characterized for operation over the temperature range of 0°C to 70°C.

terminal assignments

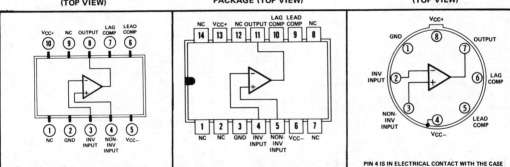

FA
FLAT PACKAGE
(TOP VIEW)

J OR N DUAL-IN-LINE
PACKAGE (TOP VIEW)

L PLUG-IN PACKAGE
(TOP VIEW)

PIN 4 IS IN ELECTRICAL CONTACT WITH THE CASE

NC—No internal connection

absolute maximum ratings over operating free-air temperature range (unless otherwise noted)

	SN52702A, SN52702	SN72702	UNIT
Supply voltage V$_{CC+}$ (see Note 1)	14	14	V
Supply voltage V$_{CC-}$ (see Note 1)	−7	−7	V
Differential input voltage (see Note 2)	±5	±5	V
Input voltage (either input, see Notes 1 and 3)	−6 to 1.5	−6 to 1.5	V
Peak output current (t$_W$ ⩽ 1 s)	50	50	mA
Continuous total dissipation at (or below) 70°C free-air temperature (see Note 4)	300	300	mW
Operating free-air temperature range	−55 to 125	0 to 70	°C
Storage temperature range	−65 to 150	−65 to 150	°C
Lead temperature 1/16 inch from case for 60 seconds FA, J, or L package	300	300	°C
Lead temperature 1/16 inch from case for 10 seconds N package	260	260	°C

NOTES: 1. All voltage values, unless otherwise noted, are with respect to the network ground terminal.
2. Differential voltages are at the noninverting input terminal with respect to the inverting input terminal.
3. The magnitude of the input voltage must never exceed the magnitude of the lesser of the two supply voltages.
4. For operation of SN52702A and SN52702 above 70°C free-air temperature, refer to Dissipation Derating Curve, Figure 3.

SN52702A

electrical characteristics at specified free-air temperature

PARAMETER		TEST CONDITIONS[†]		SN52702A V_{CC+} = 12 V V_{CC-} = −6 V MIN	TYP	MAX	V_{CC+} = 6 V V_{CC-} = −3 V MIN	TYP	MAX	UNIT
V_{IO}	Input offset voltage	$R_S \leqslant 2\,k\Omega$	25°C		0.5	2		0.7	3	mV
			Full range			3			4	
α_{VIO}	Average temperature coefficient of input offset voltage	$R_S = 50\,\Omega$	−55°C to 25°C		2	10		3	15	µV/°C
			25°C to 125°C		2.5	10		3.5	15	
I_{IO}	Input offset current		25°C		0.2	0.5		0.12	0.5	µA
			−55°C		0.4	1.5		0.3	1.5	
			125°C		0.08	0.5		0.05	0.5	
α_{IIO}	Average temperature coefficient of input offset current		−55°C to 25°C		3	16		2	13	nA/°C
			25°C to 125°C		1	5		0.7	4	
I_{IB}	Input bias current		25°C		2	5		1.2	3.5	µA
			−55°C		4.3	10		2.6	7.5	
V_I	Input voltage range	Positive swing	25°C	0.5	1		0.5	1		V
		Negative swing		−4	−5		−1.5	−2		
V_{OPP}	Maximum peak-to-peak output voltage swing	$R_L \geqslant 100\,k\Omega$	25°C	10	10.6		5	5.4		V
			Full range	10			5			
		$R_L = 10\,k\Omega$	25°C	7	8		3	4		
		$R_L \geqslant 10\,k\Omega$	Full range	7			3			
A_{VD}	Large-signal differential voltage amplification	$R_L \geqslant 100\,k\Omega$, $V_O = \pm 5\,V$	25°C	2500	3600	6000				
			Full range	2000		7000				
		$V_O = \pm 2.5\,V$	25°C				600	900	1500	
			Full range				500		1750	
r_i	Input resistance		25°C	16	40		22	67		kΩ
			Full range	6			8			
r_o	Output resistance	$V_O = 0$, See Note 3	25°C		200	500		300	700	Ω
CMRR	Common-mode rejection ratio	$R_S \leqslant 2\,k\Omega$	25°C	80	100		80	100		dB
			Full range	70			70			
$\Delta V_{IO}/\Delta V_{CC}$	Supply voltage sensitivity	$R_S \leqslant 2\,k\Omega$	25°C		75			75		µV/V
			Full range			200			200	
I_{CC}	Supply current	No load, No signal	25°C		5	6.7		2.1	3.3	mA
			−55°C		5	7.5		2.1	3.9	
			125°C		4.4	6.7		1.7	3.3	
P_D	Total power dissipation	No load, No signal	25°C		90	120		19	30	mW
			−55°C		90	135		19	35	
			125°C		80	120		15	30	

[†] All characteristics are specified under open-loop operation. Full range for SN52702A is −55°C to 125°C.
NOTE 3: This typical value applies only at frequencies above a few hundred hertz because of the effects of drift and thermal feedback.

TEXAS INSTRUMENTS
INCORPORATED
POST OFFICE BOX 5012 • DALLAS, TEXAS 75222

SN52702

electrical characteristics at specified free-air temperature

PARAMETER		TEST CONDITIONS[†]		SN52702 V_{CC+} = 12 V V_{CC-} = −6 V MIN	TYP	MAX	V_{CC+} = 6 V V_{CC-} = −3 V MIN	TYP	MAX	UNIT
V_{IO}	Input offset voltage	$R_S \leqslant 2 \, k\Omega$	25°C		2	5		2	5	mV
			Full range			6			6	
αVIO	Average temperature coefficient of input offset voltage	$R_S = 50 \, \Omega$	−55°C to 25°C		10			10		μV/°C
			25°C to 125°C		5			5		
I_{IO}	Input offset current		25°C		0.5	2		0.3	2	μA
			−55°C		1	3			3	
			125°C		0.2	3			3	
αIIO	Average temperature coefficient of input offset current		−55°C to 25°C		6			5		nA/°C
			25°C to 125°C		3			2		
I_{IB}	Input bias current		25°C		4	10		2.5	7	μA
			−55°C		6.5	20			14	
V_I	Input voltage range	Positive swing	25°C	0.5	1		0.5	1		V
		Negative swing		−4	−5		−1.5	−2		
V_{OPP}	Maximum peak-to-peak output voltage swing	$R_L \geqslant 100 \, k\Omega$		10	10.6		5	5.4		V
		$R_L = 10 \, k\Omega$			8			4		
A_{VD}	Large-signal differential voltage amplification	$R_L \geqslant 100 \, k\Omega$	$V_O = \pm 5$ V 25°C	1400	2600					
			Full range	1000						
			$V_O = \pm 2.5$ V 25°C				380	700		
r_i	Input resistance		25°C	8	25		12	40		kΩ
			Full range	3			4			
r_o	Output resistance	$V_O = 0$, See Note 3	25°C		200	500		300	700	Ω
CMRR	Common-mode rejection ratio	$R_S \leqslant 2 \, k\Omega$	25°C	70	80		70	80		dB
$\Delta V_{IO}/\Delta V_{CC}$	Supply voltage sensitivity	$R_S \leqslant 2 \, k\Omega$	25°C		60	300		60	300	μV/V
I_{CC}	Supply current	No load, No signal	25°C		5	6.7		2.1	3.9	mA
P_D	Total power dissipation	No load, No signal	25°C		90	120		19	35	mW

[†] All characteristics are specified under open-loop operation. Full range for SN52702 is −55°C to 125°C.

NOTE 3: This typical value applies only at frequencies above a few hundred hertz because of the effects of drift and thermal feedback.

4

TEXAS INSTRUMENTS
INCORPORATED
POST OFFICE BOX 5012 • DALLAS, TEXAS 75222

SN72702

electrical characteristics at specified free-air temperature, V_{CC+} = 12 V, V_{CC-} = −6 V

PARAMETER		TEST CONDITIONS[†]		SN72702 MIN	SN72702 TYP	SN72702 MAX	UNIT
V_{IO}	Input offset voltage	$R_S \leqslant 2\,k\Omega$	25°C		5	10	mV
			Full Range			15	
αV_{IO}	Average temperature coefficient of input offset voltage	$R_S = 50\,\Omega$	Full Range		5		µV/°C
I_{IO}	Input offset current		25°C		0.5	5	µA
			Full Range			7.5	
αI_{IO}	Average temperature coefficient of input offset current		0°C to 25°C		5		nA/°C
			25°C to 70°C		3		
I_{IB}	Input bias current		25°C		4	15	µA
			0°C		4.5	20	
V_I	Input voltage range	Positive swing	25°C	0.5	1		V
		Negative swing		−4	−5		
V_{OPP}	Maximum peak-to-peak output voltage swing	$R_L \geqslant 100\,k\Omega$	25°C	10	10.6		V
A_{VD}	Large-signal differential voltage amplification	$R_L \geqslant 100\,k\Omega$, $V_O = \pm 5$ V	25°C	1000	2600		
			Full Range	800			
r_i	Input resistance		25°C	6	25		$k\Omega$
			Full Range	3.5			
r_o	Output resistance	$V_O = 0$, See Note 3	25°C		200	600	Ω
CMRR	Common-mode rejection ratio	$R_S \leqslant 2\,k\Omega$	25°C	65	80		dB
$\Delta V_{IO}/\Delta V_{CC}$	Supply voltage sensitivity	$R_S \leqslant 2\,k\Omega$	25°C		60	300	µV/V
I_{CC}	Supply current	No load, No signal	25°C		5	7	mA
P_D	Total power dissipation	No load, No signal	25°C		90	125	mW

[†]All characteristics are specified under open-loop operation. Full range for SN72702 is 0°C to 70°C.

NOTE 3: This typical value applies only at frequencies above a few hundred hertz because of the effects of drift and thermal feedback.

SN52702A, SN52702, SN72702

operating characteristics V_{CC+} = 12 V, V_{CC-} = −6 V, T_A = 25°C

PARAMETER		TEST FIGURE	TEST CONDITIONS		ALL TYPES MIN	ALL TYPES TYP	ALL TYPES MAX	UNIT
t_r	Rise time	1	V_I = 10 mV,	$C_L = 0$		25	120	ns
		2	V_I = 1 mV			10	30	ns
	Overshoot	1	V_I = 10 mV,	$C_L = 100$ pF		10%	50%	
		2	V_I = 1 mV			20%	40%	
SR	Slew rate	1	V_I = 6 V,	$C_L = 100$ pF		1.7		V/µs
		2	V_I = 100 mV			11		

DEFINITION OF TERMS

Input Offset Voltage (V_{IO}) The d-c voltage which must be applied between the input terminals to force the quiescent d-c output voltage to zero. The input offset voltage may also be defined for the case where two equal resistances (R_S) are inserted in series with the input leads.

Average Temperature Coefficient of Input Offset Voltage (α_{VIO}) The ratio of the change in input offset voltage to the change in free-air temperature. This is an average value for the specified temperature range.

$$\alpha_{VIO} = \left| \frac{(V_{IO} @ T_{A(1)}) - (V_{IO} @ T_{A(2)})}{T_{A(1)} - T_{A(2)}} \right| \text{ where } T_{A(1)} \text{ and } T_{A(2)} \text{ are the specified temperature extremes.}$$

Input Offset Current (I_{IO}) The difference between the currents into the two input terminals with the output at zero volts.

Average Temperature Coefficient Of Input Offset Current (α_{IIO}) The ratio of the change in input offset current to the change in free-air temperature. This is an average value for the specified temperature range.

$$\alpha_{IIO} = \left| \frac{(I_{IO} @ T_{A(1)}) - (I_{IO} @ T_{A(2)})}{T_{A(1)} - T_{A(2)}} \right| \text{ where } T_{A(1)} \text{ and } T_{A(2)} \text{ are the specified temperature extremes.}$$

Input Bias Current (I_{IB}) The average of the currents into the two input terminals with the output at zero volts.

Input Voltage Range (V_I) The range of voltage which if exceeded at either input terminal will cause the amplifier to cease functioning properly.

Maximum Peak-to-Peak Output Voltage Swing (V_{OPP}) The maximum peak-to-peak output voltage which can be obtained without waveform clipping when the quiescent d-c output voltage is zero.

Large-Signal Differential Voltage Amplification (A_{VD}) The ratio of the peak-to-peak output voltage swing to the change in differential input voltage required to drive the output.

Input Resistance (r_i) The resistance between the input terminals with either input grounded.

Output Resistance (r_o) The resistance between the output terminal and ground.

Common-Mode Rejection Ratio (CMRR) The ratio of differential voltage amplification to common-mode voltage amplification. This is measured by determining the ratio of a change in input common-mode voltage to the resulting change in input offset voltage.

Supply Voltage Sensitivity ($\Delta V_{IO}/\Delta V_{CC}$) The ratio of the change in input offset voltage to the change in supply voltages producing it. For these devices, both supply voltages are varied symmetrically.

Total Power Dissipation (P_D) The total d-c power supplied to the device less any power delivered from the device to a load. At no load: $P_D = V_{CC+} \cdot I_{CC+} + V_{CC-} \cdot I_{CC-}$.

Rise Time (t_r) The time required for an output voltage step to change from 10% to 90% of its final value.

Overshoot The quotient of: (1) the largest deviation of the output signal value from its steady-state value after a step-function change of the input signal, and (2) the difference between the output signal values in the steady state before and after the step-function change of the input signal.

Slew Rate (SR) The average time rate of change of the closed-loop amplifier output voltage for a step-signal input.

PARAMETER MEASUREMENT INFORMATION

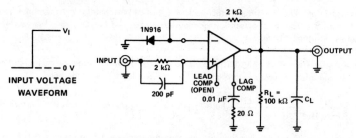

FIGURE 1—UNITY-GAIN AMPLIFIER

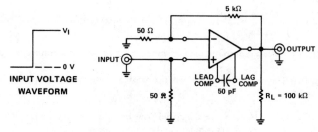

FIGURE 2—GAIN-OF-100 AMPLIFIER

THERMAL INFORMATION

SN52702A, SN52702
DISSIPATION DERATING CURVE

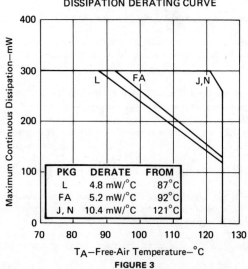

PKG	DERATE	FROM
L	4.8 mW/°C	87°C
FA	5.2 mW/°C	92°C
J, N	10.4 mW/°C	121°C

FIGURE 3

TEXAS INSTRUMENTS
INCORPORATED
POST OFFICE BOX 5012 • DALLAS, TEXAS 75222

TYPICAL CHARACTERISTICS

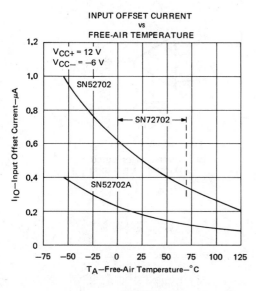

FIGURE 4

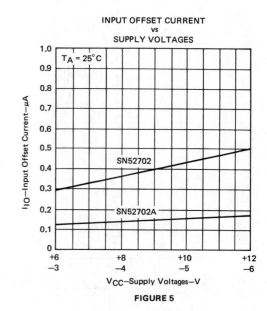

FIGURE 5

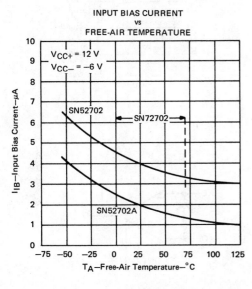

FIGURE 6

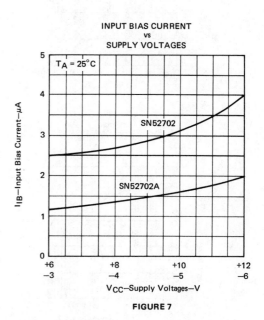

FIGURE 7

4

1

TYPES SN52702A, SN52702, SN72702
GENERAL-PURPOSE OPERATIONAL AMPLIFIERS

TYPICAL CHARACTERISTICS

MAXIMUM PEAK-TO-PEAK OUTPUT VOLTAGE
vs
FREQUENCY
(for various lag compensations)

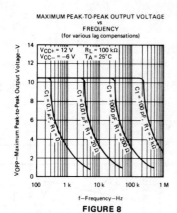

FIGURE 8

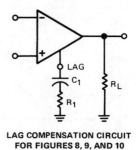

LAG COMPENSATION CIRCUIT
FOR FIGURES 8, 9, AND 10

SN52709A
LARGE-SIGNAL DIFFERENTIAL
VOLTAGE AMPLIFICATION
vs
FREQUENCY

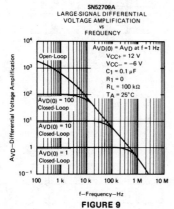

FIGURE 9

SN52702A
LARGE-SIGNAL DIFFERENTIAL
VOLTAGE AMPLIFICATION
vs
FREQUENCY
(for various lag compensations)

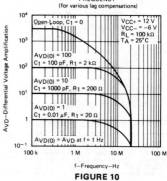

FIGURE 10

SN52702A
LARGE-SIGNAL DIFFERENTIAL
VOLTAGE AMPLIFICATION
vs
FREQUENCY
(for various lag compensations)

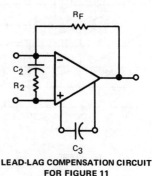

FIGURE 11

LEAD-LAG COMPENSATION CIRCUIT
FOR FIGURE 11

TEXAS INSTRUMENTS
INCORPORATED
POST OFFICE BOX 5012 • DALLAS, TEXAS 75222

TYPICAL CHARACTERISTICS

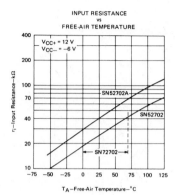

FIGURE 12

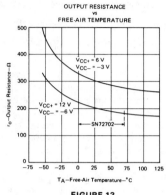

FIGURE 13

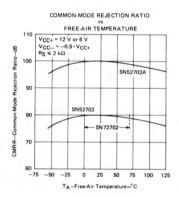

FIGURE 14

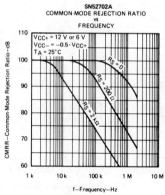

FIGURE 15

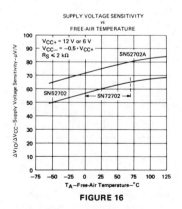

FIGURE 16

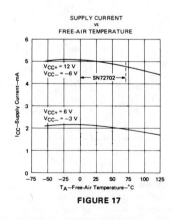

FIGURE 17

4

TEXAS INSTRUMENTS
INCORPORATED
POST OFFICE BOX 5012 • DALLAS, TEXAS 75222

SERIES 52/72 OPERATIONAL AMPLIFIERS
featuring

- **Common-Mode Input Range . . . ±10 V Typical**
- **Designed to be Interchangeable with Fairchild μA709A, μA709, and μA709C**
- **Maximum Peak-to-Peak Output Voltage Swing . . . 28 V Typical with 15 V Supplies**

description

These circuits are general-purpose operational amplifiers, each having high-impedance differential inputs and a low-impedance output. Component matching, inherent with silicon monolithic circuit-fabrication techniques, produces an amplifier with low-drift and low-offset characteristics. Provisions are incorporated within the circuit whereby external components may be used to compensate the amplifier for stable operation under various feedback or load conditions. These amplifiers are particularly useful for applications requiring transfer or generation of linear or nonlinear functions.

schematic

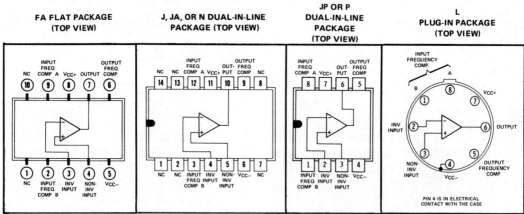

The SN52709A circuit features improved offset characteristics, reduced input-current requirements, and lower power dissipation when compared to the SN52709 circuit. In addition, maximum values of the average temperature coefficients of offset voltage and current are guaranteed.

The SN52709A and SN52709 are characterized for operation over the full military temperature range of −55°C to 125°C. The SN72709 is characterized for operation from 0°C to 70°C.

| FA FLAT PACKAGE (TOP VIEW) | J, JA, OR N DUAL-IN-LINE PACKAGE (TOP VIEW) | JP OR P DUAL-IN-LINE PACKAGE (TOP VIEW) | L PLUG-IN PACKAGE (TOP VIEW) |

NC—No internal connection

voltages specified

Throughout this data sheet, supply voltages are specified either as a range or as a specific value. A positive voltage within the specified range (or of the specified value) is applied to V_{CC+}, and an equal negative voltage is applied to V_{CC-}.

TEXAS INSTRUMENTS
INCORPORATED
POST OFFICE BOX 5012 • DALLAS, TEXAS 75222

absolute maximum ratings over operating free-air temperature range (unless otherwise noted)

		SN52709A, SN52709	SN72709	UNIT
Supply voltage V_{CC+} (see Note 1)		18	18	V
Supply voltage V_{CC-} (see Note 1)		−18	−18	V
Differential input voltage (see Note 2)		±5	±5	V
Input voltage (either input, see Notes 1 and 3)		±10	±10	V
Duration of output short-circuit (see Note 4)		5	5	s
Continuous total dissipation at (or below) 70°C free-air temperature (see Note 5)		300	300	mW
Operating free-air temperature range		−55 to 125	0 to 70	°C
Storage temperature range		−65 to 150	−65 to 150	°C
Lead temperature 1/16 inch from case for 60 seconds	FA, J, JA, JP, or L package	300	300	°C
Lead temperature 1/16 inch from case for 10 seconds	N or P package	260	260	°C

NOTES: 1. All voltage values, unless otherwise noted, are with respect to the zero reference level (ground) of the supply voltages where the zero reference level is the midpoint between V_{CC+} and V_{CC-}.
2. Differential voltages are at the noninverting input terminal with respect to the inverting input terminal.
3. The magnitude of the input voltage must never exceed the magnitude of the supply voltage or 10 volts, whichever is less.
4. The output may be shorted to ground or either power supply.
5. For operation of SN52709A and SN52709 above 70°C free-air temperature, refer to Dissipation Derating Curve, Figure 1.

electrical characteristics at specified free-air temperature, $V_{CC\pm}$ = ±9 V to ±15 V (unless otherwise noted)

PARAMETER		TEST CONDITIONS†		SN52709A			SN52709			UNIT
				MIN	TYP‡	MAX	MIN	TYP‡	MAX	
V_{IO}	Input offset voltage	$R_S \leqslant 10\ k\Omega$	25°C		0.6	2		1	5	mV
			Full range			3			6	
α_{VIO}	Average temperature coefficient of input offset voltage	$R_S = 50\ \Omega$	Full range		1.8	10		3		μV/°C
		$R_S = 10\ k\Omega$	−55°C to 25°C		4.8	25		6		
			25°C to 125°C		2	15		6		
I_{IO}	Input offset current		25°C		10	50		50	200	nA
			−55°C		40	250		100	500	
			125°C		3.5	50		20	200	
α_{IIO}	Average temperature coefficient of input offset current		−55°C to 25°C		0.45	2.8				nA/°C
			25°C to 125°C		0.08	0.5				
I_{IB}	Input bias current		25°C		0.1	0.2		0.2	0.5	μA
			−55°C		0.3	0.6		0.5	1.5	
V_I	Input voltage range	$V_{CC\pm} = \pm 15\ V$	25°C	±8	±10		±8	±10		V
			Full range	±8			±8			
V_{OPP}	Maximum peak-to-peak output voltage swing	$V_{CC\pm} = \pm 15\ V$, $R_L \geqslant 10\ k\Omega$	25°C	24	28		24	28		V
			Full range	24			24			
		$V_{CC\pm} = \pm 15\ V$, $R_L = 2\ k\Omega$	25°C	20	26		20	26		
		$V_{CC\pm} = \pm 15\ V$, $R_L \geqslant 2\ k\Omega$	Full range	20			20			
A_{VD}	Large-signal differential voltage amplification	$V_{CC\pm} = \pm 15\ V$, $R_L \geqslant 2\ k\Omega$, $V_O = \pm 10\ V$	25°C		45,000			45,000		
			Full range	25,000		70,000	25,000		70,000	
r_i	Input resistance		25°C	350	750		150	400		kΩ
			−55°C	85	185		40	100		
r_o	Output resistance	$V_O = 0$, See Note 6	25°C		150			150		Ω
CMRR	Common-mode rejection ratio	$R_S \leqslant 10\ k\Omega$	25°C	80	110		70	90		dB
			Full range	80			70			
$\Delta V_{IO}/\Delta V_{CC}$	Power supply sensitivity	$R_S \leqslant 10\ k\Omega$	25°C		40	100		25	150	μV/V
			Full range			100			150	
I_{CC}	Supply current	$V_{CC\pm} = \pm 15\ V$, No load, No signal	25°C		2.5	3.6		2.6	5.5	mA
			−55°C		2.7	4.5				
			125°C		2.1	3				
P_D	Total power dissipation	$V_{CC\pm} = \pm 15\ V$, No load, No signal	25°C		75	108		78	165	mW
			−55°C		81	135				
			125°C		63	90				

†All characteristics are specified under open-loop operation. Full range for SN52709A and SN52709 is −55°C to 125°C.

‡All typical values are at $V_{CC\pm} = \pm 15\ V$.

Note 6: This typical value applies only at frequencies above a few hundred hertz because of the effects of drift and thermal feedback.

TEXAS INSTRUMENTS
INCORPORATED
POST OFFICE BOX 5012 • DALLAS, TEXAS 75222

electrical characteristics at specified free-air temperature (unless otherwise noted $V_{CC\pm} = \pm 15$ V)

PARAMETER		TEST CONDITIONS†		SN72709			UNIT
				MIN	TYP	MAX	
V_{IO}	Input offset voltage	$V_{CC\pm} = \pm 9$ V to ± 15 V, $R_S \leqslant 10$ kΩ	25°C		2	7.5	mV
			Full range			10	
I_{IO}	Input offset current	$V_{CC\pm} = \pm 9$ V to ± 15 V	25°C		100	500	nA
			Full range			750	
I_{IB}	Input bias current	$V_{CC\pm} = \pm 9$ V to ± 15 V	25°C		0.3	1.5	μA
			Full range			2	
V_I	Input voltage range		25°C	± 8	± 10		V
V_{OPP}	Maximum peak-to-peak output voltage swing	$R_L \geqslant 10$ kΩ	25°C	24	28		V
			Full range	24			
		$R_L = 2$ kΩ	25°C	20	26		
		$R_L \geqslant 2$ kΩ	Full range	20			
A_{VD}	Large-signal differential voltage amplification	$R_L \leqslant 2$ kΩ, $V_O = \pm 10$ V	25°C	15,000	45,000		
			Full range	12,000			
r_i	Input resistance		25°C	50	250		kΩ
			Full range	35			
r_o	Output resistance	$V_O = 0$, See Note 6	25°C		150		Ω
CMRR	Common-mode rejection ratio	$R_S \leqslant 10$ kΩ	25°C	65	90		dB
$\Delta V_{IO}/\Delta V_{CC}$	Supply voltage sensitivity	$R_S \leqslant 10$ kΩ	25°C		25	200	μV/V
P_D	Total power dissipation	No load, No signal	25°C		80	200	mW

†All characteristics are specified under open-loop operation. Full range for SN72709 is 0°C to 70°C.
NOTE 6: This typical value applies only at frequencies above a few hundred hertz because of the effects of drift and thermal feedback.

operating characteristics $V_{CC\pm} = \pm 9$ V to ± 15 V, $T_A = 25$°C

PARAMETER		TEST CONDITIONS		SN52709A SN52709 SN72709			UNIT
				MIN	TYP	MAX	
t_r	Rise time	$V_I = 20$ mV, $R_L = 2$ kΩ, See Figure 2	$C_L = 0$		0.3	1	μs
	Overshoot		$C_L = 100$ pF		6%	30%	

THERMAL INFORMATION
SN52709A, SN52709

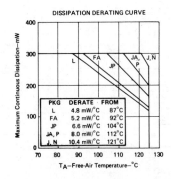

FIGURE 1

PARAMETER MEASUREMENT INFORMATION

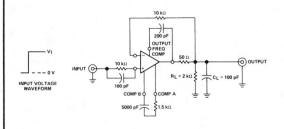

FIGURE 2—RISE TIME AND SLEW RATE

TEXAS INSTRUMENTS
INCORPORATED
POST OFFICE BOX 5012 • DALLAS, TEXAS 75222

DEFINITION OF TERMS

Input Offset Voltage (V_{IO}) The d-c voltage which must be applied between the input terminals to force the quiescent d-c output voltage to zero. The input offset voltage may also be defined for the case where two equal resistances (R_S) are inserted in series with the input leads.

Average Temperature Coefficient of Input Offset Voltage (α_{VIO}) The ratio of the change in input offset voltage to the change in free-air temperature. This is an average value for the specified temperature range.

$$\alpha_{VIO} = \left| \frac{(V_{IO} @ T_{A(1)}) - (V_{IO} @ T_{A(2)})}{T_{A(1)} - T_{A(2)}} \right| \text{ where } T_{A(1)} \text{ and } T_{A(2)} \text{ are the specified temperature extremes.}$$

Input Offset Current (I_{IO}) The difference between the currents into the two input terminals with the output at zero volts.

Average Temperature Coefficient of Input Offset Current (α_{IIO}) The ratio of the change in input offset current to the change in free-air temperature. This is an average value for the specified temperature range.

$$\alpha_{IIO} = \left| \frac{(I_{IO} @ T_{A(1)}) - (I_{IO} @ T_{A(2)})}{T_{A(1)} - T_{A(2)}} \right| \text{ where } T_{A(1)} \text{ and } T_{A(2)} \text{ are the specified temperature extremes.}$$

Input Bias Current (I_{IB}) The average of the currents into the two input terminals with the output at zero volts.

Input Voltage Range (V_I) The range of voltage which if exceeded at either input terminal will cause the amplifier to cease functioning properly.

Maximum Peak-to-Peak Output Voltage Swing (V_{OPP}) The maximum peak-to-peak output voltage which can be obtained without waveform clipping when the quiescent d-c output voltage is zero.

Large-Signal Differential Voltage Amplification (A_{VD}) The ratio of the peak-to-peak output voltage swing to the change in differential input voltage required to drive the output.

Input Resistance (r_i) The resistance between the input terminals with either input grounded.

Output Resistance (r_o) The resistance between the output terminal and ground.

Common-Mode Rejection Ratio (CMRR) The ratio of differential voltage amplification to common-mode voltage amplification. This is measured by determining the ratio of a change in input common-mode voltage to the resulting change in input offset voltage.

Supply Voltage Sensitivity ($\Delta V_{IO}/\Delta V_{CC}$) The ratio of the change in input offset voltage to the change in supply voltages producing it. For these deivces, both supply voltages are varied symmetrically.

Total Power Dissipation (P_D) The total d-c power supplied to the device less any power delivered from the device to a load. At no load: $P_D = V_{CC+} \cdot I_{CC+} + V_{CC-} \cdot I_{CC-}$.

Rise Time (t_r) The time required for an output voltage step to change from 10% to 90% of its final value.

Overshoot The quotient of: (1) the largest deviation of the output signal value from its steady-state value after a step-function change of the input signal, and (2) the difference between the output signal values in the steady state before and after the step-function change of the input signal.

Slew Rate (SR) The average time rate of change of the closed-loop amplifier output for a step-signal input. Slew rate is measured between specified output levels (0 and 10 volts for this device) with feedback adjusted for gain as specified.

4

TYPICAL CHARACTERISTICS
(unless designated maximum or minimum)

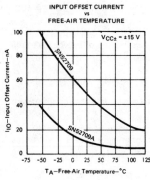

INPUT OFFSET CURRENT
vs
FREE-AIR TEMPERATURE

FIGURE 3

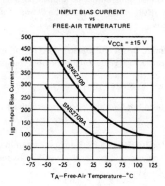

INPUT BIAS CURRENT
vs
FREE-AIR TEMPERATURE

FIGURE 4

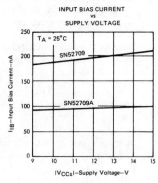

INPUT BIAS CURRENT
vs
SUPPLY VOLTAGE

FIGURE 5

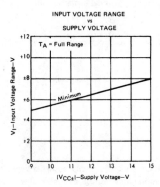

INPUT VOLTAGE RANGE
vs
SUPPLY VOLTAGE

FIGURE 6

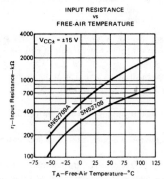

INPUT RESISTANCE
vs
FREE-AIR TEMPERATURE

FIGURE 7

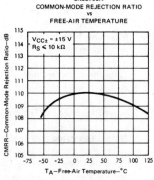

SN52709A
COMMON-MODE REJECTION RATIO
vs
FREE-AIR TEMPERATURE

FIGURE 8

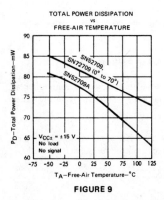

TOTAL POWER DISSIPATION
vs
FREE-AIR TEMPERATURE

FIGURE 9

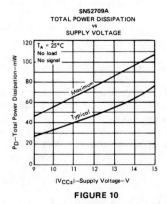

SN52709A
TOTAL POWER DISSIPATION
vs
SUPPLY VOLTAGE

FIGURE 10

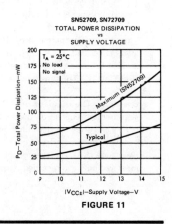

SN52709, SN72709
TOTAL POWER DISSIPATION
vs
SUPPLY VOLTAGE

FIGURE 11

TEXAS INSTRUMENTS
INCORPORATED
POST OFFICE BOX 5012 • DALLAS, TEXAS 75222

TYPICAL CHARACTERISTICS
(unless designated maximum or minimum)

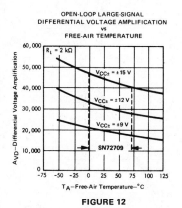

OPEN-LOOP LARGE-SIGNAL
DIFFERENTIAL VOLTAGE AMPLIFICATION
vs
FREE-AIR TEMPERATURE

FIGURE 12

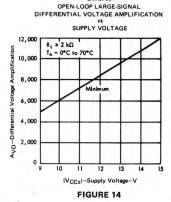

SN52709A, SN52709
OPEN-LOOP LARGE-SIGNAL
DIFFERENTIAL VOLTAGE AMPLIFICATION
vs
SUPPLY VOLTAGE

FIGURE 13

SN72709
OPEN-LOOP LARGE-SIGNAL
DIFFERENTIAL VOLTAGE AMPLIFICATION
vs
SUPPLY VOLTAGE

FIGURE 14

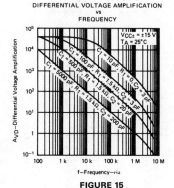

OPEN-LOOP LARGE-SIGNAL
DIFFERENTIAL VOLTAGE AMPLIFICATION
vs
FREQUENCY

FIGURE 15

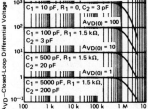
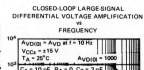

CLOSED-LOOP LARGE-SIGNAL
DIFFERENTIAL VOLTAGE AMPLIFICATION
vs
FREQUENCY

FIGURE 16

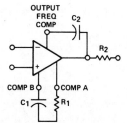
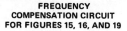

When the amplifier is operated with
capacitive loading, R_2 = 50 Ω.

**FREQUENCY
COMPENSATION CIRCUIT
FOR FIGURES 15, 16, AND 19**

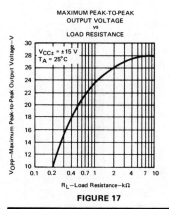

MAXIMUM PEAK-TO-PEAK
OUTPUT VOLTAGE
vs
LOAD RESISTANCE

FIGURE 17

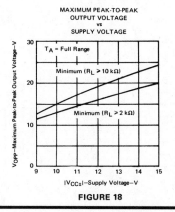

MAXIMUM PEAK-TO-PEAK
OUTPUT VOLTAGE
vs
SUPPLY VOLTAGE

FIGURE 18

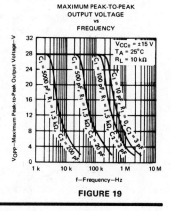

MAXIMUM PEAK-TO-PEAK
OUTPUT VOLTAGE
vs
FREQUENCY

FIGURE 19

4

TYPICAL CHARACTERISTICS

SN52709A, SN52709
VOLTAGE TRANSFER
CHARACTERISTICS

SN72709
VOLTAGE TRANSFER
CHARACTERISTICS

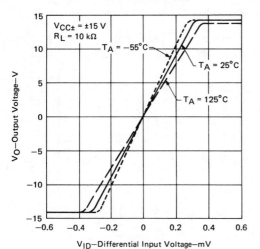

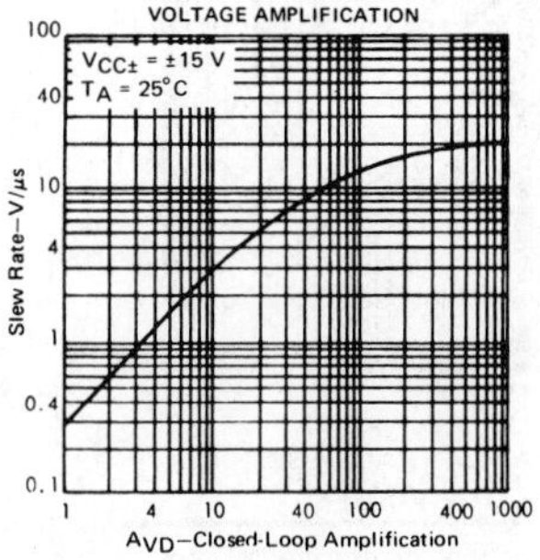

FIGURE 20

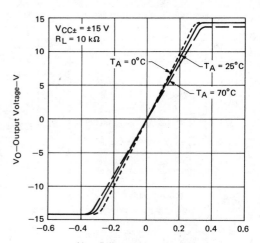

FIGURE 21

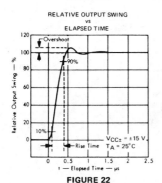

FIGURE 22

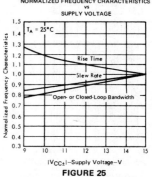

FIGURE 23

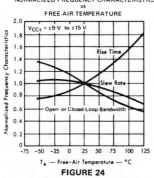

FIGURE 24

FIGURE 25

TEXAS INSTRUMENTS
INCORPORATED
POST OFFICE BOX 5012 • DALLAS, TEXAS 75222

LINEAR INTEGRATED CIRCUITS

TYPES SN52741, SN72741
GENERAL-PURPOSE OPERATIONAL AMPLIFIERS
BULLETIN NO. DL-S 7311363, NOVEMBER 1970—REVISED SEPTEMBER 1973

- Short-Circuit Protection
- Offset-Voltage Null Capability
- Large Common-Mode and Differential Voltage Ranges
- No Frequency Compensation Required
- Low Power Consumption
- No Latch-up
- Same Pin Assignments as SN52709/SN72709

description

The SN52741 and SN72741 are general-purpose operational amplifiers, featuring offset-voltage null capability.

The high common-mode input voltage range and the absence of latch-up make the amplifier ideal for voltage-follower applications. The devices are short-circuit protected and the internal frequency compensation ensures stability without external components. A low-value potentiometer may be connected between the offset null inputs to null out the offset voltage as shown in Figure 11.

The SN52741 is characterized for operation over the full military temperature range of −55°C to 125°C; the SN72741 is characterized for operation from 0°C to 70°C.

schematic

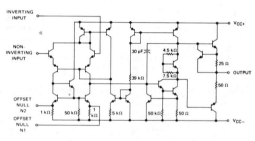

COMPONENT VALUES SHOWN ARE NOMINAL

terminal assignments

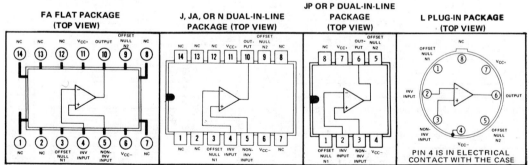

| FA FLAT PACKAGE (TOP VIEW) | J, JA, OR N DUAL-IN-LINE PACKAGE (TOP VIEW) | JP OR P DUAL-IN-LINE PACKAGE (TOP VIEW) | L PLUG-IN PACKAGE (TOP VIEW) |

NC—No internal connection

PIN 4 IS IN ELECTRICAL CONTACT WITH THE CASE

TEXAS INSTRUMENTS
INCORPORATED
POST OFFICE BOX 5012 • DALLAS, TEXAS 75222

TYPES SN52741, SN72741
GENERAL-PURPOSE OPERATIONAL AMPLIFIERS

absolute maximum ratings over operating free-air temperature range (unless otherwise noted)

		SN52741	SN72741	UNIT
Supply voltage V_{CC+} (see Note 1)		22	18	V
Supply voltage V_{CC-} (see Note 1)		−22	−18	V
Differential input voltage (see Note 2)		±30	±30	V
Input voltage (either input, see Notes 1 and 3)		±15	±15	V
Voltage between either offset null terminal (N1/N2) and V_{CC-}		±0.5	±0.5	V
Duration of output short-circuit (see Note 4)		unlimited	unlimited	
Continuous total power dissipation at (or below) 25°C free-air temperature (see Note 5)		500	500	mW
Operating free-air temperature range		−55 to 125	0 to 70	°C
Storage temperature range		−65 to 150	−65 to 150	°C
Lead temperature 1/16 inch from case for 60 seconds	FA, J, JA, JP, or L package	300	300	°C
Lead temperature 1/16 inch from case for 10 seconds	N or P package	260	260	°C

NOTES: 1. All voltage values, unless otherwise noted, are with respect to the zero reference level (ground) of the supply voltages where the zero reference level is the midpoint between V_{CC+} and V_{CC-}.
2. Differential voltages are at the noninverting input terminal with respect to the inverting input terminal.
3. The magnitude of the input voltage must never exceed the magnitude of the supply voltage or 15 volts, whichever is less.
4. The output may be shorted to ground or either power supply. For the SN52741 only, the unlimited duration of the short-circuit applies at (or below) 125°C case temperature or 75°C free-air temperature.
5. For operation above 25°C free-air temperature, refer to Dissipation Derating Curve, Figure 12.

electrical characteristics at specified free-air temperature, V_{CC+} = 15 V, V_{CC-} = −15 V

PARAMETER		TEST CONDITIONS†		SN52741			SN72741			UNIT
				MIN	TYP	MAX	MIN	TYP	MAX	
V_{IO}	Input offset voltage	$R_S \leq 10\ k\Omega$	25°C		1	5		1	6	mV
			Full range			6			7.5	
$\Delta V_{IO(adj)}$	Offset voltage adjust range		25°C		±15			±15		mV
I_{IO}	Input offset current		25°C		20	200		20	200	nA
			Full range			500			300	
I_{IB}	Input bias current		25°C		80	500		80	500	nA
			Full range			1500			800	
V_I	Input voltage range		25°C	±12	±13		±12	±13		V
			Full range	±12			±12			
V_{OPP}	Maximum peak-to-peak output voltage swing	$R_L = 10\ k\Omega$	25°C	24	28		24	28		V
		$R_L \geq 10\ k\Omega$	Full range	24			24			
		$R_L = 2\ k\Omega$	25°C	20	26		20	26		
		$R_L \geq 2\ k\Omega$	Full range	20			20			
A_{VD}	Large-signal differential voltage amplification	$R_L \geq 2\ k\Omega$, $V_O = \pm 10$ V	25°C	50,000	200,000		20,000	200,000		
			Full range	25,000			15,000			
r_i	Input resistance		25°C	0.3	2		0.3	2		MΩ
r_o	Output resistance	$V_O = 0$ V, See Note 6	25°C		75			75		Ω
C_i	Input capacitance		25°C		1.4			1.4		pF
CMRR	Common-mode rejection ratio	$R_S \leq 10\ k\Omega$	25°C	70	90		70	90		dB
			Full range	70			70			
$\Delta V_{IO}/\Delta V_{CC}$	Supply voltage sensitivity	$R_S \leq 10\ k\Omega$	25°C		30	150		30	150	μV/V
			Full range			150			150	
I_{OS}	Short-circuit output current		25°C		±25	±40		±25	±40	mA
I_{CC}	Supply current	No load, No signal	25°C		1.7	2.8		1.7	2.8	mA
			Full range			3.3			3.3	
P_D	Total power dissipation	No load, No signal	25°C		50	85		50	85	mW
			Full range			100			100	

†All characteristics are specified under open-loop operation. Full range for SN52741 is −55°C to 125°C and for SN72741 is 0°C to 70°C.
NOTE 6: This typical value applies only at frequencies above a few hundred hertz because of the effects of drift and thermal feedback.

TEXAS INSTRUMENTS
INCORPORATED
POST OFFICE BOX 5012 • DALLAS, TEXAS 75222

operating characteristics, V_{CC+} = 15 V, V_{CC-} = −15 V, T_A = 25°C

PARAMETER		TEST CONDITIONS	SN52741			SN72741			UNIT
			MIN	TYP	MAX	MIN	TYP	MAX	
t_r	Rise time	V_I = 20 mV, R_L = 2 kΩ,		0.3			0.3		μs
	Overshoot	C_L = 100 pF, See Figure 1		5%			5%		
SR	Slew rate at unity gain	V_I = 10 V, R_L = 2 kΩ, C_L = 100 pF, See Figure 1		0.5			0.5		V/μs

DEFINITION OF TERMS

Input Offset Voltage (V_{IO}) The d-c voltage which must be applied between the input terminals to force the quiescent d-c output voltage to zero. The input offset voltage may also be defined for the case where two equal resistances (R_S) are inserted in series with the input leads.

Input Offset Current (I_{IO}) The difference between the currents into the two input terminals with the output at zero volts.

Input Bias Current (I_{IB}) The average of the currents into the two input terminals with the output at zero volts.

Input Voltage Range (V_I) The range of voltage   that if exceeded at either input terminal will cause the amplifier to cease functioning properly.

Maximum Peak-to-Peak Output Voltage Swing (V_{OPP}) The maximum peak-to-peak output voltage which can be obtained without waveform clipping when the quiescent d-c output voltage is zero.

Large-Signal Differential Voltage Amplification (A_{VD}) The ratio of the peak-to-peak output voltage swing to the change in differential input voltage required to drive the output.

Input Resistance (r_i) The resistance between the input terminals with either input grounded.

Output Resistance (r_o) The resistance between the output terminal and ground.

Input Capacitance (C_i) The capacitance between the input terminals with either input grounded.

Common-Mode Rejection Ratio (CMRR) The ratio of differential voltage amplification to common-mode voltage amplification. This is measured by determining the ratio of a change in input common-mode voltage to the resulting change in input offset voltage.

Supply Voltage Sensitivity ($\Delta V_{IO}/\Delta V_{CC}$) The ratio of the change in input offset voltage to the change in supply voltages producing it. For these devices, both supply voltages are varied symmetrically.

Short-Circuit Output Current (I_{OS}) The maximum output current available from the amplifier with the output shorted to ground or to either supply.

Total Power Dissipation (P_D) The total d-c power supplied to the device less any power delivered from the device to a load. At no load: $P_D = V_{CC+} \cdot I_{CC+} + V_{CC-} \cdot I_{CC-}$.

Rise Time (t_r) The time required for an output voltage step to change from 10% to 90% of its final value.

Overshoot The quotient of: (1) the largest deviation of the output signal value from its steady-state value after a step-function change of the input signal, and (2) the difference between the output signal values in the steady state before and after the step-function change of the input signal.

Slew Rate (SR) The average time rate of change of the closed-loop amplifier output voltage for a step-signal input. Slew rate is measured between specified output levels (0 and 10 volts for this device) with feedback adjusted for unity gain.

PARAMETER MEASUREMENT INFORMATION

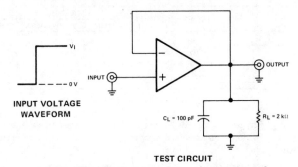

INPUT VOLTAGE WAVEFORM

$C_L = 100$ pF $R_L = 2$ kΩ

TEST CIRCUIT

FIGURE 1—RISE TIME, OVERSHOOT, AND SLEW RATE

TYPICAL CHARACTERISTICS

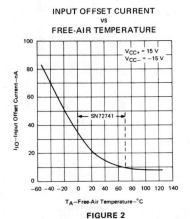

INPUT OFFSET CURRENT
vs
FREE-AIR TEMPERATURE

$V_{CC+} = 15$ V
$V_{CC-} = -15$ V

SN72741

I_{IO}—Input Offset Current—nA

T_A—Free-Air Temperature—°C

FIGURE 2

INPUT BIAS CURRENT
vs
FREE-AIR TEMPERATURE

$V_{CC+} = 15$ V
$V_{CC-} = -15$ V

SN72741

I_{IB}—Input Bias Current—nA

T_A—Free-Air Temperature—°C

FIGURE 3

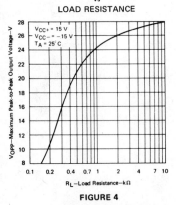

MAXIMUM PEAK-TO-PEAK OUTPUT VOLTAGE
vs
LOAD RESISTANCE

$V_{CC+} = 15$ V
$V_{CC-} = -15$ V
$T_A = 25°$C

V_{OPP}—Maximum Peak-to-Peak Output Voltage—V

R_L—Load Resistance—kΩ

FIGURE 4

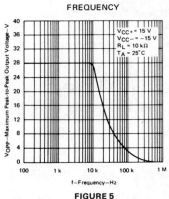

MAXIMUM PEAK-TO-PEAK OUTPUT VOLTAGE
vs
FREQUENCY

$V_{CC+} = 15$ V
$V_{CC-} = -15$ V
$R_L = 10$ kΩ
$T_A = 25°$C

V_{OPP}—Maximum Peak-to-Peak Output Voltage—V

f—Frequency—Hz

FIGURE 5

TEXAS INSTRUMENTS
INCORPORATED
POST OFFICE BOX 5012 • DALLAS, TEXAS 75222

TYPICAL CHARACTERISTICS

OPEN-LOOP LARGE-SIGNAL
DIFFERENTIAL
VOLTAGE AMPLIFICATION
vs
SUPPLY VOLTAGE

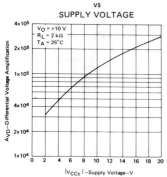

FIGURE 6

OUTPUT VOLTAGE
vs
ELAPSED TIME

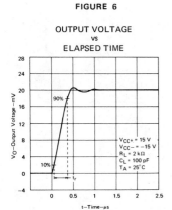

FIGURE 9

COMMON-MODE REJECTION RATIO
vs
FREQUENCY

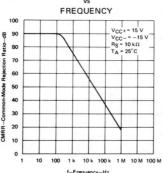

FIGURE 8

OPEN-LOOP LARGE-SIGNAL
DIFFERENTIAL
VOLTAGE AMPLIFICATION
vs
FREQUENCY

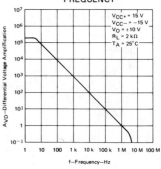

FIGURE 7

VOLTAGE-FOLLOWER
LARGE-SIGNAL PULSE RESPONSE

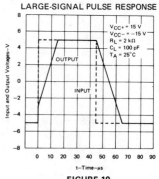

FIGURE 10

TYPICAL APPLICATION DATA

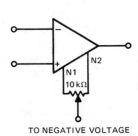

FIGURE 11—INPUT OFFSET VOLTAGE NULL CIRCUIT

THERMAL INFORMATION

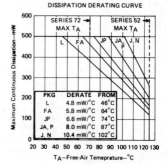

FIGURE 12

TEXAS INSTRUMENTS
INCORPORATED
POST OFFICE BOX 5012 • DALLAS, TEXAS 75222

- **No frequency Compensation Required**
- **Low Power Consumption**
- **Short-Circuit Protection**
- **Offset-Voltage Null Capability**

- **Wide Common-Mode and Differential Voltage Ranges**
- **No Latch-up**
- **Designed to be Interchangeable with Fairchild µA747 and µA747C**

description

The SN52747 and SN72747 are dual general-purpose operational amplifiers featuring offset-voltage null capability. Each half is electrically similar to SN52741/SN72741.

The high common-mode input voltage range and the absence of latch-up make the amplifiers ideal for voltage-follower applications. The devices are short-circuit protected and the internal frequency compensation ensures stability without external components. A low-value potentiometer may be connected between the offset null inputs to null out the offset voltage as shown in Figure 3.

The SN52747 is characterized for operation over the full military temperature range of −55°C to 125°C; the SN72747 is characterized for operation from 0°C to 70°C.

FA FLAT PACKAGE OR J, JA, OR N DUAL-IN-LINE PACKAGE (TOP VIEW)

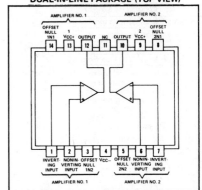

NC—No internal connection

L PLUG-IN PACKAGE (TOP VIEW)

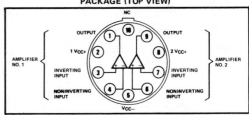

NC-No internal connection

schematic (each amplifier)

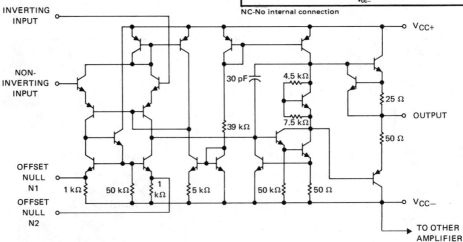

Component values shown are nominal.

TEXAS INSTRUMENTS
INCORPORATED
POST OFFICE BOX 5012 • DALLAS, TEXAS 75222

absolute maximum ratings over operating free-air temperature range (unless otherwise noted)

		SN52747	SN72747	UNIT
Supply voltage V_{CC+} (see Note 1)		22	18	V
Supply voltage V_{CC-} (see Note 1)		−22	−18	V
Differential input voltage (see Note 2)		±30	±30	V
Input voltage any input, (see Notes 1 and 3)		±15	±15	V
Voltage between any offset null terminal (N1/N2) and V_{CC-}		±0.5	±0.5	V
Duration of output short-circuit (see Note 4)		unlimited	unlimited	
Continuous total dissipation (at or below) 25°C	Each amplifier	500	500	mW
free-air temperature (see Note 5)	Total package	See Figure 2		
Operating free-air temperature range		−55 to 125	0 to 70	°C
Storage temperature range		−65 to 150	−65 to 150	°C
Lead temperature 1/16 inch from case for 60 seconds	FA, J, JA, or L package	300	300	°C
Lead temperature 1/16 inch from case for 10 seconds	N package	260	260	°C

NOTES: 1. All voltage values, unless otherwise noted, are with respect to the zero reference level (ground) of the supply voltages where the zero reference level is the midpoint between V_{CC+} and V_{CC-}.
2. Differential voltages are at the noninverting input terminal with respect to the inverting input terminal.
3. The magnitude of the input voltage must never exceed the magnitude of the supply voltage or 15 volts, whichever is less.
4. The output may be shorted to ground or either power supply. For the SN52747 only, the unlimited duration of the short-circuit applies at (or below) 125°C case temperature or 75°C free-air temperature.
5. For operation above 25°C free-air temperature and for total package ratings, refer to Dissipation Derating Curve, Figure 2.

electrical characteristics at specified free-air temperature, V_{CC+} = 15 V, V_{CC-} = −15 V

PARAMETER		TEST CONDITIONS†		SN52747			SN72747			UNIT
				MIN	TYP	MAX	MIN	TYP	MAX	
V_{IO}	Input offset voltage	$R_S \leqslant 10\ k\Omega$	25°C		1	5		1	6	mV
			Full range			6			7.5	
$\Delta V_{IO(adj)}$	Offset voltage adjust range		25°C		±15			±15		mV
I_{IO}	Input offset current		25°C		20	200		20	200	nA
			Full range			500			300	
I_{IB}	Input bias current		25°C		80	500		80	500	nA
			Full range			1500			800	
V_I	Input voltage range		25°C	±12	±13		±12	±13		V
			Full range	±12			±12			
V_{OPP}	Maximum peak-to-peak output voltage swing	$R_L = 10\ k\Omega$	25°C	24	28		24	28		V
		$R_L \geqslant 10\ k\Omega$	Full range	24			24			
		$R_L = 2\ k\Omega$	25°C	20	26		20	26		
		$R_L \geqslant 2\ k\Omega$	Full range	20			20			
A_{VD}	Large-signal differential voltage amplification	$R_L \geqslant 2\ k\Omega$, $V_O = ±10\ V$	25°C	50,000	200,000		50,000	200,000		
			Full range	25,000			25,000			
r_i	Input resistance		25°C	0.3	2		0.3	2		MΩ
r_o	Output resistance	$V_O = 0\ V$, See Note 6	25°C		75			75		Ω
C_i	Input capacitance		25°C		1.4			1.4		pF
CMRR	Common-mode rejection ratio	$R_S \leqslant 10\ k\Omega$	25°C	70	90		70	90		dB
			Full range	70			70			
$\Delta V_{IO}/\Delta V_{CC}$	Supply voltage sensitivity	$R_S \leqslant 10\ k\Omega$	25°C		30	150		30	150	μV/V
			Full range			150			150	
I_{OS}	Short-circuit output current		25°C		±25	±40		±25	±40	mA
I_{CC}	Supply current (each amplifier)	No load, No signal	25°C		1.7	2.8		1.7	2.8	mA
			Full range			3.3			3.3	
P_D	Power dissipation (each amplifier)	No load, No signal	25°C		50	85		50	85	mW
			Full range			100			100	
V_{o1}/V_{o2}	Channel separation		25°C		120			120		dB

† All characteristics are specified under open-loop operation. Full range for SN52747 is −55°C to 125°C and for SN72747 is 0°C to 70°C.
NOTE 6: This typical value applies only at frequencies above a few hundred hertz because of the effects of drift and thermal feedback.
For definitions of terms, see the SN52741/SN72741 data sheet, page 4-69.

TYPES SN52747, SN72747
DUAL GENERAL-PURPOSE OPERATIONAL AMPLIFIERS

operating characteristics, V_{CC+} = 15 V, V_{CC-} = −15 V, T_A = 25°C

	PARAMETER	TEST CONDITIONS	SN52747 MIN	SN52747 TYP	SN52747 MAX	SN72747 MIN	SN72747 TYP	SN72747 MAX	UNIT
t_r	Rise time	V_I = 20 mV, R_L = 2 kΩ,		0.3			0.3		μs
	Overshoot	C_L = 100 pF, See Figure 1		5%			5%		
SR	Slew rate at unity gain	V_I = 10 V, R_L = 2 kΩ, C_L = 100 pF, See Figure 1		0.5			0.5		V/μs

PARAMETER MEASUREMENT INFORMATION

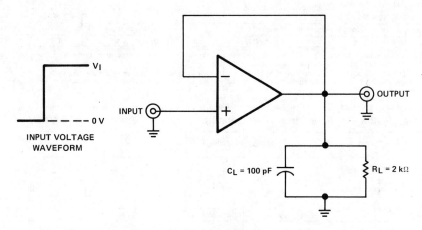

INPUT VOLTAGE
WAVEFORM

TEST CIRCUIT
FIGURE 1—RISE TIME, OVERSHOOT, AND SLEW RATE

THERMAL INFORMATION

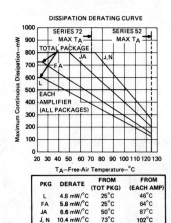

FIGURE 2

TYPICAL APPLICATION DATA

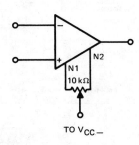

FIGURE 3—INPUT OFFSET VOLTAGE NULL CIRCUIT

TEXAS INSTRUMENTS
INCORPORATED
POST OFFICE BOX 5012 • DALLAS, TEXAS 75222

TYPICAL CHARACTERISTICS

INPUT OFFSET CURRENT
vs
FREE-AIR TEMPERATURE

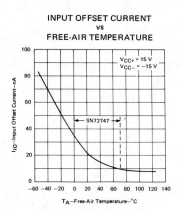

FIGURE 4

INPUT BIAS CURRENT
vs
FREE-AIR TEMPERATURE

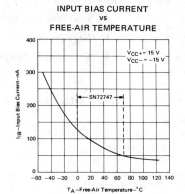

FIGURE 5

MAXIMUM PEAK-TO-PEAK
OUTPUT VOLTAGE
vs
LOAD RESISTANCE

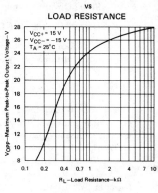

FIGURE 6

MAXIMUM PEAK-TO-PEAK
OUTPUT VOLTAGE
vs
FREQUENCY

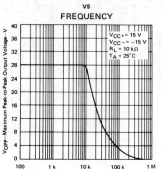

FIGURE 7

OPEN-LOOP LARGE-SIGNAL
DIFFERENTIAL
VOLTAGE AMPLIFICATION
vs
SUPPLY VOLTAGE

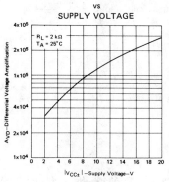

FIGURE 8

OPEN-LOOP LARGE-SIGNAL
DIFFERENTIAL
VOLTAGE AMPLIFICATION
vs
FREQUENCY

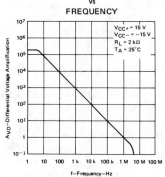

FIGURE 9

COMMON-MODE REJECTION RATIO
vs
FREQUENCY

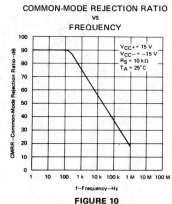

FIGURE 10

OUTPUT VOLTAGE
vs
ELAPSED TIME

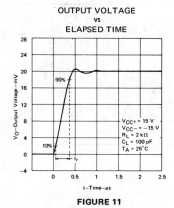

FIGURE 11

VOLTAGE-FOLLOWER
LARGE-SIGNAL PULSE RESPONSE

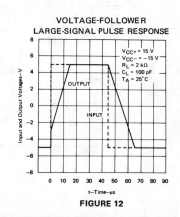

FIGURE 12

TEXAS INSTRUMENTS
INCORPORATED
POST OFFICE BOX 5012 • DALLAS, TEXAS 75222

- Frequency and Transient Response Characteristics Adjustable

- Short-Circuit Protection
- Low Power Consumption

- Offset-Voltage Null Capability
- No Latch-up

- Wide Common-Mode and Differential Voltage Ranges
- Same Pin Assignments as SN52709/SN72709

description

The SN52748 and SN72748 are general-purpose operational amplifiers. They offer the same advantages and desirable features as the SN52741 and SN72741 with the exception of internal compensation. The external compensation of the SN52748 and SN72748 allows the changing of the frequency response (when the closed-loop gain is greater than unity) for applications requiring wider bandwidth or higher slew rate. These circuits feature high gain, large differential and common-mode input voltage range, output short-circuit protection, and may be compensated under unity-gain conditions with a single 30-pF capacitor. A potentiometer may be connected between the offset null inputs, as shown in Figure 12, to null out the offset voltage.

The SN52748 is characterized for operation over the full military temperature range of $-55°C$ to $125°C$; the SN72748 is characterized for operation from $0°C$ to $70°C$.

schematic

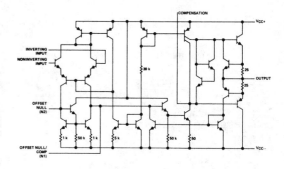

Resistor values shown are nominal and in ohms.

terminal assignments

FA FLAT PACKAGE (TOP VIEW)

J, JA, OR N DUAL-IN-LINE PACKAGE (TOP VIEW)

JP OR P DUAL-IN-LINE PACKAGE (TOP VIEW)

L PLUG-IN PACKAGE (TOP VIEW)

PIN 4 IS IN ELECTRICAL CONTACT WITH THE CASE

NC—No internal connection

TEXAS INSTRUMENTS
INCORPORATED
POST OFFICE BOX 5012 • DALLAS, TEXAS 75222

absolute maximum ratings over operating free-air temperature range (unless otherwise noted)

		SN52748	SN72748	UNIT
Supply voltage V_{CC+} (see Note 1)		22	18	V
Supply voltage V_{CC-} (see Note 1)		−22	−18	V
Differential input voltage (see Note 2)		±30	±30	V
Input voltage (either input, see Notes 1 and 3)		±15	±15	V
Voltage between either offset null terminal (N1/N2) and V_{CC-}		−0.5 to 2	−0.5 to 2	V
Duration of output short-circuit (see Note 4)		unlimited	unlimited	
Continuous total power dissipation at (or below) 25°C free-air temperature (see Note 5)		500	500	mW
Operating free-air temperature range		−55 to 125	0 to 70	°C
Storage temperature range		−65 to 150	−65 to 150	°C
Lead temperature 1/16 inch from case for 60 seconds	FA, J, JA, JP, or L package	300	300	°C
Lead temperature 1/16 inch from case for 10 seconds	N or P package	260	260	°C

NOTES: 1. All voltage values, unless otherwise noted, are with respect to the zero reference level (ground) of the supply voltages where the zero reference level is the midpoint between V_{CC+} and V_{CC-}.
2. Differential voltages are at the noninverting input terminal with respect to the inverting input terminal.
3. The magnitude of the input voltage must never exceed the magnitude of the supply voltage or 15 volts, whichever is less.
4. The output may be shorted to ground or either power supply. For the SN52748 only, the unlimited duration of the short-circuit applies at (or below) 125°C case temperature or 75°C free-air temperature.
5. For operation above 25°C free-air temperature, refer to Dissipation Derating Curve, Figure 13.

electrical characteristics at specified free-air temperature, V_{CC+} = 15 V, V_{CC-} = −15 V, C_C = 30 pF

PARAMETER		TEST CONDITIONS†		SN52748			SN72748			UNIT
				MIN	TYP	MAX	MIN	TYP	MAX	
V_{IO}	Input offset voltage	$R_S \leqslant 10$ kΩ	25°C		1	5		1	6	mV
			Full range			6			7.5	
I_{IO}	Input offset current		25°C		20	200		20	200	nA
			Full range			500			300	
I_{IB}	Input bias current		25°C		80	500		80	500	nA
			Full range			1500			800	
V_I	Input voltage range		25°C	±12	±13		±12	±13		V
			Full range	±12			±12			
V_{OPP}	Maximum peak-to-peak output voltage swing	$R_L = 10$ kΩ	25°C	24	28		24	28		V
		$R_L \geqslant 10$ kΩ	Full range	24			24			
		$R_L = 2$ kΩ	25°C	20	26		20	26		
		$R_L \geqslant 2$ kΩ	Full range	20			20			
A_{VD}	Large-signal differential voltage amplification	$R_L \geqslant 2$ kΩ, $V_O = \pm 10$ V	25°C	50,000	200,000		50,000	200,000		
			Full range	25,000			25,000			
r_i	Input resistance		25°C	0.3	2		0.3	2		MΩ
r_o	Output resistance	$V_O = 0$ V, See Note 6	25°C		75			75		Ω
C_i	Input capacitance		25°C		1.4			1.4		pF
CMRR	Common-mode rejection ratio	$R_S \leqslant 10$ kΩ	25°C	70	90		70	90		dB
			Full range	70			70			
$\Delta V_{IO}/\Delta V_{CC}$	Supply voltage sensitivity	$R_S \leqslant 10$ kΩ	25°C		30	150		30	150	μV/V
			Full range			150			150	
I_{OS}	Short-circuit output current		25°C		±25	±40		±25	±40	mA
I_{CC}	Supply current	No load, No signal	25°C		1.7	2.8		1.7	2.8	mA
			Full range			3.3			3.3	
P_D	Total power dissipation	No load, No signal	25°C		50	85		50	85	mW
			Full range			100			100	

† All characteristics are specified under open-loop operation. Full range for SN52748 is −55°C to 125°C and for SN72748 is 0°C to 70°C.
NOTE 6: This typical value applies only at frequencies above a few hundred hertz because of the effects of drift and thermal feedback.

For definitions of terms, see page 4-69.

operating characteristics, $V_{CC+} = 15$ V, $V_{CC-} = -15$ V, $T_A = 25°C$

PARAMETER		TEST CONDITIONS	SN52748			SN72748			UNIT
			MIN	TYP	MAX	MIN	TYP	MAX	
t_r	Rise time	$V_I = 20$ mV, $R_L = 2$ kΩ, $C_L = 100$ pF, $C_C = 30$ pF, See Figure 1		0.3			0.3		µs
	Overshoot			5%			5%		
SR	Slew rate at unity gain	$V_I = 10$ V, $R_L = 2$ kΩ, $C_L = 100$ pF, $C_C = 30$ pF, See Figure 1		0.5			0.5		V/µs

PARAMETER MEASUREMENT INFORMATION

INPUT VOLTAGE
WAVEFORM

TEST CIRCUIT

FIGURE 1—RISE TIME, OVERSHOOT, AND SLEW RATE

TYPICAL CHARACTERISTICS

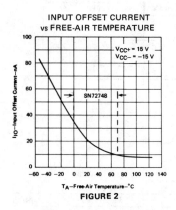

INPUT OFFSET CURRENT
vs FREE-AIR TEMPERATURE

FIGURE 2

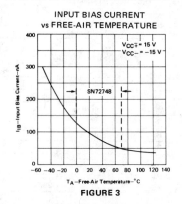

INPUT BIAS CURRENT
vs FREE-AIR TEMPERATURE

FIGURE 3

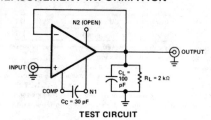

MAXIMUM PEAK-TO-PEAK OUTPUT
VOLTAGE vs LOAD RESISTANCE

FIGURE 4

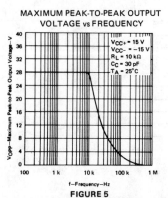

MAXIMUM PEAK-TO-PEAK OUTPUT
VOLTAGE vs FREQUENCY

FIGURE 5

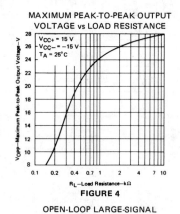

OPEN-LOOP LARGE-SIGNAL
DIFFERENTIAL VOLTAGE
AMPLIFICATION vs SUPPLY VOLTAGE

FIGURE 6

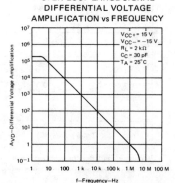

OPEN-LOOP LARGE-SIGNAL
DIFFERENTIAL VOLTAGE
AMPLIFICATION vs FREQUENCY

FIGURE 7

TEXAS INSTRUMENTS
INCORPORATED
POST OFFICE BOX 5012 • DALLAS, TEXAS 75222

TYPICAL CHARACTERISTICS

COMMON-MODE REJECTION RATIO
vs
FREQUENCY

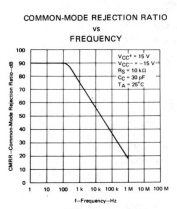

OUTPUT VOLTAGE
vs
ELAPSED TIME

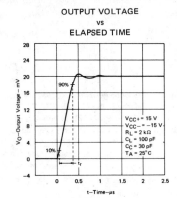

VOLTAGE-FOLLOWER
LARGE-SIGNAL PULSE RESPONSE

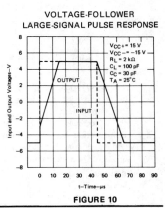

FIGURE 8   **FIGURE 9**   **FIGURE 10**

TYPICAL APPLICATION DATA

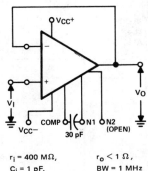

$r_i = 400\ M\Omega,$ $r_o < 1\ \Omega,$

$C_i = 1\ pF,$ $BW = 1\ MHz$

FIGURE 11—UNITY-GAIN VOLTAGE FOLLOWER

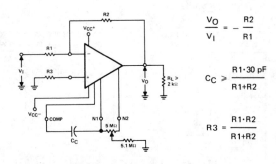

$$\frac{V_O}{V_I} = -\frac{R2}{R1}$$

$$C_C \geq \frac{R1 \cdot 30\ pF}{R1 + R2}$$

$$R3 = \frac{R1 \cdot R2}{R1 + R2}$$

**FIGURE 12—INVERTING CIRCUIT WITH ADJUSTABLE GAIN,
COMPENSATION, AND OFFSET ADJUSTMENT**

THERMAL INFORMATION

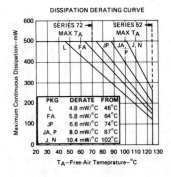

PKG	DERATE	FROM
L	4.8 mW/°C	46°C
FA	5.8 mW/°C	64°C
JP	6.6 mW/°C	74°C
JA, P	8.0 mW/°C	87°C
J, N	10.4 mW/°C	102°C

FIGURE 13

TEXAS INSTRUMENTS
INCORPORATED
POST OFFICE BOX 5012 • DALLAS, TEXAS 75222

LINEAR INTEGRATED CIRCUITS

- ● Adjustable Frequency and Transient Response Characteristics
- ● Offset-Voltage Null Capability
- ● No Latch-Up
- ● Low Power Consumption
- ● High Slew Rates
- ● Very Low Input Bias Currents
- ● Very Low Input Offset Parameters
- ● Short-Circuit Protection
- ● Wide Common-Mode and Differential Voltage Ranges

description

The SN52770 and SN72770 are high-performance general purpose integrated-circuit operational amplifiers. They offer the same advantages and desirable features as the SN52771 and SN72771 with the exception of internal compensation. The external compensation of the SN52770 and SN72770 allows the changing of the frequency response (when the closed-loop gain is greater than unity) for applications requiring wider bandwidth or higher slew rate. Unity-gain compensation is accomplished by means of a single 30-pF capacitor, and for higher gains, smaller capacitors may be used to obtain increased slew rate and bandwidth. High slew rate makes these amplifiers ideal for fast-rise-time signals, or large signals at high frequency. Very low input currents make them ideal for sample and hold, logarithmic amplifiers, and other low-level applications. A potentiometer may be connected between the offset null inputs, as shown in Figure 12, to null out the offset voltage.

The SN52770 is characterized for operation over the full military temperature range of −55°C to 125°C; the SN72770 is characterized for operation from 0°C to 70°C.

terminal assignments

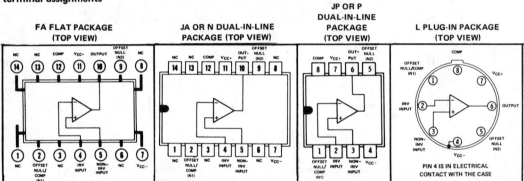

FA FLAT PACKAGE (TOP VIEW)   JA OR N DUAL-IN-LINE PACKAGE (TOP VIEW)   JP OR P DUAL-IN-LINE PACKAGE (TOP VIEW)   L PLUG-IN PACKAGE (TOP VIEW)

NC—No internal connection

absolute maximum ratings over operating free-air temperature range (unless otherwise noted)

		SN52770	SN72770	UNIT
Supply voltage V$_{CC+}$ (see Note 1)		22	18	V
Supply voltage V$_{CC-}$ (see Note 1)		−22	−18	V
Differential input voltage (see Note 2)		±30	±30	V
Input voltage (either input, see Notes 1 and 3)		±15	±15	V
Voltage between either offset null terminal (N1/N2) and V$_{CC-}$		−0.5 to 2	−0.5 to 2	V
Duration of output short-circuit (see Note 4)		unlimited	unlimited	
Continuous total dissipation at (or below) 25°C free-air temperature (see Note 5)		500	500	mW
Operating free-air temperature range		−55 to 125	0 to 70	°C
Storage temperature range		−65 to 150	−65 to 150	°C
Lead temperature 1/16 inch from case for 60 seconds	FA, JA, JP or L package	300	300	°C
Lead temperature 1/16 inch from case for 10 seconds	N or P package	260	260	°C

NOTES: 1. All voltage values, unless otherwise noted, are with respect to the zero reference level (ground) of the supply voltages where the zero reference level is the midpoint between V$_{CC+}$ and V$_{CC-}$.
2. Differential voltages are at the noninverting input terminal with respect to the inverting input terminal.
3. The magnitude of the input voltage must never exceed the magnitude of the supply voltage or 15 volts, whichever is less.
4. The output may be shorted to ground or either power supply. For the SN52770 only, the unlimited duration of the short-circuit applies at (or below) 125°C case temperature or 75°C free-air temperature.
5. For operation above 25°C free-air temperature, refer to Dissipation Derating Curve, Figure 1.

TEXAS INSTRUMENTS
INCORPORATED
POST OFFICE BOX 5012 • DALLAS, TEXAS 75222

schematic

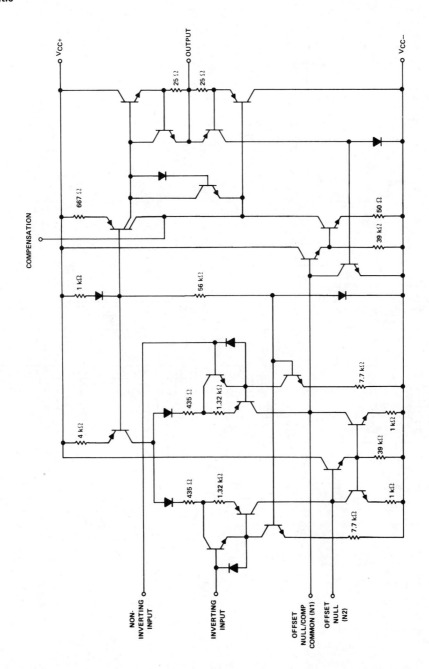

Component values shown are nominal.

TEXAS INSTRUMENTS
INCORPORATED
POST OFFICE BOX 5012 • DALLAS, TEXAS 75222

electrical characteristics at specified free-air temperature, V_{CC+} = 15 V, V_{CC-} = −15V, C_C = 30 pF

PARAMETER		TEST CONDITIONS†		SN52770			SN72770			UNIT
				MIN	TYP	MAX	MIN	TYP	MAX	
V_{IO}	Input offset voltage	$R_S \leqslant 10 k\Omega$	25°C		2	4		5	10	mV
			Full range			7			14	
I_{IO}	Input offset current		25°C		1	2		5	10	nA
			Full range			5			14	
I_{IB}	Input bias current		25°C		8	15		15	30	nA
			Full range			35			40	
V_{ICR}	Common-mode input voltage range		25°C	±12	±14		±11			V
V_{OPP}	Maximum peak-to-peak output voltage swing	$R_L = 2 k\Omega$	25°C	24	26.5		22	26.5		
		$R_L \geqslant 2 k\Omega$	Full range	24			22			
A_{VD}	Large-signal differential voltage amplification	$R_L = 2 k\Omega$, $V_O = \pm 10$ V	25°C	50,000	100,000		35,000	100,000		
		$R_L \geqslant 2 k\Omega$, $V_O = \pm 10$ V	Full range	25,000			25,000			
B_{OM}	Maximum-output-swing bandwidth (closed loop)	$R_L = 2 k\Omega$, $V_O \geqslant \pm 10$ V, $A_{VD} = 1$, THD $\leqslant 5\%$	25°C		40			40		kHz
B_1	Unity-gain bandwidth		25°C		1.3			1.3		MHz
r_{id}	Differential input resistance		25°C		100			100		MΩ
z_{ic}	Common-mode input impedance	f = 10 Hz	25°C		500			500		MΩ
z_o	Output impedance	f = 10 Hz	25°C		2			2		kΩ
CMRR	Common-mode rejection ratio	$R_S \leqslant 10 k\Omega$	25°C	80	100		70	100		dB
$\Delta V_{IO}/\Delta V_{CC}$	Supply voltage sensitivity	$R_S \leqslant 10 k\Omega$	25°C		80	150			200	μV/V
V_n	Equivalent input noise voltage (closed loop)	$A_{VD} = 100$, BW = 1 Hz, f = 1 kHz	25°C		40			40		nV/$\sqrt{Hz}$
I_{OS}	Short-circuit output current	To V_{CC+}	25°C		24			24		mA
		To V_{CC-}			−20			−20		
I_{CC}	Supply current	No load, No signal	25°C		1.3	2		1.7	4	mA
P_D	Total power dissipation	No load, No signal	25°C		40	60		50	120	mW

†All characteristics are specified under open-loop operation unless otherwise noted. Full range for SN52770 is −55°C to 125°C and for SN72770 is 0°C to 70°C.

operating characteristics, V_{CC+} = 15 V, V_{CC-} = −15 V, T_A = 25°C

PARAMETER		TEST CONDITIONS	SN52770			SN72770			UNIT
			MIN	TYP	MAX	MIN	TYP	MAX	
t_r	Rise time	V_I = 200 mV, R_L = 2 kΩ, C_L = 200 pF, C_C = 30 pF, See Figure 2		130			130		ns
SR	Slew rate at unity gain	V_I = 10 V, R_L = 2 kΩ, C_L = 200 pF, C_C = 30 pF, See Figure 2		2.5			2.5		V/μs

DEFINITION OF TERMS

Input Offset Voltage (V_{IO}) The d-c voltage which must be applied between the input terminals to force the quiescent d-c output voltage to zero. The input offset voltage may also be defined for the case where two equal resistances (R_S) are inserted in series with the input leads.

Input Offset Current (I_{IO}) The difference between the currents into the two input terminals with the output at zero volts.

Input Bias Current (I_{IB}) The average of the currents into the two input terminals with the output at zero volts.

Common-Mode Input Voltage Range (V_{ICR}) The range of common-mode voltage that if exceeded will cause the amplifier to cease functioning properly.

Maximum Peak-to-Peak Output Voltage Swing (V_{OPP}) The maximum peak-to-peak output voltage that can be obtained without waveform clipping when the quiescent d-c output voltage is zero.

Large-Signal Differential Voltage Amplification (A_{VD}) The ratio of the peak-to-peak output voltage swing to the change in differential input voltage required to drive the output.

Maximum-Output-Swing Bandwidth (B_{OM}) The range of frequencies within which the maximum output voltage swing is above a specified value.

Unity-Gain Bandwidth (B_1) The range of frequencies within which the voltage amplification is greater than unity.

Differential Input Resistance (r_{id}) The small-signal resistance between the two ungrounded input terminals.

Common-Mode Input Impedance (z_{ic}) The parallel sum of the small-signal impedances between each input terminal and ground.

Output Impedance (z_o) The small-signal impedance between the output terminal and ground.

Common-Mode Rejection Ratio (CMRR) The ratio of differential voltage amplification to common-mode voltage amplification. This is measured by determining the ratio of a change in input common-mode voltage to the resulting change in input offset voltage.

Supply Voltage Sensitivity ($\Delta V_{IO}/\Delta V_{CC}$) The ratio of the change in input offset voltage to the change in supply voltages producing it. For these devices, both supply voltages are varied symmetrically.

Short-Circuit Output Current (I_{OS}) The maximum output current available from the amplifier with the output shorted to the specified supply.

Total Power Dissipation (P_D) The total d-c power supplied to the device less any power delivered from the device to a load. At no load: $P_D = V_{CC+} \cdot I_{CC+} + V_{CC-} \cdot I_{CC-}$.

Rise Time (t_r) The time required for an output voltage step to change from 10% to 90% of its final value.

Slew Rate (SR) The average time rate of change of the closed-loop amplifier output voltage for a step-signal input. Slew rate is measured between specified output levels (0 and 10 volts for this device) with feedback adjusted for unity gain.

TEXAS INSTRUMENTS
INCORPORATED
POST OFFICE BOX 5012 • DALLAS, TEXAS 75222

TYPES SN52770, SN72770
HIGH-PERFORMANCE OPERATIONAL AMPLIFIERS

THERMAL INFORMATION

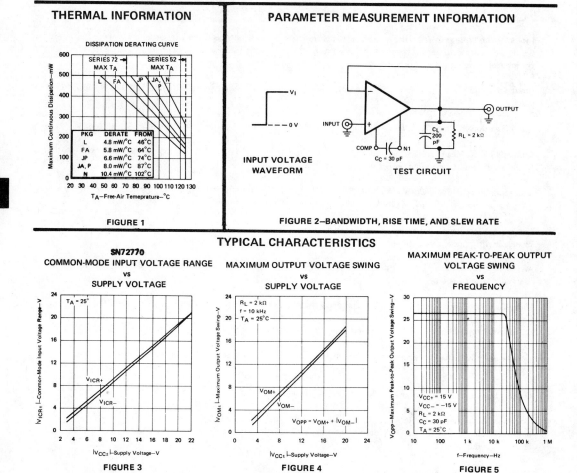

FIGURE 1

PARAMETER MEASUREMENT INFORMATION

INPUT VOLTAGE WAVEFORM

TEST CIRCUIT

FIGURE 2—BANDWIDTH, RISE TIME, AND SLEW RATE

TYPICAL CHARACTERISTICS

SN72770
COMMON-MODE INPUT VOLTAGE RANGE
vs
SUPPLY VOLTAGE

FIGURE 3

MAXIMUM OUTPUT VOLTAGE SWING
vs
SUPPLY VOLTAGE

FIGURE 4

MAXIMUM PEAK-TO-PEAK OUTPUT
VOLTAGE SWING
vs
FREQUENCY

FIGURE 5

OPEN-LOOP LARGE-SIGNAL
DIFFERENTIAL VOLTAGE
AMPLIFICATION
vs
SUPPLY VOLTAGE

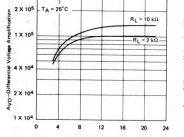

FIGURE 6

LARGE-SIGNAL DIFFERENTIAL
VOLTAGE AMPLIFICATION
vs
FREQUENCY

FIGURE 7

SHORT-CIRCUIT OUTPUT CURRENT
vs
FREE-AIR TEMPERATURE

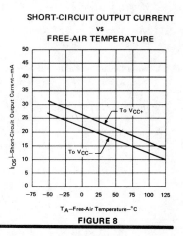

FIGURE 8

4

4-84

97

TYPICAL CHARACTERISTICS

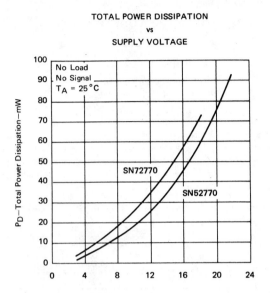

TOTAL POWER DISSIPATION
vs
SUPPLY VOLTAGE

FIGURE 9

VOLTAGE-FOLLOWER
LARGE-SIGNAL PULSE RESPONSE

FIGURE 10

TYPICAL APPLICATION DATA

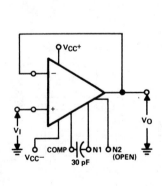

$r_i \approx 5,000$ MΩ at 10 Hz $r_o \ll 1$ Ω
$C_L \approx 1.5$ pF $B_1 \approx 1.3$ MHz

FIGURE 11—UNITY-GAIN VOLTAGE FOLLOWER

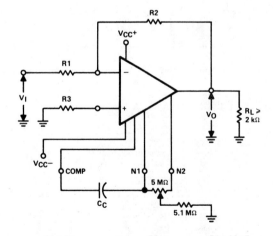

$$R3 = \frac{R1 \cdot R2}{R1 + R2} \qquad \frac{V_O}{V_1} = -\frac{R2}{R1} \qquad C_C \geq \frac{R1 \cdot 30 \text{ pF}}{R1 + R2}$$

**FIGURE 12—INVERTING CIRCUIT WITH
ADJUSTABLE GAIN, COMPENSATION, AND
OFFSET ADJUSTMENT**

TEXAS INSTRUMENTS
INCORPORATED
POST OFFICE BOX 5012 • DALLAS, TEXAS 75222

- **Very Low Input Bias Currents**
- **6-dB Roll-Off Insures Stability**
- **No Frequency Compensation Required**
- **Offset-Voltage Null Capability**
- **Low Power Consumption**
- **High Slew Rates**
- **Very Low Input Offset Parameters**
- **Short-Circuit Protection**
- **No Latch-Up**
- **Wide Common-Mode and Differential Voltage Ranges**

description

The SN52771 and SN72771 are high-performance general purpose integrated-circuit operational amplifiers. Very low input currents make these amplifiers ideal for sample and hold, logarithmic amplifiers, and other low-level applications. High slew rate makes them ideal for fast-rise-time signals, or large signals at high frequency. Internal compensation provides a 6-dB roll-off for stability under all closed-loop conditions. A potentiometer may be connected between the offset null inputs, as shown in Figure 11, to null out the offset voltage.

The SN52771 is characterized for operation over the full military temperature range of $-55°C$ to $125°C$; the SN72771 is characterized for operation from $0°C$ to $70°C$.

terminal assignments

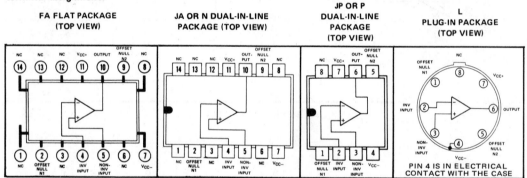

FA FLAT PACKAGE (TOP VIEW) • JA OR N DUAL-IN-LINE PACKAGE (TOP VIEW) • JP OR P DUAL-IN-LINE PACKAGE (TOP VIEW) • L PLUG-IN PACKAGE (TOP VIEW)

PIN 4 IS IN ELECTRICAL CONTACT WITH THE CASE

NC—No internal connection

absolute maximum ratings over operating free-air temperature range (unless otherwise noted)

		SN52771	SN72771	UNIT
Supply voltage V_{CC+} (see Note 1)		22	18	V
Supply voltage V_{CC-} (see Note 1)		−22	−18	V
Differential input voltage (see Note 2)		±30	±30	V
Input voltage (either input, see Notes 1 and 3)		±15	±15	V
Voltage between either offset null terminal (N1/N2) and V_{CC-}		±0.5	±0.5	V
Duration of output short-circuit (see Note 4)		unlimited	unlimited	
Continuous total dissipation at (or below) 25°C free-air temperature (see Note 5)		500	500	mW
Operating free-air temperature range		−55 to 125	0 to 70	°C
Storage temperature range		−65 to 150	−65 to 150	°C
Lead temperature 1/16 inch from case for 60 seconds	FA, JA, JP, or L package	300	300	°C
Lead temperature 1/16 inch from case for 10 seconds	N or P package	260	260	°C

NOTES: 1. All voltage values, unless otherwise noted, are with respect to the zero reference level (ground) of the supply voltages where the zero reference level is the midpoint between V_{CC+} and V_{CC-}.
2. Differential voltages are at the noninverting input terminal with respect to the inverting input terminal.
3. The magnitude of the input voltage must never exceed the magnitude of the supply voltage or 15 volts, whichever is less.
4. The output may be shorted to ground or either power supply. For the SN52771 only, the unlimited duration of the short-circuit applies at (or below) 125°C case temperature or 75°C free-air temperature.
5. For operation above 25°C free-air temperature, refer to Dissipation Derating Curve, Figure 1.

TEXAS INSTRUMENTS
INCORPORATED
POST OFFICE BOX 5012 • DALLAS, TEXAS 75222

schematic

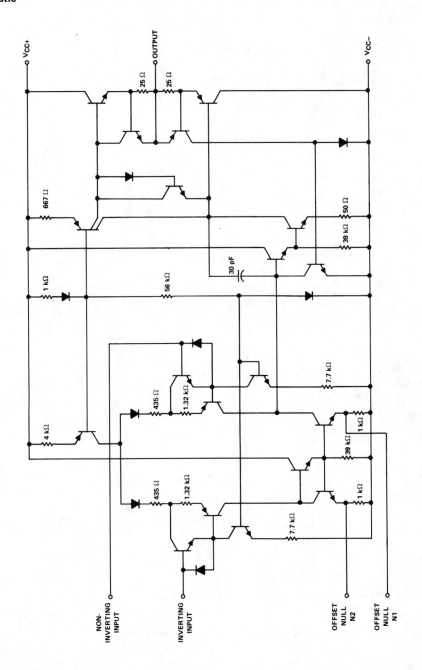

Component values shown are nominal.

4

1

TYPES SN52771, SN72771
HIGH-PERFORMANCE OPERATIONAL AMPLIFIERS

electrical characteristics at specified free-air temperature, V_{CC+} = 15 V, V_{CC-} = −15 V

PARAMETER		TEST CONDITIONS[†]		SN52771			SN72771			UNIT
				MIN	TYP	MAX	MIN	TYP	MAX	
V_{IO}	Input offset voltage	$R_S \leqslant 10\ k\Omega$	25°C		2	4		5	10	mV
			Full range			7			14	
I_{IO}	Input offset current		25°C		1	2		5	10	nA
			Full range			5			14	
I_{IB}	Input bias current		25°C		8	15		15	30	nA
			Full range			35			40	
V_{ICR}	Common-mode input voltage range		25°C	±12	±14		±11			V
V_{OPP}	Maximum peak-to-peak output voltage swing	$R_L = 2\ k\Omega$	25°C	24	26.5		22	26.5		
		$R_L \geqslant 2\ k\Omega$	Full range	24			22			
A_{VD}	Large-signal differential voltage amplification	$R_L = 2\ k\Omega$, $V_O = \pm 10$ V	25°C	50,000	100,000		35,000	100,000		
		$R_L \geqslant 2\ k\Omega$, $V_O = \pm 10$ V	Full range	25,000			25,000			
B_{OM}	Maximum-output-swing bandwidth (closed loop)	$R_L = 2\ k\Omega$, $V_O \geqslant \pm 10$ V, $A_{VD} = 1$, THD $\leqslant 5\%$	25°C		40			40		kHz
B_1	Unity-gain bandwidth		25°C		1.3			1.3		MHz
r_{id}	Differential input resistance		25°C		100			100		MΩ
z_{ic}	Common-mode input impedance	$f = 10$ Hz	25°C		500			500		MΩ
z_o	Output impedance	$f = 10$ Hz	25°C		2			2		kΩ
CMRR	Common-mode rejection ratio	$R_S \leqslant 10\ k\Omega$	25°C	80	100		70	100		dB
$\Delta V_{IO}/\Delta V_{CC}$	Supply voltage sensitivity	$R_S \leqslant 10\ k\Omega$	25°C		80	150			200	μV/V
e_n	Equivalent input noise voltage (closed loop)	$A_{VD} = 100$, BW = 1 Hz, $f = 1$ kHz	25°C		40			40		nV/√Hz
I_{OS}	Short-circuit output current	To V_{CC+}	25°C		24			24		mA
		To V_{CC-}			−20			−20		
I_{CC}	Supply current	No load, No signal	25°C		1.3	2		1.7	4	mA
P_D	Total power dissipation	No load, No signal	25°C		40	60		50	120	mW

[†]All characteristics are specified under open-loop operation unless otherwise noted. Full range for SN52771 is −55°C to 125°C and for SN72771 is 0°C to 70°C.

operating characteristics, V_{CC+} = 15 V, V_{CC-} = −15 V, T_A = 25°C

PARAMETER		TEST CONDITIONS	SN52771			SN72771			UNIT
			MIN	TYP	MAX	MIN	TYP	MAX	
t_r	Rise time	$V_I = 200$ mV, $R_L = 2\ k\Omega$, $C_L = 200$ pF, $C_C = 30$ pF, See Figure 2		130			130		ns
SR	Slew rate at unity gain	$V_I = 10$ V, $R_L = 2\ k\Omega$, $C_L = 200$ pF, $C_C = 30$ pF, See Figure 2		2.5			2.5		V/μs

For ordering instructions and mechanical data, see the SN52741/SN72741 data sheet dated November 1970.

TEXAS INSTRUMENTS
INCORPORATED
POST OFFICE BOX 5012 • DALLAS, TEXAS 75222

DEFINITION OF TERMS

Input Offset Voltage (V_{IO}) The d-c voltage which must be applied between the input terminals to force the quiescent d-c output voltage to zero. The input offset voltage may also be defined for the case where two equal resistances (R_S) are inserted in series with the input leads.

Input Offset Current (I_{IO}) The difference between the currents into the two input terminals with the output at zero volts.

Input Bias Current (I_{IB}) The average of the currents into the two input terminals with the output at zero volts.

Common-Mode Input Voltage Range (V_{ICR}) The range of common-mode voltage which if exceeded will cause the amplifier to cease functioning properly.

Maximum Peak-to-Peak Output Voltage Swing (V_{OPP}) The maximum peak-to-peak output voltage that can be obtained without waveform clipping when the quiescent d-c output voltage is zero.

Large-Signal Differential Voltage Amplification (A_{VD}) The ratio of the peak-to-peak output voltage swing to the change in differential input voltage required to drive the output.

Maximum-Output-Swing Bandwidth (B_{OM}) The range of frequencies within which the maximum output voltage swing is above a specified value.

Unity-Gain Bandwidth (B_1) The range of frequencies within which the voltage amplification is greater than unity.

Differential Input Resistance (r_{id}) The small-signal resistance between the two ungrounded input terminals.

Common-Mode Input Impedance (z_{ic}) The parallel sum of the small-signal impedances between each input terminal and ground.

Output Impedance (z_o) The impedance between the output terminal and ground.

Common-Mode Rejection Ratio (CMRR) The ratio of differential voltage amplification to common-mode voltage amplification. This is measured by determining the ratio of a change in input common-mode voltage to the resulting change in input offset voltage.

Supply Voltage Sensitivity ($\Delta V_{IO}/\Delta V_{CC}$) The ratio of the change in input offset voltage to the change in supply voltages producing it. For these devices, both supply voltages are varied symmetrically.

Short-Circuit Output Current (I_{OS}) The maximum output current available from the amplifier with the output shorted to the specified supply.

Total Power Dissipation (P_D) The total d-c power supplied to the device less any power delivered from the device to a load. At no load: $P_D = V_{CC+} \cdot I_{CC+} + V_{CC-} \cdot I_{CC-}$.

Rise Time (t_r) The time required for an output voltage step to change from 10% to 90% of its final value.

Slew Rate (SR) The average time rate of change of the closed-loop amplifier output voltage for a step-signal input. Slew rate is measured between specified output levels (0 and 10 volts for this device) with feedback adjusted for unity gain.

TYPES SN52771, SN72771
HIGH-PERFORMANCE OPERATIONAL AMPLIFIERS

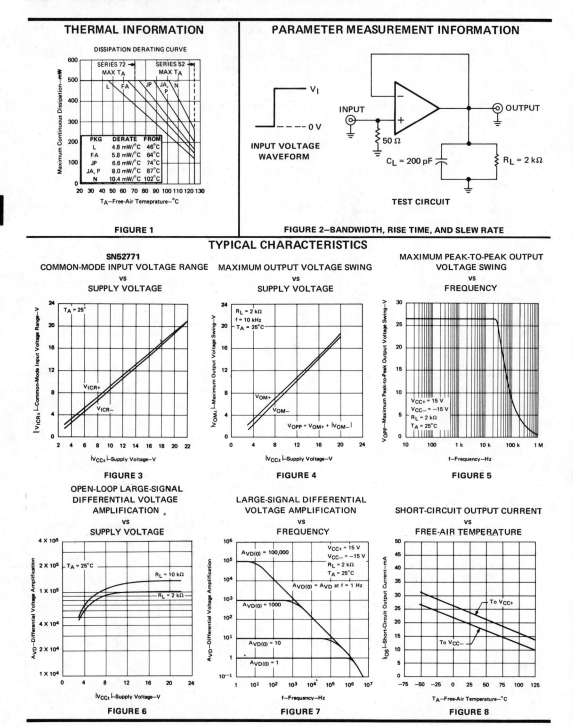

THERMAL INFORMATION

DISSIPATION DERATING CURVE

FIGURE 1

PARAMETER MEASUREMENT INFORMATION

TEST CIRCUIT

FIGURE 2—BANDWIDTH, RISE TIME, AND SLEW RATE

TYPICAL CHARACTERISTICS

SN52771
COMMON-MODE INPUT VOLTAGE RANGE
vs
SUPPLY VOLTAGE

FIGURE 3

MAXIMUM OUTPUT VOLTAGE SWING
vs
SUPPLY VOLTAGE

FIGURE 4

MAXIMUM PEAK-TO-PEAK OUTPUT
VOLTAGE SWING
vs
FREQUENCY

FIGURE 5

OPEN-LOOP LARGE-SIGNAL
DIFFERENTIAL VOLTAGE
AMPLIFICATION
vs
SUPPLY VOLTAGE

FIGURE 6

LARGE-SIGNAL DIFFERENTIAL
VOLTAGE AMPLIFICATION
vs
FREQUENCY

FIGURE 7

SHORT-CIRCUIT OUTPUT CURRENT
vs
FREE-AIR TEMPERATURE

FIGURE 8

TEXAS INSTRUMENTS
INCORPORATED
POST OFFICE BOX 5012 • DALLAS, TEXAS 75222

TYPICAL CHARACTERISTICS

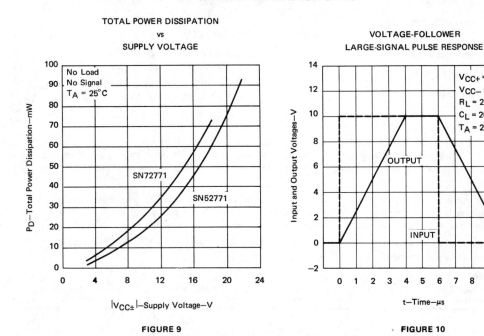

TOTAL POWER DISSIPATION
vs
SUPPLY VOLTAGE

VOLTAGE-FOLLOWER
LARGE-SIGNAL PULSE RESPONSE

FIGURE 9

FIGURE 10

TYPICAL APPLICATION DATA

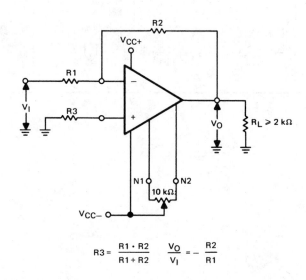

$$R3 = \frac{R1 \cdot R2}{R1 + R2} \qquad \frac{V_O}{V_I} = -\frac{R2}{R1}$$

FIGURE 11—INVERTING CIRCUIT WITH ADJUSTABLE GAIN, COMPENSATION, AND OFFSET ADJUSTMENT

TEXAS INSTRUMENTS
INCORPORATED
POST OFFICE BOX 5012 • DALLAS, TEXAS 75222

- Low Input Currents
- Low Input Offset Parameters
- Frequency and Transient Response Characteristics Adjustable
- Short-Circuit Protection
- Offset-Voltage Null Capability

- Designed to be Interchangeable with Fairchild μA777 and μA777C
- No Latch-Up
- Wide Common-Mode and Differential Voltage Ranges
- Same Pin Assignments as SN52748/SN72748, SN52709/SN72709, SN52101A/SN72301A

description

The SN52777 and SN72777 are precision operational amplifiers. Low offset and bias currents improve system accuracy when used in applications such as long-term integrators, sample-and-hold circuits, and high-source-impedance summing amplifiers. These devices are excellent choices where a performance between that of super-beta and general purpose operational amplifiers is required.

External compensation of the SN52777 and SN72777 may be implemented in either normal or feed-forward configuration to satisfy bandwidth and slew-rate requirements. These circuits feature high gain, wide differential and common-mode input voltage range, output short-circuit protection, and null capability.

The SN52777 is characterized for operation over the full military range of -55°C to 125°C; the SN72777 is characterized for operation from 0°C to 70°C.

terminal assignments

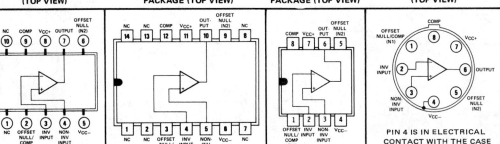

FA FLAT PACKAGE (TOP VIEW)   JA OR N DUAL-IN-LINE PACKAGE (TOP VIEW)   JP OR P DUAL-IN-LINE PACKAGE (TOP VIEW)   L PLUG-IN PACKAGE (TOP VIEW)

PIN 4 IS IN ELECTRICAL CONTACT WITH THE CASE

NC—No internal connection

schematic

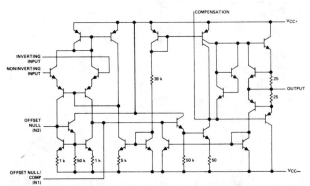

Resistor values shown are nominal and in ohms.

TEXAS INSTRUMENTS
INCORPORATED
POST OFFICE BOX 5012 • DALLAS, TEXAS 75222

absolute maximum ratings over operating free-air temperature range (unless otherwise noted)

		SN52777	SN72777	UNIT
Supply voltage V_{CC+} (see Note 1)		22	22	V
Supply voltage V_{CC-} (see Note 1)		−22	−22	V
Differential input voltage (see Note 2)		±30	±30	V
Input voltage (either input, see Notes 1 and 3)		±15	±15	V
Voltage between either offset null terminal (N1/N2) and V_{CC-}		−0.5 to 2	−0.5 to 2	V
Duration of output short-circuit (see Note 4)		unlimited	unlimited	
Continuous total dissipation at (or below) 25°C free-air temperature (see Note 5)		500	500	mW
Operating free-air temperature range		−55 to 125	0 to 70	°C
Storage temperature range		−65 to 150	−65 to 150	°C
Lead temperature 1/16 inch from case for 60 seconds	FA, JA, JP or L package	300	300	°C
Lead temperature 1/16 inch from case for 10 seconds	N or P package	260	260	°C

NOTES: 1. All voltage values, unless otherwise noted, are with respect to the zero-reference level (ground) of the supply voltages where the zero-reference level is the midpoint between V_{CC+} and V_{CC-}. If the zero-reference level of the system is not the midpoint of the supply voltages, all voltage values must be changed accordingly.
2. Differential voltages are at the noninverting input terminal with respect to the inverting input terminal.
3. The magnitude of the input voltage must never exceed the magnitude of the supply voltage or 15 volts, whichever is less.
4. The output may be shorted to ground or either power supply. For the SN52777 only, the unlimited duration of the short-circuit applies at (or below) 125°C case temperature or 75°C free-air temperature.
5. For operation above 25°C free-air temperature, refer to Dissipation Derating Curve, Figure 4.

electrical characteristics at specified free-air temperature, V_{CC+} = 15 V, V_{CC-} = −15 V, C_C = 30 pF (unless otherwise noted)

PARAMETER		TEST CONDITIONS†		SN52777			SN72777			UNIT
				MIN	TYP	MAX	MIN	TYP	MAX	
V_{IO}	Input offset voltage	$R_S \leqslant 50\ k\Omega$	25°C		0.5	2		0.7	5	mV
			Full range			3			5	
α_{VIO}	Average temperature coefficient of input offset voltage	$R_S \leqslant 50\ k\Omega$	Full range		2.5	15		4	30	µV/°C
I_{IO}	Input offset current		25°C		0.25	3		0.7	20	nA
			Full range			10			40	
α_{IIO}	Average temperature coefficient of input offset current		MIN to 25°C		6.5	150		20	600	pA/°C
			25°C to MAX		2.5	30		10	300	
I_{IB}	Input bias current		25°C		8	25		25	100	nA
			Full range			75			200	
V_I	Input voltage range		Full range	±12	±13		±12	±13		V
V_{OPP}	Maximum peak-to-peak output voltage swing	$R_L = 10\ k\Omega$	Full range	24	28		24	28		V
		$R_L = 2\ k\Omega$	Full range	20	26		20	26		
A_{VD}	Large-signal differential voltage amplification	$V_O = \pm10$ V, $R_L \geqslant 2\ k\Omega$	25°C	50,000	250,000		25,000	250,000		
			Full range	25,000			15,000			
r_i	Input resistance		25°C	2	10		1	2		MΩ
r_o	Output resistance		25°C		100			100		Ω
C_i	Input capacitance		25°C		3			3		pF
CMRR	Common-mode rejection ratio	$R_S = 50\ k\Omega$	Full range	80	95		70	95		dB
$\Delta V_{CC}/\Delta V_{IO}$	Supply voltage rejection ratio	$R_S \leqslant 50\ k\Omega$	Full range		13	100		15	150	µV/V
I_{OS}	Short-circuit output current		25°C		±25			±25		mA
I_{CC}	Supply current	No load, No signal	25°C		1.9	2.8		1.9	3.3	mA
			MIN		2	3.3			3.3	
			MAX		1.5	2.5			3.3	

†All characteristics are specified under open-loop operation. Full range (MIN to MAX) for SN52777 is −55°C to 125°C and for SN72777 is 0°C to 70°C.

operating characteristics, V_{CC+} = 15 V, V_{CC-} = −15 V, T_A = 25°C

PARAMETER		TEST CONDITIONS		SN52777 MIN	TYP	MAX	SN72777 MIN	TYP	MAX	UNIT
t_r	Rise time	V_I = 20 mV, R_L = 2 kΩ, C_L = 100 pF	A_V = 1, C_C = 30 pF		0.3			0.3		μs
			A_V = 10, C_C = 3.5 pF		0.2			0.2		
	Overshoot	V_I = 20 mV, R_L = 2 kΩ, C_L = 100 pF	A_V = 1, C_C = 30 pF		5%			5%		
			A_V = 10, C_C = 3.5 pF		5%			5%		
SR	Slew rate	R_L = 2 kΩ, C_L = 100 pF	A_V = 1, C_C = 30 pF		0.5			0.5		V/μs
			A_V = 10, C_C = 3.5 pF		5.5			5.5		

DEFINITION OF TERMS

Input Offset Voltage (V_{IO}) The d-c voltage that must be applied between the input terminals to force the quiescent d-c output voltage to zero. The input offset voltage may also be defined for the case where two equal resistances (R_S) are inserted in series with the input leads.

Average Temperature Coefficient of Input Offset Voltage (α_{VIO}) The ratio of the change in input offset voltage to the change in free-air temperature. This is an average value for the specified temperature range.

$$\alpha_{VIO} = \left| \frac{(V_{IO} @ T_{A(1)}) - (V_{IO} @ T_{A(2)})}{T_{A(1)} - T_{A(2)}} \right| \quad \text{where } T_{A(1)} \text{ and } T_{A(2)} \text{ are the specified temperature extremes.}$$

Input Offset Current (I_{IO}) The difference between the currents into the two input terminals with the output at zero volts.

Average Temperature Coefficient of Input Offset Current (α_{IIO}) The ratio of the change in input offset current to the change in free-air temperature. This is an average value for the specified temperature range.

$$\alpha_{IIO} = \left| \frac{(I_{IO} @ T_{A(1)}) - (I_{IO} @ T_{A(2)})}{T_{A(1)} - T_{A(2)}} \right| \quad \text{where } T_{A(1)} \text{ and } T_{A(2)} \text{ are the specified temperature extremes.}$$

Input Bias Current (I_{IB}) The average of the currents into the two input terminals with the output at zero volts.

Input Voltage Range (V_I) The range of voltage that if exceeded at either input terminal will cause the amplifier to cease functioning properly.

Maximum Peak-to-Peak Output Voltage Swing (V_{OPP}) The maximum peak-to-peak output voltage than can be obtained without waveform clipping when the quiescent d-c output voltage is zero.

Large-Signal Differential Voltage Amplifier (A_{VD}) The ratio of the maximum peak-to-peak output voltage swing to the change in differential input voltage required to drive the output.

Input Resistance (r_i) The resistance between the input terminals with either input grounded.

Common-Mode Rejection Ratio (CMRR) The ratio of differential voltage amplification to common-mode voltage amplification. This is measured by determining the ratio of a change in input common-mode voltage to the resulting change in input offset voltage.

Supply Voltage Rejection Ratio ($\Delta V_{CC}/\Delta V_{IO}$) The ratio of the change in power supply voltages to the change in input offset voltage. For these devices, both supply voltages are varied symmetrically.

Rise Time (t_r) The time required for an output voltage step to change from 10% to 90% of its final value.

Overshoot The quotient of: (1) the largest deviation of the output signal value from its steady-state value after a step-function change of the input signal, and (2) the difference between the output signal values in the steady state before and after the step-function change of the input signal.

Slew Rate (SR) The average time rate of change of the closed-loop amplifier output voltage for a step-signal input. Slew rate is measured between specified output levels (0 and 10 volts for this device) with feedback adjusted for unity gain.

TEXAS INSTRUMENTS
INCORPORATED
POST OFFICE BOX 5012 • DALLAS, TEXAS 75222

PARAMETER MEASUREMENT INFORMATION

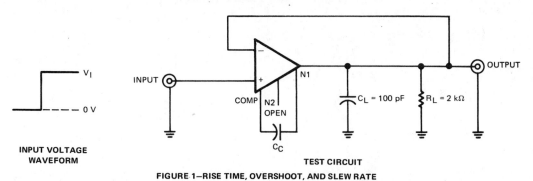

INPUT VOLTAGE WAVEFORM

TEST CIRCUIT

FIGURE 1—RISE TIME, OVERSHOOT, AND SLEW RATE

TYPICAL CHARACTERISTICS

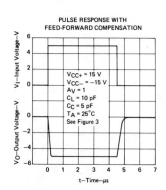

PULSE RESPONSE WITH FEED-FORWARD COMPENSATION

$V_{CC+} = 15$ V
$V_{CC-} = -15$ V
$A_V = 1$
$C_L = 10$ pF
$C_C = 5$ pF
$T_A = 25°C$
See Figure 3

FIGURE 2

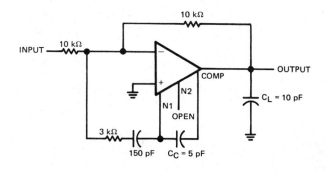

FIGURE 3—INVERTING CIRCUIT WITH UNITY GAIN AND FEED-FORWARD COMPENSATION

THERMAL INFORMATION

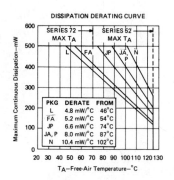

DISSIPATION DERATING CURVE

SERIES 72 MAX T_A SERIES 52 MAX T_A

PKG	DERATE	FROM
L	4.8 mW/°C	46°C
FA	5.2 mW/°C	54°C
JP	6.6 mW/°C	74°C
JA, P	8.0 mW/°C	87°C
N	10.4 mW/°C	102°C

FIGURE 4

TYPICAL APPLICATION DATA

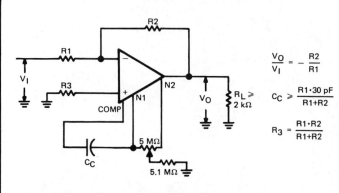

$$\frac{V_O}{V_I} = -\frac{R2}{R1}$$

$$C_C \geq \frac{R1 \cdot 30 \text{ pF}}{R1+R2}$$

$$R_3 = \frac{R1 \cdot R2}{R1+R2}$$

FIGURE 5—INVERTING CIRCUIT WITH ADJUSTABLE GAIN, SINGLE-POLE COMPENSATION, AND OFFSET ADJUSTMENT

TEXAS INSTRUMENTS
INCORPORATED
POST OFFICE BOX 5012 • DALLAS, TEXAS 75222

Voltage Regulators

Series 52 (−55°C to 125°C operating temperature range)

PARAMETER	SN52104	SN52105	SN52109	SN52723	UNIT
Input Voltage, Min	−8	8.5	7	9.5	V
Input Voltage, Max	−50	50	25	40	V
Output Voltage, Min	−0.015	4.5	5.0 Nom	2	V
Output Voltage, Max	−40	40		37	V
Input-to-Output Voltage Difference, Min	−0.5	3	2	3	V
Output Current, Max	20	12	500	150	mA
Input Regulation, Max	0.1%	0.06%/V	50 mV	0.5%	
Ripple Rejection, Min			85†	74†	dB
Ripple Sensitivity, Max	1 mV/V	0.01 %/V			
Load Regulation, Max	5 mV	0.1%	50 mV	0.6%	
Standby Current, Max	5	2	10	3.5	mA

†Typical value at 25°C

Series 72 (0°C to 70°C operating temperature range)

PARAMETER	SN72304	SN72305	SN72305A	SN72309	SN72376	SN72723	UNIT
Input Voltage, Min	−8	8	8.5	7	9	9.5	V
Input Voltage, Max	−40	40	50	25	40	40	V
Output Voltage, Min	−0.035	4.5	4.5	5.0 Nom	5	2	V
Output Voltage, Max	−30	30	40		37	37	V
Input-to-Output Voltage Difference, Min	−0.5	3	3	2	3	3	V
Output Current, Max	20	20	45	500	25	150	mA
Input Regulation, Max	0.1%	0.06%/V	0.06%/V	50 mV	0.06%	0.3%	
Ripple Rejection, Min				85†		74†	dB
Ripple Sensitivity, Max	1 mV/V	0.01 %/V	0.003 %/V†				
Load Regulation, Max	5 mV	0.1%	0.4%	50 mV	0.5%	0.6%	
Standby Current, Max	5	2	2	10	2.5	4	mA

†Typical value at 25°C

5

TEXAS INSTRUMENTS
INCORPORATED
POST OFFICE BOX 5012 • DALLAS, TEXAS 75222

- Typical Load Regulation . . . 1 mV
- Typical Input Regulation . . . 0.06%
- Designed to be Interchangeable with National Semiconductor LM104 and LM304 Respectively

description

The SN52104 and SN72304 are monolithic integrated circuit voltage regulators that can be programmed with a single external resistor to provide any voltage between −40 volts and approximately 0 volts while operating from a single unregulated negative supply. When used with a separate floating bias supply, these devices can provide regulation with the output voltage limited only by the breakdown characteristics of the external pass transistors.

Although designed primarily for application as linear series regulators at output currents up to 25 milliamperes, the SN52104/SN72304 can be used as current regulators, switching regulators, or control elements with the output current limited by the capability of the external pass transistors. The improvement factor for load regulation is approximately equal to the composite current gain of the added transistors. The devices can be used in either constant-current or fold-back current-limiting applications.

The SN52104 is characterized for operation over the full military temperature range of −55°C to 125°C; the SN72304 is characterized for operation from 0°C to 70°C.

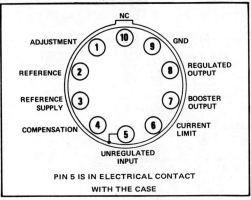

L PLUG-IN PACKAGE
(TOP VIEW)

PIN 5 IS IN ELECTRICAL CONTACT
WITH THE CASE

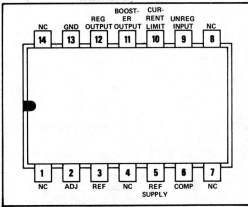

JA OR N DUAL-IN-LINE
PACKAGE (TOP VIEW)

NC—No internal connection

schematic

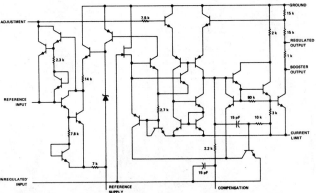

Component values shown are nominal.
Resistor values are in ohms.

TEXAS INSTRUMENTS
INCORPORATED

POST OFFICE BOX 5012 • DALLAS, TEXAS 75222

absolute maximum ratings over operating free-air temperature range (unless otherwise noted)

		SN52104	SN72104	UNIT
Input voltage (see Note 1)		−50	−40	V
Input-to-output voltage differential		−50	−40	V
Continuous total dissipation at (or below) 25°C	JA or N package	1000	1000	mW
free-air temperature (see Note 2)	L package	800	800	
Operating free-air temperature range		−55 to 125	0 to 70	°C
Storage temperature range		−65 to 150	−65 to 150	°C
Lead temperature 1/16 inch from case for 60 seconds: JA or L package		300	300	°C
Lead temperature 1/16 inch from case for 10 seconds: N package		260	260	°C

NOTES: 1. Voltage values, except input-to-output voltage differential, are with respect to network ground terminal.
2. For operation above 25°C free-air temperature, refer to Dissipation Derating Curve, Figure 1. This rating for the L package requires a heat sink that provides a thermal resistance from case to free-air, $R_{\theta CA}$, of not more than 95°C/W.

recommended operating conditions

		SN52104		SN72304		UNIT
		MIN	MAX	MIN	MAX	
Input voltage, V_I		−8	−50	−8	−40	V
Output voltage, V_O		−0.015	−40	−0.035	−30	V
Input-to-output voltage differential, $V_I - V_O$	I_O = 20 mA	−2	−50	−2	−40	V
	I_O ⩽ 5 mA	−0.5	−50	−0.5	−40	
Output current, I_O			20		20	mA
Operating free-air temperature, T_A		−55	125	0	70	°C

electrical characteristics over recommended ranges of input and output voltage and operating free-air temperature (unless otherwise noted)

PARAMETER	TEST CONDITIONS[†]		SN52104			SN72304			UNIT
			MIN	TYP	MAX	MIN	TYP	MAX	
Input regulation	V_O = −5 V to MAX, ΔV_I = 0.1 V_I, See Notes 3 and 4			0.06	0.1		0.06	0.1	%
Ripple sensitivity	C1 = 10 μF,	V_I = −15 V to MAX		0.2	0.5		0.2	0.5	mV/V
	f = 120 Hz	V_I = −7 V to −15 V		0.5	1		0.5	1	
Load regulation	I_O = 0 to 20 mA, R_{SC} = 15 Ω, See Note 3			1	5		1	5	mV
Output voltage scale factor	R1 = 2.4 kΩ, See Figure 2		1.8	2	2.2	1.8	2	2.2	V/kΩ
Output voltage change with temperature	T_A = MIN to T_A = 25°C				1			1	%
	T_A = 25°C to T_A = MAX				1			1	
Output noise voltage	V_O = −5 V to MAX,	C1 = 0		0.007			0.007		%
	f = 10 Hz to 10 kHz	C1 = 10 μF		15			15		μV
Bias current	I_O = 5 mA	V_O = 0		1.7	2.5		1.7	2.5	mA
		V_O = −30 V					3.6	5	
		V_O = −40 V		3.6	5				

[†]For conditions shown as MIN or MAX, use the appropriate value specified under recommended operating conditions.

NOTES: 3. Input regulation and load regulation are measured using pulse techniques (t_w ⩽ 10 μs, duty cycle ⩽ 5%) to limit changes in average internal dissipation. Output voltage changes due to large changes in internal dissipation must be taken into account separately.
4. At zero output voltage, the output variation can be determined using the ripple sensitivity. At low voltages (i.e., 0 to −5 V), the output variation determined from the ripple sensitivity must be added to the variation determined from the input regulation to determine the overall line regulation.

DEFINITION OF TERMS

Input Regulation The percentage change in the output voltage for a change in input voltage.

Ripple Sensitivity The ratio of the peak-to-peak output ripple voltage to the peak-to-peak input ripple voltage.

Load Regulation The change in output voltage for a change in output current.

Output Voltage Scale Factor Output voltage divided by the value of resistance between the adjustment terminal and ground.

Output Voltage Change with Temperature The percentage change in the output voltage for a change in free-air temperature. This is the net change over the specified temperature range.

Output Noise Voltage The rms output noise voltage with constant load and no input ripple. This may also be expressed as a percentage of the output voltage.

Bias Current The difference between input and output current.

THERMAL INFORMATION

DISSIPATION DERATING CURVE

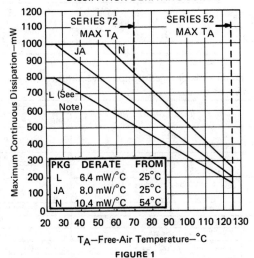

PKG	DERATE	FROM
L	6.4 mW/°C	25°C
JA	8.0 mW/°C	25°C
N	10.4 mW/°C	54°C

FIGURE 1

NOTE 2: This rating for the L package requires a heat sink that provides a thermal resistance from case to free-air, $R_{\theta CA}$, of not more than 95°C/W.

TYPICAL APPLICATION DATA

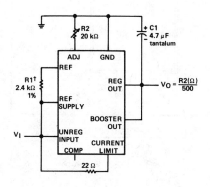

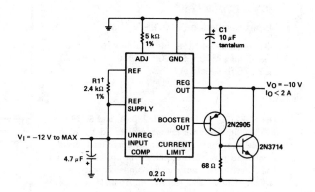

FIGURE 2—BASIC REGULATOR CIRCUIT

FIGURE 3—HIGH-CURRENT REGULATOR

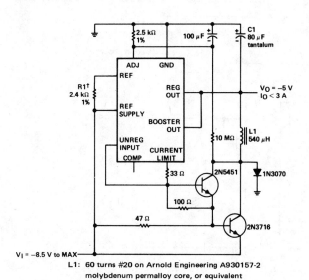

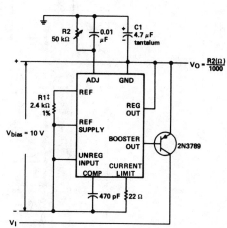

L1: 60 turns #20 on Arnold Engineering A930157-2
molybdenum permalloy core, or equivalent

FIGURE 4—SWITCHING REGULATOR

FIGURE 5—OPERATING WITH SEPARATE BAIS SUPPLY

†Trim R1 for exact scale factor.

TEXAS INSTRUMENTS
INCORPORATED
POST OFFICE BOX 5012 • DALLAS, TEXAS 75222

LINEAR
INTEGRATED CIRCUITS

TYPES SN52105, SN72305, SN72305A, SN72376
POSITIVE-VOLTAGE REGULATORS

BULLETIN NO. DL-S 7312057, SEPTEMBER 1973

- Low Standby Current . . . 0.8 mA Typ
- Adjustable Output Voltage
- Load Regulation . . . 0.1% Max
  (SN52105, SN72305)
- Input Regulation . . . 0.1%/V Max
- Designed to be Interchangeable with
  National LM105, LM305, LM305A, and
  LM376 Respectively

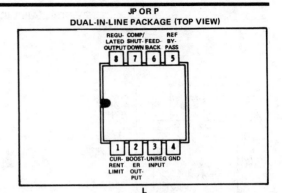

description

The SN52105, SN72305, SN72305A, and SN72376 are monolithic positive-voltage regulators designed for a wide range of applications from digital power supplies to precision regulators for analog systems. These devices will not oscillate under conditions of varying resistive and reactive loads and will start reliably with any load within the rating of the circuits.

The SN52105 is characterized for operation over the full military temperature range of −55°C to 125°C; the SN72305, SN72305A, and SN72376 are characterized for operation from 0°C to 70°C.

schematic

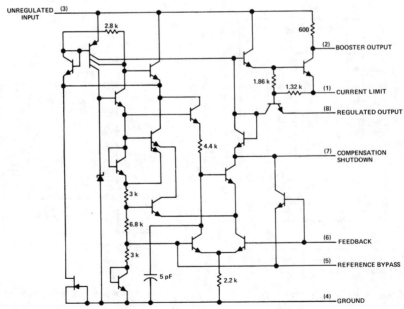

Component values shown are nominal.
Resistor values are in ohms.

TEXAS INSTRUMENTS
INCORPORATED
POST OFFICE BOX 5012 • DALLAS, TEXAS 75222

absolute maximum ratings over operating free-air temperature range (unless otherwise noted)

	SN52105	SN72305A	SN72305 SN72376	UNIT
Input voltage (see Note 1)	50	50	40	V
Input-to-output voltage differential	40	40	40	V
Continuous total dissipation at (or below) 25°C free-air temperature (see Note 2)	800	800	800	mW
Operating free-air temperature range	−55 to 125	0 to 70	0 to 70	°C
Storage temperature range	−65 to 150	−65 to 150	−65 to 150	°C
Lead temperature 1/16 inch from case for 60 seconds: JP or L package	300	300	300	°C
Lead temperature 1/16 inch from case for 10 seconds: P package	260	260	260	°C

NOTES: 1. Voltage values, except input-to-output voltage differential, are with respect to network ground terminal.
2. For operation above 25°C free-air temperature, refer to Dissipation Derating Curve, Figure 8. This rating for the L package requires a heat sink that provides a thermal resistance from case to free-air, $R_{\theta CA}$, of not more than 95°C/W.

recommended operating conditions

	SN52105		SN72305A		SN72305		SN72376		UNIT
	MIN	MAX	MIN	MAX	MIN	MAX	MIN	MAX	
Input voltage, V_I	8.5	50	8.5	50	8.5	40	9	40	V
Output voltage, V_O	4.5	40	4.5	40	4.5	30	5	37	V
Input-to-output voltage differential, $V_I - V_O$	3	30	3	30	3	30	3	30	V
Output current, I_O	0	12	0	45	0	12	0	25	mA
Operating free-air temperature, T_A	−55	125	0	70	0	70	0	70	°C

SN52105, SN72305 electrical characteristics[†] at 25°C free-air temperature (unless otherwise noted)

PARAMETER	TEST CONDITIONS[‡]			SN52105			SN72305			UNIT
				MIN	TYP	MAX	MIN	TYP	MAX	
Input regulation	$V_I - V_O \leqslant 5$ V		See Note 3		0.025	0.06		0.025	0.06	%/V
	$V_I - V_O > 5$ V				0.015	0.03		0.015	0.03	
Ripple sensitivity	$C_{ref} = 10$ μF,	f = 120 Hz			0.003	0.01		0.003	0.01	%/V
Load regulation (see Note 4)	$I_O = 0$ to $I_O = 12$ mA, See Note 3	$R_{SC} = 10$ Ω, $T_A = 25°C$			0.02	0.05		0.02	0.05	%
		$R_{SC} = 10$ Ω, $T_A = MIN$			0.03	0.1		0.03	0.1	
		$R_{SC} = 10$ Ω, $T_A = MAX$			0.03	0.1				
		$R_{SC} = 15$ Ω, $T_A = MAX$						0.03	0.1	
Output voltage change with temperature	$T_A = MIN$ to $T_A = 25°C$					1			1	%
	$T_A = 25°C$ to $T_A = MAX$					1			1	
Output noise voltage	f = 10 Hz to 10 kHz	$C_{ref} = 0$			0.005			0.005		%
		$C_{ref} > 0.1$ μF			0.002			0.002		
Feedback sense voltage				1.63	1.7	1.81	1.63	1.7	1.81	V
Current-limit sense voltage	$R_{SC} = 10$ Ω,	$V_O = 0$,	See Note 5	225	300	315	225	300	315	mV
Standby current	$V_I = 50$ V				0.8	2				mA
	$V_I = 40$ V							0.8	2	

[†] These specifications apply for input and output voltages within the ranges specified under recommended operating conditions and for a divider impedance of 2 kΩ presented to the feedback terminal, unless otherwise noted.
[‡] For conditions shown as MIN or MAX, use the appropriate value specified under recommended operating conditions.
NOTES: 3. Input regulation and load regulation are measured using pulse techniques ($t_w \leqslant 10$ μs, duty cycle ≤ 5%) to limit changes in average internal dissipation. Output voltage changes due to large changes in internal dissipation must be taken into account separately.
4. Load regulation and output current capacity can be improved by the addition of external transistors. The improvement factor will be approximately equal to the composite current gain of the added transistors.
5. Current-limit sense voltage is measured without an external pass transistor.

TEXAS INSTRUMENTS
INCORPORATED
POST OFFICE BOX 5012 • DALLAS, TEXAS 75222

SN72305A, SN72376 electrical characteristics[†] at 25°C free-air temperature (unless otherwise noted)

PARAMETER	TEST CONDITIONS[‡]			SN72305A			SN72376			UNIT
				MIN	TYP	MAX	MIN	TYP	MAX	
Input regulation	$V_I - V_O \leqslant 5$ V		See Note 3		0.025	0.06			0.03	%/V
	$V_I - V_O > 5$ V				0.015	0.03			0.03	
	$T_A = 0°C$ to 70°C								0.1	
Ripple sensitivity	$C_{ref} = 10\ \mu F$,	f = 120 Hz			0.003					%/V
	f = 120 Hz								0.1	
Load regulation (see Note 4)	$I_O = 0$ to $I_O =$ MAX, See Note 3	$R_{SC} = 0\ \Omega$,	$T_A = 25°C$		0.02	0.2			0.2	%
		$R_{SC} = 0\ \Omega$,	$T_A = 0°C$		0.03	0.4			0.5	
		$R_{SC} = 0\ \Omega$,	$T_A = 70°C$		0.03	0.4			0.5	
Output voltage change with temperature	$T_A = 0°C$ to $T_A = 25°C$					1			1	%
	$T_A = 25°C$ to $T_A = 70°C$					1			1	
Output noise voltage	f = 10 Hz to 10 kHz	$C_{ref} = 0$			0.005					%
		$C_{ref} > 0.1\ \mu F$			0.002					
Feedback sense voltage				1.55	1.7	1.85				V
	$T_A = 0°C$ to $T_A = 70°C$						1.6	1.7	1.8	
Current limit sense voltage	$R_{SC} = 10\ \Omega$,	$V_O = 0$ V,	See Note 5	225	300	375		300		mV
Standby current	$V_I = 50$ V				0.8	2				mA
	$V_I = 30$ V								2.5	

[†]These specifications apply for input and output voltages within the ranges specified under recommended operating conditions, and for a divider impedance of 2 kΩ presented to the feedback terminal, unless otherwise noted.

[‡]For conditions shown as MIN or MAX, use the appropriate value specified under recommended operating conditions.

NOTES: 3. Input regulation and load regulation are measured using pulse rechniques ($t_w \leqslant 10\ \mu s$, duty cycle $\leqslant 5$) to limit changes in average internal dissipation. Output voltage changes due to large changes in internal dissipation must be taken into account separately.
         4. Load regulation and output current capacity can be improved by the addition of external transistors. The improvement factor will be approximately equal to the composite current gain of the added transistors.
         5. Current-limit sense voltage is measured without an external pass transistor.

DEFINITION OF TERMS

Input Regulation The ratio of the change in the output voltage, expressed as a percentage, to the change in input voltage.

Ripple Sensitivity The ratio of the peak-to-peak output ripple voltage, expressed as a percentage of output voltage, to the peak-to-peak input ripple voltage.

Load Regulation The change in output voltage for a change in output current.

Output Voltage Change with Temperature The percentage change in the output voltage for a change in free-air temperature. This is the net change over the specified temperature range.

Output Noise Voltage The rms output noise voltage with constant load and no input ripple. This may be expressed as a percentage of the output voltage.

Feedback Sense Voltage The voltage that is a function of the output voltage and is used for feedback control of the regulator.

Current Limit Sense Voltage The voltage between the current-limit and regulated-output terminals required to initiate current limiting.

Standby Current The input current to the regulator with no output current.

TEXAS INSTRUMENTS
INCORPORATED
POST OFFICE BOX 5012 • DALLAS, TEXAS 75222

TYPICAL APPLICATION DATA

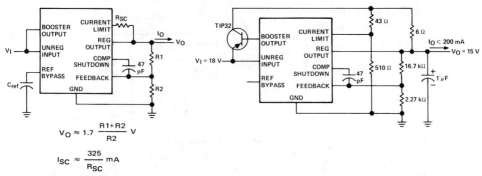

$$V_O \approx 1.7 \ \frac{R1+R2}{R2} \ V$$

$$I_{SC} \approx \frac{325}{R_{SC}} \ mA$$

**FIGURE 1—BASIC REGULATOR
WITH CURRENT LIMITING**

**FIGURE 2—LINEAR REGULATOR
WITH FOLDBACK CURRENT LIMITING**

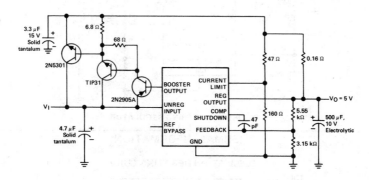

**FIGURE 3—10-A REGULATOR WITH
FOLDBACK CURRENT LIMITING**

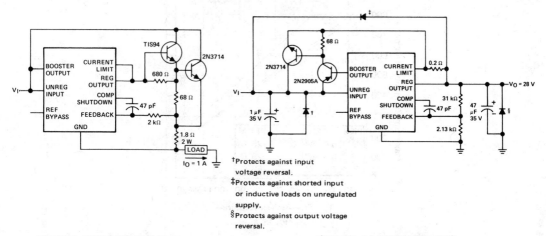

†Protects against input
   voltage reversal.

‡Protects against shorted input
   or inductive loads on unregulated
   supply.

§Protects against output voltage
   reversal.

FIGURE 4—CURRENT REGULATOR

**FIGURE 5—1-A REGULATOR WITH
PROTECTIVE DIODES**

TYPES SN52105, SN72305, SN72305A, SN72376
POSITIVE-VOLTAGE REGULATORS

TYPICAL APPLICATION DATA

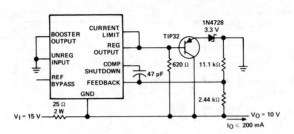

FIGURE 6—SHUNT REGULATOR

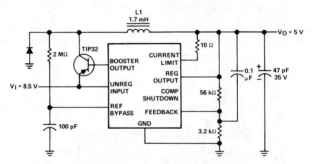

FIGURE 7—SWITCHING REGULATOR

THERMAL INFORMATION

DISSIPATION DERATING CURVE

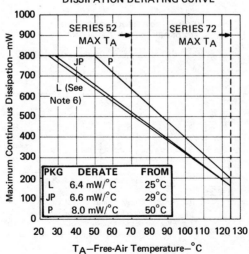

PKG	DERATE	FROM
L	6.4 mW/°C	25°C
JP	6.6 mW/°C	29°C
P	8.0 mW/°C	50°C

T_A—Free-Air Temperature—°C

FIGURE 8

NOTE 6: This rating for the L package requires a heat sink that provides a thermal resistance from case to free-air, $R_{\theta CA}$, of not more than 95°C/W.

PRINTED IN U.S.A.
TI cannot assume any responsibility for any circuits shown
or represent that they are free from patent infringement.

TEXAS INSTRUMENTS RESERVES THE RIGHT TO MAKE CHANGES AT ANY TIM
IN ORDER TO IMPROVE DESIGN AND TO SUPPLY THE BEST PRODUCT POSSIB

TEXAS INSTRUMENTS
INCORPORATED
POST OFFICE BOX 5012 • DALLAS, TEXAS 75222

LINEAR
INTEGRATED CIRCUITS

- No External Components Required for Most Applications
- Output Current . . . 500 mA Max
- Satisfies 5-V Supply Requirements of TTL and DTL
- Virtually Blow-Out Proof Due to Internal Current Limiting, Thermal Shutdown, and Safe-Operating-Area Compensation

LA PLUG-IN PACKAGE
(TOP VIEW)

INPUT — 1
OUTPUT — 2
GND — 3

PIN 3 IS IN ELECTRICAL
CONTACT WITH THE CASE

description

These monolithic 5-volt regulators are designed for use as local regulators to eliminate noise and distribution problems inherent with single-point regulation. They are specified under worst-case conditions to match the power supply requirements of TTL and DTL logic families. In other applications, these devices can be used with external components to obtain adjustable output voltages and currents or as the series-pass element in precision regulators.

schematic

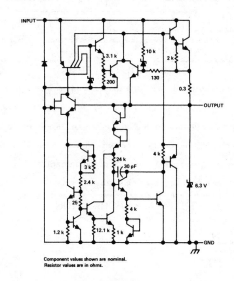

Component values shown are nominal.
Resistor values are in ohms.

absolute maximum ratings over operating case temperature range (unless otherwise noted)

	SN52109	SN72309
Input voltage	35 V	35 V
Output current	500 mA	500 mA
Continuous total dissipation at (or below) 25°C case temperature (see Note 1)	5 W	4 W
Continuous total dissipation at (or below) 25°C free-air temperature (see Note 2)	600 mW	480 mW
Operating case temperature range	−55°C to 150°C	0°C to 125°C
Storage temperature range	◄——— −65°C to 150°C ———►	
Lead temperature 1/16 inch from case for 60 seconds	◄———300°C———	

NOTES: 1. Above 25°C case temperature, derate linearly at the rate of 40 mW/°C, or refer to Dissipation Derating Curve, Figure 1.
2. Above 25°C free-air temperature, derate linearly at the rate of 4.8 mW/°C, or refer to Dissipation Derating Curve, Figure 2.

recommended operating conditions

	SN52109		SN72309		UNIT
	MIN	MAX	MIN	MAX	
Input voltage, V_I	7	25	7	25	V
Output current, I_O	0	500	0	500	mA
Operating case temperature, T_C	−55	150	0	125	°C

electrical characteristics at specified case temperature

PARAMETER	TEST CONDITIONS†		SN52109			SN72309			UNIT
			MIN	TYP	MAX	MIN	TYP	MAX	
Output voltage	V_I = 10 V, I_O = 100 mA	25°C	4.7	5.0	5.3	4.8	5.0	5.2	V
	V_I = 7 V to 25 V, I_O = 5 mA to 200 mA	Full Range	4.6		5.4	4.75		5.25	
Input regulation	V_I = 7 V to V_I = 25 V	25°C		4	50		4	50	mV
Ripple rejection	f = 120 Hz	25°C		85			85		dB
Load regulation	I_O = 5 mA to I_O = 500 mA, See Note 3	25°C		20	50		20	50	mV
Output noise voltage	f = 10 Hz to 100 kHz	25°C		40			40		µV
Standby current	V_I = 7 V to 25 V	Full range		5	10		5	10	mA
Bias current change	V_I = 7 V to V_I = 25 V, I_O = 100 mA	Full range			0.5			0.5	mA
	I_O = 5 mA to I_O = 200 mA				0.8			0.8	

†Full range for SN52109 is −55°C to 150°C and for SN72309 is 0°C to 125°C. All characteristics, except output noise voltage and ripple rejection, are measured using pulse techniques. t_w ⩽ 10 ms, duty cycle ⩽ 5%.

NOTE 3: Pulse techniques are used in testing to limit the average internal dissipation. Output voltage changes due to large changes in internal dissipation must be taken into account separately.

DEFINITION OF TERMS

Input Regulation The change in the output voltage for a change in input voltage from one level to another level.

Ripple Rejection The ratio of the peak-to-peak input ripple voltage to the peak-to-peak output ripple voltage.

Load Regulation The change in output voltage for a change in output current from one level to another level.

Output Noise Voltage The rms output noise voltage with constant load and no input ripple.

Standby Current The input current to the regulator with no output current.

Bias Current The difference between input and output current.

THERMAL INFORMATION

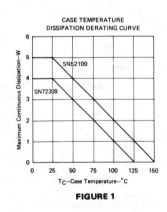

CASE TEMPERATURE
DISSIPATION DERATING CURVE

FIGURE 1

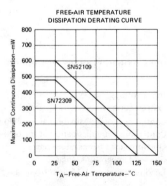

FREE-AIR TEMPERATURE
DISSIPATION DERATING CURVE

FIGURE 2

TYPICAL CHARACTERISTICS†

OUTPUT VOLTAGE
vs
CASE TEMPERATURE

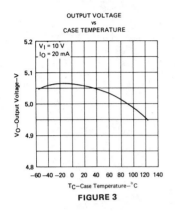

FIGURE 3

OUTPUT VOLTAGE
vs
INPUT VOLTAGE

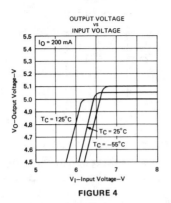

FIGURE 4

INPUT-TO-OUTPUT VOLTAGE DIFFERENTIAL
vs
CASE TEMPERATURE

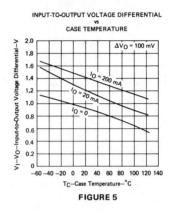

FIGURE 5

RIPPLE REJECTION
vs
FREQUENCY

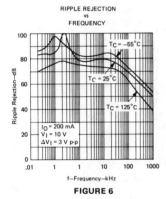

FIGURE 6

OUTPUT NOISE VOLTAGE
vs
FREQUENCY

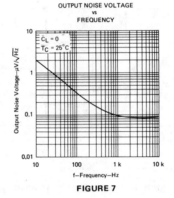

FIGURE 7

OUTPUT IMPEDANCE
vs
FREQUENCY

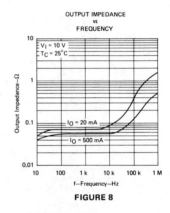

FIGURE 8

STANDBY OR BIAS CURRENT
vs
CASE TEMPERATURE

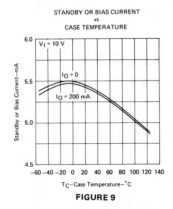

FIGURE 9

BIAS CURRENT
vs
INPUT VOLTAGE

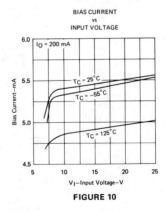

FIGURE 10

†Data for temperatures below 0°C and above 125°C are applicable for SN52109 only.

TYPES SN52109, SN72309
5-VOLT REGULATORS

TYPICAL APPLICATION DATA

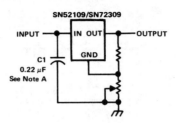

NOTE A: C1 is required if regulator is not located in close proximity to power supply filter.

FIGURE 11—ADJUSTABLE OUTPUT REGULATOR

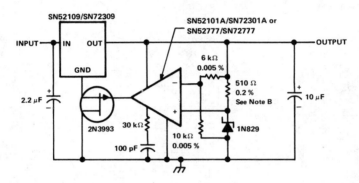

NOTES: A. All capacitors are solid tantalum.
         B. This resistor determines zener current. Adjust to minimize thermal drift.

FIGURE 12—HIGH-STABILITY REGULATOR

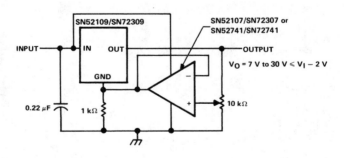

FIGURE 13—HIGH-STABILITY REGULATOR WITH ADJUSTABLE OUTPUT

TEXAS INSTRUMENTS
INCORPORATED
POST OFFICE BOX 5012 • DALLAS, TEXAS 75222

LINEAR INTEGRATED CIRCUITS

TYPES SN52723, SN72723
PRECISION VOLTAGE REGULATORS

BULLETIN NO. DL-S 7311533, AUGUST 1972—REVISED SEPTEMBER 1973

- 150-mA Load Current without External Power Transistor
- Typically 0.02% Input Regulation and 0.03% Load Regulation (SN52723)
- Adjustable Current Limiting Capability
- Input Voltages to 40 Volts
- Output Adjustable from 2 to 37 Volts
- Designed to be Interchangeable with Fairchild μA723 and μA723C Respectively

description

The SN52723 and SN72723 are monolithic integrated circuit voltage regulators featuring high ripple rejection, excellent input and load regulation, excellent temperature stability, and low standby current. The circuit consists of a temperature-compensated reference voltage amplifier, an error amplifier, a 150-milliampere output transistor, and an adjustable output current limiter.

The SN52723 and SN72723 are designed for use in positive or negative power supplies as a series, shunt, switching, or floating regulator. For output currents exceeding 150 mA, additional pass elements may be connected as shown in Figures 4 and 5.

The SN52723 is characterized for operation over the full military temperature range of −55°C to 125°C; the SN72723 is characterized for operation from 0°C to 70°C.

terminal assignments

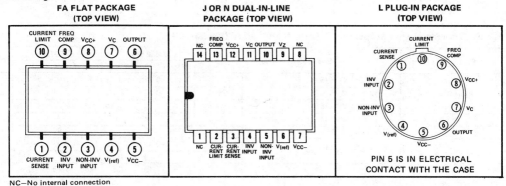

NC—No internal connection

PIN 5 IS IN ELECTRICAL CONTACT WITH THE CASE

functional block diagram

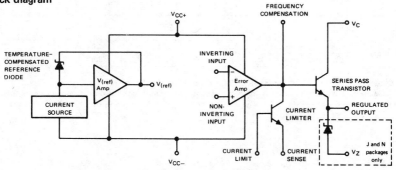

TEXAS INSTRUMENTS
INCORPORATED

POST OFFICE BOX 5012 • DALLAS, TEXAS 75222

TYPES SN52723, SN72723
PRECISION VOLTAGE REGULATORS

absolute maximum ratings over operating free-air temperature range (unless otherwise noted)

Peak voltage from V_{CC+} to V_{CC-} ($t_w \leqslant 50$ ms)	50 V
Continuous voltage from V_{CC+} to V_{CC-}	40 V
Input-to-output voltage differential	40 V
Current from V_Z	25 mA
Current from $V_{(ref)}$	15 mA
Continuous total dissipation at (or below) 25°C free-air temperature (see Note 1):	
J or N package	1000 mW
L package (see Note 2)	800 mW
FA package	650 mW
Operating free-air temperature range: SN52723 Circuits	-55°C to 125°C
SN72723 Circuits	0°C to 70°C
Storage temperature range	-65°C to 150°C
Lead temperature 1/16 inch from case for 60 seconds, FA, J, or L package	300°C
Lead temperature 1/16 inch from case for 10 seconds, N package	260°C

NOTES: 1. Power dissipation = $[I_{(standby)} + I_{(ref)}]\ V_{CC} + [V_C - V_O]\ I_O$. For operation at elevated temperature, refer to Dissipation Derating Curve, Figure 13.
2. This rating for the L package requires a heat sink that provides a thermal resistance from case to free-air, $R_{\theta CA}$, of not more than 95°C/W.

recommended operating conditions

	MIN	MAX	UNIT
Input voltage, V_I	9.5	40	V
Output voltage, V_O	2	37	V
Input-to-output voltage differential, $V_C - V_O$	3	38	V
Output current, I_O		150	mA

electrical characteristics at specified free-air temperature (see note 3)

PARAMETER	TEST CONDITIONS[†]		SN52723			SN72723			UNIT
			MIN	TYP	MAX	MIN	TYP	MAX	
Input regulation	$V_I = 12$ V to $V_I = 15$ V	25°C		0.01%	0.1%		0.01%	0.1%	%
	$V_I = 12$ V to $V_I = 40$ V	25°C		0.02%	0.2%		0.1%	0.5%	
	$V_I = 12$ V to $V_I = 15$ V	Full range			0.5%			0.3%	
Ripple rejection	$f = 50$ Hz to 10 kHz, $C_{(ref)} = 0$	25°C		74			74		dB
	$f = 50$ Hz to 10 kHz, $C_{(ref)} = 5\ \mu$F	25°C		86			86		
Load regulation	$I_O = 1$ mA to $I_O = 50$ mA	25°C		−0.03%	−0.15%		−0.03%	−0.2%	
		Full range			−0.6%			−0.6%	
Reference voltage, $V_{(ref)}$		25°C	6.95	7.15	7.35	6.8	7.15	7.5	V
Standby current	$V_I = 30$ V, $I_O = 0$	25°C		2.3	3.5		2.3	4	mA
Temperature coefficient of output voltage		Full range		0.002	0.015		0.003	0.015	%/$^\circ$C
Short-circuit output current	$R_{SC} = 10\ \Omega$, $V_O = 0$	25°C		65			65		mA
Output noise voltage	BW = 100 Hz to 10 kHz, $C_{(ref)} = 0$	25°C		20			20		μV
	BW = 100 Hz to 10 kHz, $C_{(ref)} = 5\ \mu$F	25°C		2.5			2.5		

[†]Full range for SN52723 is -55°C to 125°C and for SN72723 is 0°C to 70°C.

NOTE 3: For all values in this table the device is connected as shown in Figure 1 with the divider resistance as seen by the error amplifier $\leqslant 10$ kΩ. Unless otherwise specified, $V_I = V_{CC+} = V_C = 12$ V, $V_{CC-} = 0$, $V_O = 5$ V, $I_O = 1$ mA, $R_{SC} = 0$, and $C_{(ref)} = 0$.

TEXAS INSTRUMENTS
INCORPORATED
POST OFFICE BOX 5012 • DALLAS, TEXAS 75222

DEFINITION OF TERMS

Input Regulation The percentage change in the output voltage for a change in input voltage from one level to another level.

$$\text{Input Regulation} = \left[\frac{\Delta V_O}{V_O \text{ at } V_I = 12 \text{ V}} \right] 100\%$$

Ripple Rejection The ratio of the peak-to-peak input ripple voltage to the peak-to-peak output ripple voltage.

Load Regulation The percentage change in the output voltage for a change in output current from one level to another level.

$$\text{Load Regulation} = \left[\frac{V_O \text{ at } I_{O(2)} - V_O \text{ at } I_{O(1)}}{V_O \text{ at } I_{O(1)}} \right] 100\%$$

where $I_{O(1)}$ and $I_{)(2)}$ are the specified low and high current extremes, respectively.

Reference Voltage The output of the reference amplifier measured with respect to the negative supply.

Standby Current The input current to the regulator from V_{CC+} with no output current and the $V_{(ref)}$ terminal open.

Average Temperature Coefficient of Output Voltage (α_{VO}) The ratio of the change in output voltage expressed as a percentage to the change in free-air temperature. This is an average value for the specified temperature range.

$$\alpha_{VO} = \pm \left[\frac{V_O \text{ at } T_{A(2)} - V_O \text{ at } T_{A(1)}}{V_O \text{ at } 25°C} \right] \frac{100\%}{(T_{A(2)} - T_{A(1)})}$$

Short-Circuit Output Current The output current of the regulator with the output shorted to V_{CC-}.

Output Noise Voltage The rms output noise voltage with constant load and no input ripple.

schematic

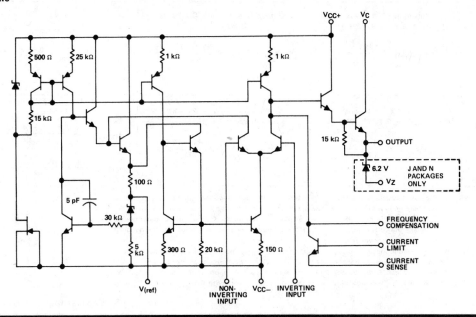

TEXAS INSTRUMENTS
INCORPORATED
POST OFFICE BOX 5012 • DALLAS, TEXAS 75222

TABLE I
RESISTOR VALUES (kΩ) FOR STANDARD OUTPUT VOLTAGES

OUTPUT VOLTAGE (V)	APPLICABLE FIGURES (SEE NOTE 4)	FIXED OUTPUT ±5% R1 (kΩ)	FIXED OUTPUT ±5% R2 (kΩ)	OUTPUT ADJUSTABLE ±10% (SEE NOTE 5) R1 (kΩ)	P1 (kΩ)	R2 (kΩ)	OUTPUT VOLTAGE (V)	APPLICABLE FIGURES (SEE NOTE 4)	FIXED OUTPUT ±5% R1 (kΩ)	FIXED OUTPUT ±5% R2 (kΩ)	OUTPUT ADJUSTABLE ±10% (SEE NOTE 5) R1 (kΩ)	P1 (kΩ)	R2 (kΩ)
+3.0	1, 5, 6, 9, 11, 12 (4)	4.12	3.01	1.8	0.5	1.2	+100	7	3.57	105	2.2	10	91
+3.6	1, 5, 6, 9, 11, 12 (4)	3.57	3.65	1.5	0.5	1.5	+250	7	3.57	255	2.2	10	240
+5.0	1, 5, 6, 9, 11, 12 (4)	2.15	4.99	0.75	0.5	2.2	−6 (Note 6)	3, (10)	3.57	2.43	1.2	0.5	0.75
+6.0	1, 5, 6, 9, 11, 12 (4)	1.15	6.04	0.5	0.5	2.7	−9	3, 10	3.48	5.36	1.2	0.5	2.0
+9.0	2, 4, (5, 6, 9, 12)	1.87	7.15	0.75	1.0	2.7	−12	3, 10	3.57	8.45	1.2	0.5	3.3
+12	2, 4, (5, 6, 9, 12)	4.87	7.15	2.0	1.0	3.0	−15	3, 10	3.57	11.5	1.2	0.5	4.3
+15	2, 4, (5, 6, 9, 12)	7.87	7.15	3.3	1.0	3.0	−28	3, 10	3.57	24.3	1.2	0.5	10
+28	2, 4, (5, 6, 9, 12)	21.0	7.15	5.6	1.0	2.0	−45	8	3.57	41.2	2.2	10	33
+45	7	3.57	48.7	2.2	10	39	−100	8	3.57	95.3	2.2	10	91
+75	7	3.57	78.7	2.2	10	68	−250	8	3.57	249	2.2	10	240

TABLE II
FORMULAS FOR INTERMEDIATE OUTPUT VOLTAGES

Outputs from +2 to +7 volts [Figures 1, 5, 6, 9, 11, 12, (4)]	Outputs from +4 to +250 volts [Figure 7]	Current Limiting
$$V_O = V_{(ref)} \times \frac{R2}{R1 + R2}$$	$$V_O = \frac{V_{(ref)}}{2} \times \frac{R2 - R1}{R1};$$ R3 = R4	$$I_{(limit)} \approx \frac{0.65\ V}{R_{sc}}$$
Outputs from +7 to +37 volts [Figures 2, 4, (5, 6, 9, 11, 12)]	Outputs from −6 to −250 volts [Figures 3, 8, 10]	Foldback Current Limiting [Figure 6]
$$V_O = V_{(ref)} \times \frac{R1 + R2}{R2}$$	$$V_O = -\frac{V_{(ref)}}{2} \times \frac{R1 + R2}{R1};$$ R3 = R4	$$I_{(knee)} \approx \frac{V_O R3 + (R3 + R4)\ 0.65\ V}{R_{sc} R4};$$ $$I_{OS} \approx \frac{0.65\ V}{R_{sc}} \times \frac{R3 + R4}{R4}$$

NOTES: 4. Figures 1 through 12 show the R1/R2 divider across either V_O or $V_{(ref)}$. Figure numbers in parentheses may be used if the R1/R2 divider is placed across the other voltage ($V_{(ref)}$ or V_O) that it was not placed across in the figures without parentheses.

5. To make the voltage adjustable, the R1/R2 divider shown in the figures must be replaced by the divider shown at the right.

6. For negative output voltages less than 9 V, V_{CC+} and V_C must be connected to a positive supply such that the voltage between V_{CC+} and V_{CC-} is greater than 9 V.

7. When 10-lead SN52723/SN72723 devices are used in applications requiring V_Z, an external 6.2-V regulator diode must be connected in series with the V_O terminal.

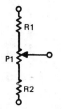

ADJUSTABLE OUTPUT CIRCUITS

TEXAS INSTRUMENTS
INCORPORATED
POST OFFICE BOX 5012 • DALLAS, TEXAS 75222

TYPICAL APPLICATION DATA

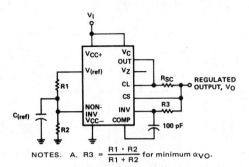

NOTES: A. $R3 = \dfrac{R1 \cdot R2}{R1 + R2}$ for minimum α_{V_O}.

B. R3 may be eliminated for minimum component count. Use direct connection (i.e., $R_3 = 0$).

FIGURE 1—BASIC LOW-VOLTAGE REGULATOR
(V_O = 2 TO 7 VOLTS)

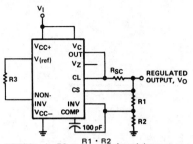

NOTES: A. $R3 = \dfrac{R1 \cdot R2}{R1 + R2}$ for minimum α_{V_O}.

B. R3 may be eliminated for minimum component count. Use direct connection (i.e., $R_3 = 0$).

FIGURE 2—BASIC HIGH-VOLTAGE REGULATOR
(V_O = 7 TO 37 VOLTS)

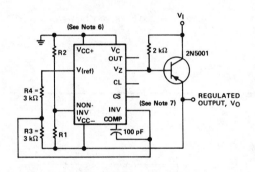

FIGURE 3—NEGATIVE VOLTAGE REGULATOR

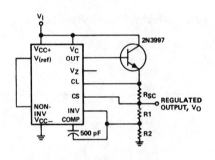

FIGURE 4—POSITIVE VOLTAGE REGULATOR
(EXTERNAL N-P-N PASS TRANSISTOR)

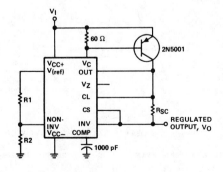

FIGURE 5—POSITIVE VOLTAGE REGULATOR
(EXTERNAL P-N-P PASS TRANSISTOR)

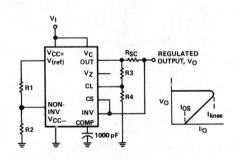

FIGURE 6—FOLDBACK CURRENT LIMITING

TYPES SN52723, SN72723
PRECISION VOLTAGE REGULATORS

TYPICAL APPLICATION DATA

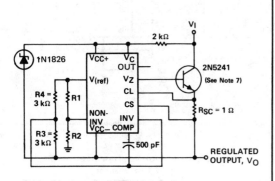

FIGURE 7—POSITIVE FLOATING REGULATOR

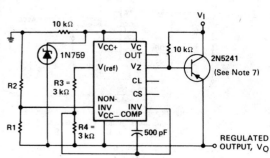

FIGURE 8—NEGATIVE FLOATING REGULATOR

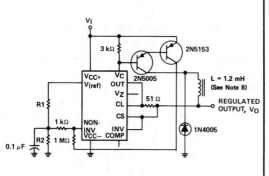

FIGURE 9—POSITIVE SWITCHING REGULATOR

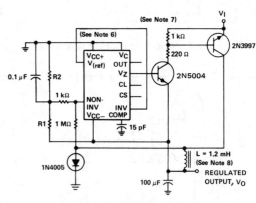

FIGURE 10—NEGATIVE SWITCHING REGULATOR

NOTES: 6. For negative output voltages less than 9 V, V_{CC+} and V_C must be connected to a positive supply such that the voltage between V_{CC+} and V_{CC-} is greater than 9 V.

7. When 10-lead SN52723/SN72723 devices are used in applications requiring V_Z, an external 6.2-V regulator diode must be connected in series with the V_O terminal.

8. L is 40 turns of No. 20 enameled copper wire wound on Ferroxcube P36/22-3B7 potted core, or equivalent, with 0.009-inch air gap.

TEXAS INSTRUMENTS
INCORPORATED

POST OFFICE BOX 5012 • DALLAS, TEXAS 75222

TYPICAL APPLICATION DATA

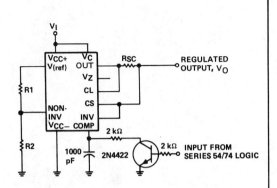

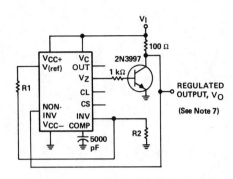

NOTE A: Current limit transistor may be used for shutdown
if current limiting is not required.

**FIGURE 11—REMOTE SHUTDOWN REGULATOR WITH
CURRENT LIMITING**

FIGURE 12—SHUNT REGULATOR

NOTE 7. When 10-lead SN52723/SN72723 devices are used in applications requiring V_Z, an external 6.2-V regulator diode must be connected
in series with the V_O terminal.

THERMAL INFORMATION

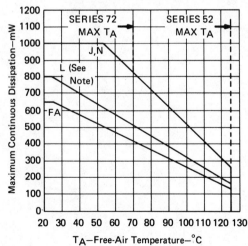

FIGURE 13

PACKAGE DERATING

PKG	DERATE	FROM
FA	5.2 mW/°C	25°C
L	6.4 mW/°C	25°C
J, N	10.4 mW/°C	54°C

NOTE 2: This rating for the L package requires a heat sink that provides a thermal resistance from case to free-air, $R_{\theta CA}$, of not more than
95°C/W.

TEXAS INSTRUMENTS
INCORPORATED
POST OFFICE BOX 5012 • DALLAS, TEXAS 75222

5

Voltage Comparators

Series 52 (−55°C to 125°C operating temperature range)

DIFFERENTIAL COMPARATORS

FEATURES		SINGLE					DUAL CHANNEL		DUAL			UNIT
		SN52106	SN52111	SN52510	SN52710	SN52810	SN52711	SN52811	SN52506	SN52514	SN52820	
Input Offset Voltage, Max		2	3	4	5	2	3.5	3.5	2	2	2	mV
Input Offset Current, Max		3	0.01	3	10	3	10	3	3	3	3	μA
Input Bias Current, Max		20	0.1	15	75	15	75	20	20	15	15	μA
Voltage Amplification, Typ		40 000	200 000	33 000	1500	33 000	1500	17 500	40 000	33 000	33 000	
Low-Level Output Current, Min		16	8	2	1.6	2	0.5	0.5	16	2	2	mA
Avg Response Time, Typ		28	140	30	40	30	40	33	28	30	30	ns
Power Supplies	V_{CC+}	12	5† to 15	12	12	12	12	12	12	12	12	V
Required, Nom	V_{CC-}	−3 to −12	0 to −15	−6	−6	−6	−6	−6	−3 to −12	−6	−6	
Comments		Strobe	Strobe	Strobe		Improved SN52710	Strobes	Improved SN52811	Dual SN52106	Dual SN52510	Dual SN52810	

Series 72 (0°C to 70°C operating temperature range)

DIFFERENTIAL COMPARATORS

FEATURES		SINGLE					DUAL CHANNEL		DUAL				UNIT
		SN72306	SN72311	SN72510	SN72710	SN72810	SN72711	SN72811	SN72506	SN72514	SN72720	SN72820	
Input Offset Voltage, Min		5	7.5	3.5	7.5	3.5	5	5	5	3.5	7.5	3.5	mV
Input Offset Current, Max		5	0.05	5	15	5	15	5	5	5	15	5	μA
Input Bias Current, Max		25	0.25	20	100	20	100	30	25	20	100	20	μA
Voltage Amplification, Typ		40 000	200	33 000	1500	33 000	1500	17 500	40 000	33 000	1500	33 000	
Low-Level Output Current, Min		16	8	1.6	NS	1.6	0.5	0.5	16	1.6	NS	1.6	mA
Avg Response Time, Typ		28	140	30	40	30	40	33	28	30	40	30	ns
Power Supplies	V_{CC+}	12	5† to 15	12	12	12	12	12	12	12	12	12	V
Required, Nom	V_{CC-}	−3 to −12	0 to −15	−6	−6	−6	−6	−6	−3 to −12	−6	−6	−6	
Comments		Strobe	Strobe	Strobe		Improved SN72710	Strobe	Improved SN72811	Dual SN72306	Dual SN72510	Dual SN72710	Dual SN72810	

NS ≡ Not specified

† Capable of operating with a single 5-V supply

6

LINEAR INTEGRATED CIRCUITS

TYPES SN52106, SN72306
DIFFERENTIAL COMPARATORS WITH STROBES
BULLETIN NO. DL-S 7311586, JANUARY 1972—REVISED SEPTEMBER 1973

- Fast Response Times
- Improved Gain and Accuracy
- Fan-Out to 10 Series 54/74 TTL Loads
- Strobe Capability
- Short-Circuit and Surge Protection
- Designed to be interchangeable with National Semiconductor LM106 and LM306

description

The SN52106 and SN72306 are high-speed voltage comparators with differential inputs, a low-impedance output with high-sink-current capability (100 mA), and two strobe inputs. These devices detect low-level analog or digital signals and can drive digital logic or lamps and relays directly. Short-circuit protection and surge-current limiting is provided.

The circuit is similar to an SN52810/SN72810 with gated output. A low-level input at either strobe causes the output to remain high regardless of the differential input. When both strobe inputs are either open or at a high logic level, the output voltage is controlled by the differential input voltage. The circuit will operate with any negative supply voltage between −3 V and −12 V with little difference in performance.

The SN52106 is characterized for operation over the full military temperature range of −55°C to 125°C; the SN72306 is characterized for operation from 0°C to 70°C.

terminal assignments

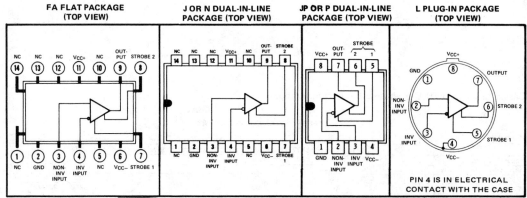

FA FLAT PACKAGE (TOP VIEW) | J OR N DUAL-IN-LINE PACKAGE (TOP VIEW) | JP OR P DUAL-IN-LINE PACKAGE (TOP VIEW) | L PLUG-IN PACKAGE (TOP VIEW)

PIN 4 IS IN ELECTRICAL CONTACT WITH THE CASE

NC—No internal connection

absolute maximum ratings over operating free-air temperature range (unless otherwise noted)

Supply voltage V_{CC+} (see Note 1)	15 V
Supply voltage V_{CC-} (see Note 1)	−15 V
Differential input voltage (see Note 2)	±5 V
Input voltage (either input, see Notes 1 and 3)	±7 V
Strobe voltage range (see Note 1)	0 V to V_{CC+}
Output voltage (see Note 1)	24 V
Voltage from output to V_{CC-}	30 V
Duration of output short-circuit (see Note 4)	10 s
Continuous total power dissipation at (or below) 25°C free-air temperature (see Note 5)	600 mW
Operating free-air temperature range: SN52106 Circuits	−55°C to 125°C
SN72306 Circuits	0°C to 70°C
Storage temperature range	−65°C to 150°C
Lead temperature 1/16 inch from case for 60 seconds: FA, J, JP, or L package	300°C
Lead temperature 1/16 inch from case for 10 seconds: N or P package	260°C

NOTES: 1. All voltage values, except differential voltages and the voltage from the output to V_{CC-}, are with respect to the network ground terminal.
2. Differential voltages are at the noninverting input terminal with respect to the inverting input terminal.
3. The magnitude of the input voltage must never exceed the magnitude of the supply voltage or 7 volts, whichever is less.
4. The output may be shorted to ground or either power supply.
5. For operation above 25°C free-air temperature, refer to Dissipation Derating Curve, Figure 14.

TEXAS INSTRUMENTS
INCORPORATED
POST OFFICE BOX 5012 • DALLAS, TEXAS 75222

electrical characteristics at specified free-air temperature, V_{CC+} = 12 V, V_{CC-} = −3 V to −12 V (unless otherwise noted)

PARAMETER		TEST CONDITIONS[†]		SN52106 MIN	SN52106 TYP	SN52106 MAX	SN72306 MIN	SN72306 TYP	SN72306 MAX	UNIT
V_{IO}	Input offset voltage	$R_S \leq 200\,\Omega$, See Note 6	25°C		0.5[§]	2		1.6[§]	5	mV
			Full range			3			6.5	
α_{VIO}	Average temperature coefficient of input offset voltage	R_S = 50 Ω, See Note 6	Full range		3	10		5	20	µV/°C
I_{IO}	Input offset current	See Note 6	25°C		0.7[§]	3		1.8[§]	5	µA
			MIN		2	7		1	7.5	
			MAX		0.4	3		0.5		
α_{IIO}	Average temperature coefficient of input offset current	See Note 6	MIN to 25°C		15	75		24	100	nA/°C
			25°C to MAX		5	25		15	50	
I_{IB}	Input bias current	V_O = 0.5 V to 5 V	25°C		7[§]	20		16[§]	25	µA
			Full range			45			40	
I_{SL}	Low-level strobe current	$V_{(strobe)}$ = 0.4 V	Full range		−1.7[§]	−3.3		−1.7[§]	−3.3	mA
$V_{IH(strobe)}$	High-level strobe voltage		Full range	2.5			2.5			V
$V_{IL(strobe)}$	Low-level strobe voltage		Full range			0.9			0.9	V
V_{ICR}	Common-mode input voltage range	V_{CC-} = −7 V to −12 V	Full range	±5			±5			V
V_{ID}	Differential input voltage range		Full range	±5			±5			V
A_{VD}	Large-signal differential voltage amplification	No load, V_O = 0.5 V to 5 V	25°C		40 000[§]			40 000[§]		
V_{OH}	High-level output voltage	V_{ID} = 5 mV, I_{OH} = −400 µA	Full range	2.5		5.5	2.5		5.5	V
V_{OL}	Low-level output voltage	V_{ID} = −5 mV, I_{OL} = 100 mA	25°C		0.8[§]	1.5		0.8[§]	2	V
		V_{ID} = −5 mV, I_{OL} = 50 mA	Full range			1			1	
		V_{ID} = −5 mV, I_{OL} = 16 mA	Full range			0.4			0.4	
I_{OH}	High-level output current	V_{ID} = 5 mV, V_{OH} = 8 V to 24 V	25°C		0.02[§]	1		0.02[§]	2	µA
			Full range			100			100	
I_{CC+}	Supply current from V_{CC+}	V_{ID} = −5 mV, No load	Full range		6.6[§]	10		6.6[§]	10	mA
I_{CC-}	Supply current from V_{CC-}	No load	Full range		1.9[§]	3.6		1.9[§]	3.6	mA

[†]Unless otherwise noted, all characteristics are measured with the strobe open.

[§]These typical values are at V_{CC+} = 12 V, V_{CC-} = −6 V, T_A = 25°C. Full range (MIN to MAX) for SN52106 is −55°C to 125°C and for the SN72306 is 0°C to 70°C.

NOTE 6: The offset voltages and offset currents given are the maximum values required to drive the output down to the low range (V_{OL}) or up to the high range (V_{OH}). Thus these parameters actually define an error band and take into account the worst-case effects of voltage gain and input impedance.

switching characteristics, V_{CC+} = 12 V, V_{CC-} = −6 V, T_A = 25°C

PARAMETER	TEST CONDITIONS[†]	SN52506 MIN	SN52506 TYP	SN52506 MAX	SN72506 MIN	SN72506 TYP	SN72506 MAX	UNIT
Response time, low-to-high-level output	R_L = 390 Ω to 5 V, C_L = 15 pF, See Note 7		28	40		28		ns

NOTE 7: The response time specified is for a 100-mV input step with 5-mV overdrive. The typical value is specified for a nominal threshold voltage of 1.4 V.

DEFINITION OF TERMS

Input Offset Voltage (V_{IO}) The d-c voltage which must be applied between the input terminals to force the quiescent d-c output voltage to the specified level. The input offset voltage may also be defined for the case where two equal resistances (R_S) are inserted in series with the input leads.

Average Temperature Coefficient of Input Offset Voltage (α_{VIO}) The ratio of the change in input offset voltage to the change in free-air temperature. This is an average value for the specified temperature range.

$$\alpha_{VIO} = \left| \frac{(V_{IO} @ T_{A(1)}) - (V_{IO} @ T_{A(2)})}{T_{A(1)} - T_{A(2)}} \right| \text{ where } T_{A(1)} \text{ and } T_{A(2)} \text{ are the specified temperature extremes.}$$

Input Offset Current (I_{IO}) The difference between the currents into the two input terminals with the output at the specified level.

Average Temperature Coefficient of Input Offset Current (α_{IIO}) The ratio of the change in input offset current to the change in free-air temperature. This is an average value for the specified temperature range.

$$\alpha_{IIO} = \left| \frac{(I_{IO} @ T_{A(1)}) - (I_{IO} @ T_{A(2)})}{T_{A(1)} - T_{A(2)}} \right| \text{ where } T_{A(1)} \text{ and } T_{A(2)} \text{ are the specified temperature extremes.}$$

Input Bias Current (I_{IB}) The average of the currents into the two input terminals with the output at the specified level.

Low-Level Strobe Current (I_{SL}) The current flowing out of the strobe at a low-level voltage.

High-Level Strobe Voltage ($V_{IH(strobe)}$) A voltage within the range that is guaranteed not to interfere with the operation of the comparator.

Low-Level Strobe Voltage ($V_{IL(strobe)}$) A voltage within the range that is guaranteed to force the output high independently of the differential inputs.

Common-Mode Input Voltage Range (V_{ICR}) The range of common-mode voltage which if exceeded will cause the comparator to cease functioning properly.

Differential Input Voltage Range (V_{ID}) The range of voltage between the two input terminals which if exceeded will cause the comparator to cease functioning properly.

Large-Signal Differential Voltage Amplification (A_{VD}) The ratio of the change in output voltage to the change in differential input voltage producing it.

High-Level Output Voltage (V_{OH}) The voltage at the output with the specified input conditions applied which should establish a high level at the output.

Low-Level Output Voltage (V_{OL}) The voltage at the output with the specified input conditions applied which should establish a low level at the output.

High-Level Output Current (I_{OH}) The current flowing into the output with a specified high-level output voltage, V_{OH}, applied.

Response Time, Low-To-High-Level Output The interval between the application of an input step function and the time when the output crosses the logic threshold voltage. The input step drives the comparator from some initial condition sufficient to saturate the output to an input level just barely in excess of that required to bring the output back to the logic threshold voltage. This excess is referred to as the voltage overdrive.

TEXAS INSTRUMENTS
INCORPORATED

POST OFFICE BOX 5012 • DALLAS, TEXAS 75222

schematic

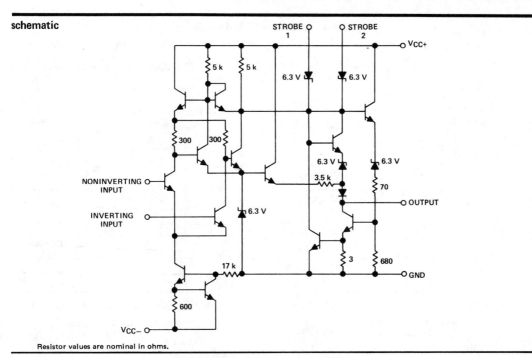

Resistor values are nominal in ohms.

TYPICAL CHARACTERISTICS

INPUT OFFSET CURRENT
vs
FREE-AIR TEMPERATURE

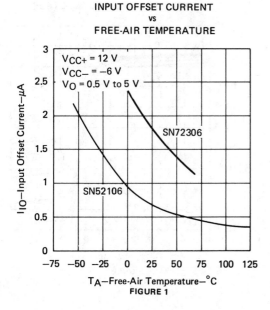

FIGURE 1

INPUT BIAS CURRENT
vs
FREE-AIR TEMPERATURE

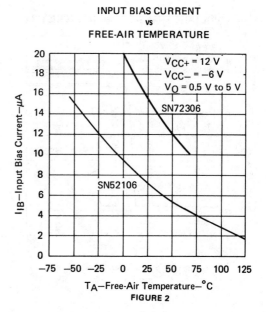

FIGURE 2

TYPICAL CHARACTERISTICS [‡]

HIGH-LEVEL OUTPUT VOLTAGE
vs
FREE-AIR TEMPERATURE

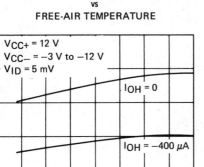
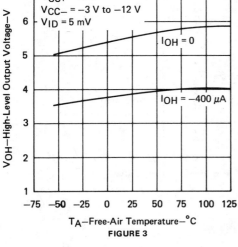

FIGURE 3

LOW-LEVEL OUTPUT VOLTAGE
vs
FREE-AIR TEMPERATURE

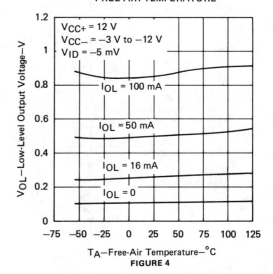

FIGURE 4

VOLTAGE TRANSFER CHARACTERISTICS

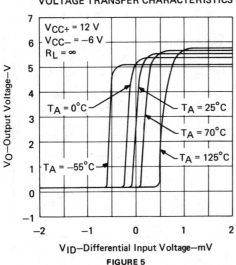

FIGURE 5

OUTPUT CURRENT
vs
DIFFERENTIAL INPUT VOLTAGE

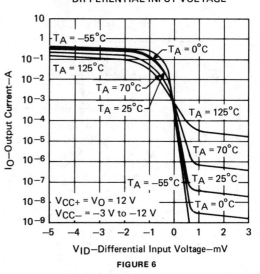

FIGURE 6

[‡]Data for temperatures below 0°C and above 70°C is applicable to SN52106 circuits only.

TEXAS INSTRUMENTS
INCORPORATED
POST OFFICE BOX 5012 • DALLAS, TEXAS 75222

TYPICAL CHARACTERISTICS[‡]

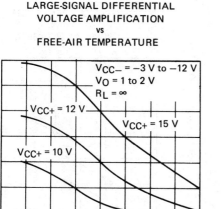

LARGE-SIGNAL DIFFERENTIAL
VOLTAGE AMPLIFICATION
vs
FREE-AIR TEMPERATURE

$V_{CC-} = -3$ V to -12 V
$V_O = 1$ to 2 V
$R_L = \infty$

$V_{CC+} = 12$ V
$V_{CC+} = 15$ V
$V_{CC+} = 10$ V

FIGURE 7

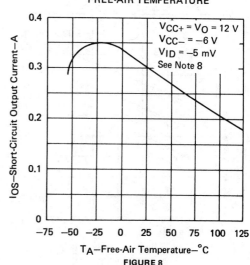

SHORT-CIRCUIT OUTPUT CURRENT
vs
FREE-AIR TEMPERATURE

$V_{CC+} = V_O = 12$ V
$V_{CC-} = -6$ V
$V_{ID} = -5$ mV
See Note 8

FIGURE 8

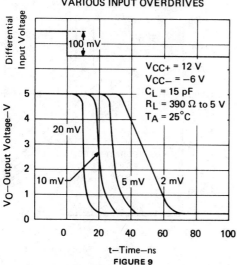

OUTPUT RESPONSE FOR
VARIOUS INPUT OVERDRIVES

100 mV

$V_{CC+} = 12$ V
$V_{CC-} = -6$ V
$C_L = 15$ pF
$R_L = 390$ Ω to 5 V
$T_A = 25°C$

20 mV
10 mV
5 mV
2 mV

FIGURE 9

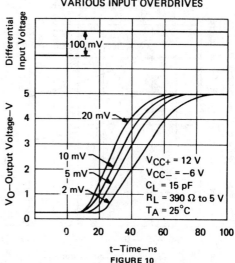

OUTPUT RESPONSE FOR
VARIOUS INPUT OVERDRIVES

100 mV

20 mV
10 mV
5 mV
2 mV

$V_{CC+} = 12$ V
$V_{CC-} = -6$ V
$C_L = 15$ pF
$R_L = 390$ Ω to 5 V
$T_A = 25°C$

FIGURE 10

[‡]Data for temperatures below 0°C and above 70°C is applicable to SN52106 circuits only
NOTE 8: This parameter was measured using a single 5-ms pulse.

TYPICAL CHARACTERISTICS ‡

SUPPLY CURRENT FROM V$_{CC+}$
vs
SUPPLY VOLTAGE V$_{CC+}$

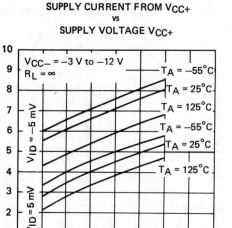

FIGURE 11

SUPPLY CURRENT FROM V$_{CC-}$
vs
SUPPLY VOLTAGE V$_{CC-}$

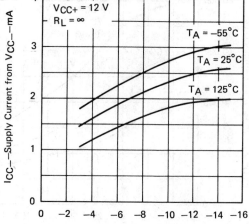

FIGURE 12

TOTAL POWER DISSIPATION
vs
FREE-AIR TEMPERATURE

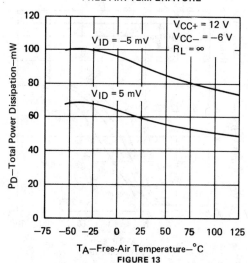

FIGURE 13

‡Data for temperatures below 0°C and above 70°C is applicable to SN52106 circuits only.

THERMAL INFORMATION

DISSIPATION DERATING CURVE

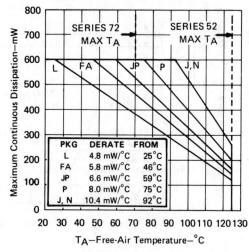

PKG	DERATE	FROM
L	4.8 mW/°C	25°C
FA	5.8 mW/°C	46°C
JP	6.6 mW/°C	59°C
P	8.0 mW/°C	75°C
J, N	10.4 mW/°C	92°C

FIGURE 14

PRINTED IN U.S.A.

TEXAS INSTRUMENTS
INCORPORATED
POST OFFICE BOX 5012 • DALLAS, TEXAS 75222

LINEAR
INTEGRATED CIRCUITS

TYPES SN52111, SN72311
DIFFERENTIAL COMPARATORS WITH STROBE

BULLETIN NO. DL-S 7311797, SEPTEMBER 1973

- Fast Response Times
- Strobe Capability
- SN52111 and SN72311 Designed to be Interchangeable with National Semiconductor LM111 and LM311, Respectively

- Maximum Input Bias Current . . . 300 nA
- Maximum Input Offset Current . . . 70 nA
- Can Operate From Single 5-V Supply

description

The SN52111 and SN72311 are single high-speed voltage comparators. These devices are designed to operate from a wide range of power supply voltage, including ±15-volt supplies for operational amplifiers and 5-volt supplies for logic systems. The output levels are compatible with most DTL, TTL, and MOS circuits. These comparators are capable of driving lamps or relays and switching voltages up to 50 volts at 50 milliamperes. All inputs and outputs can be isolated from system ground. The outputs can drive loads referenced to ground, V_{CC+}, or V_{CC-}. Offset balancing and strobe capability are available and the outputs can be wire-OR connected. If the strobe input is low, the output will be in the off state regardless of the differential input. Although slower than the SN52506 and SN52514, these devices are not as sensitive to spurious oscillations.

The SN52111 is characterized for operation over the full military temperature range of −55°C to 125°C; the SN72311 is characterized for operation from 0°C to 70°C.

terminal assignments

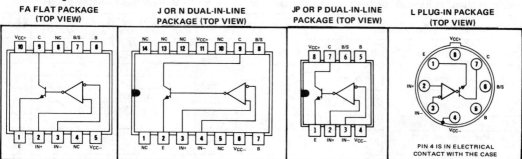

FA FLAT PACKAGE (TOP VIEW)

J OR N DUAL-IN-LINE PACKAGE (TOP VIEW)

JP OR P DUAL-IN-LINE PACKAGE (TOP VIEW)

L PLUG-IN PACKAGE (TOP VIEW)

PIN 4 IS IN ELECTRICAL CONTACT WITH THE CASE

schematic

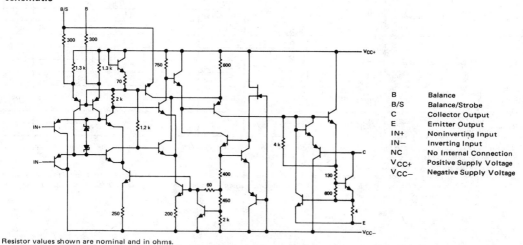

B	Balance
B/S	Balance/Strobe
C	Collector Output
E	Emitter Output
IN+	Noninverting Input
IN−	Inverting Input
NC	No Internal Connection
V_{CC+}	Positive Supply Voltage
V_{CC-}	Negative Supply Voltage

Resistor values shown are nominal and in ohms.

TEXAS INSTRUMENTS
INCORPORATED
POST OFFICE BOX 5012 • DALLAS, TEXAS 75222

6-9

TYPES SN52111, SN72311,
DIFFERENTIAL COMPARATORS WITH STROBE

absolute maximum ratings over operating free-air temperature range (unless otherwise noted)

		SN52111	SN72111	UNIT
Supply voltage, V_{CC+} (see Note 1)		18	18	V
Supply voltage, V_{CC-} (see Note 1)		−18	−18	V
Differential input voltage (see Note 2)		±30	±30	V
Input voltage (either input, see Notes 1 and 3)		±15	±15	V
Voltage from emitter output to V_{CC-}		30	30	V
Voltage from collector output to V_{CC-}		50	40	V
Duration of output short-circuit (see Note 4)		10	10	s
Continuous total dissipation at (or below) 25°C free-air temperature (see Note 5)		500	500	mW
Operating free-air temperature range		−55 to 125	0 to 70	°C
Storage temperature range		−65 to 150	−65 to 150	°C
Lead temperature 1/16 inch from case for 10 seconds	FA, J, JP or L package	300	300	°C
Lead temperature 1/16 inch from case for 60 seconds	N or P package	260	260	°C

NOTES: 1. All voltage values, unless otherwise noted, are with respect to the zero-reference level (ground) of the supply voltages where the zero-reference level is at the midpoint between V_{CC+} and V_{CC-}. If the zero-reference level of the system is not the midpoint of the supply voltages, all voltage values must be adjusted accordingly.
2. Differential voltages are at the noninverting input terminal with respect to the inverting input terminal.
3. The magnitude of the input voltage must never exceed the magnitude of the supply voltage or ±15 V, whichever is less.
4. The output may be shorted to ground or either power supply.
5. For operation above 25°C free-air temperature, refer to Dissipation Derating Curve, Figure 11.

electrical characteristics at specified free-air temperature, $V_{CC\pm} = \pm 15$ V (unless otherwise noted)

PARAMETER		TEST CONDITIONS[†]			SN52111 MIN	TYP[‡]	MAX	SN72311 MIN	TYP[‡]	MAX	UNIT
V_{IO}	Input offset voltage	$R_S \leqslant 50$ kΩ,	See Note 6	25°C		0.7	3		2	7.5	mV
				Full range			4			10	
I_{IO}	Input offset current	See Note 6		25°C		4	10		6	50	nA
				Full range			20			70	
I_{IB}	Input bias current	$V_O = 1$ V to 14 V		25°C		75	100		100	250	nA
				Full range			150			300	
I_{SL}	Low-level strobe current	$V_{(strobe)} = 0.3$ V, $V_{ID} \leqslant -10$ mV		25°C		−3			−3		mA
V_{ICR}	Common-mode input voltage range	$V_{CC-} = -15$ V		Full range		±14			±14		V
A_{VD}	Large-signal differential voltage amplification	$V_O = 5$ V to 35 V, $R_L = 1$ kΩ		25°C		200,000			200,000		
I_{OH}	High-level output current	$V_{ID} = 5$ mV,	$V_{OH} = 35$ V	25°C		0.2	10				nA
				Full range			0.5				µA
		$V_{ID} = 10$ mV	$V_{OH} = 35$ V	25°C					0.2	50	nA
V_{OL}	Low-level output voltage	$I_{OL} = 50$ mA	$V_{ID} = -5$ mV	25°C		0.75	1.5				V
			$V_{ID} = -10$ mV	25°C					0.75	1.5	
		$I_{OL} = 8$ mA	$V_{ID} = -6$ mV	Full range		0.23	0.4				
			$V_{ID} = -10$ mV	Full range					0.23	0.4	
I_{CC+}	Supply current from V_{CC+}, output low	$V_{ID} = -10$ mV,	No load	25°C		5.1	6		5.1	7.5	mA
I_{CC-}	Supply current from V_{CC-}, output high	$V_{ID} = 10$ mV,	No load	25°C		−4.1	−5		−4.1	−5	mA

[†]Unless otherwise noted, all characteristics are measured with the balance and balance/strobe terminals open and the emitter output grounded.
Full range for SN52111 is −55°C to 125°C and for SN72311 is 0°C to 70°C.
[‡]All typical values are at $T_A = 25$°C.
NOTE 6: The offset voltages and offset currents given are the maximum values required to drive the collector output up to 14 V or down to 1 V with a pull-up resistor of 7.5 kΩ to V_{CC+}. Thus these parameters actually define an error band and take into account the worst-case effects of voltage gain and input impedance.

TEXAS INSTRUMENTS
INCORPORATED
POST OFFICE BOX 5012 • DALLAS, TEXAS 75222

switching characteristics, V_{CC+} = 15 V, V_{CC-} = −15 V, T_A = 25°C

PARAMETER	TEST CONDITIONS	MIN	TYP	MAX	UNIT
Response time, low-to-high-level output	R_C = 500 Ω to 5 V, C_L = 5 pF, See Note 7		115		ns
Response time, high-to-low-level output			165		ns

NOTE 7: The response time specified is for a 100-mV input step with 5-mV overdrive. The typical values are specified for a nominal threshold voltage of 1.4 V.

DEFINITION OF TERMS

Input Offset Voltage (V_{IO}) The d-c voltage that must be applied between the input terminals to force the quiescent d-c output voltage to the specified level. The input offset voltage may also be defined for the case where two equal resistances (R_S) are inserted in series with the input leads.

Input Offset Current (I_{IO}) The difference between the currents into the two input terminals with the output at the specified level.

Input Bias Current (I_{IB}) The average of the currents into the two input terminals with the output at the specified level.

Low-Level Strobe Current (I_{SL}) The current flowing out of the strobe at a low-level voltage.

Common-Mode Input Voltage Range (V_{ICR}) The range of common-mode voltage that if exceeded will cause the comparator to cease functioning properly.

Large-Signal Differential Voltage Amplification (A_{VD}) The ratio of the change in output voltage to the change in differential input voltage producing it.

High-Level Output Current (I_{OH}) The current flowing into the collector output with a specified high-level output voltage, V_{OH}, applied.

Low-Level Output Voltage (V_{OL}) The voltage at the collector output with the emitter output grounded and the specified input conditions applied that should establish a low level at the output.

Response Time, Low-To-High-Level Output The interval between the application of an input step function and the time when the output crosses the specified threshold voltage. The input step drives the comparator from some initial condition sufficient to saturate the output to an input level just barely in excess of that required to bring the output back to the specified threshold voltage. This excess is referred to as the voltage overdrive.

Response Time, High-To-Low-Level Output The interval between the application of an input step function and the time when the output crosses the specified threshold voltage. The input step drives the comparator from some initial condition sufficient to turn the output off to an input level just barely in excess of that required to bring the output back to the specified threshold voltage. This excess is referred to as the voltage overdrive.

6

TEXAS INSTRUMENTS
INCORPORATED
POST OFFICE BOX 5012 • DALLAS, TEXAS 75222

TYPICAL CHARACTERISTICS

INPUT OFFSET CURRENT
vs
FREE-AIR TEMPERATURE

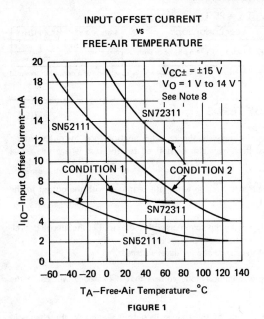

FIGURE 1

INPUT BIAS CURRENT
vs
FREE-AIR TEMPERATURE

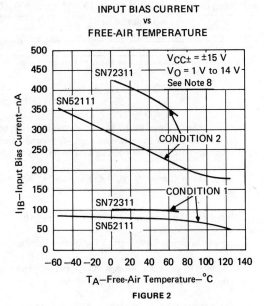

FIGURE 2

VOLTAGE TRANSFER CHARACTERISTICS

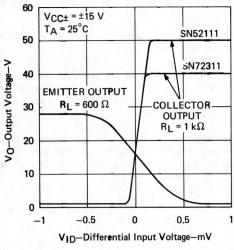

FIGURE 3

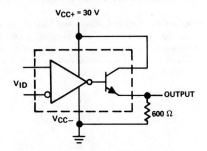

**COLLECTOR OUTPUT TRANSFER CHARACTERISTIC
TEST CIRCUIT FOR FIGURE 3**

**EMITTER OUTPUT TRANSFER CHARACTERISTIC
TEST CIRCUIT FOR FIGURE 3**

NOTE 8: Condition 1 is with the balance and balance/strobe terminals open. Condition 2 is with the balance and balance/strobe terminals connected to V_{CC+}.

TEXAS INSTRUMENTS
INCORPORATED
POST OFFICE BOX 5012 • DALLAS, TEXAS 75222

TYPICAL CHARACTERISTICS

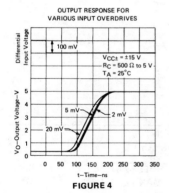

TEST CIRCUIT FOR FIGURES 4 AND 5

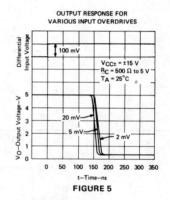

TEST CIRCUIT FOR FIGURES 6 AND 7

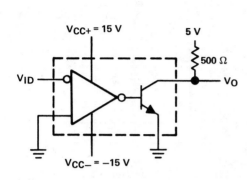

FIGURE 4

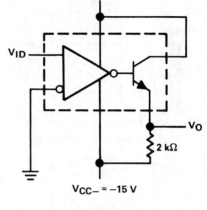

FIGURE 5

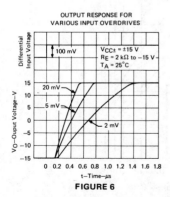

FIGURE 6

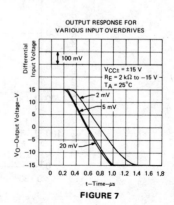

FIGURE 7

TYPICAL CHARACTERISTICS

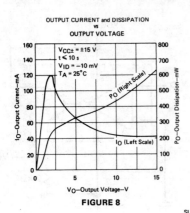

FIGURE 8

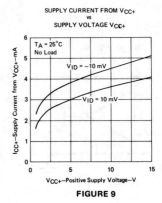

FIGURE 9

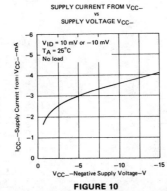

FIGURE 10

THERMAL INFORMATION
DISSIPATION DERATING CURVE

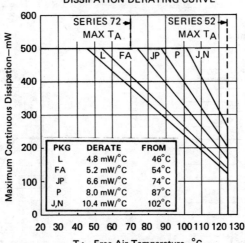

PKG	DERATE	FROM
L	4.8 mW/°C	46°C
FA	5.2 mW/°C	54°C
JP	6.6 mW/°C	74°C
P	8.0 mW/°C	87°C
J,N	10.4 mW/°C	102°C

FIGURE 11

TEXAS INSTRUMENTS
INCORPORATED
POST OFFICE BOX 5012 • DALLAS, TEXAS 75222

TYPICAL APPLICATION DATA

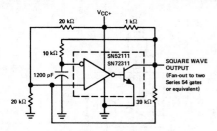

FIGURE 12—100-kHz
FREE-RUNNING MULTIVIBRATOR

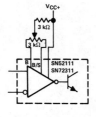

FIGURE 13
OFFSET BALANCING

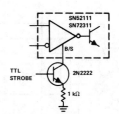

FIGURE 14—STROBING

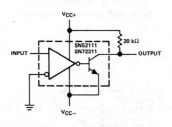

FIGURE 15—ZERO-CROSSING DETECTOR

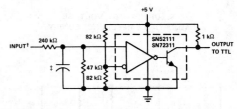

† Resistor values shown are for a 0-to-30-V logic swing and a
15-V threshold.
‡ May be added to control speed and reduce susceptibility
to noise spikes.

FIGURE 16—TTL INTERFACE WITH HIGH-LEVEL LOGIC

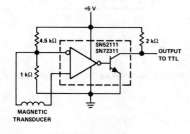

FIGURE 17—DETECTOR FOR MAGNETIC TRANSDUCER

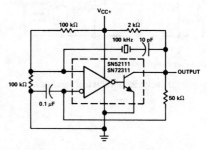

FIGURE 18—100-kHz CRYSTAL OSCILLATOR

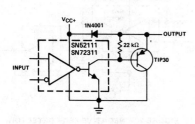

FIGURE 19—COMPARATOR AND SOLENOID DRIVER

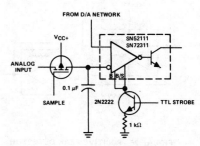

Typical input current is 50 pA with inputs strobed off.

FIGURE 20—STROBING BOTH INPUT AND
OUTPUT STAGES SIMULTANEOUSLY

6

TYPICAL APPLICATION DATA

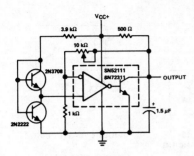

**FIGURE 21—LOW-VOLTAGE
ADJUSTABLE REFERENCE SUPPLY**

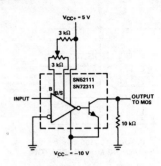

**FIGURE 22— ZERO-CROSSING
DETECTOR DRIVING MOS LOGIC**

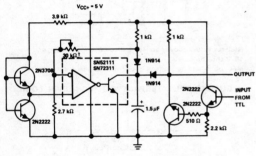

†Adjust to set clamp level.

FIGURE 23—PRECISION SQUARER

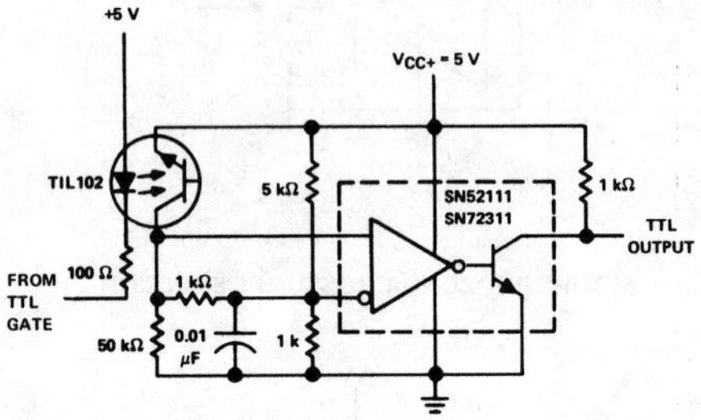

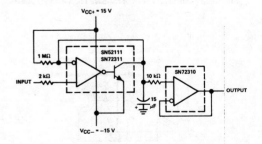

FIGURE 24—DIGITAL TRANSMISSION ISOLATOR

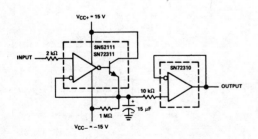

FIGURE 25— POSITIVE-PEAK DETECTOR

FIGURE 26— NEGATIVE-PEAK DETECTOR

TEXAS INSTRUMENTS
INCORPORATED
POST OFFICE BOX 5012 • DALLAS, TEXAS 75222

TYPICAL APPLICATIONS DATA

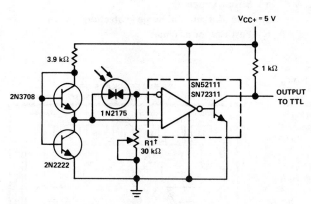

† R1 sets the comparision level. At comparision, the photodiode has less than 5 mV across it, decreasing dark current
by an order of magnitude.

FIGURE 27—PRECISION PHOTODIODE COMPARATOR

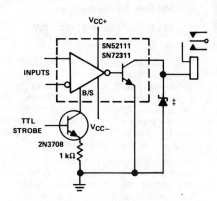

‡Transient voltage and inductive kickback protection.

FIGURE 28—RELAY DRIVER WITH STROBE

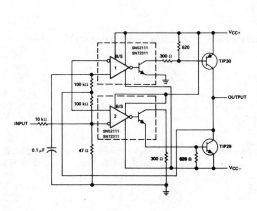

FIGURE 29—SWITCHING POWER AMPLIFIER

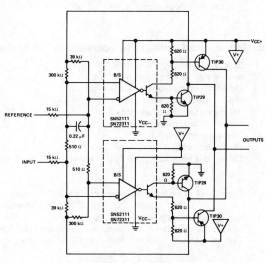

FIGURE 30—SWITCHING POWER AMPLIFIERS

TEXAS INSTRUMENTS
INCORPORATED
POST OFFICE BOX 5012 • DALLAS, TEXAS 75222

LINEAR
INTEGRATED CIRCUITS

TYPES SN52506, SN72506
DUAL DIFFERENTIAL COMPARATORS
WITH STROBES

BULLETIN NO. DL-S 7311671, MARCH 1972–REVISED SEPTEMBER 1973

- Each Comparator Identical to SN52106 or SN72306 with Common V_{CC+}, V_{CC-}, and Ground Connections
- Improved Gain and Accuracy
- Fan-Out to 10 Series 54/74 TTL Loads
- Strobe Capability
- Short-Circuit and Surge Protection
- Fast Response Times

description

The SN52506 and SN72506 are dual high-speed voltage comparators, with each half having differential inputs, a low-impedance output with high-sink-current capability (100 mA), and two strobe inputs. These devices detect low-level analog or digital signals and can drive digital logic or lamps and relays directly. Short-circuit protection and surge-current limiting is provided.

The circuit is similar to an SN52810/SN72810 with gated output. A low-level input at either strobe causes the output to remain high regardless of the differential input. When both strobe inputs are either open or at a high logic level, the output voltage is controlled by the differential input voltage. The circuit will operate with any negative supply voltage between −3 V and −12 V with little difference in performance.

The SN52506 is characterized for operation over the full military temperature range of −55°C to 125°C; the SN72506 is characterized for operation from 0°C to 70°C.

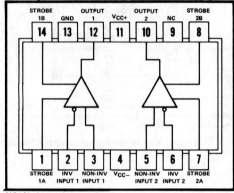

FA FLAT PACKAGE OR
J OR N DUAL-IN-LINE PACKAGE (TOP VIEW)

NC—No internal connection

absolute maximum ratings over operating free-air temperature range (unless otherwise noted)

Supply voltage V_{CC+} (see Note 1)	15 V
Supply voltage V_{CC-} (see Note 1)	−15 V
Differential input voltage (see Note 2)	±5 V
Input voltage (any input, see Notes 1 and 3)	±7 V
Strobe voltage range (see Note 1)	0 V to V_{CC+}
Output voltage (see Note 1)	24 V
Voltage from output to V_{CC-}	30 V
Duration of output short-circuit (see Note 4)	10 s
Continuous total dissipation at (or below) 25°C free-air temperature (see Note 5): Each amplifier	600 mW
Total: FA package	725 mW
J or N package	800 mW
Operating free-air temperature range: SN52506 Circuits	−55°C to 125°C
SN72506 Circuits	0°C to 70°C
Storage temperature range	−65°C to 150°C
Lead temperature 1/16 inch from case for 60 seconds: FA or J package	300°C
Lead temperature 1/16 inch from case for 10 seconds: N package	260°C

NOTES: 1. All voltage values, except differential voltages and the voltage from the output to V_{CC-}, are with respect to the network ground terminal.

2. Differential voltages are at the noninverting input terminal with respect to the inverting input terminal.

3. The magnitude of the input voltage must never exceed the magnitude of the supply voltage or 7 volts, whichever is less.

4. One output at a time may be shorted to ground or either power supply.

5. For operation above 25°C free-air temperature, refer to Dissipation Derating Curve, Figure 14.

TEXAS INSTRUMENTS
INCORPORATED

POST OFFICE BOX 5012 • DALLAS, TEXAS 75222

electrical characteristics at specified free-air temperature, V_{CC+} = 12 V, V_{CC-} = −3 V to −12 V (unless otherwise noted)

PARAMETER		TEST CONDITIONS[†]		SN52506			SN72506			UNIT
				MIN	TYP	MAX	MIN	TYP	MAX	
V_{IO}	Input offset voltage	See Note 6	25°		0.5[§]	2		1.6[§]	5	mV
			Full range			3			6.5	
α_{VIO}	Average temperature coefficient of input offset voltage	See Note 6	Full range		3	10		5	20	µV/°C
I_{IO}	Input offset current	See Note 6	25°C		0.7[§]	3		1.8[§]	5	µA
			MIN		2	7		1	7.5	
			MAX		0.4	3		0.5		
α_{IIO}	Average temperature coefficient of input offset current	See Note 6	MIN to 25°C		15	75		24	100	nA/°C
			25°C to MAX		5	25		15	50	
I_{IB}	Input bias current	V_O = 0.5 V to 5 V	25°C		7[§]	20		16[§]	25	µA
			Full range			45			40	
I_{SL}	Low-level strobe current	$V_{(strobe)}$ = 0.4 V	Full range		−1.7[§]	−3.3		−1.7[§]	−3.3	mA
$V_{IH(strobe)}$	High-level strobe voltage		Full range	2.5			2.5			V
$V_{IL(strobe)}$	Low-level strobe voltage		Full range			0.9			0.9	V
V_{ICR}	Common-mode input voltage range	V_{CC-} = −7 V to −12 V	Full range	±5			±5			V
V_{ID}	Differential input voltage range		Full range	±5			±5			V
A_{VD}	Large-signal differential voltage amplification	No load, V_O = 0.5 V to 5 V	25°C		40 000[§]			40 000[§]		
V_{OH}	High-level output voltage	V_{ID} = 5 mV, I_{OH} = −400 µA	Full range	2.5		5.5	2.5		5.5	V
V_{OL}	Low-level output voltage	V_{ID} = −5 mV, I_{OL} = 100 mA	25°C		0.8[§]	1.5		0.8[§]	2	V
		V_{ID} = −5 mV, I_{OL} = 50 mA	Full range			1			1	
		V_{ID} = −5 mV, I_{OL} = 16 mA	Full range			0.4			0.4	
I_{OH}	High-level output current	V_{ID} = 5 mV, V_{OH} = 8 V to 24 V	25°C		0.02[§]	1		0.02[§]	2	µA
			Full range			100			100	
I_{CC+}	Supply current from V_{CC+}	V_{ID} = −5 mV, See Note 7	Full range		13.9[§]	20		13.9[§]	20	mA
I_{CC-}	Supply current from V_{CC-}	See Note 7	Full range		3.2[§]	7.2		3.2[§]	7.2	mA

[†]Unless otherwise noted, all characteristics are measured with the strobe open.

[§]These typical values are at V_{CC+} = 12 V, V_{CC-} = −6 V, T_A = 25°C. Full range (MIN to MAX) for SN52506 is −55°C to 125°C and for the SN72506 is 0°C to 70°C.

NOTES: 6. The offset voltages and offset currents given are the maximum values required to drive the output down to the low range (V_{OL}) or up to the high range (V_{OH}). Thus these parameters actually define an error band and take into account the worst-case effects of voltage gain and input impedance.

7. Power supply currents are measured with the respective non-inverting inputs and inverting inputs of both comparators connected in parallel. The outputs are open.

switching characteristics, V_{CC+} = 12 V, V_{CC-} = −6 V, T_A = 25°C

PARAMETER	TEST CONDITIONS[†]	SN52506			SN72506			UNIT
		MIN	TYP	MAX	MIN	TYP	MAX	
Response time, low-to-high-level output	R_L = 390 Ω to 5 V, C_L = 15 pF, See Note 8		28	40		28		ns

NOTE 8: The response time specified is for a 100-mV input step with 5-mV overdrive. The typical value is specified for a nominal threshold voltage of 1.4 V.

6

DEFINITION OF TERMS

Input Offset Voltage (V_{IO}) The d-c voltage which must be applied between the input terminals to force the quiescent d-c output voltage to the specified level.

Average Temperature Coefficient of Input Offset Voltage (α_{VIO}) The ratio of the change in input offset voltage to the change in free-air temperature. This is an average value for the specified temperature range.

$$\alpha_{VIO} = \left| \frac{(V_{IO} @ T_{A(1)}) - (V_{IO} @ T_{A(2)})}{T_{A(1)} - T_{A(2)}} \right| \text{ where } T_{A(1)} \text{ and } T_{A(2)} \text{ are the specified temperature extremes.}$$

Input Offset Current (I_{IO}) The difference between the currents into the two input terminals with the output at the specified level.

Average Temperature Coefficient of Input Offset Current (α_{IIO}) The ratio of the change in input offset current to the change in free-air temperature. This is an average value for the specified temperature range.

$$\alpha_{IIO} = \left| \frac{(I_{IO} @ T_{A(1)}) - (I_{IO} @ T_{A(2)})}{T_{A(1)} - T_{A(2)}} \right| \text{ where } T_{A(1)} \text{ and } T_{A(2)} \text{ are the specified temperature extremes.}$$

Input Bias Current (I_{IB}) The average of the currents into the two input terminals with the output at the specified level.

Low-Level Strobe Current (I_{SL}) The current flowing out of the strobe at a low-level voltage.

High-Level Strobe Voltage ($V_{IH(strobe)}$) A voltage within the range that is guaranteed not to interfere with the operation of the comparator.

Low-Level Strobe Voltage ($V_{IL(strobe)}$) A voltage within the range that is guaranteed to force the output high independently of the differential inputs.

Common-Mode Input Voltage Range (V_{ICR}) The range of common-mode voltage which if exceeded will cause the comparator to cease functioning properly.

Differential Input Voltage Range (V_{ID}) The range of voltage between the two input terminals which if exceeded will cause the comparator to cease functioning properly.

Large-Signal Differential Voltage Amplification (A_{VD}) The ratio of the change in output voltage to the change in differential input voltage producing it.

High-Level Output Voltage (V_{OH}) The voltage at the output with the specified input conditions applied which should establish a high level at the output.

Low-Level Output Voltage (V_{OL}) The voltage at the output with the specified input conditions applied which should establish a low level at the output.

High-Level Output Current (I_{OH}) The current flowing into the output with a specified high-level output voltage, V_{OH}, applied.

Response Time, Low-To-High-Level Output The interval between the application of an input step function and the time when the output crosses the logic threshold voltage. The input step drives the comparator from some initial condition sufficient to saturate the output to an input level just barely in excess of that required to bring the output back to the logic threshold voltage. This excess is referred to as the voltage overdrive.

TEXAS INSTRUMENTS
INCORPORATED
POST OFFICE BOX 5012 • DALLAS, TEXAS 75222

schematic (each comparator)

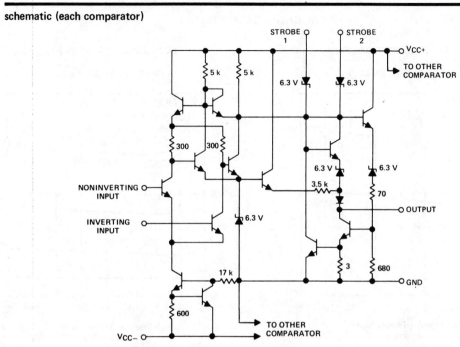

Resistor values are nominal in ohms.

TYPICAL CHARACTERISTICS

INPUT OFFSET CURRENT
vs
FREE-AIR TEMPERATURE

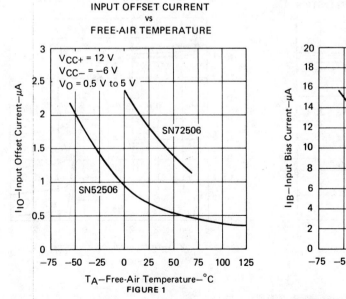

FIGURE 1

INPUT BIAS CURRENT
vs
FREE-AIR TEMPERATURE

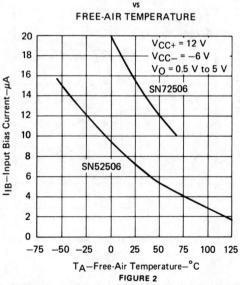

FIGURE 2

TYPICAL CHARACTERISTICS‡

HIGH-LEVEL OUTPUT VOLTAGE
vs
FREE-AIR TEMPERATURE

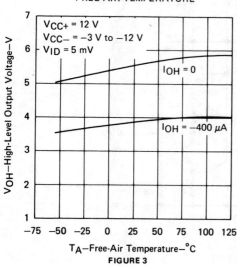

FIGURE 3

LOW-LEVEL OUTPUT VOLTAGE
vs
FREE-AIR TEMPERATURE

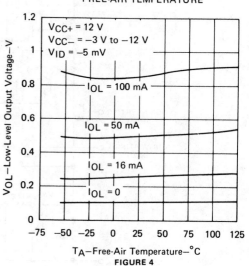

FIGURE 4

VOLTAGE TRANSFER CHARACTERISTICS

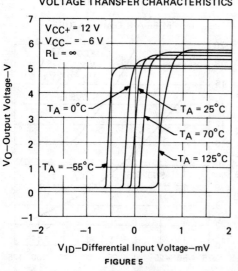

FIGURE 5

OUTPUT CURRENT
vs
DIFFERENTIAL INPUT VOLTAGE

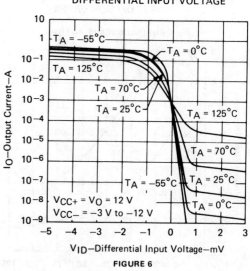

FIGURE 6

‡Data for temperatures below 0°C and above 70°C is applicable to SN52506 circuits only.

TEXAS INSTRUMENTS
INCORPORATED
POST OFFICE BOX 5012 • DALLAS, TEXAS 75222

TYPICAL CHARACTERISTICS‡

LARGE-SIGNAL DIFFERENTIAL
VOLTAGE AMPLIFICATION
vs
FREE-AIR TEMPERATURE

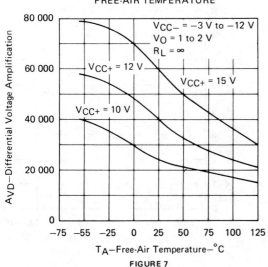

FIGURE 7

SHORT-CIRCUIT OUTPUT CURRENT
vs
FREE-AIR TEMPERATURE

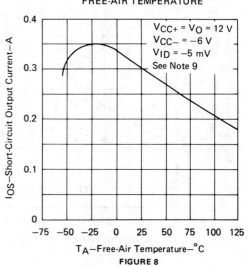

FIGURE 8

OUTPUT RESPONSE FOR
VARIOUS INPUT OVERDRIVES

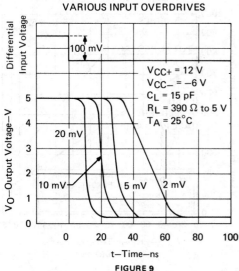

FIGURE 9

OUTPUT RESPONSE FOR
VARIOUS INPUT OVERDRIVES

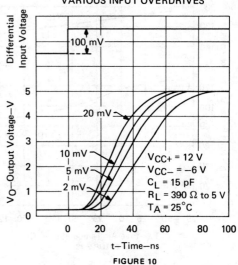

FIGURE 10

‡Data for temperatures below 0°C and above 70°C is applicable to SN52506 circuits only.

NOTE 9: This parameter was measured using a single 5-ms pulse.

TYPCIAL CHARACTERISTICS‡

SUPPLY CURRENT FROM V$_{CC+}$
vs
SUPPLY VOLTAGE V$_{CC+}$

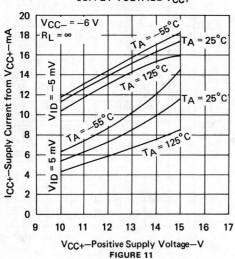

FIGURE 11

SUPPLY CURRENT FROM V$_{CC-}$
vs
SUPPLY VOLTAGE V$_{CC-}$

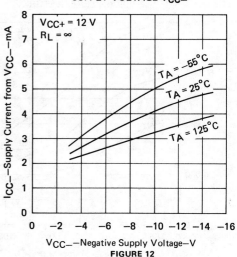

FIGURE 12

TOTAL POWER DISSIPATION
vs
FREE-AIR TEMPERATURE

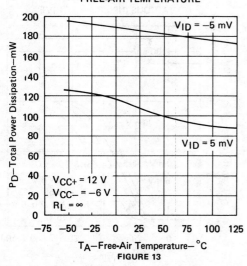

FIGURE 13

THERMAL INFORMATION

DISSIPATION DERATING CURVE

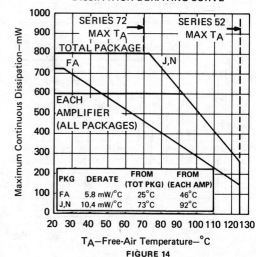

PKG	DERATE	FROM (TOT PKG)	FROM (EACH AMP)
FA	5.8 mW/°C	25°C	46°C
J,N	10.4 mW/°C	73°C	92°C

FIGURE 14

‡Data for temperatures below 0°C and above 70°C is applicable to SN52506 circuits only.

PRINTED IN U.S.A.

TEXAS INSTRUMENTS
INCORPORATED
POST OFFICE BOX 5012 • DALLAS, TEXAS 75222

TEXAS INSTRUMENTS RESERVES THE RIGHT TO MAKE CHANGES AT ANY TIM
IN ORDER TO IMPROVE DESIGN AND TO SUPPLY THE BEST PRODUCT POSSIBL

6

LINEAR
INTEGRATED CIRCUITS

TYPES SN52510, SN72510
DIFFERENTIAL COMPARATORS WITH STROBE
BULLETIN NO. DL-S 7311452, MARCH 1971—REVISED SEPTEMBER 1973

- Low Offset Characteristics
- High Differential Voltage Amplification
- Fast Response Times
- Output Compatible with Most TTL and DTL Circuits

schematic

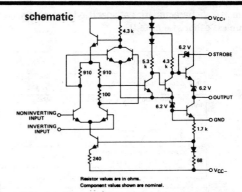

Resistor values are in ohms.
Component values shown are nominal.

description

The SN52510 and SN72510 monolithic high-speed voltage comparators are improved versions of the SN52710 and SN72710 with an extra stage added to increase voltage amplification and accuracy, and a strobe input for greater flexibility. Typical voltage amplification is 33,000. Since the output cannot be more positive than the strobe, a low-level input at the strobe will cause the output to go low regardless of the differential input. Component matching, inherent in integrated circuit fabrication techniques, produces a comparator with low-drift and low-offset characteristics. These circuits are particularly useful for applications requiring an amplitude discriminator, memory sense amplifier, or a high-speed limit detector.

The SN52510 is characterized for operation over the full military temperature range of −55°C to 125°C; the SN72510 is characterized for operation from 0°C to 70°C.

terminal assignments

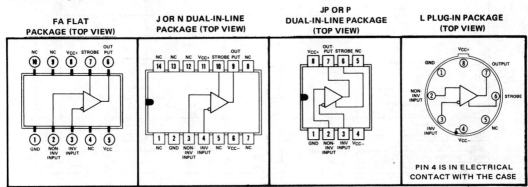

FA FLAT PACKAGE (TOP VIEW)

J OR N DUAL-IN-LINE PACKAGE (TOP VIEW)

JP OR P DUAL-IN-LINE PACKAGE (TOP VIEW)

L PLUG-IN PACKAGE (TOP VIEW)

PIN 4 IS IN ELECTRICAL CONTACT WITH THE CASE

NC—No internal connection

absolute maximum ratings over operating free-air temperature range (unless otherwise noted)

Supply voltage V_{CC+} (see Note 1)	14 V
Supply voltage V_{CC-} (see Note 1)	−7 V
Differential input voltage (see Note 2)	±5 V
Input voltage (either input, see Note 1)	±7 V
Strobe Voltage (see Note 1)	6 V
Peak output current ($t_W \leqslant 1$ s)	10 mA
Continuous total power dissipation at (or below) 70°C free-air temperature (see Note 3)	300 mW
Operating free-air temperature range: SN52510 Circuits	−55°C to 125°C
SN72510 Circuits	0°C to 70°C
Storage temperature range	−65°C to 150°C
Lead temperature 1/16 inch from case for 60 seconds: FA, J, JP, or L package	300°C
Lead temperature 1/16 inch from case for 10 seconds: N or P package	260°C

NOTES: 1. All voltage values, except differential voltages, are with respect to the network ground terminal.
2. Differential voltages are at the noninverting input terminal with respect to the inverting input terminal.
3. For operation of the SN52510 above 70°C free-air temperature, refer to Dissipating Derating Curve, Figure 13.

73

TEXAS INSTRUMENTS
INCORPORATED
POST OFFICE BOX 5012 • DALLAS, TEXAS 75222

electrical characteristics at specified free-air temperature, V$_{CC+}$ = 12 V, V$_{CC-}$ = −6 V (unless otherwise noted)

PARAMETER		TEST CONDITIONS†		SN52510			SN72510			UNIT
				MIN	TYP	MAX	MIN	TYP	MAX	
V$_{IO}$	Input offset voltage	R$_S$ ⩽ 200 Ω,	25°C		0.6	2		1.6	3.5	mV
		See Note 4	Full range			3			4.5	
α$_{VIO}$	Average temperature coefficient of input offset voltage	R$_S$ = 50 Ω, See Note 4	MIN to 25°C		3	10		3	20	μV/°C
			25°C to MAX		3	10		3	20	
I$_{IO}$	Input offset current	See Note 4	25°C		0.75	3		1.8	5	μA
			MIN		1.8	7			7.5	
			MAX		0.25	3			7.5	
α$_{IIO}$	Average temperature coefficient of input offset current	See Note 4	MIN to 25°C		15	75		24	100	nA/°C
			25°C to MAX		5	25		15	50	
I$_{IB}$	Input bias current	See Note 4	25°C		7	15		7	20	μA
			MIN		12	25		9	30	
I$_{SH}$	High-level strobe current	V$_{(strobe)}$ = 5 V, V$_{ID}$ = −5 mV,	25°C			±100			±100	μA
I$_{SL}$	Low-level strobe current	V$_{(strobe)}$ = −100 mV, V$_{ID}$ = 5 mV,	25°C		−1	−2.5		−1	−2.5	mA
V$_{ICR}$	Common-mode input voltage range	V$_{CC-}$ = −7 V	Full range		±5			±5		V
V$_{ID}$	Differential input voltage range		Full range		±5			±5		V
A$_{VD}$	Large-signal differential voltage amplification	No load, V$_O$ = 0 to 2.5 V	25°C	12,500	33,000		10,000	33,000		
			Full range	10,000			8,000			
V$_{OH}$	High-level output voltage	V$_{ID}$ = 5 mV, I$_{OH}$ = 0	Full range		4§	5		4§	5	V
		V$_{ID}$ = 5 mV, I$_{OH}$ = −5 mA	Full range	2.5	3.6§		2.5	3.6§		
V$_{OL}$	Low-level output voltage	V$_{ID}$ = −5 mV, I$_{OL}$ = 0	Full range	−1	−0.5§	0‡	−1	−0.5§	0‡	V
		V$_{(strobe)}$ = 0.3 V, V$_{ID}$ = 5 mV, I$_{OL}$ = 0	Full range	−1		0‡	−1		0‡	V
I$_{OL}$	Low-level output current	V$_{ID}$ = −5 mV, V$_O$ = 0	25°C	2	2.4		1.6	2.4		mA
			MIN	1	2.3		0.5	2.4		
			MAX	0.5	2.3		0.5	2.4		
r$_o$	Output resistance	V$_O$ = 1.4 V	25°C		200			200		Ω
CMRR	Common-mode rejection ratio	R$_S$ ⩽ 200 Ω	Full range	80	100§		70	100§		dB
I$_{CC+}$	Supply current from V$_{CC+}$	V$_{ID}$ = −5 mV, No load	Full range		5.5§	9		5.5§	9	mA
I$_{CC-}$	Supply current from V$_{CC-}$		Full range		−3.5§	−7		−3.5§	−7	mA
P$_D$	Total power dissipation		Full range		90§	150		90§	150	mW

†Unless otherwise noted, all characteristics are measured with the strobe open. Full range (MIN to MAX) for SN52510 is −55°C to 125°C and for the SN72510 is 0°C to 70°C.

‡The algebraic convention where the most-positive (least-negative) limit is designated as maximum is used in this data sheet for logic levels only, e.g., when 0 V is the maximum, the minimum limit is a more-negative voltage.

§These typical values are at T$_A$ = 25°C.

NOTE 4: These characteristics are verified by measurements at the following temperatures and output voltage levels: for SN52510, V$_O$ = 1.8 V at T$_A$ = −55°C, V$_O$ = 1.4 V at T$_A$ = 25°C, and V$_O$ = 1V at T$_A$ = 125°C; for SN72510, V$_O$ = 1.5 V at T$_A$ = 0°C, V$_O$ = 1.4 V at 25°C, and V$_O$ = 1.2 V at T$_A$ = 70°C. These output voltage levels were selected to approximate the logic threshold voltages of the types of digital logic circuits these comparators are intended to drive.

switching characteristics, V$_{CC+}$ = 12 V, V$_{CC-}$ = −6 V, T$_A$ = 25°C

PARAMETER	TEST CONDITIONS			MIN	TYP	MAX	UNIT
Response time	R$_L$ = ∞,	C$_L$ = 5 pF,	See Note 5		30	80	ns
Strobe release time	R$_L$ = ∞,	C$_L$ = 5 pF,	See Note 6		5	25	ns

NOTES: 5. The response time specified is for a 100-mV input step with 5-mV overdrive.

6. For testing purposes, the input bias conditions are selected to produce an output voltage of 1.4 V. A 5-mV overdrive is then added to the input bias voltage to produce an output voltage which rises above 1.4 V. The time interval is measured from the 50% point of the strobe voltage curve to the point where the overdriven output voltage crosses the 1.4 V level.

TEXAS INSTRUMENTS
INCORPORATED
POST OFFICE BOX 5012 • DALLAS, TEXAS 75222

DEFINITION OF TERMS

Input Offset Voltage (V_{IO}) The d-c voltage which must be applied between the input terminals to force the quiescent d-c output voltage to the specified level. The input offset voltage may also be defined for the case where two equal resistances (R_S) are inserted in series with the input leads.

Average Temperature Coefficient of Input Offset Voltage (α_{VIO}) The ratio of the change in input offset voltage to the change in free-air temperature. This is an average value for the specified temperature range.

$$\alpha_{VIO} = \left| \frac{(V_{IO} @ T_{A(1)}) - (V_{IO} @ T_{A(2)})}{T_{A(1)} - T_{A(2)}} \right| \qquad \text{where } T_{A(1)} \text{ and } T_{A(2) } \text{ are the specified temperature extremes.}$$

Input Offset Current (I_{IO}) The difference between the currents into the two input terminals with the output at the specified level.

Average Temperature Coefficient of Input Offset Current (α_{IIO}) The ratio of the change in input offset current to the change in free-air temperature. This is an average value for the specified temperature range.

$$\alpha_{IIO} = \left| \frac{(I_{IO} @ T_{A(1)}) - (I_{IO} @ T_{A(2)})}{T_{A(1)} - T_{A(2)}} \right| \qquad \text{where } T_{A(1)} \text{ and } T_{A(2)} \text{ are the specified temperature extremes.}$$

Input Bias Current (I_{IB}) The average of the currents into the two input terminals with the output at the specified level.

High-Level Strobe Current (I_{SH}) The current flowing into or out of the strobe at a high-level voltage.

Low-Level Strobe Current (I_{SL}) The current flowing out of the strobe at a low-level voltage.

Common-Mode Input Voltage Range (V_{ICR}) The range of common-mode voltage which if exceeded will cause the comparator to cease functioning properly.

Differential Input Voltage Range (V_{ID}) The range of voltage between the two input terminals which if exceeded will cause the comparator to cease functioning properly.

Large-Signal Differential Voltage Amplification (A_{VD}) The ratio of the change in output voltage to the change in differential input voltage producing it.

High-Level Output Voltage (V_{OH}) The voltage at the output with the specified input conditions applied which should establish a high level at the output.

Low-Level Output Voltage (V_{OL}) The voltage at the output with the specified input conditions applied which should establish a low level at the output.

Low-Level Output Current (I_{OL}) The current flowing into the output at a specified low-level output voltage.

Output Resistance (r_o) The resistance between the output terminal and ground.

Common-Mode Rejection Ratio (CMRR) The ratio of differential voltage amplification to common-mode voltage amplification. This is measured by determining the ratio of a change in input common-mode voltage to the resulting change in input offset voltage.

Total Power Dissipation (P_D) The total d-c power supplied to the device less any power delivered from the device to a load. At no load: $P_D = V_{CC+} \cdot I_{CC+} + V_{CC-} \cdot I_{CC-}$.

Response Time The interval between the application of an input step function and the time when the output crosses the logic threshold voltage. The input step drives the comparator from some initial condition sufficient to saturate the output to an input level just barely in excess of that required to bring the output back to the logic threshold voltage. This excess is referred to as the voltage overdrive.

Strobe Release Time The time required for the output to rise to the logic threshold voltage after the strobe terminal has been driven from the low logic level to the high logic level. Appropriate input conditions are assumed.

TYPICAL CHARACTERISTICS

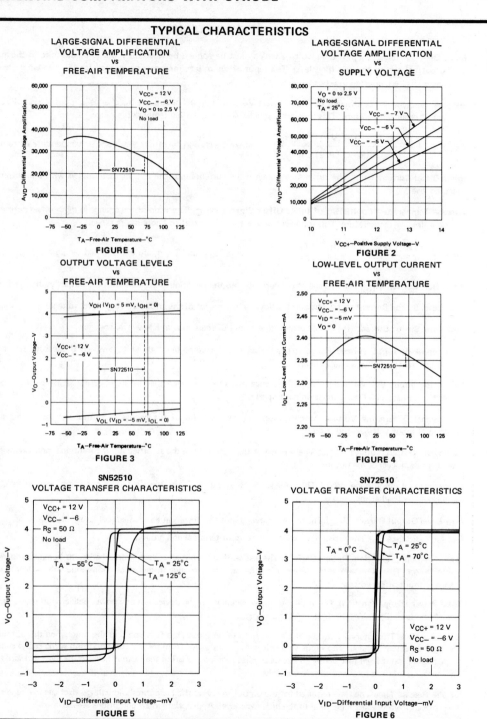

LARGE-SIGNAL DIFFERENTIAL
VOLTAGE AMPLIFICATION
vs
FREE-AIR TEMPERATURE

FIGURE 1

LARGE-SIGNAL DIFFERENTIAL
VOLTAGE AMPLIFICATION
vs
SUPPLY VOLTAGE

FIGURE 2

OUTPUT VOLTAGE LEVELS
vs
FREE-AIR TEMPERATURE

FIGURE 3

LOW-LEVEL OUTPUT CURRENT
vs
FREE-AIR TEMPERATURE

FIGURE 4

SN52510
VOLTAGE TRANSFER CHARACTERISTICS

FIGURE 5

SN72510
VOLTAGE TRANSFER CHARACTERISTICS

FIGURE 6

TEXAS INSTRUMENTS
INCORPORATED
POST OFFICE BOX 5012 • DALLAS, TEXAS 75222

TYPICAL CHARACTERISTICS

INPUT BIAS CURRENT
vs
FREE-AIR TEMPERATURE

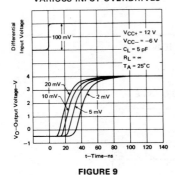

FIGURE 7

COMMON-MODE REJECTION RATIO
vs
FREE-AIR TEMPERATURE

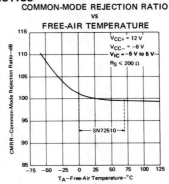

FIGURE 8

OUTPUT RESPONSE FOR
VARIOUS INPUT OVERDRIVES

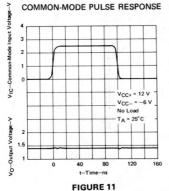

FIGURE 9

STROBE RELEASE TIME
FOR VARIOUS INPUT OVERDRIVES

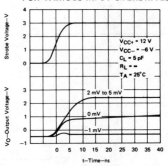

FIGURE 10

COMMON-MODE PULSE RESPONSE

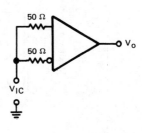

FIGURE 11

TEST CIRCUIT
FOR FIGURE 11

NOTE 4: These characteristics are verified by measurements at the following temperatures and output voltage levels: for SN52510, $V_O = 1.8$ V at $T_A = -55°$C, $V_O = 1.4$ V at $T_A = 25°$C, and $V_O = 1$V at $T_A = 125°$C; for SN72510, $V_O = 1.5$ V at $T_A = 0°$C, $V_O = 1.4$ V at 25°C, and $V_O = 1.2$ V at $T_A = 70°$C. These output voltage levels were selected to approximate the logic threshold voltages of the types of digital logic circuits these comparators are intended to drive.

TYPICAL CHARACTERISTICS

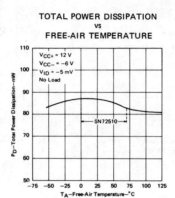

TOTAL POWER DISSIPATION
VS
FREE-AIR TEMPERATURE

FIGURE 12

THERMAL INFORMATION

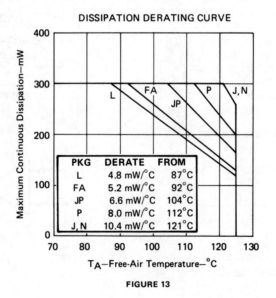

DISSIPATION DERATING CURVE

PKG	DERATE	FROM
L	4.8 mW/°C	87°C
FA	5.2 mW/°C	92°C
JP	6.6 mW/°C	104°C
P	8.0 mW/°C	112°C
J, N	10.4 mW/°C	121°C

FIGURE 13

TEXAS INSTRUMENTS
INCORPORATED
POST OFFICE BOX 5012 • DALLAS, TEXAS 75222

LINEAR INTEGRATED CIRCUITS

TYPES SN52514, SN72514
DUAL DIFFERENTIAL COMPARATORS WITH STROBES

BULLETIN NO. DL-S 7311451, MARCH 1971–REVISED SEPTEMBER 1973

- Fast Response Times
- High Differential Voltage Amplification
- Low Offset Characteristics
- Outputs Compatible with Most TTL and DTL Circuits

schematic (each comparator)

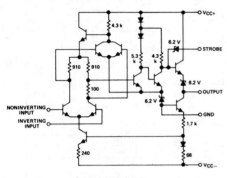

Resistor values are in ohms.
Component values shown are nominal.

J OR N
DUAL-IN-LINE PACKAGE (TOP VIEW)

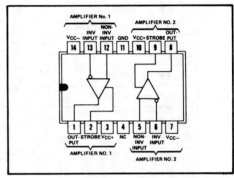

NC—No internal connection

description

The SN52514 and SN72514 are improved versions of the SN72720 dual high-speed voltage comparator. When compared with the SN72720, these circuits feature higher amplification (typically 33,000) due to an extra amplification stage, increased accuracy because of lower offset characterisitcs, and greater flexibility with the addition of a strobe to each comparator. Since the output cannot be more positive than the strobe, a low-level input at the strobe will cause the output to go low regardless of the differential input.

These circuits are especially useful in applications requiring an amplitude discriminator, memory sense amplifier, or a high-speed limit detector. The SN52514 is characterized for operation over the full military temperature range of −55°C to 125°C; the SN72514 is characterized for operation from 0°C to 70°C.

absolute maximum ratings over operating free-air temperature range (unless otherwise noted)

Supply voltage V_{CC+} (see Note 1) . . . . 14 V
Supply voltage V_{CC-} (see Note 1) . . . . −7 V
Differential input voltage (see Note 2) . . . . ±5 V
Input voltage (any input, see Note 1) . . . . ±7 V
Strobe voltage (see Note 1) . . . . 6 V
Peak output current ($t_w \leqslant 1$ s) . . . . 10 mA
Continuous total power dissipation: each comparator . . . . 300 mW
total package (see Note 3) . . . . 600 mW
Operating free-air temperature range: SN52514 Circuits . . . . −55°C to 125°C
SN72714 Circuits . . . . 0°C to 70°C
Storage temperature range . . . . −65°C to 150°C
Lead temperature 1/16 inch from case for 60 seconds: J package . . . . 300°C
Lead temperature 1/16 inch from case for 10 seconds: N package . . . . 260°C

NOTES: 1. All voltage values, except differential voltages, are with respect to the network ground terminal.
2. Differential voltages are at the noninverting input terminal with respect to the inverting input terminal.
3. For SN52514, this rating applies at (or below) 92°C free-air temperature. For operation above this temperature, derate linearly at the rate of 10.4 mW/°C. For SN72514, this rating applies at (or below) 70°C free-air temperature without derating.

electrical characteristics at specified free-air temperature, $V_{CC+} = 12$ V, $V_{CC-} = -6$ V (unless otherwise noted)

PARAMETER		TEST CONDITIONS[†]		SN52514 MIN	TYP	MAX	SN72514 MIN	TYP	MAX	UNIT
V_{IO}	Input offset voltage	$R_S \leq 200\ \Omega$, See Note 4	25°C		0.6	2		1.6	3.5	mV
			Full range			3			4.5	
α_{VIO}	Average temperature coefficient of input offset voltage	$R_S = 50\ \Omega$, See Note 4	MIN to 25°C		3	10		3	20	µV/°C
			25°C to MAX		3	10		3	20	
I_{IO}	Input offset current	See Note 4	25°C		0.75	3		1.8	5	µA
			MIN		1.8	7			7.5	
			MAX		0.25	3			7.5	
α_{IIO}	Average temperature coefficient of input offset current	See Note 4	MIN to 25°C		15	75		24	100	nA/°C
			25°C to MAX		5	25		15	50	
I_{IB}	Input bias current	See Note 4	25°C		7	15		7	20	µA
			MIN		12	25		9	30	
I_{SH}	High-level strobe current	$V_{(strobe)} = 5$ V, $V_{ID} = -5$ mV	25°C			±100			±100	µA
I_{SL}	Low-level strobe current	$V_{(strobe)} = -100$ mV, $V_{ID} = 5$ mV	25°C		-1	-2.5		-1	-2.5	mA
V_{ICR}	Common-mode input voltage range	$V_{CC-} = -7$ V	Full range	±5			±5			V
V_{ID}	Differential input voltage range		Full range	±5			±5			V
A_{VD}	Large-signal differential voltage amplification	No load, $V_O = 0$ to 2.5 V	25°C	12,500	33,000		10,000	33,000		
			Full range	10,000			8,000			
V_{OH}	High-level output voltage	$V_{ID} = 5$ mV, $I_{OH} = 0$	Full range		4§	5		4§	5	V
		$V_{ID} = 5$ mV, $I_{OH} = -5$ mA	Full range	2.5	3.6§		2.5	3.6§		
V_{OL}	Low-level output voltage	$V_{ID} = -5$ mV, $I_{OL} = 0$	Full range	-1	-0.5§	0‡	-1	-0.5§	0‡	V
		$V_{(strobe)} = 0.3$ V, $V_{ID} = 5$ mV, $I_{OL} = 0$	Full range	-1		0‡	-1		0‡	V
I_{OL}	Low-level output current	$V_{ID} = -5$ mV, $V_O = 0$	25°C	2	2.4		1.6	2.4		mA
			MIN	1	2.3		0.5	2.4		
			MAX	0.5	2.3		0.5	2.4		
r_o	Output resistance	$V_O = 1.4$ V	25°C		200			200		Ω
CMRR	Common-mode rejection ratio	$R_S \leq 200\ \Omega$	Full range	80	100§		70	100§		dB
I_{CC+}	Supply current from V_{CC+} ¶	$V_{ID} = -5$ mV, No load	Full range		5.5§	9		5.5§	9	mA
I_{CC-}	Supply current from V_{CC-} ¶		Full range		-3.5§	-7		-3.5§	-7	mA
P_D	Total power dissipation ¶		Full range		90§	150		90§	150	mW

[†] Unless otherwise noted, all characteristics are measured with the strobe open. Full range (MIN to MAX) for SN52514 is -55°C to 125°C and for the SN72514 is 0°C to 70°C.

[‡] The algebraic convention where the most-positive (least-negative) limit is designated as maximum is used in this data sheet for logic levels only, e.g., when 0 V is the maximum, the minimum limit is a more-negative voltage.

[§] These typical values are at $T_A = 25$°C.

[¶] Suppy current and power dissipation limits apply for each comparator.

NOTE 4: These characteristics are verified by measurements at the following temperatures and output voltage levels: for SN52514, $V_O = 1.8$ V at $T_A = -55$°C, $V_O = 1.4$ V at $T_A = 25$°C, and $V_O = 1$V at $T_A = 125$°C; for SN72514, $V_O = 1.5$ V at $T_A = 0$°C, $V_O = 1.4$ V at $T_A = 25$°C, and $V_O = 1.2$ V at $T_A = 70$°C. These output voltage levels were selected to approximate the logic threshold voltages of the types of digital logic circuits these comparators are intended to drive.

switching characteristics, $V_{CC+} = 12$ V, $V_{CC-} = -6$ V, $T_A = 25$°C

PARAMETER	TEST CONDITIONS			MIN	TYP	MAX	UNIT
Response time	$R_L = \infty$,	$C_L = 5$ pF,	See Note 5		30	80	ns
Strobe release time	$R_L = \infty$,	$C_L = 5$ pF,	See Note 6		5	25	ns

NOTES: 5. The response time specified is for a 100-mV input step with 5-mV overdrive.

6. For testing purposes, the input bias conditions are selected to produce an output voltage of 1.4 V. A 5-mV overdrive is then added to the input bias voltage to produce an output voltage which rises above 1.4 V. The time interval is measured from the 50% point of the strobe voltage curve to the point where the overdriven output voltage crosses the 1.4 V level.

For definition of terms and typical characteristic curves, see the SN52510/SN72510 data sheet on page 6-25.

TEXAS INSTRUMENTS
INCORPORATED
POST OFFICE BOX 5012 • DALLAS, TEXAS 75222

- **Fast Response Times**
- **Low Offset Characteristics**
- **Output Compatible with Most TTL and DTL Circuits**

schematic

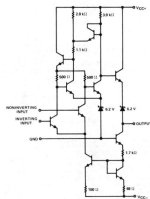

Component values shown are nominal.

description

The SN52710 and SN72710 are monolithic high-speed comparators having differential inputs and a low-impedance output. Component matching, inherent in silicon integrated circuit fabrication techniques, produces a comparator with low-drift and low-offset characteristics. These circuits are especially useful for applications requiring an amplitude discriminator, memory sense amplifier, or a high-speed voltage comparator. The SN52710 is characterised for operation over the full military temperature range of $-55°C$ to $125°C$; the SN72710 is characterized for operation from $0°C$ to $70°C$.

terminal assignments

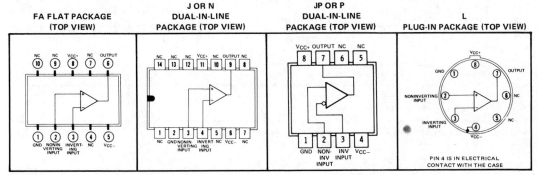

NC—No internal connection

absolute maximum ratings over operating free-air temperature range (unless otherwise noted)

		SN52710	SN72710	UNIT
Supply voltage V_{CC+} (see Note 1)		14	14	V
Supply voltage V_{CC-} (see Note 1)		−7	−7	V
Differential input voltage (see Note 2)		±5	±5	V
Input voltage (either input, see Note 1)		±7	±7	V
Peak output current ($t_W \leqslant 1$ s)		10	10	mA
Continuous total power dissipation at (or below) $70°C$ free-air temperature (see Note 3)		300	300	mW
Operating free-air temperature range		−55 to 125	0 to 70	°C
Storage temperature range		−65 to 150	−65 to 150	°C
Lead temperature 1/16 inch from case for 60 seconds	FA, J, JP, or L package	300	300	°C
Lead temperature 1/16 inch from case for 10 seconds	N or P package	260	260	°C

NOTES: 1. All voltage values, except differential voltages, are with respect to the network ground terminal.
2. Differential voltages are at the noninverting input terminal with respect to the inverting input terminal.
3. For operation of the SN52710 above $70°C$ free-air temperature, refer to Dissipation Derating Curve, Figure 8.

TEXAS INSTRUMENTS
INCORPORATED
POST OFFICE BOX 5012 • DALLAS, TEXAS 75222

electrical characteristics at specified free-air temperature, V_{CC+} = 12 V, V_{CC-} = −6 V (unless otherwise noted)

PARAMETER		TEST CONDITIONS†		SN52710 MIN	TYP	MAX	SN72710 MIN	TYP	MAX	UNIT
V_{IO}	Input offset voltage	$R_S \leq 200\ \Omega$, See Note 4	25°C		2	5		2	7.5	mV
			Full range			6			10	
α_{VIO}	Average temperature coefficient of input offset voltage	$R_S \leq 200\ \Omega$, See Note 4	Full range		5			7.5		μV/°C
I_{IO}	Input offset current	See Note 4	25°C		1	10		1	15	μA
			Full range			20			25	
I_{IB}	Input bias current	See Note 4	25°C		25	75		25	100	μA
			Full range			150			150	
V_I	Input voltage range	V_{CC-} = −7 V	25°C	±5			±5			V
V_{ID}	Differential input voltage range		25°C	±5			±5			V
A_{VD}	Large-signal differential voltage amplification	No load, See Note 4	25°C	750	1500		700	1500		
			Full range	500			500			
V_{OH}	High-level output voltage	V_{ID} = 15 mV, I_{OH} = −0.5 mA	25°C	2.5	3.2	4	2.5	3.2	4	V
V_{OL}	Low-level output voltage	V_{ID} = −15 mV, I_{OL} = 0	25°C	−1	−0.5	0‡	−1	−0.5	0‡	V
I_{OL}	Low-level output current	V_{ID} = −15 mV, V_O = 0	25°C	1.6	2.5					mA
r_o	Output resistance	V_O = 1.4 V	25°C		200			200		Ω
CMRR	Common-mode rejection ratio	$R_S \leq 200\ \Omega$	25°C	70	90		65	90		dB
I_{CC+}	Supply current from V_{CC+}	V_{ID} = −5 V to 5 V	25°C		5.4	10.1		5.4		mA
I_{CC-}	Supply current from V_{CC-}	(−10 mV for typ),	25°C		−3.8	−8.9		−3.8		mA
P_D	Total power dissipation	No load	25°C		88	175		88		mW

NOTE 4: These characteristics are verified by measurements at the following temperatures and output voltage levels: for SN52710, V_O = 1.8 V at T_A = −55°C, V_O = 1.4 V at T_A = 25°C, and V_O = 1 V at T_A = 125°C; for SN72710, V_O = 1.5 V at T_A = 0°C, V_O = 1.4 V at T_A = 25°C, and V_O = 1.2 V at T_A = 70°C. These output voltage levels were selected to approximate the logic threshold voltages of the types of digital logic circuits these comparators are intended to drive.

†Full range for SN52710 is −55°C to 125°C and for SN72710 is 0°C to 70°C.

‡The algebraic convention where the most-positive (least-negative) limit is designated as maximum is used in this data sheet for logic levels only, e.g., when 0 V is the maximum, the minimum limit is a more-negative voltage.

switching characteristics, V_{CC+} = 12 V, V_{CC-} = −6 V, T_A = 25°C

PARAMETER	TEST CONDITIONS	SN52710 TYP	SN72710 TYP	UNIT
Response time	No load, See Note 5	40	40	ns

NOTE 5: The response time specified is for a 100-mV input step with 5-mV overdrive.

For definitions of terms, see the SN52711/SN72711 data sheet on page 6-37.

TEXAS INSTRUMENTS
INCORPORATED
POST OFFICE BOX 5012 • DALLAS, TEXAS 75222

TYPICAL CHARACTERISTICS

OUTPUT RESPONSE FOR VARIOUS
INPUT OVERDRIVES

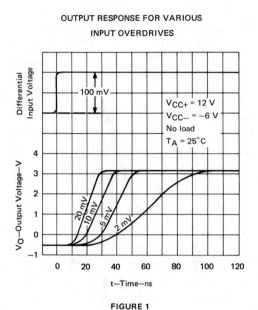

FIGURE 1

OUTPUT RESPONSE FOR VARIOUS
INPUT OVERDRIVES

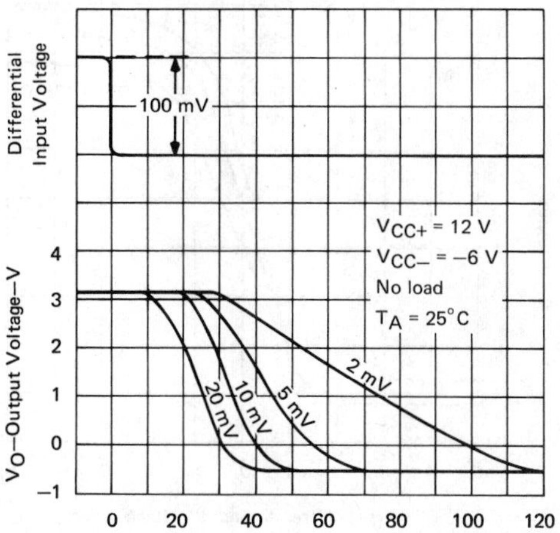

FIGURE 2

COMMON-MODE PULSE RESPONSE
vs
ELAPSED TIME

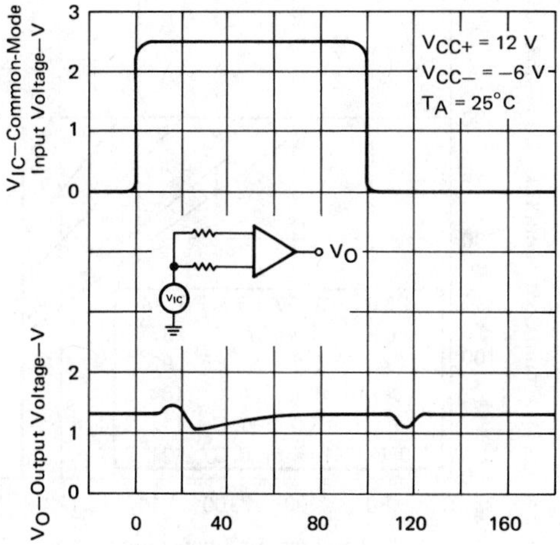

FIGURE 3

OUTPUT VOLTAGE
vs
FREE-AIR TEMPERATURE

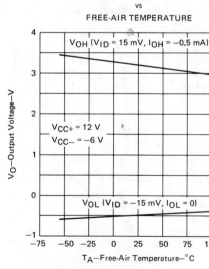

FIGURE 4

TYPICAL CHARACTERISTICS

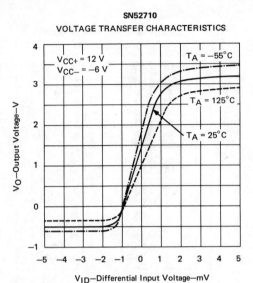

SN52710
VOLTAGE TRANSFER CHARACTERISTICS

FIGURE 5

SN72710
VOLTAGE TRANSFER CHARACTERISTICS

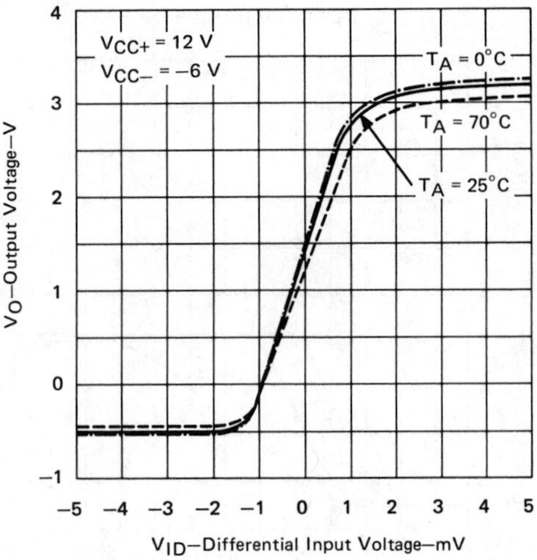

FIGURE 6

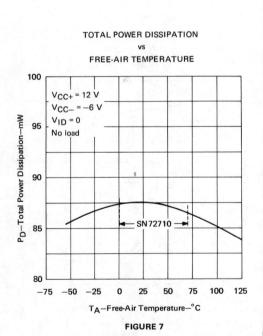

TOTAL POWER DISSIPATION
vs
FREE-AIR TEMPERATURE

FIGURE 7

THERMAL INFORMATION

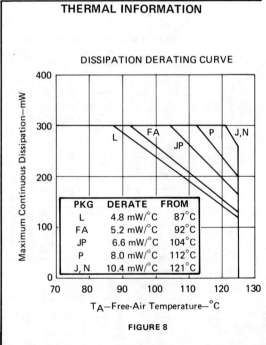

DISSIPATION DERATING CURVE

PKG	DERATE	FROM
L	4.8 mW/°C	87°C
FA	5.2 mW/°C	92°C
JP	6.6 mW/°C	104°C
P	8.0 mW/°C	112°C
J, N	10.4 mW/°C	121°C

FIGURE 8

TEXAS INSTRUMENTS
INCORPORATED
POST OFFICE BOX 5012 • DALLAS, TEXAS 75222

- **Fast Response Times** • **Low Offset Characteristics**
- **Output Compatible with Most TTL and DTL Circuits**
- **Designed to be Interchangeable with Fairchild μA711 and μA711C**

description

The SN52711 and SN72711 circuits are high-speed dual-channel comparators with differential inputs and a low-impedance output. Component matching, inherent with silicon monolithic circuit fabrication techniques, produces a comparator circuit with low-drift and low-offset characteristics. An independent strobe input is provided for each of the two channels, which when taken low, inhibits the associated channel. If both strobes are simultaneously low, the output will be low regardless of the conditions applied to the differential inputs. The comparator output pulse width may be "stretched" by varying the capacitive loading. These dual comparators are particularly useful for applications requiring an amplitude-discriminating sense amplifier with an adjustable threshold voltage. The SN52711 is characterized for operation over the full military temperature range of −55°C to 125°C; the SN72711 is characterized for operation from 0°C to 70°C.

schematic

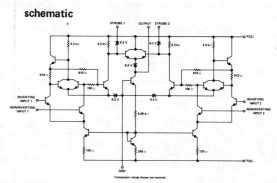

Component values shown are nominal.

terminal assignments

FA FLAT PACKAGE (TOP VIEW)	J OR N DUAL-IN-LINE PACKAGE (TOP VIEW)	L PLUG-IN PACKAGE (TOP VIEW)

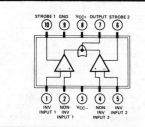 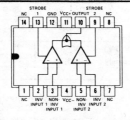 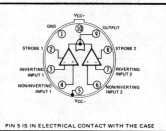

PIN 5 IS IN ELECTRICAL CONTACT WITH THE CASE

NC—No Internal Connection

absolute maximum ratings over operating free-air temperature range (unless otherwise noted)

		SN52711	SN72711	UNIT
Supply voltage V_{CC+} (see Note 1)		14	14	V
Supply voltage V_{CC-} (see Note 1)		−7	−7	V
Differential input voltage (see Note 2)		±5	±5	V
Input voltage (any input, see Note 1)		±7	±7	V
Strobe voltage (see Note 1)		6	6	V
Peak output current ($t_w \leqslant 1$ s)		50	50	mA
Continuous total power dissipation at (or below) 70°C free-air temperature (see Note 3)		300	300	mW
Operating free-air temperature range		−55 to 125	0 to 70	°C
Storage temperature range		−65 to 150	−65 to 150	°C
Lead temperature 1/16 inch from case for 60 seconds	FA, J, or L package	300	300	°C
Lead temperature 1/16 inch from case for 10 seconds	N package	260	260	°C

NOTES: 1. All voltage values, except differential voltages, are with respect to network ground terminal.
2. Differential voltages are at the noninverting input terminal with respect to the inverting input terminal.
3. For operation of SN52711 above 70°C free-air temperature, refer to Dissipation Derating Curve, Figure 9.

TEXAS INSTRUMENTS
INCORPORATED
POST OFFICE BOX 5012 • DALLAS, TEXAS 75222

electrical characteristics at specified free-air temperature, V_{CC+} = 12 V, V_{CC-} = −6 V (unless otherwise noted)

PARAMETER		TEST CONDITIONS[†]		SN52711			SN72711			UNIT
				MIN	TYP	MAX	MIN	TYP	MAX	
V_{IO}	Input offset voltage	$R_S \leqslant 200\ \Omega$, V_{IC} = 0, See Note 4	25°C		1	3.5		1	5	mV
			Full range			4.5			6	
		$R_S \leqslant 200\ \Omega$, See Note 4	25°C		1	5		1	7.5	
			Full range			6			10	
α_{VIO}	Average temperature coefficient of input offset voltage	$R_S \leqslant 200\ \Omega$, V_{IC} = 0, See Note 4	Full range		5			5		μV/°C
I_{IO}	Input offset current	See Note 4	25°C		0.5	10		0.5	15	μA
			Full range			20			25	
I_{IB}	Input bias current	See Note 4	25°C		25	75		25	100	μA
			Full range			150			150	
I_{SL}	Low-level strobe current	$V_{(strobe)}$ = 0, V_{ID} = 10 mV	25°C		−1.2	−2.5		−1.2	−2.5	mA
V_I	Input voltage range	V_{CC-} = −7 V	25°C	±5			±5			V
V_{ID}	Differential input voltage range		25°C	±5			±5			V
A_{VD}	Large-signal differential voltage amplification	No load, V_O = 0 to 2.5 V	25°C	750	1500		700	1500		
			Full range	500			500			
V_{OH}	High-level output voltage	V_{ID} = 10 mV, I_{OH} = 0	25°C		4.5	5		4.5	5	V
		V_{ID} = 10 mV, I_{OH} = −5 mA	25°C	2.5	3.5		2.5	3.5		
V_{OL}	Low-level output voltage	V_{ID} = −10 mV, I_{OL} = 0	25°C	−1	−0.5	0[‡]	−1	−0.5	0[‡]	V
		V_{ID} = 10 mV, $V_{(strobe)}$ = 0.3 V, I_{OL} = 0	25°C	−1		0[‡]	−1		0[‡]	
I_{OL}	Low-level output current	V_{ID} = −10 mV, V_O = 0	25°C	0.5	0.8		0.5	0.8		mA
r_o	Output resistance	V_O = 1.4 V	25°C		200			200		Ω
CMRR	Common-mode rejection ratio	$R_S \leqslant 200\ \Omega$	25°C	70	90		65	90		dB
I_{CC+}	Supply current from V_{CC+}	V_{ID} = −5 V to 5 V (−10 mV for typ),	25°C		9			9		mA
I_{CC-}	Supply current from V_{CC-}	Strobes alternately grounded,	25°C		−4			−4		mA
P_D	Total power dissipation	No load	25°C		130	200		130	230	mW

NOTE 4: These characteristics are verified by measurements at the following temperatures and output voltage levels: for SN52711, V_O = 1.8 V at T_A = −55°C, V_O = 1.4 V at T_A = 25°C, and V_O = 1 V at T_A = 125°C; for SN72711, V_O = 1.5 V at T_A = 0°C, V_O = 1.4 V at T_A = 25°C, and V_O = 1.2 V at 70°C. These output voltage levels were selected to approximate the logic threshold voltages of the types of digital logic circuits these comparators are intended to drive.

[†]Unless otherwise noted, all characteristics are measured with the strobe of the channel under test open. The strobe of the other channel is grounded. Full range for SN52711 is −55°C to 125°C and for the SN72711 is 0°C to 70°C.

[‡]The algebraic convention where the most-positive (least-negative) limit is designated as maximum is used in this data sheet for logic levels only, e.g., when 0 V is the maximum, the minimum limit is a more-negative voltage.

switching characteristics, V_{CC+} = 12 V, V_{CC-} = −6 V, T_A = 25°C

PARAMETER	TEST CONDITIONS		SN52711			SN72711			UNIT
			MIN	TYP	MAX	MIN	TYP	MAX	
Response time	No load,	See Note 5		40	80		40		ns
Strobe release time	No load,	See Note 6		7	25		7		ns

NOTES: 5. The response time specified is for a 100-mV input step with 5-mV overdrive.

6. For testing purposes, the input bias conditions are selected to produce an output voltage of 1.4 V. A 5-mV overdrive is then added to the input bias voltage to produce an output voltage which rises above 1.4 V. The time interval is measured from the 50% point of the strobe voltage curve to the point where the overdriven output voltage crosses the 1.4 V level.

TEXAS INSTRUMENTS
INCORPORATED
POST OFFICE BOX 5012 • DALLAS, TEXAS 75222

DEFINITION OF TERMS

Input Offset Voltage (V_{IO}) The d-c voltage which must be applied between the input terminals to force the quiescent d-c output voltage to the specified level. The input offset voltage may also be defined for the case where two equal resistances (R_S) are inserted in series with the input leads.

Average Temperature Coefficient of Input Offset Voltage (α_{VIO}) The ratio of the change in input offset voltage to the change in free-air temperature. This is an average value for the specified temperature range.

$$\alpha_{VIO} = \left| \frac{(V_{IO} @ T_{A(1)}) - (V_{IO} @ T_{A(2)})}{T_{A(1)} - T_{A(2)}} \right| \quad \text{where } T_{A(1)} \text{ and } T_{A(2)} \text{ are the specified temperature extremes.}$$

Input Offset Current (I_{IO}) The difference between the currents into the two input terminals with the output at the specified level.

Input Bias Current (I_{IB}) The average of the currents into the two input terminals with the output at the specified level.

Low-Level Strobe Current (I_{SL}) The current flowing out of the strobe at a low-level voltage.

Input Voltage Range (V_I) The range of voltage which if exceeded at either input terminal will cause the comparator to cease functioning properly.

Differential Input Voltage Range (V_{ID}) The range of voltage between the two input terminals which if exceeded will cause the comparator to cease functioning properly.

Large-Signal Differential Voltage Amplification (A_{VD}) The ratio of the change in output voltage to the change in differential input voltage producing it.

High-Level Output Voltage (V_{OH}) The voltage at the output with the specified input conditions applied which should establish a high level at the output.

Low-Level Output Voltage (V_{OL}) The voltage at the output with the specified input conditions applied which should establish a low level at the output.

Low-Level Output Current (I_{OL}) The current flowing into the output at a specified low-level output voltage.

Output Resistance (r_o) The resistance between the output terminal and ground.

Common-Mode Rejection Ratio (CMRR) The ratio of differential voltage amplification to common-mode voltage amplification. This is measured by determining the ratio of a change in input common-mode voltage to the resulting change in input offset voltage.

Total Power Dissipation (P_D) The total d-c power supplied to the device less any power delivered from the device to a load. At no load: $P_D = V_{CC+} \cdot I_{CC+} + V_{CC-} \cdot I_{CC-}$.

Response Time The interval between the application of an input step function and the time when the output crosses the logic threshold voltage. The input step drives the comparator from some initial condition sufficient to saturate the output to an input level just barely in excess of that required to bring the output back to the logic threshold voltage. This excess is referred to as the voltage overdrive.

Strobe Release Time The time required for the output to rise to the logic threshold voltage after the strobe terminal has been driven from the low logic level to the high logic level. Appropriate input conditions are assumed.

6

TYPES SN52711, SN72711
DUAL-CHANNEL DIFFERENTIAL COMPARATORS WITH STROBES

TYPICAL CHARACTERISTICS

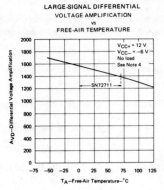

LARGE-SIGNAL DIFFERENTIAL
VOLTAGE AMPLIFICATION
vs
FREE-AIR TEMPERATURE

FIGURE 1

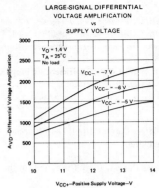

LARGE-SIGNAL DIFFERENTIAL
VOLTAGE AMPLIFICATION
vs
SUPPLY VOLTAGE

FIGURE 2

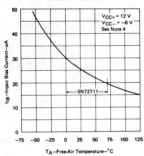

INPUT BIAS CURRENT
vs
FREE-AIR TEMPERATURE

FIGURE 3

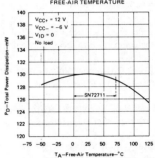

TOTAL POWER DISSIPATION
vs
FREE-AIR TEMPERATURE

FIGURE 4

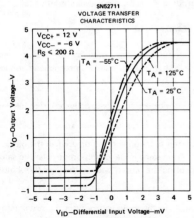

SN52711
VOLTAGE TRANSFER
CHARACTERISTICS

FIGURE 5

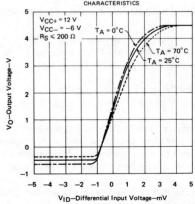

SN72711
VOLTAGE TRANSFER
CHARACTERISTICS

FIGURE 6

NOTE 4: These characteristics are verified by measurements at the following temperatures and output voltage levels: for SN52711, V_O = 1.8 V at T_A = −55°C, V_O = 1.4 V at T_A = 25°C, and V_O = 1 V at T_A = 125°C; for SN72711, V_O = 1.5 V at T_A = 0°C, V_O = 1.4 V at T_A = 25°C, and V_O = 1.2 V at 70°C. These output voltage levels were selected to approximate the logic threshold voltages of the types of digital logic circuits these comparators are intended to drive.

TEXAS INSTRUMENTS
INCORPORATED
POST OFFICE BOX 5012 • DALLAS, TEXAS 75222

TYPICAL CHARACTERISTICS

OUTPUT RESPONSE FOR
VARIOUS INPUT OVERDRIVES

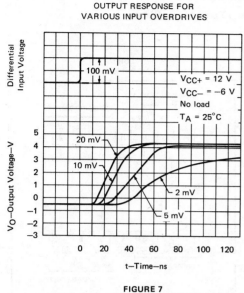

FIGURE 7

STROBE RELEASE TIME
FOR VARIOUS INPUT OVERDRIVES

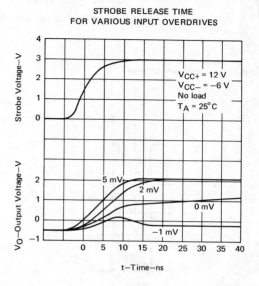

FIGURE 8

6

THERMAL INFORMATION

DISSIPATION DERATING CURVE

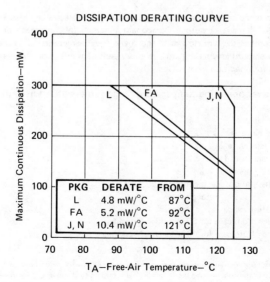

PKG	DERATE	FROM
L	4.8 mW/°C	87°C
FA	5.2 mW/°C	92°C
J, N	10.4 mW/°C	121°C

FIGURE 9

TEXAS INSTRUMENTS
INCORPORATED
POST OFFICE BOX 5012 • DALLAS, TEXAS 75222

- **Fast Response Times** • **Low Offset Characteristics**
- **Output Compatible with Most TTL and DTL Circuits**

schematic (each comparator)

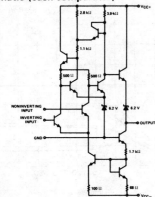

Component values shown are nominal.

**J OR N
DUAL-IN-LINE PACKAGE (TOP VIEW)**

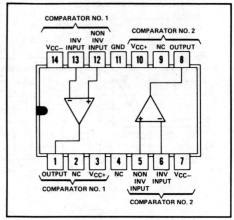

NC—No internal connection

description

The SN72720 is two high-speed comparators in a single package, each electrically identical to the SN72710 and having differential inputs and a low-impedance output. Component matching, inherent in silicon monolithic circuit fabrication techniques, produces a comparator with low-drift and low-offset characteristics. This circuit is especially useful for applications requiring an amplitude discriminator, memory sense amplifier, or a high-speed voltage comparator. The SN72720 is characterized for operation from 0°C to 70°C.

absolute maximum ratings over operating temperature range (unless otherwise noted)

Supply voltage V_{CC+} (see Note 1) . . . . 14 V
Supply voltage V_{CC-} (see Note 1) . . . . −7 V
Differential input voltage (see Note 2) . . . . ±5 V
Input voltage (any input, see Note 1) . . . . ±7 V
Peak output current, each comparator ($t_w \leqslant 1$ s) . . . . 10 mA
Continuous total power dissipation: each comparator . . . . 300 mW
                               total package . . . . 600 mW
Operating free-air temperature range . . . . 0°C to 70°C
Lead temperature 1/16 inch from case for 60 seconds: J package . . . . 300°C
Lead temperature 1/16 inch from case for 10 seconds: N package . . . . 260°C

NOTES: 1. All voltage values, except differential voltages, are with respect to the network ground terminal.
         2. Differential voltages are at the noninverting input terminal with respect to the inverting input terminal.

TEXAS INSTRUMENTS
INCORPORATED
POST OFFICE BOX 5012 • DALLAS, TEXAS 75222

electrical characteristics at specified free-air temperature, $V_{CC+} = 12$ V, $V_{CC-} = -6$ V (unless otherwise noted)

	PARAMETER	TEST CONDITIONS			MIN	TYP	MAX	UNIT
V_{IO}	Input offset voltage	$R_S \leqslant 200\ \Omega$,	See Note 3	25°C		2	7.5	mV
				0°C to 70°C			10	
α_{VIO}	Average temperature coefficient of input offset voltage	$R_S \leqslant 200\ \Omega$,	See Note 3	0°C to 70°C		7.5		μV/°C
I_{IO}	Input offset current	See Note 3		25°C		1	15	μA
				0°C to 70°C			25	
I_{IB}	Input bias current	See Note 3		25°C		25	100	μA
				0°C to 70°C			150	
V_I	Input voltage range	$V_{CC-} = -7$ V		25°C	±5			V
V_{ID}	Differential input voltage range			25°C	±5			V
A_{VD}	Large-signal differential voltage amplification	No load,	See Note 3	25°C	700	1500		
				0°C to 70°C	500			
V_{OH}	High-level output voltage	$V_{ID} = 15$ mV,	$I_{OH} = -0.5$ mA	25°C	2.5	3.2	4	V
V_{OL}	Low-level output voltage	$V_{ID} = -15$ mV,	$I_{OL} = 0$	25°C	-1	-0.5	0‡	V
r_o	Output resistance	$V_O = 1.4$ V		25°C		200		Ω
CMRR	Common-mode rejection ratio	$R_S \leqslant 200\ \Omega$		25°C	65	90		dB
I_{CC+}	Supply current from V_{CC+} (each comparater)	$V_{ID} = -5$ V to 5 V		25°C		5.4		mA
I_{CC-}	Supply current from V_{CC-} (each comparator)	(−10 mV for typ),		25°C		-3.8		mA
P_D	Total power dissipation (each comparator)	No load		25°C		88		mW

NOTE 3: These characteristics are verified by measurements at the following temperatures and output voltage levels: $V_O = 1.5$ V at $T_A = 0$°C, $V_O = 1.4$ V at $T_A = 25$°C, and $V_O = 1.2$ V at $T_A = 70$°C. These output voltage levels were selected to approximate the logic threshold voltages of the types of digital logic circuits these comparators are intended to drive.

‡The algebraic convention where the most-positive (least-negative) limit is designated as maximum is used in this data sheet for logic levels only, e.g., when 0 V is the maximum, the minimum limit is a more-negative voltage.

switching characteristics, $V_{CC+} = 12$ V, $V_{CC-} = -6$ V, $T_A = 25$°C

PARAMETER	TEST CONDITIONS		TYP	UNIT
Response time	No load,	See Note 4	40	ns

NOTE 4: The response time specified is for a 100-mV input step with 5-mV overdrive.

For definition of terms, refer to page 6-39. Typical characteristic curves on the SN52710/SN72710 data sheet, pages 6-35 and 6-36, are applicable for the SN72720.

TEXAS INSTRUMENTS
INCORPORATED
POST OFFICE BOX 5012 • DALLAS, TEXAS 75222

- **Low Offset Characteristics**
- **High Differential Voltage Amplification**
- **Fast Response Times**
- **Output Compatible with Most TTL and DTL Circuits**

schematic

Resistor values are nominal in ohms.

description

The SN52810 and SN72810 are improved versions of the SN52710 and SN72710 high-speed voltage comparators with an extra stage added to increase voltage amplification and accuracy. Typical amplification is 33,000. Component matching, inherent in monolithic integrated circuit fabrication techniques, produces a comparator with low-drift and low-offset characteristics. These circuits are particularly useful for applications requiring an amplitude discriminator, memory sense amplifier, or a high-speed limit detector.

The SN52810 is characterized for operation over the full military temperature range of $-55°C$ to $125°C$; the SN72810 is characterized for operation from $0°C$ to $70°C$.

terminal assignments

NC—No internal connection

absolute maximum ratings over operating free-air temperature range (unless otherwise noted)

Supply voltage V_{CC+} (see Note 1)	14 V
Supply voltage V_{CC-} (see Note 1)	−7 V
Differential input voltage (see Note 2)	±5 V
Input voltage (either input, see Note 1)	±7 V
Peak output current ($t_W \leqslant 1$ s)	10 mA
Continuous total power dissipation at (or below) 70°C free-air temperature (see Note 3)	300 mW
Operating free-air temperature range: SN52810 Circuits	−55°C to 125°C
SN72810 Circuits	0°C to 70°C
Storage temperature range	−65°C to 150°C
Lead temperature 1/16 inch from case for 60 seconds: FA, J, JP, or L package	300°C
Lead temperature 1/16 inch from case for 10 seconds: N or P package	260°C

NOTES: 1. All voltage values, except differential voltages, are with respect to the network ground terminal.
2. Differential voltages are at the noninverting input terminal with respect to the inverting input terminal.
3. For operation of the SN52810 above 70°C free-air temperature, refer to Dissipating Derating Curve, Figure 1.

TEXAS INSTRUMENTS
INCORPORATED
POST OFFICE BOX 5012 • DALLAS, TEXAS 75222

electrical characteristics at specified free-air temperature, V_{CC+} = 12 V, V_{CC-} = −6 V (unless otherwise noted)

PARAMETER		TEST CONDITIONS[†]		SN52810			SN72810			UNIT
				MIN	TYP	MAX	MIN	TYP	MAX	
V_{IO}	Input offset voltage	$R_S \leqslant 200 \ \Omega$, See Note 4	25°C		0.6	2		1.6	3.5	mV
			Full range			3			4.5	
α_{VIO}	Average temperature coefficient of input offset voltage	$R_S = 50 \ \Omega$, See Note 4	MIN to 25°C		3	10		3	20	μV/°C
			25°C to MAX		3	10		3	20	
I_{IO}	Input offset current	See Note 4	25°C		0.75	3		1.8	5	μA
			MIN		1.8	7			7.5	
			MAX		0.25	3			7.5	
α_{IIO}	Average temperature coefficient of input offset current	See Note 4	MIN to 25°C		15	75		24	100	nA/°C
			25°C to MAX		5	25		15	50	
I_{IB}	Input bias current	See Note 4	25°C		7	15		7	20	μA
			MIN		12	25		9	30	
V_{ICR}	Common-mode input voltage range	V_{CC-} = −7 V	Full range	±5			±5			V
V_{ID}	Differential input voltage range		Full range	±5			±5			V
A_{VD}	Large-signal differential voltage amplification	No load, V_O = 0 to 2.5 V	25°C	12,500	33,000		10,000	33,000		
			Full range	10,000			8,000			
V_{OH}	High-level output voltage	V_{ID} = 5 mV, I_{OH} = 0	Full range		4[§]	5		4[§]	5	V
		V_{ID} = 5 mV, I_{OH} = −5 mA	Full range	2.5	3.6[§]		2.5	3.6[§]		
V_{OL}	Low-level output voltage	V_{ID} = −5 mV, I_{OL} = 0	Full range	−1	−0.5[§]	0[‡]	−1	−0.5[§]	0[‡]	V
I_{OL}	Low-level output current	V_{ID} = −5 mV, V_O = 0	25°C	2	2.4		1.6	2.4		mA
			MIN	1	2.3		0.5	2.4		
			MAX	0.5	2.3		0.5	2.4		
r_o	Output resistance	V_O = 1.4 V	25°C		200			200		Ω
CMRR	Common-mode rejection ratio	$R_S \leqslant 200 \ \Omega$	Full range	80	100[§]		70	100[§]		dB
I_{CC+}	Supply current from V_{CC+}	V_{ID} = −5 mV, No load	Full range		5.5[§]	9		5.5[§]	9	mA
I_{CC-}	Supply current from V_{CC-}		Full range		−3.5[§]	−7		−3.5[§]	−7	mA
P_D	Total power dissipation		Full range		90[§]	150		90[§]	150	mW

[†] Full range (MIN to MAX) for SN52810 is −55°C to 125°C and for the SN72810 is 0°C to 70°C.

[‡] The algebraic convention where the most-positive (least-negative) limit is designated as maximum is used in this data sheet for logic levels only, e.g., when 0 V is the maximum, the minimum limit is a more-negative voltage.

[§] These typical values are at T_A = 25°C.

NOTE 4: These characteristics are verified by measurements at the following temperatures and output voltage levels: for SN52810, V_O = 1.8 V at T_A = −55°C, V_O = 1.4 V at T_A = 25°C, and V_O = 1V at T_A = 125°C; for SN72810, V_O = 1.5 V at T_A = 0°C, V_O = 1.4 V at 25°C, and V_O = 1.2 V at T_A = 70°C. These output voltage levels were selected to approximate the logic threshold voltages of the types of digital logic circuits these comparators are intended to drive.

switching characteristics, V_{CC+} = 12 V, V_{CC-} = −6 V, T_A = 25°C

PARAMETER	TEST CONDITIONS			MIN	TYP	MAX	UNIT
Response time	$R_L = \infty$,	C_L = 5 pF,	See Note 5		30	80	ns

NOTE 5: The response time specified is for a 100-mV input step with 5-mV overdrive.

DEFINITION OF TERMS

Input Offset Voltage (V_{IO}) The d-c voltage which must be applied between the input terminals to force the quiescent d-c output voltage to the specified level. The input offset voltage may also be defined for the case where two equal resistances (R_S) are inserted in series with the input leads.

Average Temperature Coefficient of Input Offset Voltage (α_{VIO}) The ratio of the change in input offset voltage to the change in free-air temperature. This is an average value for the specified temperature range.

$$\alpha_{VIO} = \left| \frac{(V_{IO} @ T_{A(1)}) - (V_{IO} @ T_{A(2)})}{T_{A(1)} - T_{A(2)}} \right| \quad \text{where } T_{A(1)} \text{ and } T_{A(2)} \text{ are the specified temperature extremes.}$$

Input Offset Current (I_{IO}) The difference between the currents into the two input terminals with the output at the specified level.

Average Temperature Coefficient of Input Offset Current (α_{IIO}) The ratio of the change in input offset current to the change in free-air temperature. This is an average value for the specified temperature range.

$$\alpha_{IIO} = \left| \frac{(I_{IO} @ T_{A(1)}) - (I_{IO} @ T_{A(2)})}{T_{A(1)} - T_{A(2)}} \right| \quad \text{where } T_{A(1)} \text{ and } T_{A(2)} \text{ are the specified temperature extremes.}$$

Input Bias Current (I_{IB}) The average of the currents into the two input terminals with the output at the specified level.

Common-Mode Input Voltage Range (V_{ICR}) The range of common-mode voltage which if exceeded will cause the comparator to cease functioning properly.

Differential Input Voltage Range (V_{ID}) The range of voltage between the two input terminals which if exceeded will cause the comparator to cease functioning properly.

Large-Signal Differential Voltage Amplification (A_{VD}) The ratio of the change in output voltage to the change in differential input voltage producing it.

High-Level Output Voltage (V_{OH}) The voltage at the output with the specified input conditions applied which should establish a high level at the output.

Low-Level Output Voltage (V_{OL}) The voltage at the output with the specified input conditions applied which should establish a low level at the output.

Low-Level Output Current (I_{OL}) The current flowing into the output at a specified low-level output voltage.

Output Resistance (r_o) The resistance between the output terminal and ground.

Common-Mode Rejection Ratio (CMRR) The ratio of differential voltage amplification to common-mode voltage amplification. This is measured by determining the ratio of a change in input common-mode voltage to the resulting change in input offset voltage.

Total Power Dissipation (P_D) The total d-c power supplied to the device less any power delivered from the device to a load. At no load: $P_D = V_{CC+} \cdot I_{CC+} + V_{CC-} \cdot I_{CC-}$.

Response Time The interval between the application of an input step function and the time when the output crosses the logic threshold voltage. The input step drives the comparator from some initial condition sufficient to saturate the output to an input level just barely in excess of that required to bring the output back to the logic threshold voltage. This excess is referred to as the voltage overdrive.

TEXAS INSTRUMENTS
INCORPORATED
POST OFFICE BOX 5012 • DALLAS, TEXAS 75222

THERMAL INFORMATION

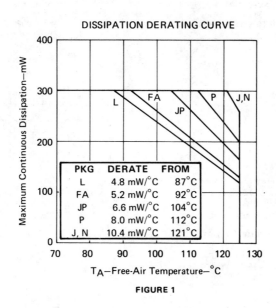

DISSIPATION DERATING CURVE

PKG	DERATE	FROM
L	4.8 mW/°C	87°C
FA	5.2 mW/°C	92°C
JP	6.6 mW/°C	104°C
P	8.0 mW/°C	112°C
J, N	10.4 mW/°C	121°C

FIGURE 1

TYPICAL CHARACTERISTICS

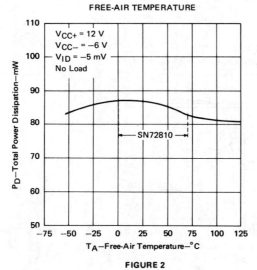

TOTAL POWER DISSIPATION
vs
FREE-AIR TEMPERATURE

V_{CC+} = 12 V
V_{CC-} = −6 V
V_{ID} = −5 mV
No Load

SN72810

FIGURE 2

TEXAS INSTRUMENTS
INCORPORATED
POST OFFICE BOX 5012 • DALLAS, TEXAS 75222

TYPICAL CHARACTERISTICS

LARGE-SIGNAL DIFFERENTIAL
VOLTAGE AMPLIFICATION
vs
FREE-AIR TEMPERATURE

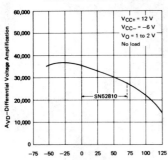

FIGURE 3

LARGE-SIGNAL DIFFERENTIAL
VOLTAGE AMPLIFICATION
vs
SUPPLY VOLTAGE

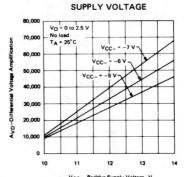

FIGURE 4

OUTPUT VOLTAGE LEVELS
vs
FREE-AIR TEMPERATURE

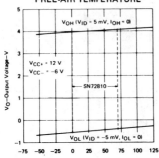

FIGURE 5

LOW-LEVEL OUTPUT CURRENT
vs
FREE-AIR TEMPERATURE

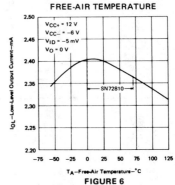

FIGURE 6

SN52810
VOLTAGE TRANSFER CHARACTERISTICS

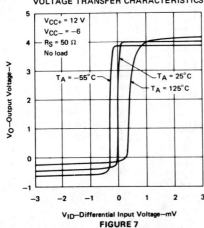

FIGURE 7

SN72810
VOLTAGE TRANSFER CHARACTERISTICS

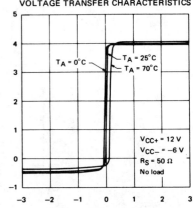

FIGURE 8

6

TEXAS INSTRUMENTS
INCORPORATED
POST OFFICE BOX 5012 • DALLAS, TEXAS 75222

TYPICAL CHARACTERISTICS

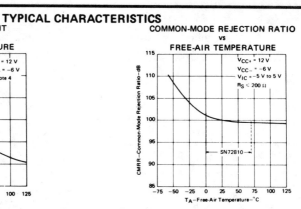

INPUT BIAS CURRENT
vs
FREE-AIR TEMPERATURE

V_{CC+} = 12 V
V_{CC-} = −6 V
See Note 4

SN72810

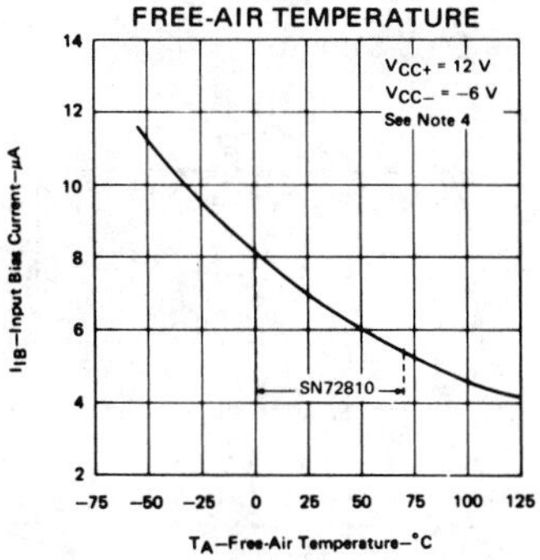

FIGURE 9

COMMON-MODE REJECTION RATIO
vs
FREE-AIR TEMPERATURE

V_{CC+} = 12 V
V_{CC-} = −6 V
V_{IC} = −5 V to 5 V
$R_S \leqslant 200\ \Omega$

SN72810

FIGURE 10

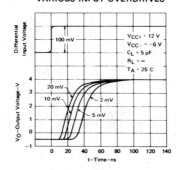

OUTPUT RESPONSE FOR
VARIOUS INPUT OVERDRIVES

100 mV

V_{CC+} = 12 V
V_{CC-} = −6 V
C_L = 5 pF
R_L = ∞
T_A = 25°C

20 mV
10 mV
2 mV
5 mV

FIGURE 11

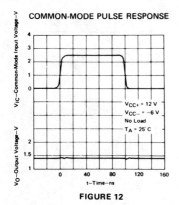

COMMON-MODE PULSE RESPONSE

V_{CC+} = 12 V
V_{CC-} = −6 V
No Load
T_A = 25°C

FIGURE 12

50 Ω

50 Ω

V_O

V_{IC}

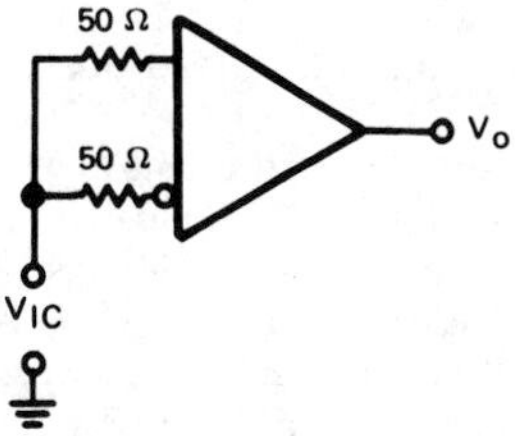

TEST CIRCUIT
FOR FIGURE 12

NOTE 4: These characteristics are verified by measurements at the following temperatures and output voltage levels: for SN52810, V_O = 1.8 V at T_A = −55°C, V_O = 1.4 V at T_A = 25°C, and V_O = 1V at T_A = 125°C; for SN72810, V_O = 1.5 V at T_A = 0°C, V_O = 1.4 V at 25°C, and V_O = 1.2 V at T_A = 70°C. These output voltage levels were selected to approximate the logic threshold voltages of the types of digital logic circuits these comparators are intended to drive.

TEXAS INSTRUMENTS
INCORPORATED
POST OFFICE BOX 5012 • DALLAS, TEXAS 75222

LINEAR
INTEGRATED CIRCUITS

TYPES SN52811, SN72811
DUAL-CHANNEL DIFFERENTIAL COMPARATORS
WITH STROBES

BULLETIN NO. DL-S 7311464, MARCH 1971—REVISED SEPTEMBER 1973

- **Fast Response Times**
- **Improved Voltage Amplification and Offset Characteristics**
- **Output Compatible with Most TTL and DTL Circuits**

description

The SN52811 and SN72811 are improved versions of the SN52711 and SN72711 high-speed dual-channel voltage comparators. Voltage amplification is higher (typically 17,500) due to an extra stage, increasing the comparator accuracy. The output pulse width may be "stretched" by varying the capacitive loading.

Each channel has differential inputs, a strobe input, and an output in common with the other channel. When either strobe is taken low, it inhibits the associated channel. If both strobes are simultaneously low, the output will be low regardless of the conditions applied to the differential inputs.

These dual-channel voltage comparators are particularly attractive for applications requiring an amplitude-discriminating sense amplifier with an adjustable threshold voltage.

schematic

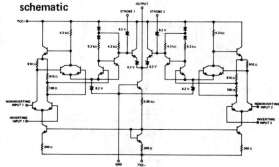

Component values shown are nominal.

The SN52811 is characterized for operation over the full military temperature range of −55°C to 125°C; the SN72811 is characterized for operation from 0°C to 70°C.

terminal assignments

| FA FLAT PACKAGE (TOP VIEW) | J OR N DUAL-IN-LINE PACKAGE (TOP VIEW) | L PLUG-IN PACKAGE (TOP VIEW) |

PIN 5 IS IN ELECTRICAL CONTACT WITH THE CASE

NC—No internal connection

absolute maximum ratings over operating free-air temperature range (unless otherwise noted)

Supply voltage V_{CC+} (see Note 1)	14 V
Supply voltage V_{CC-} (see Note 1)	−7 V
Differential input voltage (see Note 2)	±5 V
Input voltage (any input, see Note 1)	±7 V
Strobe Voltage (see Note 1)	6 V
Peak output current ($t_w \leqslant 1$ s)	50 mA
Continuous total power dissipation at (or below) 70°C free-air temperature (see Note 3)	300 mW
Operating free-air temperature range: SN52811 Circuits	−55°C to 125°C
SN72811 Circuits	0°C to 70°C
Storage temperature range	−65°C to 150°C
Lead temperature 1/16 inch from case for 60 seconds: FA, J, or L package	300°C
Lead temperature 1/16 inch from case for 10 seconds: N package	260°C

NOTES: 1. All voltage values, except differential voltages, are with respect to the network ground terminal.
2. Differential voltages are at the noninverting input terminal with respect to the inverting input terminal.
3. For operation of the SN52811 above 70°C free-air temperature, refer to Dissipating Derating Curve, Figure 10.

TEXAS INSTRUMENTS
INCORPORATED
POST OFFICE BOX 5012 • DALLAS, TEXAS 75222

electrical characteristics at specified free-air temperature, V_{CC+} = 12 V, V_{CC-} = −6 V (unless otherwise noted)

PARAMETER		TEST CONDITIONS[†]		SN52811			SN72811			UNIT
				MIN	TYP	MAX	MIN	TYP	MAX	
V_{IO}	Input offset voltage	$R_S \leqslant 200\ \Omega$, $V_{IC} = 0$, See Note 4	25°C		1	3.5		1	5	mV
			Full range			4.5			6	
		$R_S \leqslant 200\ \Omega$, See Note 4	25°C		1	5		1	7.5	
			Full range			6			10	
α_{VIO}	Average temperature coefficient of input offset voltage	$R_S \leqslant 200\ \Omega$, $V_{IC} = 0$, See Note 4	Full range		5			5		$\mu V/°C$
I_{IO}	Input offset current	See Note 4	25°C		0.5	3		0.5	5	μA
			Full range			5			10	
I_{IB}	Input bias current	See Note 4	25°C		7	20		7	30	μA
			Full range			30			50	
I_{SL}	Low-level strobe current	$V_{(strobe)} = -100\ mV$	25°C		−1.2	−2.5		−1.2	−2.5	mA
V_{ICR}	Common-mode input voltage range	$V_{CC-} = -7\ V$	25°C	±5			±5			V
V_{ID}	Differential input voltage range		25°C	±5			±5			V
A_{VD}	Large-signal differential voltage amplification	$V_O = 0\ to\ 2.5\ V$, No load	25°C	12,500	17,500		10,000	17,500		
			Full range	8,000			5,000			
V_{OH}	High-level output voltage	$V_{ID} = 10\ mV$, $I_{OH} = 0$	25°C		4	5		4	5	V
		$V_{ID} = 10\ mV$, $I_{OH} = -5\ mA$	25°C	2.5	3.6		2.5	3.6		
V_{OL}	Low-level output voltage	$V_{ID} = -10\ mV$, $I_{OL} = 0$	25°C	−1	−0.4	0[‡]	−1	−0.4	0[‡]	V
		$V_{ID} = 10\ mV$, $V_{(strobe)} = 0.3\ V$, $I_{OL} = 0$	25°C	−1		0[‡]	−1		0[‡]	
I_{OL}	Low-level output current	$V_{ID} = -10\ mV$, $V_O = 0$	25°C	0.5	0.8		0.5	0.8		mA
r_o	Output resistance	$V_O = 1.4\ V$	25°C		200			200		Ω
CMRR	Common-mode rejection ratio	$R_S \leqslant 200\ \Omega$	25°C	70	90		65	90		dB
I_{CC+}	Supply current from V_{CC+}	$V_{ID} = -5\ to\ 5\ V$	25°C		6.5			6.5		mA
I_{CC-}	Supply current from V_{CC-}	(−10 mV for typ),	25°C		−2.7			−2.7		mA
P_D	Total power dissipation	No load, See Note 5	25°C		94	150		94	200	mW

[†]Unless otherwise noted, all characteristics are measured with the strobe of the channel under test open, the strobe of the other channel is grounded. Full range for SN52811 is −55°C to 125°C and for the SN72811 is 0°C to 70°C.

[‡]The algebraic convention where the most-positive (least-negative) limit is designated as maximum is used in this data sheet for logic levels only, e.g., when 0 V is the maximum, the minimum limit is a more-negative voltage.

NOTES: 4. These characteristics are verified by measurements at the following temperatures and output voltage levels: for SN52811, $V_O = 1.8\ V$ at $T_A = -55°C$, $V_O = 1.4\ V$ at $T_A = 25°C$, and $V_O = 1\ V$ at $T_A = 125°C$; for SN72811, $V_O = 1.5\ V$ at $T_A = 0°C$, $V_O = 1.4\ V$ at $T_A = 25°C$, and $V_O = 1.2\ V$ at 70°C. These output voltage levels were selected to approximate the logic threshold voltages of the types of digital logic circuits these comparators are intended to drive.

     5. The strobes are alternately grounded.

switching characteristics, V_{CC+} = 12 V, V_{CC-} = −6 V, $T_A = 25°C$

PARAMETER	TEST CONDITIONS	SN52811			SN72811			UNIT
		MIN	TYP	MAX	MIN	TYP	MAX	
Response time	$R_L = \infty$, $C_L = 5\ pF$, See Note 6		33	80		33		ns
Strobe release time	$R_L = \infty$, $C_L = 5\ pF$, See Note 7		5	25		5		ns

NOTES: 6. The response time specified is for a 100-mV input step with 5-mV overdrive.

     7. For testing purposes, the input bias conditions are selected to produce an output voltage of 1.4 V. A 5-mV overdrive is then added to the input bias voltage to produce an output voltage which rises above 1.4 V. The time interval is measured from the 50% point of the strobe voltage curve to the point where the overdriven output voltage crosses the 1.4 V level.

TEXAS INSTRUMENTS
INCORPORATED
POST OFFICE BOX 5012 • DALLAS, TEXAS 75222

TYPES SN52811, SN72811
DUAL-CHANNEL DIFFERENTIAL COMPARATORS WITH STROBES

DEFINITION OF TERMS

Input Offset Voltage (V_{IO}) The d-c voltage which must be applied between the input terminals to force the quiescent d-c output voltage to the specified level. The input offset voltage may also be defined for the case where two equal resistances (R_S) are inserted in series with the input leads.

Average Temperature Coefficient of Input Offset Voltage (α_{VIO}) The ratio of the change in input offset voltage to the change in free-air temperature. This is an average value for the specified temperature range.

$$\alpha_{VIO} = \left| \frac{(V_{IO} @ T_{A(1)}) - (V_{IO} @ T_{A(2)})}{T_{A(1)} - T_{A(2)}} \right|$$ where $T_{A(1)}$ and $T_{A(2)}$ are the specified temperature extremes.

Input Offset Current (I_{IO}) The difference between the currents into the two input terminals with the output at the specified level.

Input Bias Current (I_{IB}) The average of the currents into the two input terminals with the output at the specified level.

Low-Level Strobe Current (I_{SL}) The current flowing out of the strobe at a low-level voltage.

Common-Mode Input Voltage Range (V_{ICR}) The range of common-mode voltage which if exceeded will cause the comparator to cease functioning properly.

Differential Input Voltage Range (V_{ID}) The range of voltage between the two input terminals which if exceeded will cause the comparator to cease functioning properly.

Large-Signal Differential Voltage Amplification (A_{VD}) The ratio of the change in output voltage to the change in differential input voltage producing it.

High-Level Output Voltage (V_{OH}) The voltage at the output with the specified input conditions applied which should establish a high level at the output.

Low-Level Output Voltage (V_{OL}) The voltage at the output with the specified input conditions applied which should establish a low level at the output.

Low-Level Output Current (I_{OL}) The current flowing into the output at a specified low-level output voltage.

Output Resistance (r_o) The resistance between the output terminal and ground.

Common-Mode Rejection Ratio (CMRR) The ratio of differential voltage amplification to common-mode voltage amplification. This is measured by determining the ratio of a change in input common-mode voltage to the resulting change in input offset voltage.

Total Power Dissipation (P_D) The total d-c power supplied to the device less any power delivered from the device to a load. At no load: $P_D = V_{CC+} \cdot I_{CC+} + V_{CC-} \cdot I_{CC-}$.

Response Time The interval between the application of an input step function and the time when the output crosses the logic threshold voltage. The input step drives the comparator from some initial condition sufficient to saturate the output to an input level just barely in excess of that required to bring the output back to the logic threshold voltage. This excess is referred to as the voltage overdrive.

Strobe Release Time The time required for the output to rise to the logic threshold voltage after the strobe terminal has been driven from the low logic level to the high logic level. Appropriate input conditions are assumed.

TEXAS INSTRUMENTS
INCORPORATED
POST OFFICE BOX 5012 • DALLAS, TEXAS 75222

TYPICAL CHARACTERISTICS

LARGE-SIGNAL DIFFERENTIAL
VOLTAGE AMPLIFICATION
vs
FREE-AIR TEMPERATURE

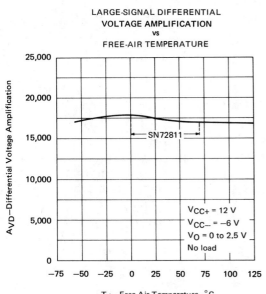

FIGURE 1

LARGE-SIGNAL DIFFERENTIAL
VOLTAGE AMPLIFICATION
vs
SUPPLY VOLTAGE

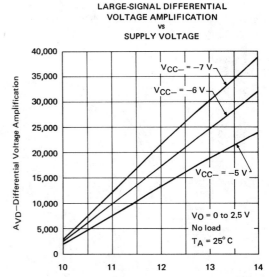

FIGURE 2

SN52811
VOLTAGE TRANSFER CHARACTERISTICS

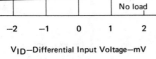

FIGURE 3

SN72811
VOLTAGE TRANSFER CHARACTERISTICS

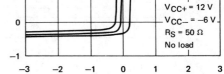

FIGURE 4

6

TYPICAL CHARACTERISTICS

OUTPUT RESPONSE FOR
VARIOUS INPUT OVERDRIVES

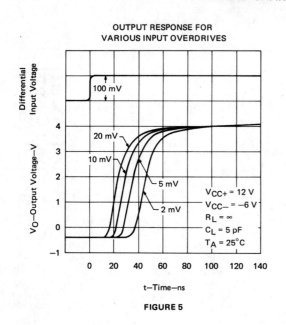

FIGURE 5

STROBE RELEASE TIME
FOR VARIOUS INPUT OVERDRIVES

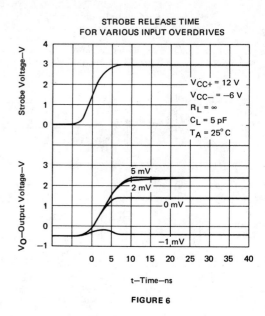

FIGURE 6

COMMON-MODE PULSE RESPONSE

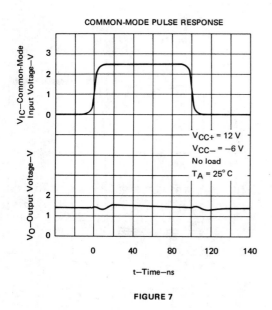

FIGURE 7

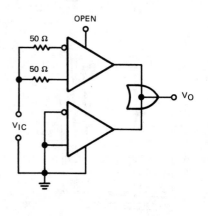

TEST CIRCUIT
FOR FIGURE 7

TEXAS INSTRUMENTS
INCORPORATED
POST OFFICE BOX 5012 • DALLAS, TEXAS 75222

TYPICAL CHARACTERISTICS

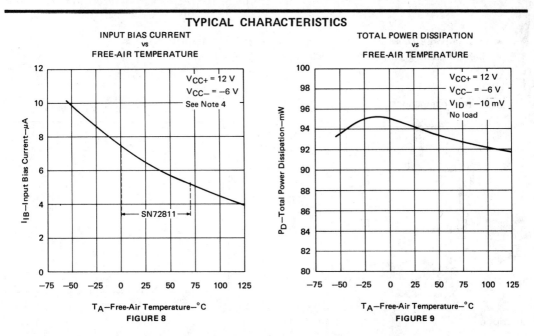

FIGURE 8

FIGURE 9

NOTE 4. These characteristics are verified by measurements at the following temperatures and output voltage levels: for SN52811, V_O = 1.8 V at T_A = −55°C, V_O = 1.4 V at T_A = 25°C, and V_O = 1 V at T_A = 125°C; for SN72811, V_O = 1.5 V at T_A = 0°C, V_O = 1.4 V at T_A = 25°C, and V_O = 1.2 V at 70°C. These output voltage levels were selected to approximate the logic threshold voltages of the types of digital logic circuits these comparators are intended to drive.

THERMAL INFORMATION

DISSIPATION DERATING CURVE

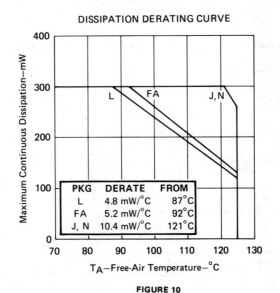

PKG	DERATE	FROM
L	4.8 mW/°C	87°C
FA	5.2 mW/°C	92°C
J, N	10.4 mW/°C	121°C

FIGURE 10

TEXAS INSTRUMENTS
INCORPORATED
POST OFFICE BOX 5012 • DALLAS, TEXAS 75222

- **Fast Response Times**
- **High Differential Voltage Amplification**
- **Low Offset Characteristics**
- **Outputs Compatible with Most TTL and DTL Circuits**

schematic (each comparator)

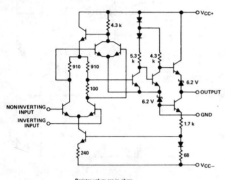

Resistor values are in ohms.
Component values shown are nominal.

J OR N
DUAL-IN-LINE PACKAGE (TOP VIEW)

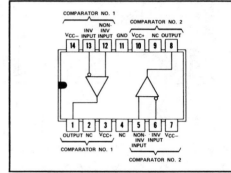

NC—No internal connection

description

The SN52820 and SN72820 are improved versions of the SN72720 dual high-speed voltage comparator. Each comparator has differential inputs and a low-impedance output. When compared with the SN72720, these circuits feature higher amplification (typically 33,000) due to an extra amplification stage and increased accuracy because of lower offset characteristics. They are particularly useful in applications requiring an amplitude discriminator, memory sense amplifier, or a high-speed limit detector. The SN52820 is characterized for operation over the full military temperature range of -55°C to 125°C; the SN72820 is characterized for operation from 0°C to 70°C.

absolute maximum ratings over operating free-air temperature range (unless otherwise noted)

Supply voltage V_{CC+} (see Note 1)	14 V
Supply voltage V_{CC-} (see Note 1)	−7 V
Differential input voltage (see Note 2)	±5 V
Input voltage (any input, see Note 1)	±7 V
Peak output current ($t_w \leqslant 1$ s)	10 mA
Continuous total power dissipation: each comparator	300 mW
total package, (see Note 3)	600 mW
Operating free-air temperature range: SN52820 Circuits	−55°C to 125°C
SN72820 Circuits	0°C to 70°C
Storage temperature range	−65°C to 150°C
Lead temperature 1/16 inch from case for 60 seconds: J package	300°C
Lead temperature 1/16 inch from case for 10 seconds: N package	260°C

NOTES: 1. All voltage values, except differential voltages, are with respect to the network ground terminal.
2. Differential voltages are at the noninverting input terminal with respect to the inverting input terminal.
3. For SN52820, this rating applies at (or below) 92°C free-air temperature. For operation above this temperature, derate linearly at the rate of 10.4 mW/°C. For SN72820, this rating applies at (or below) 70°C free-air temperature without derating.

TEXAS INSTRUMENTS
INCORPORATED
POST OFFICE BOX 5012 • DALLAS, TEXAS 75222

973

electrical characteristics at specified free-air temperature, V_{CC+} = 12 V, V_{CC-} = −6 V (unless otherwise noted)

PARAMETER		TEST CONDITIONS[†]		SN52820 MIN	TYP	MAX	SN72820 MIN	TYP	MAX	UNIT
V_{IO}	Input offset voltage	$R_S \leqslant 200\ \Omega$,	25°C		0.6	2		1.6	3.5	mV
		See Note 4	Full range			3			4.5	
α_{VIO}	Average temperature coefficient of input offset voltage	R_S = 50 Ω, See Note 4	MIN to 25°C		3	10		3	20	μV/°C
			25°C to MAX		3	10		3	20	
I_{IO}	Input offset current	See Note 4	25°C		0.75	3		1.8	5	μA
			MIN		1.8	7			7.5	
			MAX		0.25				7.5	
α_{IIO}	Average temperature coefficient of input offset current	See Note 4	MIN to 25°C		15	75		24	100	nA/°C
			25°C to MAX		5	25		15	50	
I_{IB}	Input bias current	See Note 4	25°C		7	15		7	20	μA
			MIN		12	25		9	30	
V_{ICR}	Common-mode input voltage range	V_{CC-} = −7 V	Full range	±5			±5			V
V_{ID}	Differential input voltage range		Full range	±5			±5			V
A_{VD}	Large-signal differential voltage amplification	No load, V_O = 0 to 2.5 V	25°C	12,500	33,000		10,000	33,000		
			Full range	10,000			8,000			
V_{OH}	High-level output voltage	V_{ID} = 5 mV, I_{OH} = 0	Full range		4§	5		4§	5	V
		V_{ID} = 5 mV, I_{OH} = −5 mA	Full range	2.5	3.6§		2.5	3.6§		
V_{OL}	Low-level output voltage	V_{ID} = −5 mV, I_{OL} = 0	Full range	−1	−0.5§	0‡	−1	−0.5§	0‡	V
I_{OL}	Low-level output current	V_{ID} = −5 mV, V_O = 0	25°C	2	2.4		1.6	2.4		mA
			MIN	1	2.3		0.5	2.4		
			MAX	0.5	2.3		0.5	2.4		
r_o	Output resistance	V_O = 1.4 V	25°C		200			200		Ω
CMRR	Common-mode rejection ratio	$R_S \leqslant 200\ \Omega$	Full range	80	100§		70	100§		dB
I_{CC+}	Supply current from V_{CC+} (each comparator)	V_{ID} = −5 mV, No load	Full range		5.5§	9		5.5§	9	mA
I_{CC-}	Supply current from V_{CC-} (each comparator)		Full range		−3.5§	−7		−3.5§	−7	mA
P_D	Total power dissipation (each comparator)		Full range		90§	150		90§	150	mW

[†]Full range (MIN to MAX) for SN52820 is −55°C to 125°C and for the SN72820 is 0°C to 70°C.

[‡]The algebraic convention where the most-positive (least-negative) limit is designated as maximum is used in this data sheet for logic levels only, e.g., when 0 V is the maximum, the minimum limit is a more-negative voltage.

[§]These typical values are at T_A = 25°C.

NOTE 4: These characteristics are verified by measurements at the following temperatures and output voltage levels: for SN52820, V_O = 1.8 V at T_A = −55°C, V_O = 1.4 V at T_A = 25°C, and V_O = 1V at T_A = 125°C; for SN72820, V_O = 1.5 V at T_A = 0°C, V_O = 1.4 V at 25°C, and V_O = 1.2 V at T_A = 70°C. These output voltage levels were selected to approximate the logic threshold voltages of the types of digital logic circuits these comparators are intended to drive.

switching characteristics, V_{CC+} = 12 V, V_{CC-} = −6 V, T_A = 25°C

PARAMETER	TEST CONDITIONS	MIN	TYP	MAX	UNIT
Response time	R_L = ∞, C_L = 5 pF, See Note 5		30	80	ns

NOTE 5: The response time specified is for a 100-mV input step with 5-mV overdrive.

For definition of terms and typical characteristic curves, see the SN52810/SN72810 data sheet on page 6-44.

Video Amplifiers
and
Special Functions

TYPE		SN52733, SN72733	SN5510, SN7510	SN5511, SN7511	SN5512, SN7512	SN5514, SN7514	UNIT
Differential Voltage Amplification, Typ		10 to 400 (Adjustable)	93	3000	300	300	
Bandwidth (−3 dB), Typ		200 (Gain of 10)	40	3	80	80	MHz
Bandwidth (Unity-Gain), Typ		400	300	100	400	400	MHz
Input Offset Current, Typ		0.4	3	0.6	1	1	μA
Input Offset Voltage, Typ		1.5 (Gain of 400)	5	1	1 (can be nulled)	1	mV
Output Voltage Swing, Typ		4.7	4	5	3.4	3.4	V p-p
Packages	Series 52 and 55	FA, J, L	FA, JP, L	FA, L, N	L, N	JP, L	
	Series 72 and 75	FA, J, L, N	FA, L, P	FA, L, N	L, N	L, P	

7

WIDE-BAND VIDEO AMPLIFIER
FEATURING
Flat Frequency Response with Low Phase-Shift from DC to 40 MHz

description

This wide-band video amplifier features a flat frequency response and low phase-shift from dc to 40 MHz. Differential inputs and outputs are provided which permit it to be used as a high-frequency differential amplifier.

Elements of the SN5510 video-amplifier bar include transistors with transition frequency as high as 1.2 GHz under low-current and low-V_{CE} conditions. Circuit frequency response from dc to greater than 100 MHz is possible.

schematic

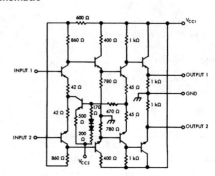

Component values shown are nominal.

terminal assignments

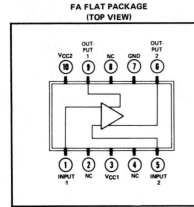

FA FLAT PACKAGE (TOP VIEW)

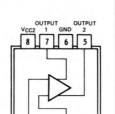

JP DUAL-IN-LINE PACKAGE (TOP VIEW)

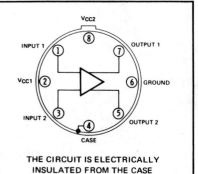

L PLUG-IN PACKAGE (TOP VIEW)

THE CIRCUIT IS ELECTRICALLY INSULATED FROM THE CASE

NC—No internal connection

TEXAS INSTRUMENTS
INCORPORATED
POST OFFICE BOX 5012 • DALLAS, TEXAS 75222

absolute maximum ratings over operating free-air temperature range (unless otherwise noted)

Supply voltages (See Note 1): V_{CC1} . . . . +8 V

V_{CC2} . . . . −8 V

Differential input voltage . . . . 5 V

Positive input voltage (See Note 1) . . . . V_{CC1}

Negative input voltage (See Note 1) . . . . V_{CC2}

Operating free-air temperature range . . . . −55°C to 100°C

Storage temperature range . . . . −65°C to 150°C

NOTE 1: These voltage values are with respect to network ground.

electrical characteristics, T_A = 25°C, V_{CC1} = +6 V, V_{CC2} = −6 V

	PARAMETER	TEST FIGURE	TEST CONDITIONS	MIN	TYP	MAX	UNIT
V_{DO}	Differential-output offset voltage	1			0.5	1.3	V
$V_{CMO(av)}$	Average common-mode output offset voltage	1		2.6	3.1	3.5	V
I_{in}	Input current	1			40	80	µA
I_{DI}	Differential-input offset current	1			3	20	µA
D_S	Single-ended output distortion	2	Load resistance = 5 kΩ, input distortion < 0.2%, V_{out} = 1 V rms, f = 10 kHz		1.5	5	%
$V_{N(in)}$	Equivalent average input noise voltage	3	Single-ended, R_s = 0, f = 10 Hz to 500 kHz		5		µV
V_{CMIM}	Maximum common-mode input voltage				±1		V
A_{vs}	Small-signal voltage gain	2	Single-ended, load resistance = 5 kΩ, f = 100 kHz	75	93	110	
A_{vcm}	Common-mode-input voltage gain	4	Single-ended, load resistance = 5 kΩ, V_{in} = 0.3 V rms, f = 100 kHz		−45	−30	dB
CMRR	Common-mode rejection ratio	4	Load resistance = 5 kΩ, f = 100 kHz		85		dB
BW	Bandwidth (−3 dB)	2			40		MHz
r_{in}	Input resistance	5	f = 100 kHz		6		kΩ
C_{in}	Input capacitance	5	f = 100 kHz		7		pF
z_{out}	Output impedance	5	f = 100 kHz		35		Ω
P_T	Total power dissipation	1	No input signal, no external load		165	220	mW
t_r	Rise time	6	Single-ended, V_{in} = 5 mV		9	12	ns
t_f	Fall time	6	Single-ended, V_{in} = 5 mV		9	12	ns

TEXAS INSTRUMENTS
INCORPORATED
POST OFFICE BOX 5012 • DALLAS, TEXAS 75222

letter symbol and parameter definitions

V_{DO} — The d-c differential voltage that exists between the output terminals when the input terminals are at ground.

$V_{CMO(av)}$ — The average of the d-c output voltages with respect to ground when the input terminals are grounded.

I_{DI} — The difference in the currents into the two input terminals.

V_{CMIM} — The maximum common-mode voltage that can be impressed on the input terminals while maintaining differential operation.

CMRR — The ratio of the differential-mode voltage gain to the common-mode voltage gain.

BW — The range of frequencies within which the open-loop voltage gain is within 3 dB of the mid-frequency value.

PARAMETER MEASUREMENT INFORMATION

test circuits

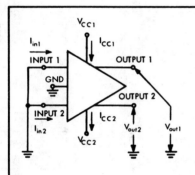

1. $V_{DO} = |V_{out1} - V_{out2}|$

2. $V_{CMO(av)} = \dfrac{V_{out1} + V_{out2}}{2}$

3. $I_{DI} = |I_{in1} - I_{in2}|$

4. $P_T = |V_{CC1} \cdot I_{CC1}| + |V_{CC2} \cdot I_{CC2}|$

FIGURE 1

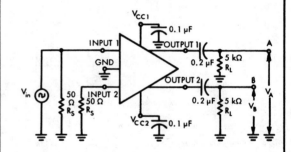

1. Single-ended output distortion is measured at A or B with V_A or $V_B = 1$ V rms, input distortion $< 0.2\%$, and $f = 10$ kHz.

2. $A_{VS} = \left| \dfrac{V_A \text{ or } V_B}{V_{in}} \right|$

   where: $V_{in} = 1$ mV rms and $f = 100$ kHz.

FIGURE 2

TEXAS INSTRUMENTS
INCORPORATED
POST OFFICE BOX 5012 • DALLAS, TEXAS 75222

PARAMETER MEASUREMENT INFORMATION

test circuits (continued)

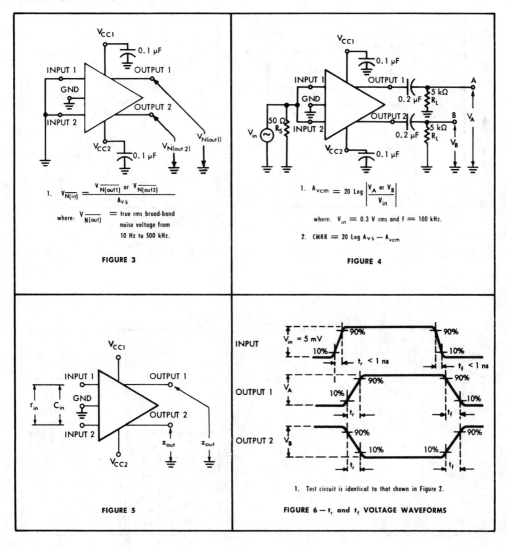

1. $V_{\overline{N(in)}} = \dfrac{V_{\overline{N(out1)}} \text{ or } V_{\overline{N(out2)}}}{A_{VS}}$

where: $V_{\overline{N(out)}}$ = true rms broad-band noise voltage from 10 Hz to 500 kHz.

FIGURE 3

1. $A_{vcm} = 20 \text{ Log} \left| \dfrac{V_A \text{ or } V_B}{V_{in}} \right|$

where: $V_{in} = 0.3$ V rms and f = 100 kHz.

2. $CMRR = 20 \text{ Log } A_{VS} - A_{vcm}$

FIGURE 4

FIGURE 5

1. Test circuit is identical to that shown in Figure 2.

FIGURE 6 — t_r and t_f VOLTAGE WAVEFORMS

TYPICAL CHARACTERISTICS†

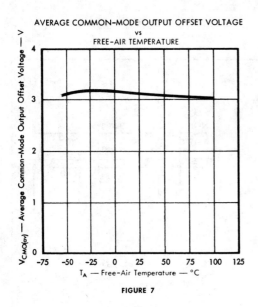

FIGURE 7

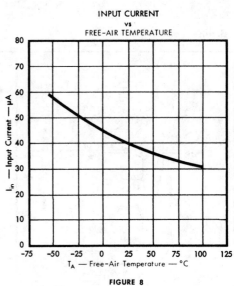

FIGURE 8

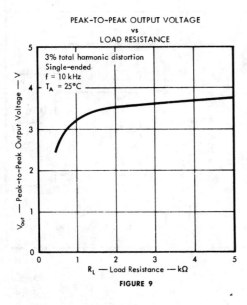

FIGURE 9

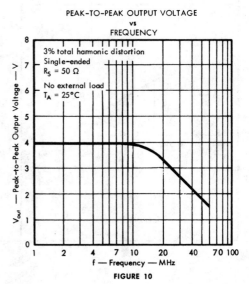

FIGURE 10

†Unless otherwise noted $V_{CC1} = +6$ V, $V_{CC2} = -6$ V.

TEXAS INSTRUMENTS
INCORPORATED
POST OFFICE BOX 5012 • DALLAS, TEXAS 75222

TYPICAL CHARACTERISTICS†

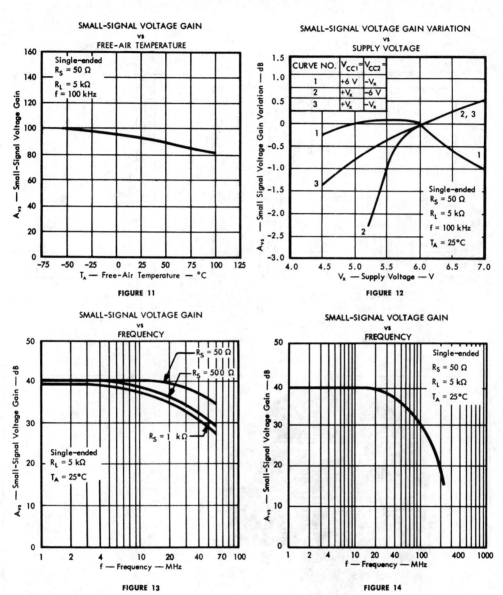

SMALL-SIGNAL VOLTAGE GAIN
vs
FREE-AIR TEMPERATURE

Single-ended
$R_S = 50 \ \Omega$
$R_L = 5 \ k\Omega$
$f = 100 \ kHz$

FIGURE 11

SMALL-SIGNAL VOLTAGE GAIN VARIATION
vs
SUPPLY VOLTAGE

CURVE NO.	$V_{CC1}=$	$V_{CC2}=$
1	+6 V	$-V_x$
2	$+V_x$	-6 V
3	$+V_x$	$-V_x$

Single-ended
$R_S = 50 \ \Omega$
$R_L = 5 \ k\Omega$
$f = 100 \ kHz$
$T_A = 25°C$

FIGURE 12

SMALL-SIGNAL VOLTAGE GAIN
vs
FREQUENCY

$R_S = 50 \ \Omega$
$R_S = 500 \ \Omega$
$R_S = 1 \ k\Omega$

Single-ended
$R_L = 5 \ k\Omega$
$T_A = 25°C$

FIGURE 13

SMALL-SIGNAL VOLTAGE GAIN
vs
FREQUENCY

Single-ended
$R_S = 50 \ \Omega$
$R_L = 5 \ k\Omega$
$T_A = 25°C$

FIGURE 14

†Unless otherwise noted $V_{CC1} = +6 \ V$, $V_{CC2} = -6 \ V$.

TYPICAL CHARACTERISTICS†

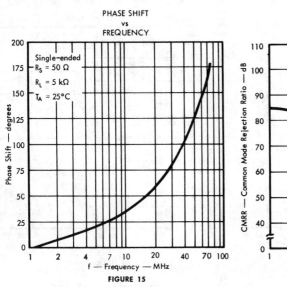

PHASE SHIFT
vs
FREQUENCY

FIGURE 15

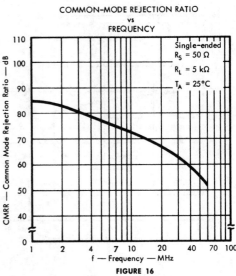

COMMON-MODE REJECTION RATIO
vs
FREQUENCY

FIGURE 16

†V_{CC1} = +6 V and V_{CC2} = −6 V.

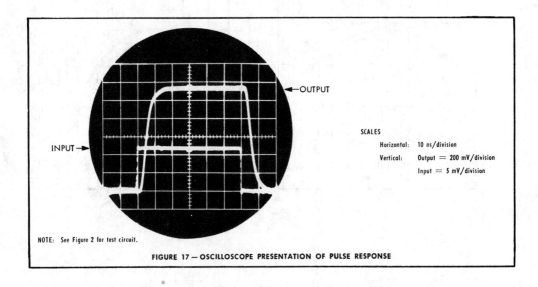

SCALES

Horizontal: 10 ns/division

Vertical: Output = 200 mV/division

Input = 5 mV/division

NOTE: See Figure 2 for test circuit.

FIGURE 17 — OSCILLOSCOPE PRESENTATION OF PULSE RESPONSE

TEXAS INSTRUMENTS
INCORPORATED
POST OFFICE BOX 5012 • DALLAS, TEXAS 75222

WIDE-BAND VIDEO AMPLIFIER
FEATURING
Flat Frequency Response with Low Phase-Shift from DC to 40 MHz

description

This wide-band video amplifier features a flat frequency response and low phase-shift from dc to 40 MHz. Differential inputs and outputs are provided which permit it to be used as a high-frequency differential amplifier.

Elements of the SN7510 video-amplifier bar include transistors with transition frequency as high as 1.2 GHz under low-current and low-V_{CE} conditions. Circuit frequency response from dc to greater than 100 MHz is possible.

schematic

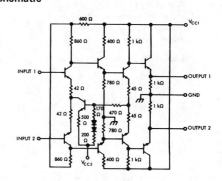

Component values shown are nominal.

terminal assignments

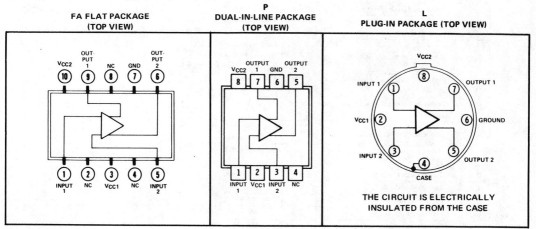

FA FLAT PACKAGE (TOP VIEW)

P DUAL-IN-LINE PACKAGE (TOP VIEW)

L PLUG-IN PACKAGE (TOP VIEW)

THE CIRCUIT IS ELECTRICALLY INSULATED FROM THE CASE

NC—No internal connection

absolute maximum ratings over operating free-air temperature range (unless otherwise noted)

Supply voltages (See Note 1): V_{CC1}	. . . .	+8 V
V_{CC2}	. . . .	−8 V
Differential input voltage		5 V
Positive input voltage (See Note 1)		V_{CC1}
Negative input voltage (See Note 1)		V_{CC2}
Operating free-air temperature range		0°C to 70°C
Storage temperature range		−65°C to 150°C

NOTE 1: These voltage values are with respect to network ground.

electrical characteristics, $T_A = 25°C$, $V_{CC1} = +6$ V, $V_{CC2} = -6$ V

	PARAMETER	TEST FIGURE	TEST CONDITIONS	MIN	TYP	MAX	UNIT
V_{DO}	Differential-output offset voltage	1			0.5	2	V
$V_{CMO(av)}$	Average common-mode output offset voltage	1		2	3	4	V
I_{in}	Input current	1			50	100	μA
I_{DI}	Differential-input offset current	1			5	30	μA
V_{OM}	Maximum peak-to-peak output voltage	2	Single-ended, load resistance = 5 kΩ, f = 100 kHz, V_{in} = 20 mV rms		4.5		V
D_S	Single-ended output distortion	2	Load resistance = 5 kΩ, input distortion < 0.2%, V_{out} = 1 V rms, f = 10 kHz		2		%
$V_{\overline{N(in)}}$	Equivalent average input noise voltage	3	Single-ended, R_S = 0, f = 10 Hz to 500 kHz		5		μV
V_{CMIM}	Maximum common-mode input voltage				±1		V
A_{vs}	Small-signal voltage gain	2	Single-ended, load resistance = 5 kΩ, f = 100 kHz	60	90	120	
A_{vcm}	Common-mode-input voltage gain	4	Single-ended, load resistance = 5 kΩ, V_{in} = 0.3 V rms, f = 100 kHz		−40	−20	dB
CMRR	Common-mode rejection ratio	4	Load resistance = 5 kΩ, f = 100 kHz		80		dB
BW	Bandwidth (−3 dB)	2			40		MHz
r_{in}	Input resistance	5	f = 100 kHz		6		kΩ
C_{in}	Input capacitance	5	f = 100 kHz		7		pF
z_{out}	Output impedance	5	f = 100 kHz		35		Ω
P_T	Total power dissipation	1	No input signal, no external load		165	220	mW
t_r	Rise time	6	Single-ended, V_{in} = 5 mV		10	15	ns
t_f	Fall time	6	Single-ended, V_{in} = 5 mV		10	15	ns

TEXAS INSTRUMENTS
INCORPORATED
POST OFFICE BOX 5012 • DALLAS, TEXAS 75222

letter symbol and parameter definitions

V_{DO} The d-c differential voltage that exists between the output terminals when the input terminals are at ground.

$V_{CMO(av)}$ The average of the d-c output voltages with respect to ground when the input terminals are grounded.

I_{DI} The difference in the currents into the two input terminals.

V_{OM} The maximum peak-to-peak output voltage swing that can be obtained without clipping.

V_{CMIM} The maximum common-mode voltage that can be impressed on the input terminals while maintaining differential operation.

CMRR   The ratio of the differential-mode voltage gain to the common-mode voltage gain.

BW   The range of frequencies within which the open-loop voltage gain is within 3 dB of the mid-frequency value.

PARAMETER MEASUREMENT INFORMATION

test circuits

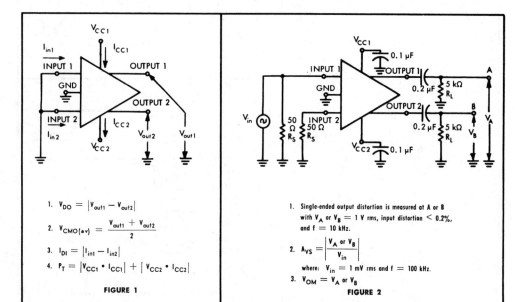

1. $V_{DO} = \left| V_{out1} - V_{out2} \right|$

2. $V_{CMO(av)} = \dfrac{V_{out1} + V_{out2}}{2}$

3. $I_{DI} = \left| I_{in1} - I_{in2} \right|$

4. $P_T = \left| V_{CC1} \cdot I_{CC1} \right| + \left| V_{CC2} \cdot I_{CC2} \right|$

FIGURE 1

1. Single-ended output distortion is measured at A or B with V_A or $V_B = 1$ V rms, input distortion $< 0.2\%$, and $f = 10$ kHz.

2. $A_{VS} = \left| \dfrac{V_A \text{ or } V_B}{V_{in}} \right|$

where: $V_{in} = 1$ mV rms and $f = 100$ kHz.

3. $V_{OM} = V_A$ or V_B

FIGURE 2

PARAMETER MEASUREMENT INFORMATION

test circuits (continued)

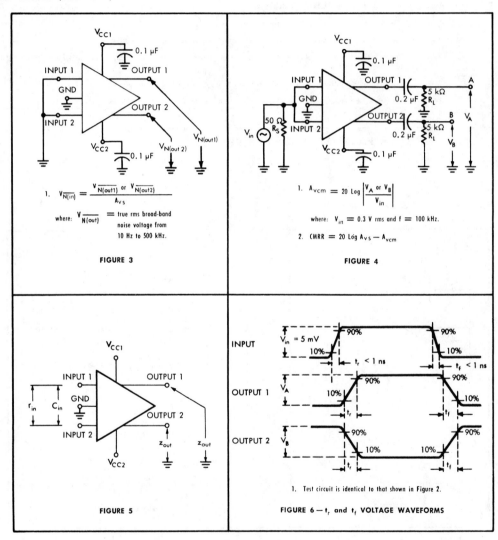

1. $V_{\overline{N(in)}} = \dfrac{V_{\overline{N(out1)}} \text{ or } V_{\overline{N(out2)}}}{A_{VS}}$

where: $V_{\overline{N(out)}}$ = true rms broad-band noise voltage from 10 Hz to 500 kHz.

FIGURE 3

1. $A_{vcm} = 20 \, \text{Log} \left| \dfrac{V_A \text{ or } V_B}{V_{in}} \right|$

where: $V_{in} = 0.3$ V rms and f = 100 kHz.

2. $CMRR = 20 \, \text{Log} \, A_{VS} - A_{vcm}$

FIGURE 4

FIGURE 5

1. Test circuit is identical to that shown in Figure 2.

FIGURE 6 — t_r and t_f VOLTAGE WAVEFORMS

TEXAS INSTRUMENTS
INCORPORATED
POST OFFICE BOX 5012 • DALLAS, TEXAS 75222

TYPICAL CHARACTERISTICS†

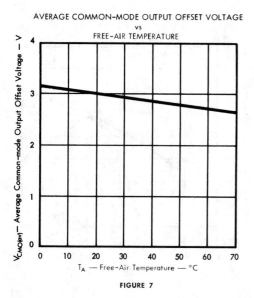

AVERAGE COMMON-MODE OUTPUT OFFSET VOLTAGE
vs
FREE-AIR TEMPERATURE

FIGURE 7

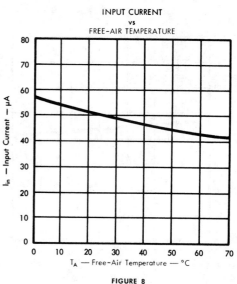

INPUT CURRENT
vs
FREE-AIR TEMPERATURE

FIGURE 8

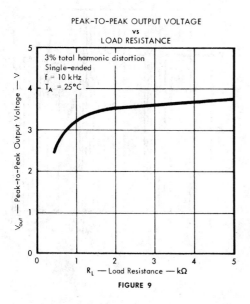

PEAK-TO-PEAK OUTPUT VOLTAGE
vs
LOAD RESISTANCE

3% total harmonic distortion
Single-ended
f = 10 kHz
T_A = 25°C

FIGURE 9

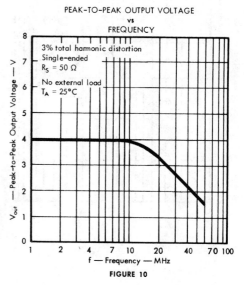

PEAK-TO-PEAK OUTPUT VOLTAGE
vs
FREQUENCY

3% total harmonic distortion
Single-ended
R_S = 50 Ω
No external load
T_A = 25°C

FIGURE 10

† Unless otherwise noted V_{CC1} = +6 V, V_{CC2} = −6 V.

TYPE SN7510
DIFFERENTIAL VIDEO AMPLIFIER

TYPICAL CHARACTERISTICS†

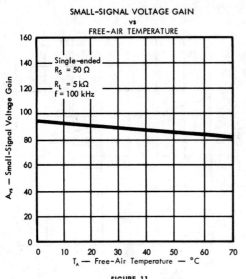

SMALL-SIGNAL VOLTAGE GAIN
vs
FREE-AIR TEMPERATURE

Single-ended
R_S = 50 Ω
R_L = 5 kΩ
f = 100 kHz

A_{vs} — Small-Signal Voltage Gain

T_A — Free-Air Temperature — °C

FIGURE 11

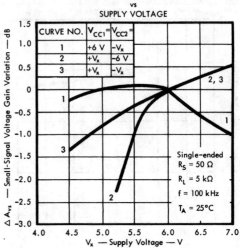

SMALL-SIGNAL VOLTAGE GAIN VARIATION
vs
SUPPLY VOLTAGE

CURVE NO.	V_{CC1} =	V_{CC2} =
1	+6 V	$-V_x$
2	$+V_x$	-6 V
3	$+V_x$	$-V_x$

Single-ended
R_S = 50 Ω
R_L = 5 kΩ
f = 100 kHz
T_A = 25°C

ΔA_{vs} — Small-Signal Voltage Gain Variation — dB

V_x — Supply Voltage — V

FIGURE 12

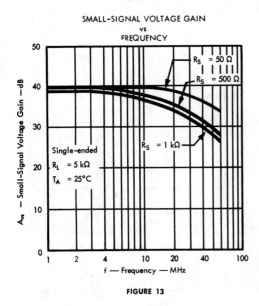

SMALL-SIGNAL VOLTAGE GAIN
vs
FREQUENCY

R_S = 50 Ω
R_S = 500 Ω
R_S = 1 kΩ

Single-ended
R_L = 5 kΩ
T_A = 25°C

A_{vs} — Small-Signal Voltage Gain — dB

f — Frequency — MHz

FIGURE 13

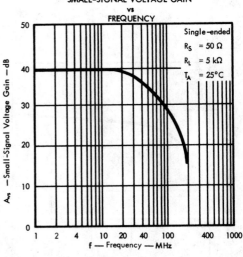

SMALL-SIGNAL VOLTAGE GAIN
vs
FREQUENCY

Single-ended
R_S = 50 Ω
R_L = 5 kΩ
T_A = 25°C

A_{vs} — Small-Signal Voltage Gain — dB

f — Frequency — MHz

FIGURE 14

† Unless otherwise noted V_{CC1} = + 6 V, V_{CC2} = −6 V.

TEXAS INSTRUMENTS
INCORPORATED
POST OFFICE BOX 5012 • DALLAS, TEXAS 75222

TYPICAL CHARACTERISTICS†

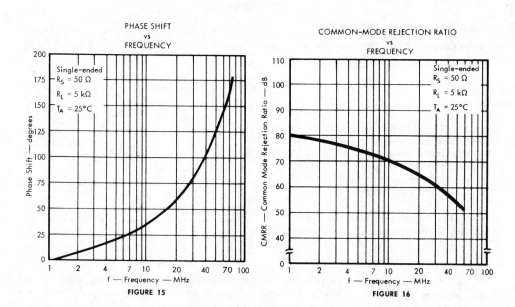

PHASE SHIFT
vs
FREQUENCY

Single-ended
$R_S = 50\ \Omega$
$R_L = 5\ k\Omega$
$T_A = 25°C$

Phase Shift — degrees

f — Frequency — MHz

FIGURE 15

COMMON-MODE REJECTION RATIO
vs
FREQUENCY

Single-ended
$R_S = 50\ \Omega$
$R_L = 5\ k\Omega$
$T_A = 25°C$

CMRR — Common Mode Rejection Ratio — dB

f — Frequency — MHz

FIGURE 16

† $V_{CC1} = +6\ V$ and $V_{CC2} = -6\ V$.

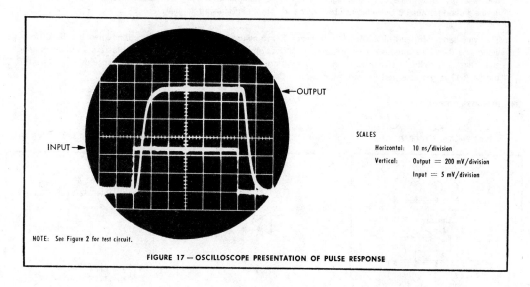

←OUTPUT

INPUT →

SCALES

Horizontal: 10 ns/division

Vertical: Output = 200 mV/division

              Input = 5 mV/division

NOTE: See Figure 2 for test circuit.

FIGURE 17 — OSCILLOSCOPE PRESENTATION OF PULSE RESPONSE

TEXAS INSTRUMENTS
INCORPORATED
POST OFFICE BOX 5012 • DALLAS, TEXAS 75222

- **Low Common-Mode Offset Voltage**
- **High Common-Mode Rejection Ratio**
- **High Gain-Bandwidth Product**

schematic

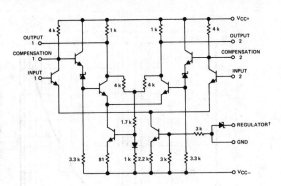

Resistor values are nominal in ohms.

† Regulator terminal is used only with single supply. See description.

description

The SN5511 and SN7511 are wide-band amplifiers with differential inputs and outputs. High gain and low offset voltage permit use in applications requiring feedback. Frequency characteristics are such that a stable closed-loop configuration with 30-dB gain results in a 30-MHz bandwidth.

Accessibility to first-stage collectors makes offset balancing and frequency compensation possible with minimal effect on input and frequency characteristics.

The base of the first-stage current-source transistor is made available to permit operation from either a single 12-volt power supply or two 6-volt power supplies. For the latter, leave the regulator terminal open and connect the positive terminal of one supply to V_{CC+}, the negative terminal of the other supply to V_{CC-}, and the remaining terminals of the two supplies to the device ground terminal. For operation from a single 12-volt supply, connect the positive terminal of the supply to both the V_{CC+} and regulator terminals and connect the negative terminal to V_{CC-}. In either case, the device ground terminal is the reference for single-ended input and output voltages.

The wide bandwidth and high gain allow this amplifier to be used in a variety of applications where a stable differential video amplifier is required. Low common-mode offset voltage extends possible uses to comparators and direct-coupled amplifiers. The SN5511 is characterized for operation over the full military temperature range of $-55°C$ to $125°C$; the SN7511 is characterized for operation from $0°C$ to $70°C$.

terminal assignments

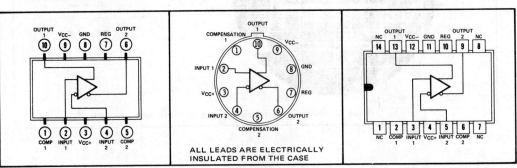

FA
FLAT PACKAGE (TOP VIEW)

L
PLUG-IN PACKAGE (TOP VIEW)

N
DUAL-IN-LINE PACKAGE (TOP VIEW)

ALL LEADS ARE ELECTRICALLY
INSULATED FROM THE CASE

NC — No internal connection

TEXAS INSTRUMENTS
INCORPORATED
POST OFFICE BOX 5012 • DALLAS, TEXAS 75222

absolute maximum ratings over operating free-air temperature range (unless otherwise noted)

Supply voltage V_{CC+} (see Note 1) . . . . 8 V
Supply voltage V_{CC-} (see Note 1) . . . . −8 V
Input voltage, either input to ground . . . . ±6 V
Differential input voltage . . . . ±6 V
Continuous total power dissipation at (or below) 25°C free-air temperature (see Note 2) . . . . 500 mW
Operating free-air temperature range: SN5511 Circuits . . . . −55°C to 125°C
　　　　　　　　　　　　　　　　　　　SN7511 Circuits . . . . 0°C to 70°C
Storage temperature range . . . . −65°C to 150°C
Lead temperature 1/16 inch from case for 60 seconds, FA or L package . . . . 300°C
Lead temperature 1/16 inch from case for 10 seconds, N package . . . . 260°C

NOTES: 1. All voltage values, unless otherwise specified, are with respect to the network ground terminal.
　　　　2. For operation above 25°C free-air temperature, refer to Dissipation Derating Curve, Figure 1.

electrical characteristics, V_{CC+} = 6 V, V_{CC-} = −6 V, T_A = 25°C (unless otherwise noted)

PARAMETER		TEST FIGURE	TEST CONDITIONS[†]	SN5511			SN7511			UNIT
				MIN	TYP	MAX	MIN	TYP	MAX	
A_{VD}	Large-signal differential voltage amplification	1	f ≤ 1 kHz, No load	3000						
			f ≤ 1 kHz, R_L = 5 kΩ	1200			600			
A_{VS}	Large-signal single-ended voltage amplification	2	f ≤ 1 kHz, R_L = 5 kΩ	400	600		250	300		
BW	Bandwidth	−3 dB	R_S = 500 Ω, No load		3			3		MHz
		Unity gain			100			100		
V_{IO}	Input offset voltage				1	5		1	5	mV
α_{VIO}	Average temperature coefficient of input offset voltage		T_A = −55°C to 25°C		4					μV/°C
			T_A = 25°C to 125°C		2					
			T_A = 0°C to 25°C					4		
			T_A = 25°C to 70°C					2		
I_{IO}	Input offset current				0.6	7		0.6	10	μA
I_{IB}	Input bias current				10	15		15	20	μA
V_I	Input voltage range	3		+2.5 −2			±1			V
V_{OO}	Output offset voltage		No load		0.35			0.35		V
			R_L = 500 Ω		0.17			0.17		
V_{OPP}	Maximum peak-to-peak output voltage swing	2	f ≤ 1 kHz, R_L = 5 kΩ	2.5	5		1.5	3		V
			f ≤ 1 kHz, R_L = 500 Ω		3			2		
z_{id}	Differential input impedance		f = 1 kHz		5			5		kΩ
z_{os}	Single-ended output impedance		f = 1 kHz		800			800		Ω
CMRR	Common-mode rejection ratio	3	f ≤ 100 kHz, No load, See Note 3	59	95		52	90		dB
P_D	Total power dissipation		No load, No signal		180			180		mW

NOTE 3: For SN5511, V_{IC} = +2.5 V to −2 V; for SN7511, V_{IC} = + 1 V to −1 V.

[†]Unless otherwise specified, V_{IO} is applied and the regulator terminal is open.

DEFINITION OF TERMS

Large-Signal Differential Voltage Amplification (A_{VD}) The ratio of the change in voltage between the output terminals to the change in voltage between the input terminals producing it.

Large-Signal Single-Ended Voltage Amplification (A_{VS}) The ratio of the change in single-ended output voltage to the change in single-ended input voltage.

Input Offset Voltage (V_{IO}) The d-c voltage which must be applied between the input terminals to force the quiescent d-c differential output voltage to zero.

Average Temperature Coefficient of Input Offset Voltage (α_{VIO}) The ratio of the change in input offset voltage to the change in free-air temperature. This is an average value for the specified temperature range.

$$\alpha_{VIO} = \left| \frac{(V_{IO} @ T_{A(1)}) - (V_{IO} @ T_{A(2)})}{T_{A(1)} - T_{A(2)}} \right| \quad \text{where } T_{A(1)} \text{ and } T_{A(2)} \text{ are the specified temperature extremes.}$$

Input Offset Current (I_{IO}) The difference between the currents into the two input terminals with the inputs grounded.

Input Bias Current (I_{IB}) The average of the currents into the two input terminals with the inputs grounded.

Input Voltage Range (V_I) The range of voltage which if exceeded at either input terminal will cause the amplifier to cease functioning properly.

Output Offset Voltage (V_{OO}) The difference between the d-c voltages at the two output terminals when the input terminals are grounded.

Maximum Peak-to-Peak Output Voltage Swing (V_{OPP}) The maximum peak-to-peak output voltage swing that can be obtained without clipping. This includes the unbalance caused by output offset voltage.

Differential Input Impedance (z_{id}) The small-signal impedance between the two input terminals.

Single-Ended Output Impedance (z_{os}) The small-signal impedance between one output terminal and ground.

Common-Mode Rejection Ratio (CMRR) The ratio of differential voltage amplification to common-mode voltage amplification. This is measured by determining the ratio of a change in input common-mode voltage to the resulting change in input offset voltage.

Total Power Dissipation (P_D) The total d-c power supplied to the device less any power delivered from the device to a load. At no load; $P_D = V_{CC+} \cdot I_{CC+} + V_{CC-} \cdot I_{CC-}$.

THERMAL INFORMATION
DISSIPATION DERATING CURVE

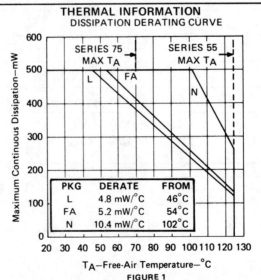

PKG	DERATE	FROM
L	4.8 mW/°C	46°C
FA	5.2 mW/°C	54°C
N	10.4 mW/°C	102°C

T_A—Free-Air Temperature—°C

FIGURE 1

TEXAS INSTRUMENTS
INCORPORATED
POST OFFICE BOX 5012 • DALLAS, TEXAS 75222

PARAMETER MEASUREMENT INFORMATION

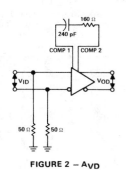

FIGURE 2 – A_{VD}

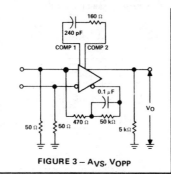

FIGURE 3 – A_{VS}, V_{OPP}

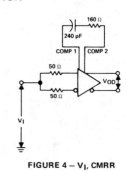

FIGURE 4 – V_I, CMRR

TYPICAL CHARACTERISTICS

SN5511
SINGLE-ENDED OPEN-LOOP
VOLTAGE AMPLIFICATION
vs
FREQUENCY

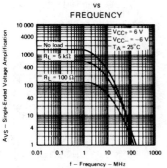

FIGURE 5

SN5511
SINGLE-ENDED OPEN-LOOP
VOLTAGE AMPLIFICATION
vs
FREE-AIR TEMPERATURE

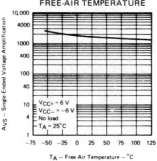

FIGURE 6

SN5511
SINGLE-ENDED OPEN-LOOP
VOLTAGE AMPLIFICATION
vs
SUPPLY VOLTAGES

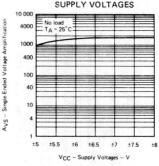

FIGURE 7

SN5511

INPUT BIAS CURRENT
vs
FREE-AIR TEMPERATURE

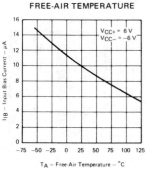

FIGURE 8

SN5511
MAXIMUM PEAK-TO-PEAK
OUTPUT VOLTAGE (OPEN-LOOP)
vs
LOAD RESISTANCE

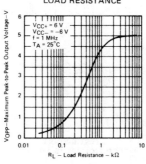

FIGURE 9

SN5511
MAXIMUM PEAK-TO-PEAK
OUTPUT VOLTAGE (OPEN-LOOP)
vs
FREQUENCY

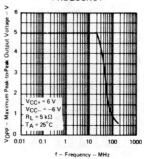

FIGURE 10

TEXAS INSTRUMENTS
INCORPORATED
POST OFFICE BOX 5012 • DALLAS, TEXAS 75222

TYPES SN5511, SN7511
DIFFERENTIAL VIDEO AMPLIFIERS

TYPICAL CHARACTERISTICS

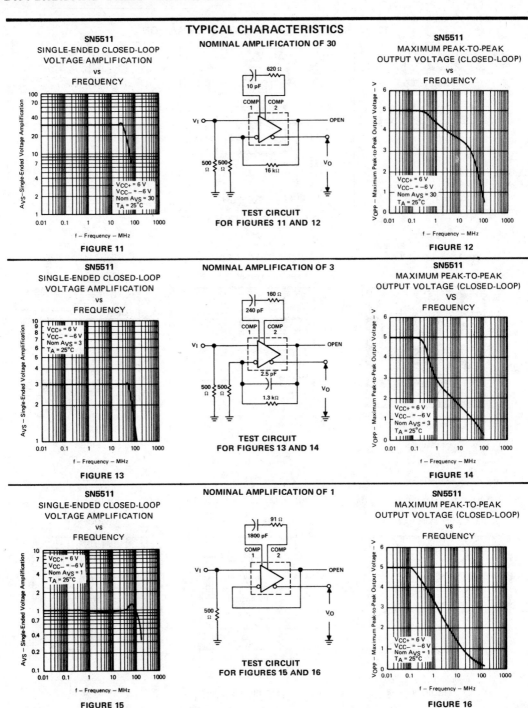

SN5511
SINGLE-ENDED CLOSED-LOOP
VOLTAGE AMPLIFICATION
vs
FREQUENCY

FIGURE 11

NOMINAL AMPLIFICATION OF 30

TEST CIRCUIT
FOR FIGURES 11 AND 12

SN5511
MAXIMUM PEAK-TO-PEAK
OUTPUT VOLTAGE (CLOSED-LOOP)
vs
FREQUENCY

FIGURE 12

SN5511
SINGLE-ENDED CLOSED-LOOP
VOLTAGE AMPLIFICATION
vs
FREQUENCY

FIGURE 13

NOMINAL AMPLIFICATION OF 3

TEST CIRCUIT
FOR FIGURES 13 AND 14

SN5511
MAXIMUM PEAK-TO-PEAK
OUTPUT VOLTAGE (CLOSED-LOOP)
vs
FREQUENCY

FIGURE 14

SN5511
SINGLE-ENDED CLOSED-LOOP
VOLTAGE AMPLIFICATION
vs
FREQUENCY

FIGURE 15

NOMINAL AMPLIFICATION OF 1

TEST CIRCUIT
FOR FIGURES 15 AND 16

SN5511
MAXIMUM PEAK-TO-PEAK
OUTPUT VOLTAGE (CLOSED-LOOP)
vs
FREQUENCY

FIGURE 16

7

TEXAS INSTRUMENTS
INCORPORATED
POST OFFICE BOX 5012 • DALLAS, TEXAS 75222

TYPICAL CHARACTERISTICS

INPUT IMPEDANCE
vs
FREE-AIR TEMPERATURE

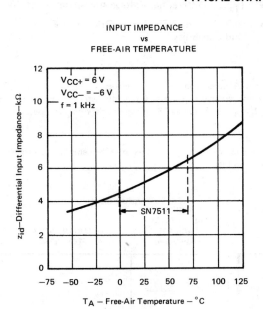

FIGURE 17

SN5511
COMMON-MODE REJECTION RATIO
vs
FREQUENCY

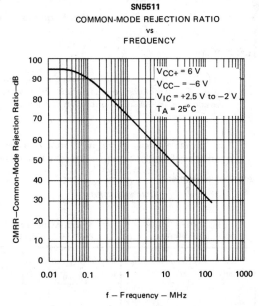

FIGURE 18

TOTAL POWER DISSIPATION
vs
FREE-AIR TEMPERATURE

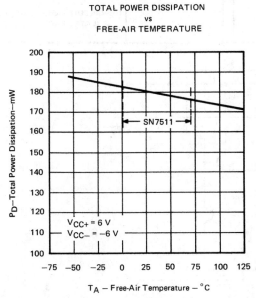

FIGURE 19

SPOT NOISE FIGURE
vs
FREQUENCY

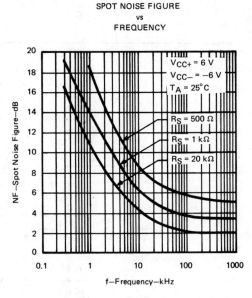

FIGURE 20

TEXAS INSTRUMENTS
INCORPORATED
POST OFFICE BOX 5012 • DALLAS, TEXAS 75222

LINEAR
INTEGRATED CIRCUITS

TYPES SN5512, SN5514, SN7512, SN7514
DIFFERENTIAL VIDEO AMPLIFIERS

BULLETIN NO. DL-S 7311496, AUGUST 1971–REVISED SEPTEMBER 1973

- 80-MHz Bandwidth
- No Frequency Compensation Required
- Typical Differential Voltage Amplification of 300
- SN5512 and SN7512 Have Offset-Voltage Null Capability

description

These wide-band video amplifiers feature a flat frequency response and low phase distortion from dc to typically 80 MHz. Emitter-follower outputs enable the devices to drive capacitive loads. A potentiometer may be connected between the offset null inputs of the SN5512 and SN7512, as shown in Figure 18, to null out the offset voltage.

These circuits are designed for use as sense amplifiers in high-speed thin-film or plated-wire memories, as magnetic tape-read amplifiers, or as general purpose pulse or video amplifiers.

terminal assignments

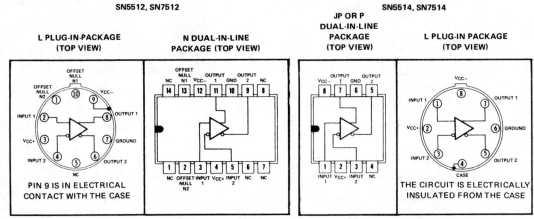

SN5512, SN7512

L PLUG-IN-PACKAGE (TOP VIEW)

PIN 9 IS IN ELECTRICAL CONTACT WITH THE CASE

N DUAL-IN-LINE PACKAGE (TOP VIEW)

JP OR P DUAL-IN-LINE PACKAGE (TOP VIEW)

SN5514, SN7514

L PLUG-IN PACKAGE (TOP VIEW)

THE CIRCUIT IS ELECTRICALLY INSULATED FROM THE CASE

NC-No internal connection

schematic

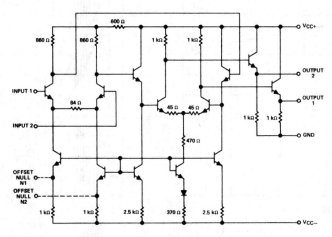

NOTES: 1. Component values shown are nominal.
2. Offset null terminals (shown with dashed lines) are provided on the SN5512 and SN7512 only.

TEXAS INSTRUMENTS
INCORPORATED
POST OFFICE BOX 5012 • DALLAS, TEXAS 75222

7

absolute maximum ratings over operating free-air temperature range (unless otherwise noted)

		SN5512 SN5514	SN7512 SN7514	UNIT
Supply voltage V_{CC+} (See Note 3)		8	8	V
Supply voltage V_{CC-} (See Note 3)		−8	−8	V
Differential input voltage		±5	±5	V
Common-mode input voltage		±6	±6	V
Voltage between either offset null terminal (N1/N2) and V_{CC-} (SN5512 and SN7512)		±0.5	±0.5	V
Output current		10	10	mA
Continuous total power dissipation at (or below) 25°C free-air temperature (See Note 4)		500	500	mW
Operating free-air temperature range		−55 to 125	0 to 70	°C
Storage temperature range		−65 to 150	−65 to 150	°C
Lead temperature 1/16 inch from case for 60 seconds	JP or L package	300	300	°C
Lead temperature 1/16 inch from case for 10 seconds	N or P package	260	260	°C

NOTES: 3. All voltage values, except differential input voltages, are with respect to the network ground terminal.
     4. For operation above 25°C free-air temperature, refer to Dissipation Derating Curve, Figure 19.

electrical characteristics, T_A = 25°C, V_{CC+} = 6 V, V_{CC-} = −6 V

PARAMETER		TEST FIGURE	TEST CONDITIONS	SN5512 SN5514 MIN	TYP	MAX	SN7512 SN7514 MIN	TYP	MAX	UNIT
A_{vd}	Small-signal differential voltage amplification	1	V_{OD} = ±0.5 V	250	300	350	200	300	400	
BW	Bandwidth	2	R_S = 50 Ω		80			80		MHz
I_{IO}	Input offset current				1	3		1	5	μA
I_{IB}	Input bias current				50	80		50	80	μA
V_I	Input voltage range	1		±1			±1			V
V_{OC}	Common-mode output voltage	1		2.4	2.8	3.4	2.4	2.8	3.4	V
V_{OO}	Output offset voltage	1			0.5	1.3		0.5	1.3	V
V_{OPP}	Maximum peak-to-peak output voltage swing	3	$V_I \geqslant$ 50 mV	3	5		3	5		V
		2	THD = 3%		4			4		
r_i	Input resistance	3	$V_{OD} \leqslant$ 1 V		6			6		kΩ
r_o	Output resistance				35			35		Ω
C_i	Input capacitance	3	$V_{OD} \leqslant$ 1 V		7			7		pF
CMRR	Common-mode rejection ratio	4	V_{IC} = ± 1 V, f ⩽ 100 kHz		84			84		dB
$\Delta V_{CC}/\Delta V_{IO}$	Supply voltage rejection ratio	1	ΔV_{CC+} = from 6 V to 5.5 V, ΔV_{CC-} = from −6 V to −5.5 V	50	80		50	80		dB
V_n	Broadband equivalent input noise voltage	5	See Note 5		3			3		μV
t_{pd}	Propagation delay time	2	R_S = 50 Ω, Output voltage step = from 0 to 1 V		6			6		ns
t_r	Rise time	2	R_S = 50 Ω, Output voltage step = from 0 to 1 V		5			5		ns
$I_{sink(max)}$	Maximum output sink current			2.5	3.2		2.5	3.2		mA
I_{CC+}	Supply current from V_{CC+}		No load, No signal		19	25		19	25	mA
I_{CC-}	Supply current from V_{CC-}		No load, No signal		−13	−20		−13	−20	mA

NOTE 5: This parameter is measured in a system with response down 3 dB at 10 Hz and 500 kHz with a 6-dB/octave rolloff.

DEFINITION OF TERMS

Small-Signal Differential Voltage Amplification (A_{vd}) The ratio of the change in voltage between the output terminals to the change in voltage between the input terminals producing it.

Bandwidth (BW) The range of frequencies within which the differential gain of the amplifier is not more than 3 dB below its low-frequency value.

Input Offset Current (I_{IO}) The difference between the currents into the two input terminals with the inputs grounded.

Input Bias Current (I_{IB}) The average of the currents into the two input terminals with the inputs grounded.

Input Voltage Range (V_I) The range of voltage which if exceeded at either input terminal will cause the amplifier to cease functioning properly.

Common-Mode Output Voltage (V_{OC}) The average of the d-c voltages at the two output terminals.

Output Offset Voltage (V_{OO}) The difference between the d-c voltages at the two output terminals when the input terminals are grounded.

Maximum Peak-to-Peak Output Voltage Swing (V_{OPP}) The maximum peak-to-peak output voltage swing that can be obtained under the specified conditions. This includes the unbalance caused by output offset voltage.

Input Resistance (r_i) The resistance between the input terminals with either input grounded.

Output Resistance (r_o) The resistance between either output terminal and ground.

Input Capacitance (C_i) The capacitance between the input terminals with either input grounded.

Common-Mode Rejection Ratio (CMRR) The ratio of differential voltage amplification to common-mode voltage amplification. This is measured by determining the ratio of a change in input common-mode voltage to the resulting change in input offset voltage.

Supply Voltage Rejection Ratio ($\Delta V_{CC}/\Delta V_{IO}$) The ratio of the change in power supply voltages to the change in input offset voltage. For these devices, both supply voltages are varied symmetrically.

Propagation Delay Time (t_{pd}) The interval between the application of an input voltage step and its arrival at either output, measured at 50% of the final value.

Rise Time (t_r) The time required for an output voltage step to change from 10% to 90% of its final value.

Maximum Output Sink Current ($I_{sink(max)}$) The maximum available current into either output terminal when that output is at its most negative potential.

TEXAS INSTRUMENTS
INCORPORATED
POST OFFICE BOX 5012 • DALLAS, TEXAS 75222

PARAMETER MEASUREMENT INFORMATION

test circuits

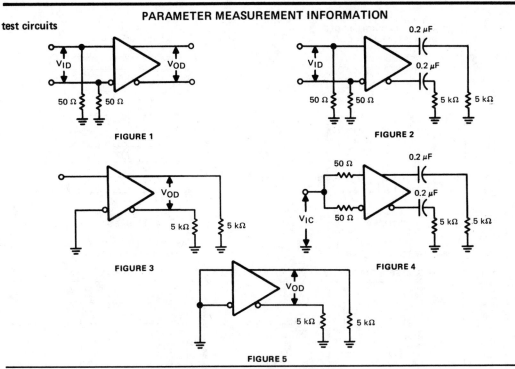

FIGURE 1

FIGURE 2

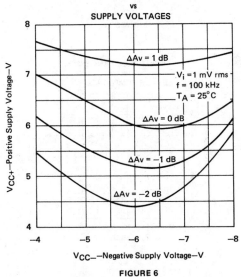

FIGURE 3

FIGURE 4

FIGURE 5

7

TYPICAL CHARACTERISTICS

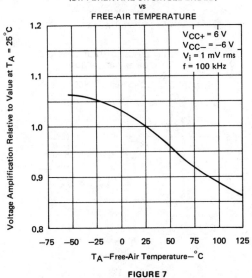

CONTOURS OF CONSTANT VARIATION IN
SMALL-SIGNAL VOLTAGE AMPLIFICATION
(DIFFERENTIAL OR SINGLE-ENDED)
vs
SUPPLY VOLTAGES

FIGURE 6

SMALL-SIGNAL VOLTAGE AMPLIFICATION
(DIFFERENTIAL OR SINGLE-ENDED)
vs
FREE-AIR TEMPERATURE

FIGURE 7

TEXAS INSTRUMENTS
INCORPORATED
POST OFFICE BOX 5012 • DALLAS, TEXAS 75222

TYPICAL CHARACTERISTICS

SMALL-SIGNAL SINGLE-ENDED
VOLTAGE AMPLIFICATION
vs
FREQUENCY

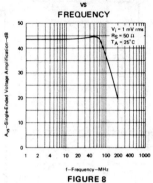

FIGURE 8

INPUT BIAS CURRENT
vs
FREE-AIR TEMPERATURE

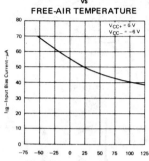

FIGURE 9

COMMON-MODE OUTPUT VOLTAGE
vs
FREE-AIR TEMPERATURE

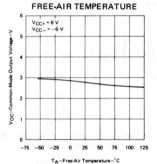

FIGURE 10

PEAK-TO-PEAK OUTPUT VOLTAGE
(FOR 3% DISTORTION)
vs
FREQUENCY

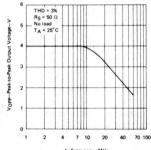

FIGURE 11

PEAK-TO-PEAK OUTPUT VOLTAGE
(FOR 3% DISTORTION)
vs
LOAD RESISTANCE

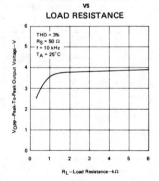

FIGURE 12

INPUT RESISTANCE
vs
FREE-AIR TEMPERATURE

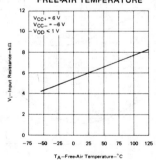

FIGURE 13

TEXAS INSTRUMENTS
INCORPORATED
POST OFFICE BOX 5012 • DALLAS, TEXAS 75222

TYPICAL CHARACTERISTICS

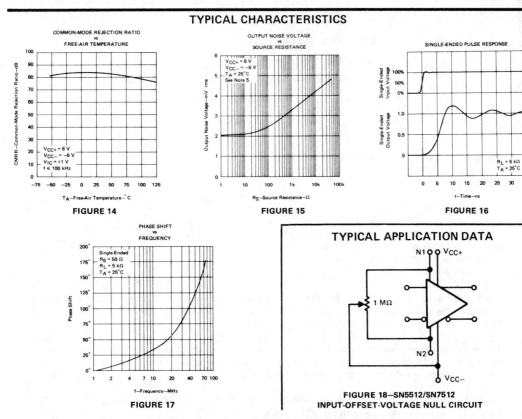

FIGURE 14

FIGURE 15

FIGURE 16

FIGURE 17

TYPICAL APPLICATION DATA

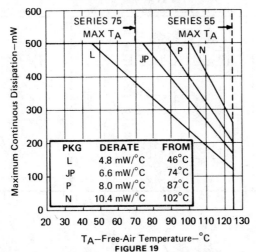

FIGURE 18—SN5512/SN7512
INPUT-OFFSET-VOLTAGE NULL CIRCUIT

NOTE 5: This parameter is measured in a system with response down 3 dB at 10 Hz and 500 kHz with a 6-dB/octave rolloff.

THERMAL INFORMATION
DISSIPATION DERATING CURVE

PKG	DERATE	FROM
L	4.8 mW/$^\circ$C	46°C
JP	6.6 mW/$^\circ$C	74°C
P	8.0 mW/$^\circ$C	87°C
N	10.4 mW/$^\circ$C	102°C

FIGURE 19

TEXAS INSTRUMENTS
INCORPORATED
POST OFFICE BOX 5012 • DALLAS, TEXAS 75222

- **200 MHz Bandwidth**
- **250 kΩ Input Resistance**
- **Selectable Nominal Amplification of 10, 100, or 400**
- **No Frequency Compensation Required**

description

The SN52733 and SN72733 are monolithic two-stage video amplifiers with differential inputs and differential outputs.

Internal series-shunt feedback provides wide bandwidth, low phase distortion, and excellent gain stability. Emitter-follower outputs enable the device to drive capacitive loads and all stages are current-source biased to obtain high common-mode and supply-voltage rejection ratios.

schematic

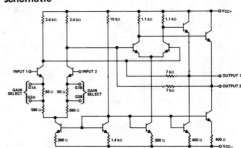

Component values shown are nominal

Fixed differential amplification of 10, 100, or 400 may be selected without external components, or amplification may be adjusted from 10 to 400 by the use of a single external resistor connected between G1A and G1B. No external frequency-compensating components are required for any gain option.

The device is particularly useful in magnetic-tape or disc-file systems using phase or NRZ encoding and in high-speed thin-film or plated-wire memories. Other applications include general purpose video and pulse amplifiers where wide bandwidth, low phase shift, and excellent gain stability are required.

The SN52733 is characterized for operation over the full military temperature range of −55°C to 125°C; the SN72733 is characterized for operation from 0°C to 70°C.

terminal assignments

FA FLAT PACKAGE (TOP VIEW)

10	9	8	7	6
INPUT 2	GAIN SELECT G2B	GAIN SELECT G1B	Vcc+	OUTPUT 2

1	2	3	4	5
INPUT 1	GAIN SELECT G2A	GAIN SELECT G1A	Vcc−	OUTPUT 1

J OR N DUAL-IN-LINE PACKAGE (TOP VIEW)

14	13	12	11	10	9	8
INPUT 2	NC	GAIN SELECT G2B	GAIN SELECT G1B	Vcc+	NC	OUTPUT 2

1	2	3	4	5	6	7
INPUT 1	NC	GAIN SELECT G2A	GAIN SELECT G1A	Vcc−	NC	OUTPUT 1

L PLUG-IN PACKAGE (TOP VIEW)

GAIN SELECT 2A
INPUT 1
GAIN SELECT 1A
INPUT 2
Vcc+
GAIN SELECT 2B
OUTPUT 1
GAIN SELECT 1B
OUTPUT 2
Vcc−

PIN 5 IS IN ELECTRICAL CONTACT WITH THE CASE

NC—No internal connection

TEXAS INSTRUMENTS
INCORPORATED

POST OFFICE BOX 5012 • DALLAS, TEXAS 75222

absolute maximum ratings over operating free-air temperature range (unless otherwise noted)

		SN52733	SN72733	UNIT
Supply voltage V_{CC+} (See Note 1)		8	8	V
Supply voltage V_{CC-} (See Note 1)		−8	−8	V
Differential input voltage		±5	±5	V
Common-mode input voltage		±6	±6	V
Output current		10	10	mA
Continuous total power dissipation (See Note 2 on the following page)		500	500	mW
Operating free-air temperature range		−55 to 125	0 to 70	°C
Storage temperature range		−65 to 150	−65 to 150	°C
Lead temperature 1/16" from case for 60 seconds	FA, J, or L package	300	300	°C
Lead temperature 1/16" from case for 10 seconds	N package	260	260	°C

NOTE 1: All voltage values, except differential input voltages, are with respect to the zero reference level (ground) of the supply voltages where the zero reference level is the midpoint between V_{CC+} and V_{CC-}.

electrical characteristics, $T_A = 25°C$, $V_{CC+} = 6$ V, $V_{CC-} = -6$ V

PARAMETER		TEST FIGURE	TEST CONDITIONS	GAIN† SELECT	SN52733 MIN	SN52733 TYP	SN52733 MAX	SN72733 MIN	SN72733 TYP	SN72733 MAX	UNIT
A_{VD}	Large-signal differential voltage amplification	1	$V_{OD} = 1$ V	1	300	400	500	250	400	600	
				2	90	100	110	80	100	120	
				3	9	10	11	8	10	12	
BW	Bandwidth	2	$R_S = 50$ Ω	1		50			50		MHz
				2		90			90		
				3		200			200		
I_{IO}	Input offset current			Any		0.4	3		0.4	5	µA
I_{IB}	Input bias current			Any		9	20		9	30	µA
V_I	Input voltage range	1		Any	±1			±1			V
V_{OC}	Common-mode output voltage	1		Any	2.4	2.9	3.4	2.4	2.9	3.4	V
V_{OO}	Output offset voltage	1		1		0.6	1.5		0.6	1.5	V
				2 & 3		0.35	1		0.35	1.5	
V_{OPP}	Maximum peak-to-peak output voltage swing	1		Any	3	4.7		3	4.7		V
r_i	Input resistance	3	$V_{OD} \leqslant 1$ V	1		4			4		kΩ
				2	20	24		10	24		
				3		250			250		
r_o	Output resistance					20			20		Ω
C_i	Input capacitance	3	$V_{OD} \leqslant 1$ V	2		2			2		pF
CMRR	Common-mode rejection ratio	4	$V_{IC} = ±1$ V, $f \leqslant 100$ kHz	2	60	86		60	86		dB
			$V_{IC} = ±1$ V, $f = 5$ MHz	2		70			70		
$\Delta V_{CC}/\Delta V_{IO}$	Supply voltage rejection ratio	1	$\Delta V_{CC+} = ± 0.5$ V, $\Delta V_{CC-} = ± 0.5$ V	2	50	70		50	70		dB
V_n	Broadband equivalent input noise voltage	5	BW = 1 kHz to 10 MHz	Any		12			12		µV
t_{pd}	Propagation delay time	2	$R_S = 50$ Ω, Output voltage step = 1 V	1		7.5			7.5		ns
				2		6.0	10		6.0	10	
				3		3.6			3.6		
t_r	Rise time	2	$R_S = 50$ Ω, Output voltage step = 1 V	1		10.5			10.5		ns
				2		4.5	10		4.5	12	
				3		2.5			2.5		
$I_{sink(max)}$	Maximum output sink current			Any	2.5	3.6		2.5	3.6		mA
I_{CC}	Supply current		No load, no signal	Any		16	24		16	24	mA

†The gain selection is made as follows:
Gain 1 . . . Gain Select pin G1A is connected to pin G1B, and pins G2A and G2B are open.
Gain 2 . . . Gain Select pin G1A and pin G1B are open, pin G2A is connected to pin G2B.
Gain 3 . . . All four gain-select pins are open.

TEXAS INSTRUMENTS
INCORPORATED
POST OFFICE BOX 5012 • DALLAS, TEXAS 75222

DEFINITION OF TERMS

Large-Signal Differential Voltage Amplification (A_{VD}) The ratio of the change in voltage between the output terminals to the change in voltage between the input terminals producing it.

Bandwidth (BW) The range of frequencies within which the differential gain of the amplifier is not more than 3 dB below its low-frequency value.

Input Offset Current (I_{IO}) The difference between the currents into the two input terminals with the inputs grounded.

Input Bias Current (I_{IB}) The average of the currents into the two input terminals with the inputs grounded.

Input Voltage Range (V_I) The range of voltage which if exceeded at either input terminal will cause the amplifier to cease functioning properly.

Common-Mode Output Voltage (V_{OC}) The average of the d-c voltages at the two output terminals.

Output Offset Voltage (V_{OO}) The difference between the d-c voltages at the two output terminals when the input terminals are grounded.

Maximum Peak-to-Peak Output Voltage Swing (V_{OPP}) The maximum peak-to-peak output voltage swing that can be obtained without clipping. This includes the unbalance caused by output offset voltage.

Input Resistance (r_i) The resistance between the input terminals with either input grounded.

Output Resistance (r_o) The resistance between either output terminal and ground.

Input Capacitance (C_i) The capacitance between the input terminals with either input grounded.

Common-Mode Rejection Ratio (CMRR) The ratio of differential voltage amplification to common-mode voltage amplification. This is measured by determining the ratio of a change in input common-mode voltage to the resulting change in input offset voltage.

Supply Voltage Rejection Ratio ($\Delta V_{CC}/\Delta V_{IO}$) The ratio of the change in power supply voltages to the change in input offset voltage. For these devices, both supply voltages are varied symmetrically.

Propagation Delay Time (t_{pd}) The interval between the application of an input voltage step and its arrival at either output, measured at 50% of the final value.

Rise Time (t_r) The time required for an output voltage step to change from 10% to 90% of its final value.

Maximum Output Sink Current ($I_{sink(max)}$) The maximum available current into either output terminal when that output is at its most negative potential.

Supply Current (I_{CC}) The average of the magnitudes of the two supply currents.

NOTE 2: For devices in the L package, this rating applies at (or below) 46°C free-air temperature with derating above that temperature at the rate of 4.8 mW/°C. For devices in the FA package, this rating applies at (or below) 54°C free-air temperature with derating above that temperature at the rate of 5.2 mW/°C. For devices in either the J or N package, this rating applies at (or below) 102°C free-air temperature with derating above that temperature at the rate of 10.4 mW/°C.

TEXAS INSTRUMENTS
INCORPORATED
POST OFFICE BOX 5012 • DALLAS, TEXAS 75222

PARAMETER MEASUREMENT INFORMATION

test circuits

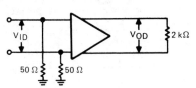

FIGURE 1

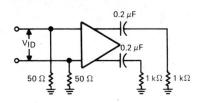

FIGURE 2

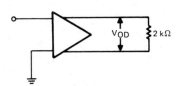

FIGURE 3

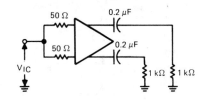

FIGURE 4

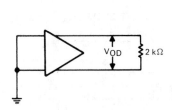

FIGURE 5

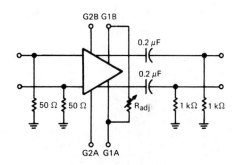

VOLTAGE AMPLIFICATION ADJUSTMENT

FIGURE 6

TYPICAL CHARACTERISTICS

PHASE SHIFT
vs
FREQUENCY

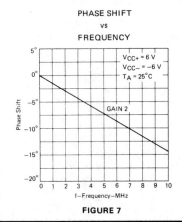

FIGURE 7

PHASE SHIFT
vs
FREQUENCY

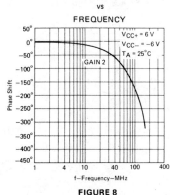

FIGURE 8

TEXAS INSTRUMENTS
INCORPORATED
POST OFFICE BOX 5012 • DALLAS, TEXAS 75222

TYPICAL CHARACTERISTICS

VOLTAGE AMPLIFICATION
(SINGLE-ENDED OR DIFFERENTIAL)
vs
TEMPERATURE

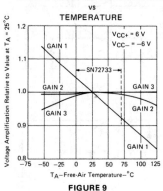

FIGURE 9

VOLTAGE AMPLIFICATION
(SINGLE-ENDED OR DIFFERENTIAL)
vs
SUPPLY VOLTAGE

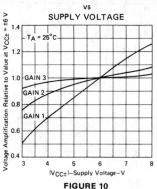

FIGURE 10

DIFFERENTIAL VOLTAGE AMPLIFICATION
vs
RESISTANCE BETWEEN G1A AND G1B

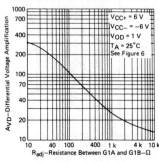

FIGURE 11

SINGLE-ENDED VOLTAGE AMPLIFICATION
vs
FREQUENCY

FIGURE 12

SUPPLY CURRENT
vs
FREE-AIR TEMPERATURE

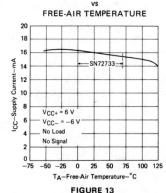

FIGURE 13

SUPPLY CURRENT
vs
SUPPLY VOLTAGE

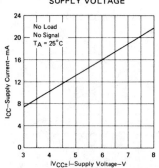

FIGURE 14

TEXAS INSTRUMENTS
INCORPORATED
POST OFFICE BOX 5012 • DALLAS, TEXAS 75222

TYPICAL CHARACTERISTICS

MAXIMUM PEAK-TO-PEAK OUTPUT VOLTAGE
vs
LOAD RESISTANCE

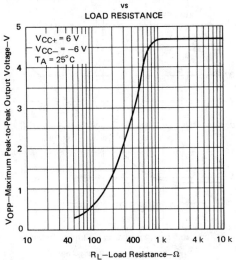

FIGURE 15

MAXIMUM PEAK-TO-PEAK OUTPUT VOLTAGE
vs
SUPPLY VOLTAGE

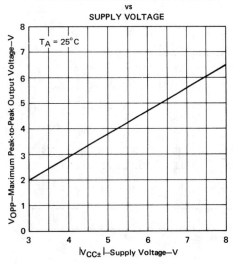

FIGURE 16

MAXIMUM PEAK-TO-PEAK OUTPUT VOLTAGE
vs
FREQUENCY

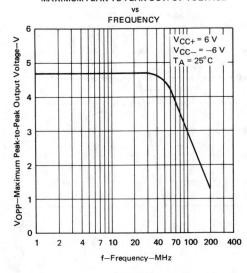

FIGURE 17

INPUT RESISTANCE
vs
FREE-AIR TEMPERATURE

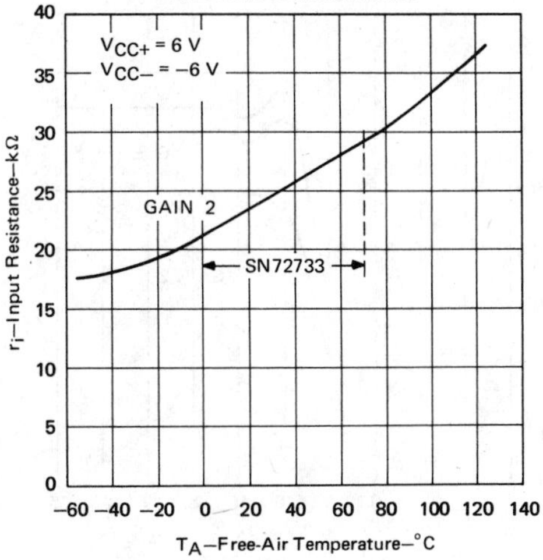

FIGURE 18

7

TEXAS INSTRUMENTS
INCORPORATED
POST OFFICE BOX 5012 • DALLAS, TEXAS 75222

TYPES SN52733, SN72733
DIFFERENTIAL VIDEO AMPLIFIERS

TYPICAL CHARACTERISTICS

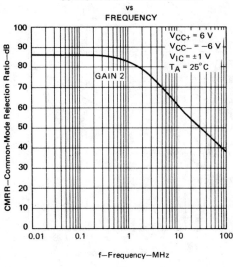

COMMON-MODE REJECTION RATIO
vs
FREQUENCY

FIGURE 19

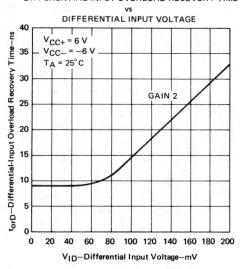

DIFFERENTIAL INPUT OVERLOAD RECOVERY TIME
vs
DIFFERENTIAL INPUT VOLTAGE

FIGURE 20

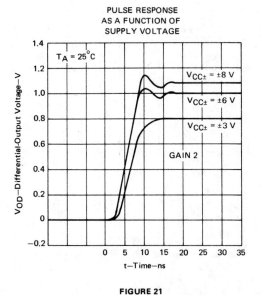

PULSE RESPONSE
AS A FUNCTION OF
SUPPLY VOLTAGE

FIGURE 21

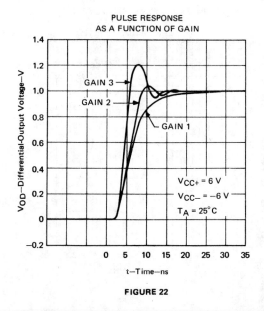

PULSE RESPONSE
AS A FUNCTION OF GAIN

FIGURE 22

TEXAS INSTRUMENTS
INCORPORATED
POST OFFICE BOX 5012 • DALLAS, TEXAS 75222

- Differential Amplifier Inputs
- A-C Line Operation
- Capable of Triggering Several Types of Triacs

- Internal Active Elements of Saw-Tooth Generator for Proportional Control
- Wide Variety of Possible Connections of Input Section and of Output Section

description

The SN72440 is a combination threshold detector and zero-crossing trigger, intended primarily for a-c power-control circuits. It allows a triac or SCR to be fired when the a-c input signal crosses through zero volts, thereby minimizing undesirable electromagnetic interference. In this manner, the load utilizes full cycles of line voltage as opposed to partial cycles typical with SCR phase-control power circuits.

The circuit includes a zero-voltage detector, a differential amplifier that may be used in conjuction with a resistance bridge to sense the parameter being controlled, the active elements of a saw-tooth generator, and an output section. Also included are resistors which may be used as a voltage divider for the reference side of the resistance bridge. An external sensor suitable for the application and an external potentiometer form the input side of the resistance bridge.

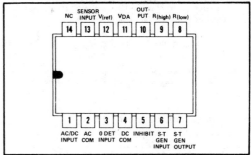

J OR N
DUAL-IN-LINE PACKAGE (TOP VIEW)

NC—No internal connection.

The SN72440 can be used either as an on-off control with or without hysteresis, or as a proportional control with the use of the internal saw-tooth generator. Although the principal application of this device is in temperature control, it can be used for many power control applications such as a photosensitive control, voltage level sensor, a-c lamp flasher, small relay driver, or a miniature lamp driver.

The inhibit function prevents any output pulses from occurring when the applied voltage at the inhibit input is typically 1 volt or greater. Conversely, if the inhibit input is shorted to dc common, an output pulse will be obtained for each zero-crossing of the a-c power input waveform regardless of the sensor input conditions.

The SN72440 is characterized for operation from 0°C to 70°C.

schematic

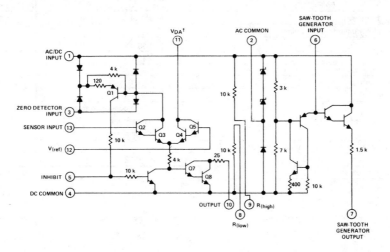

Resistor values shown are nominal and in ohms.

†Pin 11 is usually connected to the AC/DC input, pin 1, unless a control circuit requiring hysteresis is desired. See Figure 4.

TEXAS INSTRUMENTS
INCORPORATED
POST OFFICE BOX 5012 • DALLAS, TEXAS 75222

TYPE SN72440
ZERO-VOLTAGE SWITCH

absolute maximum ratings over operating free-air temperature range (unless otherwise noted)

Voltage applied to AC/DC input (See Note 1)	15 V
Peak current into AC/DC input	40 mA
Peak current into zero-detector input	30 mA
Peak output sink current (See Note 2)	250 mA
Continuous total power dissipation at (or below) 70°C free-air temperature range	500 mW
Operating free-air temperature range	0°C to 70°C
Storage temperature range	−65°C to 150°C
Lead temperature 1/16 inch from case for 60 seconds: J package	300°C
Lead temperature 1/16 inch from case for 10 seconds: N package	260°C

NOTES: 1. Voltage values are with respect to the dc common terminal unless otherwise specified.
        2. This value applies for a maximum pulse width of 400 μs and for a maximum duty cycle of 2%.

recommended operating conditions

	MIN	NOM	MAX	UNIT
D-c voltage applied to AC/DC input (See Note 3)		12		V
Differential input voltage, $V_{13} - V_{12}$			±2	V
Voltage at sensor or $V_{(ref)}$ input, V_{13} or V_{12}		6		V
Peak output current (See Note 4)			200	mA
Output pulse width	100		400	μs
Operating free-air temperature, T_A	0		70	°C

NOTES: 3. This is the recommended d-c supply voltage when the voltage across pins 1 and 4 is not being maintained by charging an
           electrolytic capacitor from the line voltage. See typical application data.
        4. This value applies for $t_w \leqslant 400$ μs, duty cycle $\leqslant 2\%$.

electrical characteristics at 25°C free-air temperature (unless otherwise noted)

PARAMETER	TEST CONDITIONS	MIN	TYP	MAX	UNIT
Sensor input voltage hysterysis	Pin 11 connected to Pin 1		30		mV
Voltage required at inhibit input to inhibit output			1	3	V
Current into sensor input	$V_{13} = 6$ V, $V_{12} = 4$ V			5	μA
Current into $V_{(ref)}$ input	$V_{12} = 6$ V, $V_{13} = 4$ V			5	μA
Current into inhibit terminal required to inhibit output				20	μA
Peak output current (pulsing)	$V_5 = 0$	75	100		mA
Output current (inhibited)	$V_{10} = 13.5$ V			1	μA
Output pulse width into resistive load	25 kΩ connected to zero-detector input, 60-Hz power source		150		μs
Average temperature coefficient of output pulse width (0°C to 70°C)			0.7		μs/°C
Peak output voltage of saw-tooth generator	$V_1 = 12$ V		9		V
Voltage at AC/DC input(See Note 5)		9	11.5		V

NOTE 5: This is the voltage across an electrolytic capacitor connected between pins 1 and 4 whose charge is maintained by the a-c line voltage.
        See Figures 1 and 3.

TEXAS INSTRUMENTS
INCORPORATED
POST OFFICE BOX 5012 • DALLAS, TEXAS 75222

TYPICAL APPLICATION DATA

The circuit shown in Figure 1 provides on-off temperature control. Electrolytic capacitor C1 maintains the d-c operating voltage. Since the series combination of D5 and D6 is in parallel with the series combination of C1 and D7, the voltage developed across C1 is limited to approximately 12 V. Because the energy to fire the triac comes from C1, the voltage across pins 1 and 4 will fluctuate as the triac fires. If a more stable operation of the circuit is desired, a 12-volt d-c supply should be connected between pins 1 and 4 in lieu of C1. The temperature sensor must have a negative coefficient in this circuit.

During most of the a-c cycle, Q1 is turned on by the current flow through either D1, Q1, D4 or D2, Q1, D3, depending on the polarity of the a-c voltage between pins 1 and 3. The collector current of Q1 turns on Q6. With Q6 on, base drive to Q7 and Q8 is inhibited, resulting in no output pulse to fire the triac. When the a-c voltage crosses zero, Q1 and Q6 are turned off. This enables Q7 and Q8 to turn on, thereby connecting d-c common to the triac trigger and firing the triac. This one output pulse per zero crossing is either inhibited or permitted by the action of the differential amplifier and resistance bridge circuit.

As the controlled temperature begins to rise, the positive voltage applied to pin 13 increases. The differential control amplifier acts to lower the potential of the base of Q1 enough to allow Q1 to stay on for the complete cycle, thus inhibiting the output pulses as explained above. Similarly when the temperature being controlled falls, Q1 is allowed to turn off during the intervals where the line voltage passes through zero, thus generating output pulses.

The width of the output pulse at pin 10 can be varied to suit the triggering characteristics of the triac to be used. Table I shows the output pulse lengths obtained as R20 is changed. For small load currents (less than 4-5 amps) a triac with high gate sensitivity may be required due to the high value of "latch-up" current of medium to high power triacs.

TABLE I

R20	OUTPUT PULSE WIDTH
15 kΩ	100 µs
22 kΩ	150 µs
42 kΩ	300 µs

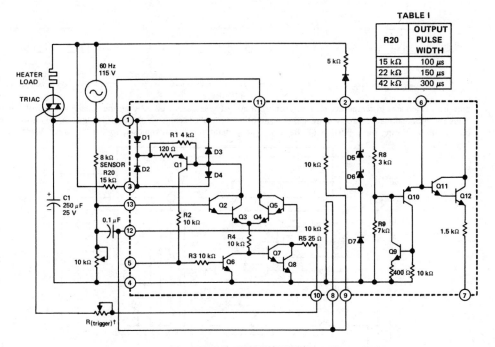

FIGURE 1—ON-OFF HEATER CONTROL

† R(trigger) is adjusted so that the peak output is less than 200 mA.

TEXAS INSTRUMENTS
INCORPORATED
POST OFFICE BOX 5012 • DALLAS, TEXAS 75222

TYPE SN72440
ZERO-VOLTAGE SWITCH

TYPICAL APPLICATION DATA

The circuit shown in Figure 3 provides proportional control of a heating system. With the exception of the saw-tooth generator, the circuit of Figure 3 functions the same as that of Figure 1. The sensor of Figure 3 has a negative temperature coefficient.

Transistors Q9 and Q10 are connected to function as an SCR in order to discharge external capacitor C2 very quickly. The time constant of the saw-tooth generator can be varied by changing either the external capacitor or the external resistor. However it is suggested that the capacitor be varied and not the resistor since too low a value of resistance would allow Q9 and Q10 to stay on continuously. The period of the saw-tooth generator is usually 10 to 100 times the period of the line voltage.

At the start of the saw-tooth waveform the base of Q1 is high and output pulses occur at pin 10. At the desired temperature a certain number of output pulses occur during each saw-tooth cycle as shown in Figure 2(a). At a slightly decreased temperature the resistance of the sensor increases, lowering the d-c potential of pin 13. This lowers the potential of the entire saw-tooth waveform as shown in Figure 2(b) which causes a few more output pulses to occur. At greatly decreased temperatures many more pulses occur each saw-tooth cycle as shown in Figure 2(c).

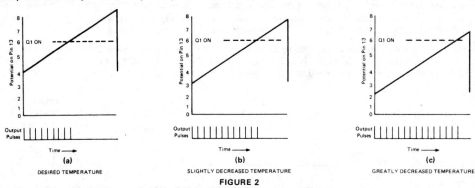

FIGURE 2

Similarly, increases in temperature cause proportionately fewer output pulses than the normal number of Figure 2(a). Thus the proportional control feature allows a smoother control of temperature in this application by always providing output pulses during some portion of the saw-tooth generator cycle as opposed to the "full on/full off" circuit of Figure 1.

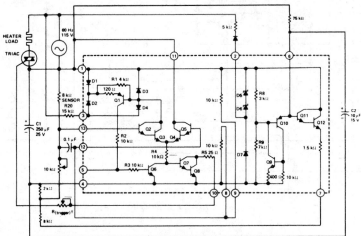

FIGURE 3—PROPORTIONAL HEATER CONTROL

†R(trigger) is adjusted so that the peak output is less than 200 mA.

TEXAS INSTRUMENTS
INCORPORATED
POST OFFICE BOX 5012 • DALLAS, TEXAS 75222

TYPICAL APPLICATION DATA

Hysteresis may be added to the SN72440 by externally making the differential amplifier appear in Schmitt-trigger configuration. This is done by applying positive feedback from pin 11 to pin 13 through hysteresis resistors R_A and R_H. When the output is enabled, the voltage drop developed across resistor R_A is fed through R_H to the sensor input of the differential amplifier. This lowers the voltage at this point from the voltage level present when the output is inhibited. The resistance of the sensor must now decrease enough to overcome this additional ("hysteresis") voltage in order to inhibit the output. R_H should have a typical value close to the value of the sensor used. The value of R_A, which determines the amount of hysteresis, should be approximately one tenth the value of R_H. In Figure 4 the 10 kΩ potentiometer is adjusted to set the voltage at pin 13 to the level at which the output is enabled. When precise control is not needed, such a circuit eliminates the small "uncertainty range" observed in time-proportioning systems.

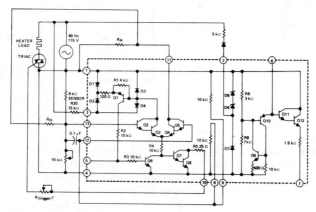

†$R_{(trigger)}$ is adjusted so that the peak output is less than 200 mA.

FIGURE 4—ON-OFF HEATER CONTROL WITH HYSTERSIS ADDED

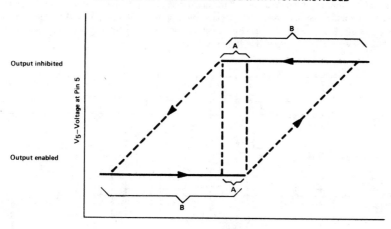

V₁₃—Voltage at Pin 13

FIGURE 5—HYSTERESIS CURVE FOR FIGURE 4

A—Circuit without added hysteresis ($\Delta V_{13} \approx$ 15 to 20 mV residual hysteresis)
B—Circuit with added hysteresis ($\Delta V_{13} \approx$ 200 to 300 mV added hysteresis)
NOTE 1: Dotted lines represent discontinuous changes where the differential amplifier changes from inhibit to enable or vice-versa. Solid lines represent stable states (inhibit or enable) of the differential amplifier.

TEXAS INSTRUMENTS
INCORPORATED
POST OFFICE BOX 5012 • DALLAS, TEXAS 75222

J OR N DUAL-IN-LINE PACKAGES (TOP VIEW)

OUTPUTS

NC	C_{B2}	C_{B2}'	GND	INPUT B1	Z	$\overline{Z}$	INPUT B2
16	15	14	13	12	11	10	9

log B1

log A1

Σ

Σ

log B2

log A2

1	2	3	4	5	6	7	8
C_{A2}	V_{CC-}	C_{A2}'	INPUT A1	Y	$\overline{Y}$	INPUT A2	V_{CC+}

OUTPUTS

- **Excellent Dynamic Range**
- **Wide Bandwidth**
- **Built-In Temperature Compensation**
- **Log Linearity (30 dBV Sections) ... 1 dBV**
- **Wide Input Voltage Range**

$Y \propto \log A1 + \log A2$; $Z \propto \log B1 + B2$;
where: A1, A2, B1, and B2 are in dBV, 0 dBV = 1 V.
C_{A2}, C_{A2}', C_{B2}, and C_{B2}', are detector compensation inputs.
NC—No internal connection

description

This monolithic logarithmic amplifier circuit contains four 30-dBV log stages. Gain in each stage is such that the output of each stage is proportional to the logarithm of the input voltage over the 30-dBV input voltage range. Each half of the circuit contains two of these 30-dBV stages summed together in one differential output which is proportional to the sum of the logs of the input voltages of the two stages. The four stages may be interconnected to obtain a theoretical input voltage range of 120 dBV. In practice, this permits the input voltage range to be typically greater than 80 dBV with log linearity of ±0.5 dBV (see application data). Bandwidth is from dc to 40 megahertz.

These circuits are useful in military weapons systems, broadband radar, and infrared reconnaissance systems. They serve for data compression and analog compensation. The logarithmic amplifiers are used in log IF circuitry as well as video and log amplifiers. The SN56502 is characterized for operation over the full military temperature range of −55°C to 125°C; the SN76502 is characterized for operation from 0°C to 70°C.

schematic

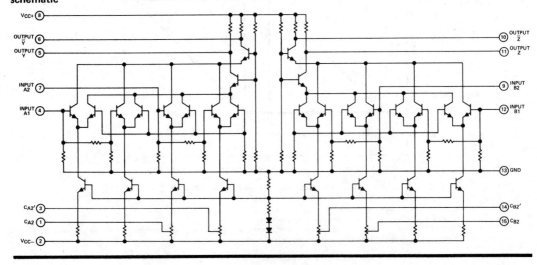

TEXAS INSTRUMENTS
INCORPORATED
POST OFFICE BOX 5012 • DALLAS, TEXAS 75222

absolute maximum ratings over operating free-air temperature range (unless otherwise noted)

Supply voltages (see Note 1):

V_{CC+} 8V

V_{CC-} . . . . −8V

Input voltage (see Note 1) 6V

Output sink current (any one output) . . . . 30 mA

Continuous total dissipation at (or below) $102°C$ free-air temperature (see Note 2) . . . . 500 mW

Operating free-air temperature range: SN56502 Circuits . . . . −55°C to 125°C

                              SN76502 Circuits . . . . 0°C to 70°C

Storage temperature range . . . . −65°C to 150°C

NOTES: 1. All voltages, except differential output voltages, are with respect to network ground terminal.
       2. Derate linearly to 260 mW at 125°C free-air temperature at the rate of 10.4 mW/°C.

recommended operating conditions

	SN56502			SN76502			UNIT
	MIN	NOM	MAX	MIN	NOM	MAX	
Input voltage for each 30-dBV stage	0.01		1	0.01		1	V_{p-p}
Operating free-air temperature, T_A	−55		125	0		70	°C

electrical characteristics, $V_{CC+} = 6$ V, $V_{CC-} = -6$ V, $T_A = 25°C$

PARAMETER	TEST FIGURE	SN56502			SN76502			UNIT
		MIN	TYP	MAX	MIN	TYP	MAX	
Differential output offset voltage	1		±25	±60		±40		mV
Quiescent output voltage	2	5.45	5.6	5.85	5.45	5.6	5.85	V
D-c scale factor (differential output), each 30-dBV stage, −35 dBV to −5 dBV	3	7	8	10	6	8	12	mV/dBV
A-c scale factor (differential output)			8			8		mV/dBV
D-c error at −20 dBV (midpoint of −35 dBV to −5 dBV range)	3		1	2		1		dBV
Input impedance			500			500		Ω
Output impedance			200			200		Ω
Rise time, 10% to 90% points, $C_L = 24$ pF	4		20	30		20	30	ns
Supply current from V_{CC+}	2	14.5	18.5	23	14.5	18.5	23	mA
Supply current from V_{CC-}	2	−6	−8.5	−10.5	−6	−8.5	−10.5	mA
Power dissipation	2	123	162	201	123	162	201	mW

PARAMETER MEASUREMENT INFORMATION

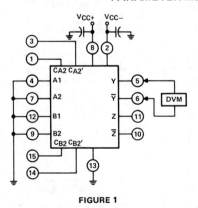

FIGURE 1

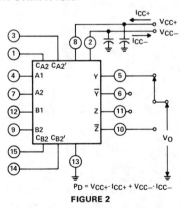

$P_D = V_{CC+} \cdot I_{CC+} + V_{CC-} \cdot I_{CC-}$

FIGURE 2

TYPES SN56502, SN76502
LOGARITHMIC AMPLIFIERS

PARAMETER MEASUREMENT INFORMATION

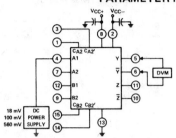

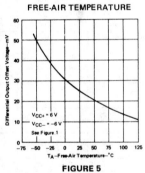

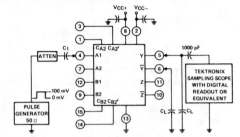

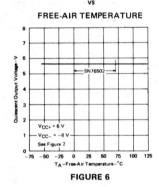

$$\text{Scale Factor} = \frac{[V_{out(560\ mV)} - V_{out(18\ mV)}]\ mV}{30\ dBV}$$

$$\text{Error} = \frac{|V_{out(100\ mV)} - 0.5\ V_{out(560\ mV)} - 0.5\ V_{out(18\ mV)}|}{\text{Scale Factor}}$$

FIGURE 3

NOTES: A. The input pulse has the following characteristics: $t_w = 50$ ns, $t_r \leq 2$ ns, $t_f \leq 2$ ns, PRR = 10 MHz.

      B. Capacitor C_I consists of three capacitors in parallel: 1 μF, 0.1 μF, and 0.01 μF.

      C. C_L includes probe and jig capacitance.

FIGURE 4

TYPICAL CHARACTERISTICS

SN56502
DIFFERENTIAL OUTPUT OFFSET VOLTAGE
vs
FREE-AIR TEMPERATURE

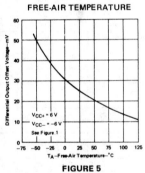

FIGURE 5

SN56502
QUIESCENT OUTPUT VOLTAGE
vs
FREE-AIR TEMPERATURE

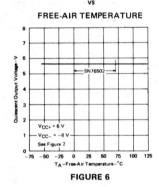

FIGURE 6

SN56502
D-C SCALE FACTOR
vs
FREE-AIR TEMPERATURE

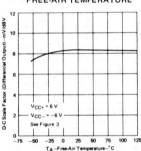

FIGURE 7

SN56502
D-C ERROR
vs
FREE-AIR TEMPERATURE

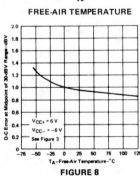

FIGURE 8

OUTPUT RISE TIME
vs
LOAD CAPACITANCE

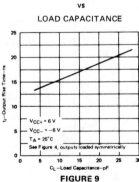

FIGURE 9

POWER DISSIPATION
vs
FREE-AIR TEMPERATURE

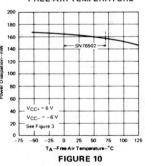

FIGURE 10

7

7-42

TEXAS INSTRUMENTS
INCORPORATED
POST OFFICE BOX 5012 • DALLAS, TEXAS 75222

TYPICAL APPLICATION DATA

Although designed for high-performance applications such as broadband radar infrared detection, and weapons systems, this device has a wide range of applications in data compression and analog computation.

basic log function

The basic log response is derived from the exponential current-voltage relationship of collector current and base-emitter voltage. This relationship is given in the equation:

$$m \cdot V_{BE} = \ln{[(I_C + I_{CES})/I_{CES}]}$$

where: I_C = collector current
I_{CES} = collector current at $V_{BE} = 0$
$m = q/kT$ (in V^{-1})
V_{BE} = base-emitter voltage

The differential input amplifier allows dual-polarity inputs, is self-compensating for temperature variations, and is relatively insensitive to noise.

functional block diagram

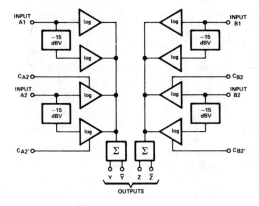

FIGURE 11

log sections

As can be seen from the schematic, there are eight differential pairs. Each pair is a 15-dBV log subsection, and each input feeds two pairs for a range of 30 dBV per stage.

Four compensation points are made available to allow slight variations in the gain (slope) of the two individual 15-dBV stages of input A2 and B2. By slightly changing the voltage on any of the compensation pins from its quiescent value, the gain of that particular 15-dBV stage can be adjusted to match the other 15-dBV stage in the pair. The compensation pins may also be used to match the transfer characteristics of input A2 to A1 or B2 to B1.

The log stages in each half of the circuit are summed by directly connecting their collectors together and summing through a common-base output stage. The two sets of output collectors are used to give two log outputs, Y and $\overline{Y}$ (or Z and $\overline{Z}$) which are equal in amplitude but opposite in polarity. This increases the versatility of the device.

By proper choice of external connections, linear amplification, linear attentuation, and many different applications requiring logarithmic signal processing are possible.

input levels

The recommended input voltage range of any one stage is given as 0.01 volt to one volt. Input levels in excess of one volt may result in a distorted output. When several log sections are summed together, the distorted area of one section overlaps with the next section and the resulting distortion is insignificant. However, there is a limit to the amount of overdrive that may be applied. As the input drive reaches ±3.5 volts, saturation occurs, clamping the collector-summing line and severely distorting the output. Therefore, the signal to any input must be limited to approximately ±3 volts to ensure a clean output.

output levels

Differential-output-voltage levels are low, generally less than 0.6 volt. As demonstrated in Figure 12, the output swing and the slope of the output response can be adjusted by varying the gain by means of the slope control. The coordinate origin may also be adjusted by positioning the offset of the output buffer.

TYPES SN56502, SN76502
LOGARITHMIC AMPLIFIERS

TYPICAL APPLICATION DATA

circuits

Figures 12 through 19 show typical circuits using these logarithmic amplifiers. Operational amplifiers not otherwise designated are SN52741 or SN72741. For operation at higher frequency, use of SN52733/SN72733 is recommended instead of SN52741/SN72741, with the differential outputs connected as in Figure 14. The SN5510/SN7510 or SN5511/SN7511 wideband amplifiers may also be used.

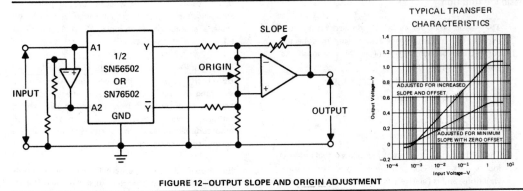

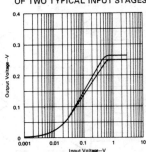

FIGURE 12–OUTPUT SLOPE AND ORIGIN ADJUSTMENT

FIGURE 13–UTILIZATION OF SEPARATE STAGES

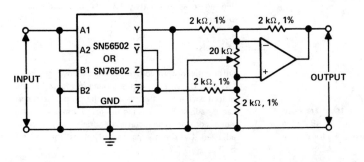

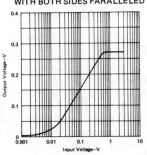

FIGURE 14–UTILIZATION OF PARALLELED INPUTS

TEXAS INSTRUMENTS
INCORPORATED
POST OFFICE BOX 5012 • DALLAS, TEXAS 75222

TYPICAL APPLICATION DATA

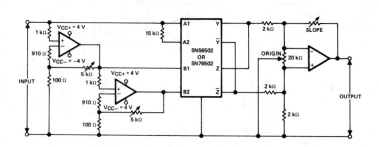

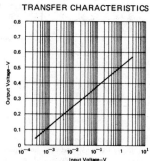

TRANSFER CHARACTERISTICS

NOTES: A. Inputs are limited by reducing the supply voltages for the input amplifiers to ±4 V.
B. The gains of the input amplifiers are adjusted to achieve smooth transitions.

FIGURE 15—LOGARITHMIC AMPLIFIER WITH INPUT VOLTAGE RANGE GREATER THAN 80 dBV

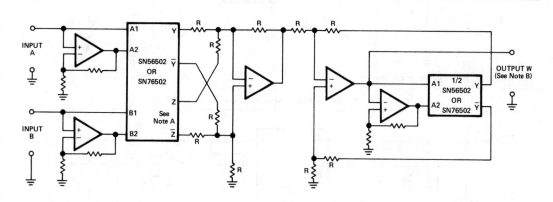

NOTES: A. Connections shown are for multiplication. For division, Z and $\overline{Z}$ connections are reversed.
B. Output W may need to be amplified to give actual product or quotient of A and B.
C. R designates resistors of equal value, typically 2 kΩ to 10 kΩ.

Multiplication: $W = A \cdot B \Rightarrow \log W = \log A + \log B$, or $W = a^{(\log_a A + \log_a B)}$

Division: $W = A/B \Rightarrow \log W = \log A - \log B$, or $W = a^{(\log_a A - \log_a B)}$

FIGURE 16—MULTIPLICATION OR DIVISION

TEXAS INSTRUMENTS
INCORPORATED
POST OFFICE BOX 5012 • DALLAS, TEXAS 75222

TYPES SN56502, SN76502
LOGARITHMIC AMPLIFIERS

TYPICAL APPLICATION DATA

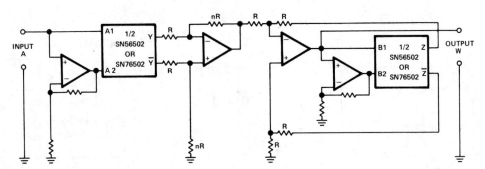

NOTE: R designates resistors of equal value, typically 2 kΩ to 10 kΩ. The power to which the input variable is raised is fixed by setting nR. Output W may need to be amplified to give the correct value.

Exponential: $W = A^n \Rightarrow \log W = n \log A$, or $W = a^{(n \log_a A)}$

FIGURE 17—RAISING A VARIABLE TO A FIXED POWER

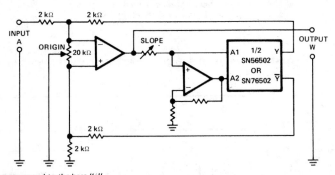

NOTE: Adjust the slope to correspond to the base "a".

Exponential to any base: $W = a$

FIGURE 18—RAISING A FIXED NUMBER TO A VARIABLE POWER

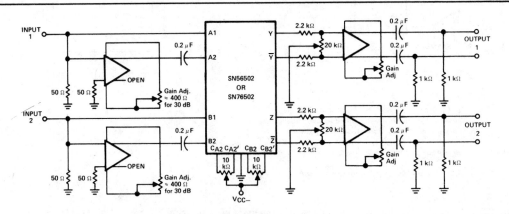

FIGURE 19—DUAL-CHANNEL RF LOGARITHMIC AMPLIFIER WITH 50-dB INPUT RANGE PER CHANNEL AT 10 MHz

TEXAS INSTRUMENTS
INCORPORATED
POST OFFICE BOX 5012 • DALLAS, TEXAS 75222

LINEAR INTEGRATED CIRCUITS

TYPES SN56514, SN76514 BALANCED MIXERS

BULLETIN NO. DL-S 7311430, JANUARY 1971—REVISED SEPTEMBER 1973

- Flat Response to 100 MHz
- Local Oscillator IF Isolation . . . 30 dB Typ
- Local Oscillator RF Isolation . . . 60 dB Typ
- RF-IF Isolation . . . 30 dB Typ
- Conversion Gain . . . 14 dB Typ
- Use with 12-V or ±6-V Power Supplies

schematic

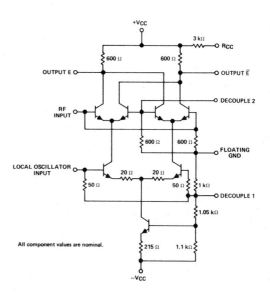

All component values are nominal.

description

The SN56514 and SN76514 are doubly balanced mixers which utilize two cross-coupled, differential transistor pairs driven by a third balanced pair. The circuit features a flat response over a wide band of frequencies. The SN56514 is characterized for operation over the full military temperature range of −55°C to 125°C; the SN76514 is characterized for operation from 0°C to 70°C.

terminal assignments

J OR N DUAL-IN-LINE PACKAGE (TOP VIEW)

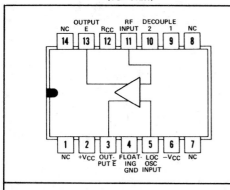

L PLUG-IN PACKAGE (TOP VIEW)

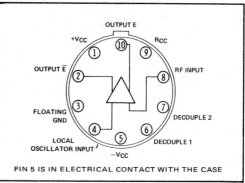

PIN 5 IS IN ELECTRICAL CONTACT WITH THE CASE

For operation from a single 12-V supply, connect the positive terminal of the supply to +V$_{CC}$, the negative terminal to −V$_{CC}$, and the floating-ground terminal to R$_{CC}$. For operation from two 6-V supplies, leave R$_{CC}$ open and connect the positive terminal of one supply to +V$_{CC}$, the negative terminal of the other supply to −V$_{CC}$, and the remaining terminals of the two supplies to the floating-ground terminal. See Figure 19.

NC—No internal connection

TEXAS INSTRUMENTS
INCORPORATED
POST OFFICE BOX 5012 • DALLAS, TEXAS 75222

absolute maximum ratings over operating free-air temperature range (unless otherwise noted)

Supply voltage, V_{CC} (see Note 1)	18 V
Input voltage (see Notes 1 and 2)	7 V
Continuous output current (see Note 3)	10 mA
Continuous total power dissipation at (or below) 25°C free-air temperature (see Note 4)	500 mW
Operating free-air temperature range: SN56514 Circuits	−55°C to 125°C
SN76514 Circuits	0°C to 70°C
Storage temperature range	−65°C to 150°C

recommended operating conditions

	MIN	NOM	MAX	UNIT
Supply voltage, V_{CC}		12		V
Local oscillator input voltage (see Note 5)		250	300	mV rms
RF input voltage (see Note 5)		10	30	mV rms
Operating free-air temperature range: SN56514 Circuits	−55		125	°C
SN76514 Circuits	0		70	°C

electrical characteristics at 25°C free-air temperature, V_{CC} = 12 V

PARAMETER		TEST FIGURE	TEST CONDITIONS	SN56514			SN76514			UNIT
				MIN	TYP	MAX	MIN	TYP	MAX	
V_O	Quiescent output voltage	1		9.6	10.5	11.3	9.6	10.5	11.3	V
I_{CC}	Supply current	1		5.5	7.4	10.9	5.5	7.4	10.9	mA
G_C	Conversion gain (single-ended output)	2	f_{RF} and f_{LO} = 100 kHz thru 40 MHz	11	14	17	11	14	17	dB
LOIFI	Local oscillator to IF isolation	3	f_{LO} = 100 kHz thru 40 MHz	15	29†			29†		dB
LORFI	Local oscillator to RF isolation	3	f_{LO} = 100 kHz thru 40 MHz	40	52†			52†		dB
RFIFI	RF to IF isolation	4	f_{RF} = 100 kHz thru 40 MHz	15	28†			28†		dB

†The typical values are at 40 MHz.

NOTES: 1. All d-c voltage values are with respect to $-V_{CC}$ terminal.
2. This rating applies to the local-oscillator input, RF input, and Decouple 2.
3. This value applies for both outputs simultaneously.
4. For operation above 25°C free-air temperature, refer to Dissipation Derating Curve, Figure 18.
5. All signal voltages are with respect to the floating-ground terminal. Alternatively, the RF input may be applied differentially between the RF input terminal and Decouple 2.

TEXAS INSTRUMENTS
INCORPORATED
POST OFFICE BOX 5012 • DALLAS, TEXAS 75222

PARAMETER MEASUREMENT INFORMATION

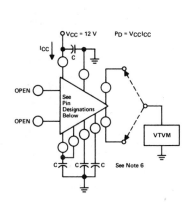

FIGURE 1–V_O, I_{CC}, and P_D

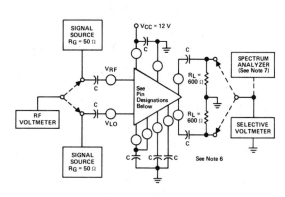

FIGURE 2–G_C

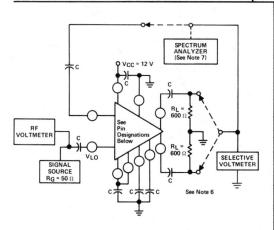

FIGURE 3–LOIFI and LORFI

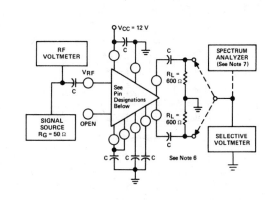

FIGURE 4–RFIFI

Pin Designations: For all test circuits appearing in this data sheet, terminal functions are defined by their relative positions as shown in the drawings in this block.

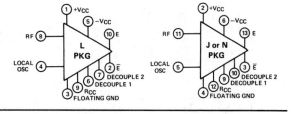

NOTES: 6. Capacitor C comprises the following capacitors in parallel: 1 μF, 0.1 μF, and 0.0015 μF.
7. The spectrum analyzer is used for frequencies above the normal range of the selective voltmeter.

TEXAS INSTRUMENTS
INCORPORATED
POST OFFICE BOX 5012 • DALLAS, TEXAS 75222

TYPICAL CHARACTERISTICS

QUIESCENT OUTPUT VOLTAGE
vs
FREE-AIR TEMPERATURE

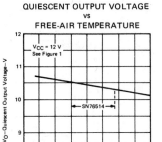

FIGURE 5

TOTAL POWER DISSIPATION
vs
FREE-AIR TEMPERATURE

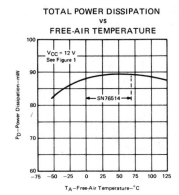

FIGURE 6

CONVERSION GAIN
vs
SUPPLY VOLTAGES

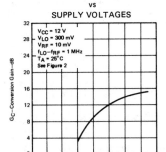

FIGURE 7

CONVERSION GAIN
vs
LOCAL OSCILLATOR VOLTAGE

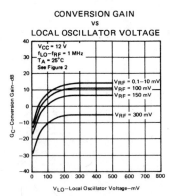

FIGURE 8

CONVERSION GAIN
vs
FREQUENCY

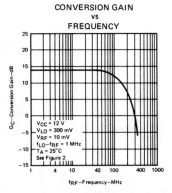

FIGURE 9

CONVERSION GAIN
vs
FREE-AIR TEMPERATURE

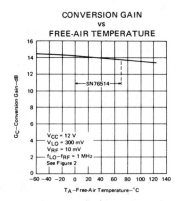

FIGURE 10

TEXAS INSTRUMENTS
INCORPORATED
POST OFFICE BOX 5012 • DALLAS, TEXAS 75222

TYPICAL CHARACTERISTICS

LOCAL OSCILLATOR TO IF ISOLATION
vs
FREQUENCY

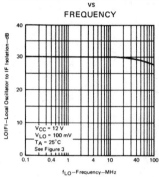

FIGURE 11

LOCAL OSCILLATOR TO IF ISOLATION
vs
FREE-AIR TEMPERATURE

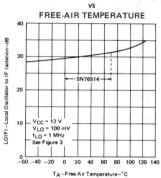

FIGURE 12

LOCAL OSCILLATOR TO RF ISOLATION
vs
FREQUENCY

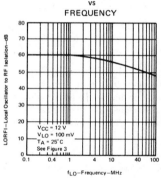

FIGURE 13

LOCAL OSCILLATOR TO RF ISOLATION
vs
FREE-AIR TEMPERATURE

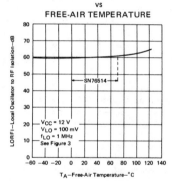

FIGURE 14

RF TO IF ISOLATION
vs
FREQUENCY

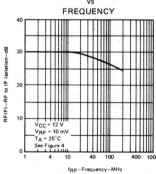

FIGURE 15

RF TO IF ISOLATION
vs
FREE-AIR TEMPERATURE

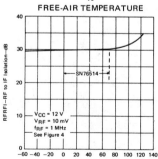

FIGURE 16

7

TEXAS INSTRUMENTS
INCORPORATED
POST OFFICE BOX 5012 • DALLAS, TEXAS 75222

TYPICAL CHARACTERISTICS

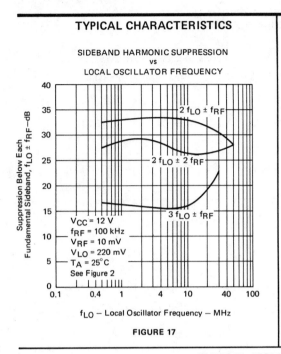

SIDEBAND HARMONIC SUPPRESSION
vs
LOCAL OSCILLATOR FREQUENCY

V_{CC} = 12 V
f_{RF} = 100 kHz
V_{RF} = 10 mV
V_{LO} = 220 mV
T_A = 25°C
See Figure 2

f_{LO} — Local Oscillator Frequency — MHz

FIGURE 17

THERMAL INFORMATION

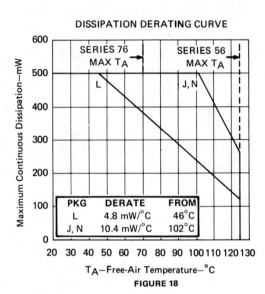

DISSIPATION DERATING CURVE

SERIES 76 MAX T_A

SERIES 56 MAX T_A

PKG	DERATE	FROM
L	4.8 mW/°C	46°C
J, N	10.4 mW/°C	102°C

T_A—Free-Air Temperature—°C

FIGURE 18

TYPICAL APPLICATION DATA

The SN56514 and SN76514 balanced mixers are designed to have considerable circuit flexibility which results in a wide range of applications. Typical applications include use as balanced modulators for sideband-suppressed-carrier generation, product detectors for demodulation, frequency converters, and frequency or phase modulators. In addition, the SN56514 and SN76514 may be used in control systems and analog computers as low-level multipliers or squaring circuits.

The circuits are designed to operate from either a single 12-V supply or two 6-V supplies. Electrical characteristics will be unchanged with the use of either power supply option. External bypass capacitors, as shown in Figure 19, should be used for optimum performance.

The mixer's electrical performance and the inherent IC advantages of size, reliability, and component matching make it very desirable for use in communication and control systems.

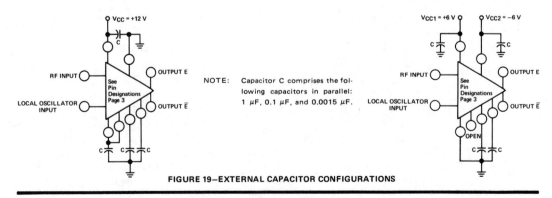

NOTE: Capacitor C comprises the following capacitors in parallel: 1 µF, 0.1 µF, and 0.0015 µF.

FIGURE 19—EXTERNAL CAPACITOR CONFIGURATIONS

TEXAS INSTRUMENTS
INCORPORATED
POST OFFICE BOX 5012 • DALLAS, TEXAS 75222

LINEAR
INTEGRATED CIRCUITS

TYPES SN52555, SN72555
PRECISION TIMERS

BULLETIN NO. DL-S 7312053, SEPTEMBER 1973

- Timing from Microseconds to Hours
- Astable or Monostable Operation
- Adjustable Duty Cycle
- Up to 200-mA Sink or Source Output Current
- TTL Compatible Output
- Designed to be Interchangeable with Signetics SE555/NE555

description

The SN52555 and SN72555 are monolithic timing circuits capable of producing accurate time delays or oscillation. In the time-delay or monostable mode of operation, the timed interval is controlled by a single external resistor and capacitor network. In the astable mode of operation, the frequency and duty cycle may be independently controlled with two external resistors and a single external capacitor.

The threshold and trigger levels are normally two-thirds and one-third, respectively, of V_{CC}. These levels can be altered by use of the control voltage terminal. When the trigger input falls below the trigger level, the flip-flop is set and the output goes high. When the threshold input rises above the threshold level, the flip-flop is reset and the output goes low. The reset input can override all other inputs and can be used to initiate a new timing cycle. When the reset input goes low, the flip-flop is reset and the output goes low. When the output is low, a low-impedance path is provided between the discharge terminal and ground.

The output circuit is capable of sinking or sourcing current up to 200 milliamperes. Operation is specified for supplies of 5 to 15 volts. With a 5-volt supply, output levels are compatible with TTL inputs.

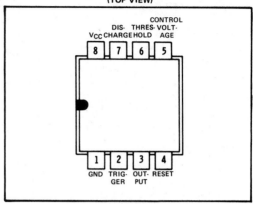

**JP OR P DUAL-IN-LINE PACKAGE
(TOP VIEW)**

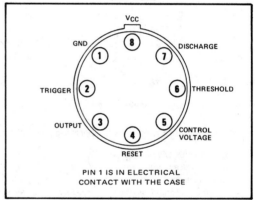

**L PLUG-IN PACKAGE
(TOP VIEW)**

PIN 1 IS IN ELECTRICAL
CONTACT WITH THE CASE

functional block diagram

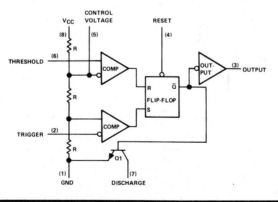

TEXAS INSTRUMENTS
INCORPORATED
POST OFFICE BOX 5012 • DALLAS, TEXAS 75222

TYPES SN52555, SN72555
PRECISION TIMERS

schematic

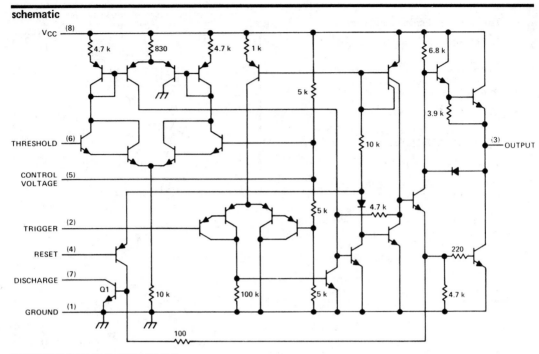

Resistor values shown are nominal and in ohms.

absolute maximum ratings over operating free-air temperature range (unless otherwise noted)

Supply voltage, V_{CC} (see Note 1) . . . . 18 V
Input voltage (control voltage, reset, threshold, trigger) . . . . V_{CC}
Output current . . . . ±225 mA
Continuous total dissipation at (or below) 25°C free-air temperature (see Note 2) . . . . 600 mW
Operating free-air temperature range: SN52555 . . . . −55°C to 125°C
                                  SN72555 . . . . 0°C to 70°C
Storage temperature range . . . . −65°C to 150°C
Lead temperature 1/16 inch from case for 60 seconds: JP or L package . . . . 300°C
Lead temperature 1/16 inch from case for 10 seconds: P package . . . . 260°C

NOTES: 1. All voltage values are with respect to network ground terminal.
         2. For operation above 25°C free-air temperature, refer to Dissipation Derating Curve, Figure 1.

recommended operating conditions

	SN52555			SN72555			UNIT
	MIN	NOM	MAX	MIN	NOM	MAX	
Supply voltage, V_{CC}	4.5		18	4.5		16	V
Input voltage, V_I (control voltage, reset, threshold, trigger)			V_{CC}			V_{CC}	V
Output Current, I_O			±200			±200	mA
Operating free-air temperature, T_A	−55		125	0		70	°C

7

TEXAS INSTRUMENTS
INCORPORATED
POST OFFICE BOX 5012 • DALLAS, TEXAS 75222

electrical characteristics at 25°C free-air temperature, V_{CC} = 5 V to 15 V (unless otherwise noted)

PARAMETER	TEST CONDITIONS		SN52555 MIN	SN52555 TYP	SN52555 MAX	SN72555 MIN	SN72555 TYP	SN72555 MAX	UNIT
Threshold voltage level as a percentage of supply voltage				66.7			66.7		%
Threshold current (see Note 3)				0.1	0.25		0.1	0.25	µA
Trigger voltage level	V_{CC} = 15 V		4.8	5	5.2		5		V
	V_{CC} = 5 V		1.45	1.67	1.9		1.67		
Trigger current				0.5			0.5		µA
Reset voltage level			0.4	0.7	1	0.4	0.7	1	V
Reset current				0.1			0.1		mA
Control voltage (open-circuit)	V_{CC} = 15 V		9.6	10	10.4	9	10	11	V
	V_{CC} = 5 V		2.9	3.3	3.8	2.6	3.3	4	
Low-level output voltage	V_{CC} = 15 V	I_{OL} = 10 mA		0.1	0.15		0.1	0.25	V
		I_{OL} = 50 mA		0.4	0.5		0.4	0.75	
		I_{OL} = 100 mA		2	2.2		2	2.5	
		I_{OL} = 200 mA		2.5			2.5		
	V_{CC} = 5 V	I_{OL} = 5 mA		0.1	0.25				
		I_{OL} = 8 mA					0.16	0.35	
High-level output voltage	V_{CC} = 15 V	I_{OH} = −100 mA	13	13.3		12.75	13.3		V
		I_{OH} = −200 mA		12.5			12.5		
	V_{CC} = 5 V	I_{OH} = −100 mA	3	3.3		2.75	3.3		
Supply current	Output low, No load	V_{CC} = 15 V		10	12		10	15	mA
		V_{CC} = 5 V		3	5		3	6	
	Output high, No load	V_{CC} = 15 V		9	11		9	14	
		V_{CC} = 5 V		2	4		2	5	

NOTE 3: This parameter influences the maximum value of the timing resistors R_A and R_B. For example when V_{CC} = 5 V the maximum value is R = $R_A + R_B$ ≈ 20 MΩ.

operating characteristics, V_{CC} = 5 V and 15 V

PARAMETER	TEST CONDITIONS†		SN52555 MIN	SN52555 TYP	SN52555 MAX	SN72555 MIN	SN72555 TYP	SN72555 MAX	UNIT
Initial accuracy of timing interval	R_A = 1 kΩ to 100 kΩ,	T_A = 25°C		0.5	2		1		%
Temperature coefficient of timing interval	R_B = 0 to 100 kΩ,	T_A = MIN to MAX		30			50		ppm/°C
Supply voltage sensitivity of timing interval	C = 0.1 µF	T_A = 25°C		0.005	0.02		0.01		%/V
Output pulse rise time	C_L = 15 pF,	T_A = 25°C		100			100		ns
Output pulse fall time				100			100		ns

†For conditions shown as MIN or MAX, use the appropriate value specified under recommended operating conditions.

THERMAL INFORMATION
DISSIPATION DERATING CURVE

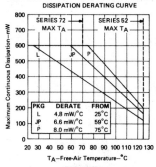

PKG	DERATE	FROM
L	4.8 mW/°C	25°C
JP	6.6 mW/°C	59°C
P	8.0 mW/°C	75°C

FIGURE 1

TEXAS INSTRUMENTS
INCORPORATED
POST OFFICE BOX 5012 • DALLAS, TEXAS 75222

TYPICAL CHARACTERISTICS†

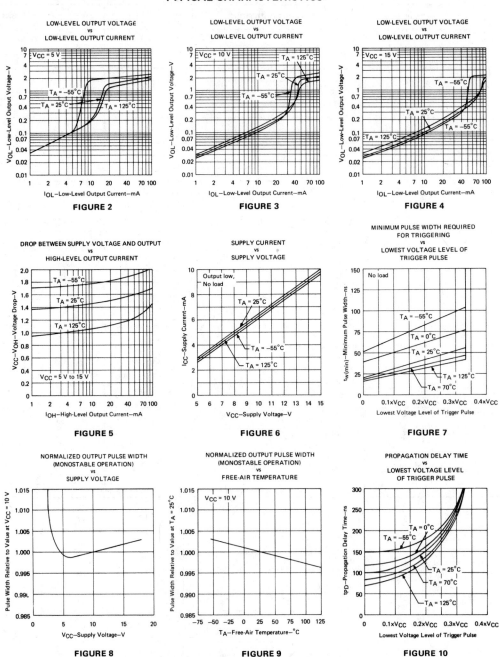

FIGURE 2

FIGURE 3

FIGURE 4

FIGURE 5

FIGURE 6

FIGURE 7

FIGURE 8

FIGURE 9

FIGURE 10

†Data for temperatures below 0°C and above 70°C are applicable for SN52555 circuits only.

TEXAS INSTRUMENTS
INCORPORATED
POST OFFICE BOX 5012 • DALLAS, TEXAS 75222

TYPICAL APPLICATION DATA

monostable operation

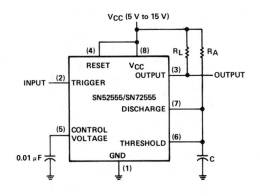

FIGURE 11—CIRCUIT FOR MONOSTABLE OPERATION

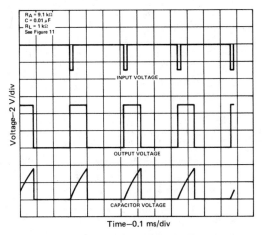

FIGURE 12—TYPICAL MONOSTABLE WAVEFORMS

The SN52555 and SN72555 may be connected as shown in Figure 11 for monostable operation producing an output pulse width independent of the input waveform and controlled by the $R_A \cdot C$ time constant. Prior to the negative-going input pulse, capacitor C is held discharged by transistor Q1 (see schematic). Application of a negative-going input-trigger-pulse sets the flip-flop, turns off Q1, and drives the output high. Capacitor C is now charged through R_A with a time constant $\tau = R_A C$. When the voltage across capacitor C reaches the threshold voltage of the comparator, the flip-flop is reset, energizing Q1 and discharging C; therefore driving the output back to the low level. Figure 12 shows the actual resultant waveforms.

Monostable operation is initiated when the negative-going input pulse reaches the trigger level. Once initiated, the timing interval will complete even if retriggering occurs during the timing interval. Because of the threshold level and saturation voltage of Q1, the output pulse width is approximately $t_W = 1.1 \, R_A C$. Figure 13 is a plot of the time constant for various values of R_A and C. The threshold levels and charge rates are both directly proportional to the supply voltage, V_{CC}. The timing interval is therefore independent of the supply voltage, so long as the supply voltage is constant during the time interval.

Applying a negative-going trigger pulse simultaneously to the reset and trigger terminals during the timing interval will discharge C and re-initiate the cycle, commencing on the positive edge of the reset pulse. The output is held low as long as the reset pulse is low. When the reset input is not used, it should be connected to V_{CC} to prevent false triggering.

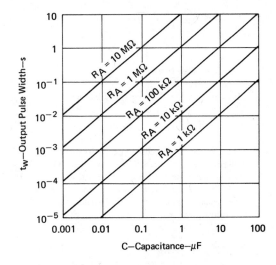

FIGURE 13—OUTPUT PULSE WIDTH vs CAPACITANCE

TYPICAL APPLICATION DATA

astable operation

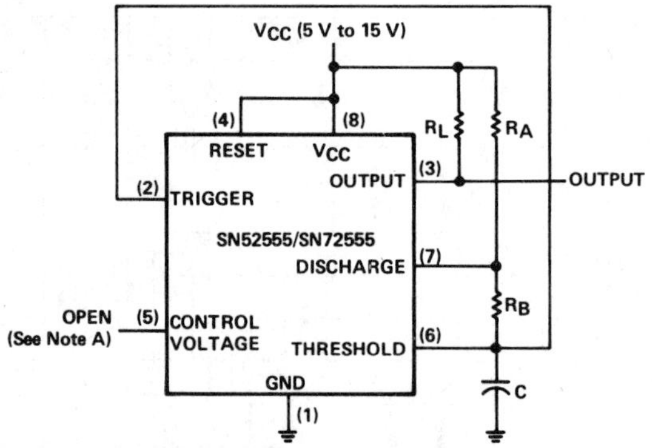

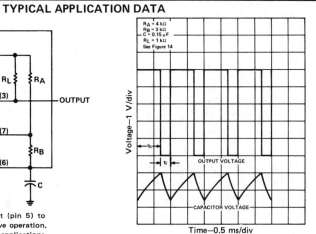

NOTE A: Decoupling the control voltage input (pin 5) to
ground with a capacitor may improve operation.
This should be evaluated for individual applications.

FIGURE 14—CIRCUIT FOR ASTABLE OPERATION

FIGURE 15—TYPICAL ASTABLE WAVEFORMS

Addition of a second resistor, R_B, to the circuit of Figure 11; as shown in Figure 14, and connection of the trigger input to the threshold input will cause the SN52555/SN72555 to self-trigger and run as a multivibrator. The capacitor C will charge through R_A and R_B then discharge through R_B only. The duty cycle may be controlled, therefore, by the values of R_A and R_B.

This astable connection results in capacitor C charging and discharging between the threshold-voltage level ($\approx 0.67 \cdot V_{CC}$) and the trigger-voltage level ($\approx 0.33 \cdot V_{CC}$). As in the monostable circuit, charge and discharge times (and therefore the frequency and duty cycle) are independent of the supply voltage.

Figure 15 shows typical waveforms generated during astable operation. The output high-level duration, t_h, is calculated as:

$$t_h = 0.693 \ (R_A + R_B)C,$$

output low-level duration, t_l, as:

$$t_l = 0.693 \ (R_B)C.$$

The total period is $T = t_h + t_l$ and frequency is

$$f = \frac{1}{T}, \text{ or } f = \frac{1.44}{(R_A + 2R_B)C}.$$

The frequency of oscillation may be determined by referring to the chart shown in Figure 16, which relates free-running frequency, f, to the external resistors R_A and R_B and the external capacitor C. Duty cycle, D, is determined by the values selected for R_A and R_B and may be calculated as:

$$D = \frac{R_B}{R_A + R_B}.$$

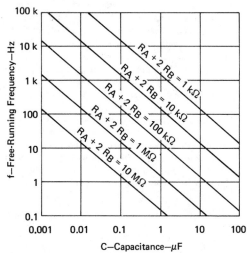

FIGURE 16—FREE-RUNNING FREQUENCY

TEXAS INSTRUMENTS
INCORPORATED
POST OFFICE BOX 5012 • DALLAS, TEXAS 75222

TYPICAL APPLICATION DATA

missing-pulse detector

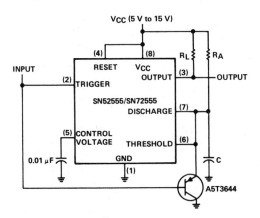

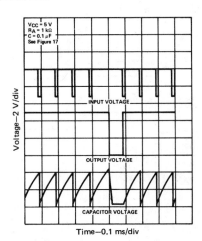

FIGURE 17—CIRCUIT FOR MISSING-PULSE DETECTOR

FIGURE 18—MISSING-PULSE-DETECTOR WAVEFORMS

The circuit shown in Figure 17 may be utilized to detect a missing pulse or abnormally long spacing between consecutive pulses in a train of pulses. The timing interval of the monostable circuit is continuously retriggered by the input pulse train as long as the pulse spacing is less than the timing interval. A longer pulse spacing, missing pulse, or terminated pulse train will permit the timing interval to be completed, thereby generating an output pulse as illustrated in Figure 18.

frequency divider

By adjusting the length of the timing cycle, the basic circuit of Figure 11 can be made to operate as a frequency divider. Figure 19 illustrates a divide-by-3 circuit that makes use of the fact that retriggering cannot occur during the timing cycle.

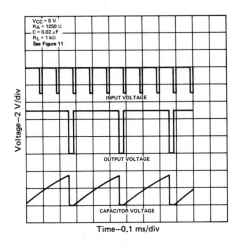

FIGURE 19—DIVIDE-BY-THREE CIRCUIT WAVEFORMS

TEXAS INSTRUMENTS
INCORPORATED
POST OFFICE BOX 5012 • DALLAS, TEXAS 75222

TYPICAL APPLICATION DATA

pulse-width modulation

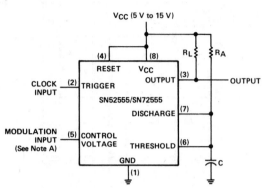

NOTE A: The modulating signal may be direct or capacitively coupled to the control voltage terminal. For direct coupling, the effects of modulation source voltage and impedance on the bias of the SN52555/SN72555 should be considered.

FIGURE 20—CIRCUIT FOR PULSE-WIDTH MODULATION

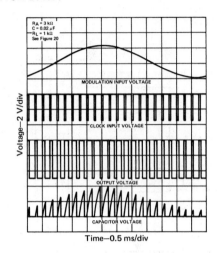

FIGURE 21—PULSE-WIDTH-MODULATION WAVEFORMS

The operation of the timer may be modified by modulating the internal threshold and trigger voltages. This is accomplished by applying an external voltage (or current) to the control voltage pin. Figure 20 is a circuit for pulse-width modulation. The monostable circuit is triggered by a continuous input pulse train and the threshold voltage is modulated by a control signal. The resultant effect is a modulation of the output pulse width, as shown in Figure 21. A sine-wave modulation signal is illustrated, but any wave-shape could be used.

pulse-position modulation

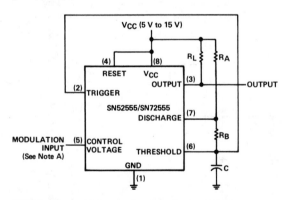

NOTE A: The modulating signal may be direct or capacitively coupled to the control voltage terminal. For direct coupling, the effects of modulation source voltage and impedance on the bias of the SN52555/SN72555 should be considered.

FIGURE 22—CIRCUIT FOR PULSE-POSITION MODULATION

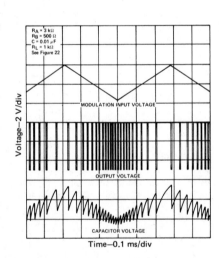

FIGURE 23—PULSE POSITION-MODULATION WAVEFORMS

The SN52555/SN72555 may be used as a pulse-position modulator as shown in Figure 22. In this application, the threshold voltage, and thereby the time delay, of a free-running oscillator is modulated. Figure 23 shows such a circuit, with a triangular-wave modulation signal, however, any modulating wave-shape could be used.

TEXAS INSTRUMENTS
INCORPORATED
POST OFFICE BOX 5012 • DALLAS, TEXAS 75222

TYPICAL APPLICATION DATA

sequential timer

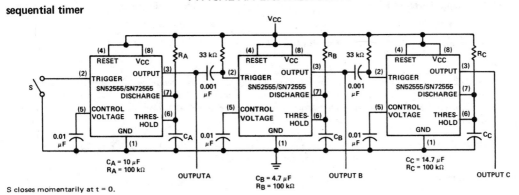

S closes momentarily at t = 0.

FIGURE 24—SEQUENTIAL TIMER CIRCUIT

Many applications, such as computers, require signals for initializing conditions during start-up. Other applications such as test equipment require activation of test signals in sequence. SN52555/SN72555 circuits may be connected to provide such sequential control. The timers may be used in various combinations of astable or monostable circuit connections, with or without modulation, for extremely flexible waveform control. Figure 24 illustrates a sequencer circuit with possible applications in many systems and Figure 25 shows the output waveforms.

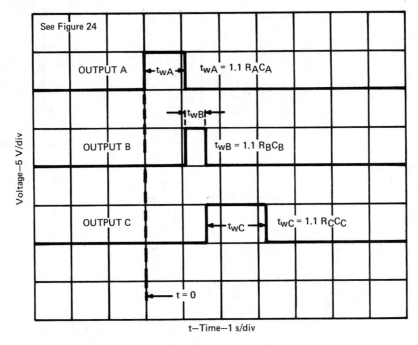

FIGURE 25—SEQUENTIAL TIMER WAVEFORMS

TEXAS INSTRUMENTS
INCORPORATED
POST OFFICE BOX 5012 • DALLAS, TEXAS 75222

- Stable Threshold Level
- Low Input Current
- High Output Sink Current Capability

- Threshold Hysteresis
- Wide Supply Voltage Range

description

The SN72560 is a precision level detector intended for applications that require a Schmitt-trigger function. The detector has excellent voltage and temperature stability and an internal voltage reference for the input threshold level. For the SN72560 only; the reference-voltage pin is available for external adjustment of the positive-going threshold voltage level.

The SN72D560 is a dual precision level detector, each half of which is electrically similar to SN72560. Both the SN72560 and SN72D560 are characterized for operation from $0°C$ to $70°C$.

terminal assignments

| | SN72560 L PLUG-IN PACKAGE (TOP VIEW) | SN72560 P DUAL-IN-LINE PACKAGE (TOP VIEW) | SN72D560 L PLUG-IN PACKAGE (TOP VIEW) | SN72D560 P DUAL-IN-LINE PACKAGE (TOP VIEW) |

SN72560 L PLUG-IN PACKAGE (TOP VIEW) — ALL TERMINALS ARE INSULATED FROM THE CASE

Vcc, GND, REF, NC, NC, OUTPUT, NC, INPUT

SN72560 P DUAL-IN-LINE PACKAGE (TOP VIEW)

8 Vcc, 7 NC, 6 INPUT, 5 NC, 1 GND, 2 REF, 3 NC, 4 OUTPUT

SN72D560 L PLUG-IN PACKAGE (TOP VIEW) — ALL TERMINALS ARE INSULATED FROM THE CASE

DETECTOR NO. 2, Vcc, GND, OUTPUT, INPUT, DETECTOR NO. 1, Vcc, INPUT, OUTPUT, GND

SN72D560 P DUAL-IN-LINE PACKAGE (TOP VIEW)

DETECTOR NO. 2: 8 Vcc, 7 INPUT, 6 OUTPUT, 5 GND
DETECTOR NO. 1: 1 GND, 2 OUTPUT, 3 INPUT, 4 Vcc

NC—No internal connection

schematic (each detector)

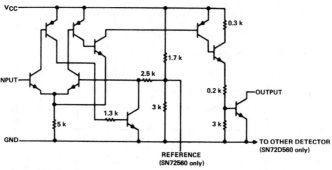

Vcc, INPUT, GND, 0.3 k, 1.7 k, 2.5 k, 0.2 k, OUTPUT, 1.3 k, 3 k, 5 k, 3 k, REFERENCE (SN72560 only), TO OTHER DETECTOR (SN72D560 only)

Resistor values shown are nominal and in ohms.

TEXAS INSTRUMENTS
INCORPORATED
POST OFFICE BOX 5012 • DALLAS, TEXAS 75222

absolute maximum ratings over operating free-air temperature range (unless otherwise noted)

Supply voltage, V_{CC} (see Note 1) . . . . 7 V
Input voltage (see Note 1) . . . . V_{CC}
Output voltage (see Note 1) . . . . 25 V
Output sink current . . . . 160 mA
Continuous total dissipation at (or below) 25°C free-air temperature (see Note 2) . . . . 800 mW
Operating free-air temperature range . . . . 0°C to 70°C
Storage temperature range . . . . −65°C to 150°C
Lead temperature 1/16 inch from case for 60 seconds: L package . . . . 300°C
Lead temperature 1/16 inch from case for 10 seconds: P package . . . . 260°C

NOTES: 1. All voltage values are with respect to the network ground terminal.
2. For operation above 25°C free-air temperature refer to Dissipation Derating Curve, Figure 3. This rating for the L package requires a heat sink that provides a thermal resistance from case to free-air, $R_{\theta CA}$, of not more than 95°C/W.

recommended operating conditions

	MIN	NOM	MAX	UNIT
Supply voltage, V_{CC}	2.5	5	7	V
Low-level output current, I_{OL}			48	mA
Operating free-air temperature, T_A	0		70	°C

electrical characteristics over recommended operating free-air temperature range, V_{CC} = 5V (unless otherwise noted)

	PARAMETER	TEST CONDITIONS		MIN	TYP	MAX	UNIT
V_{T+}	Positive-going threshold voltage[†]			2.8	3	3.2	V
V_{T+}/V_{CC}	Ratio of positive-going threshold voltage to supply voltage	V_{CC} = 2.5 V to 7 V			0.6		
V_{T-}	Negative-going threshold voltage[‡]			0.4	0.6	0.8	V
I_{T+}	Input current below positive-going threshold voltage	V_I = 2.75 V,	Output on		2	30	nA
I_{T-}	Input current above negative-going threshold voltage	V_I = 1 V,	Output off		1.2		µA
$I_{O(off)}$	Off-state output current	V_I = 4 V,	V_O = 25 V			10	µA
$V_{O(on)}$	On-state output voltage	V_I = 0,	I_O = 48 mA		0.2	0.4	V
$I_{CC(off)}$	Supply current, output off (each detector)	V_I = 4 V			4.8	6.5	mA
$I_{CC(on)}$	Supply current, output on (each detector)	V_I = 0			10	15	mA

[†]Positive-going threshold voltage, V_{T+}, is the input voltage level at which the output changes state as the input voltage is increased.
[‡]Negative-going threshold voltage, V_{T-}, is the input voltage level at which the output changes state as the input voltage is decreased.

TEXAS INSTRUMENTS
INCORPORATED
POST OFFICE BOX 5012 • DALLAS, TEXAS 75222

TYPES SN72560, SN72D560
PRECISION LEVEL DETECTORS

TYPICAL CHARACTERISTICS

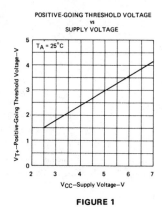

POSITIVE-GOING THRESHOLD VOLTAGE
vs
SUPPLY VOLTAGE

FIGURE 1

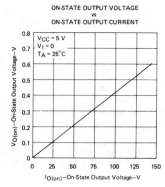

ON-STATE OUTPUT VOLTAGE
vs
ON-STATE OUTPUT CURRENT

FIGURE 2

THERMAL INFORMATION

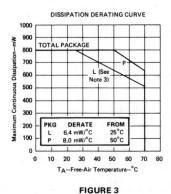

DISSIPATION DERATING CURVE

PKG	DERATE	FROM
L	6,4 mW/°C	25°C
P	8,0 mW/°C	50°C

FIGURE 3

NOTE 3: This rating for the L package requires a heat sink that provides a thermal resistance from case to free-air, $R_{\theta CA}$, of not more than 95°C/W.

TYPICAL APPLICATION DATA

The SN72560 and SN72D560 perform the function of a Schmitt trigger circuit. The logic function is noninverting and has a wide hysteresis between the positive-going and negative-going threshold voltage levels (see Figure 4).

Operation of the SN72560 and SN72D560 is specified at a V_{CC} of 5 V, although 2.5-V to 7-V supply operation is possible. The devices can be used with popular logic systems (such as Series 54/74 TTL) and standard battery voltages.

Figure 5 is used to illustrate operation of the SN72560 and SN72D560 circuits. The input stage is a differential amplifier composed of Q1, Q2, Q3, and Q4. The input signal is applied at the base of Q1 while the base of Q2 is connected to an internal reference voltage determined by resistors R4 and R5 and V_{CC}; $V_{ref} = V_{CC} \cdot R5/(R4 + R5)$.

TEXAS INSTRUMENTS
INCORPORATED
POST OFFICE BOX 5012 • DALLAS, TEXAS 75222

TYPICAL APPLICATION DATA

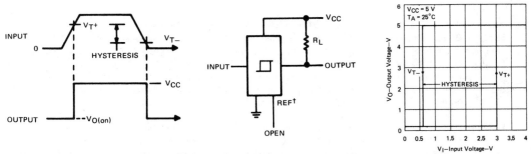

FIGURE 4—INPUT-OUTPUT TRANSFER FUNCTION

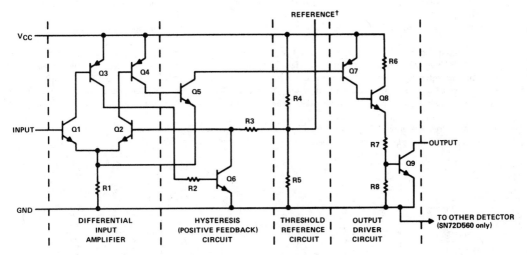

FIGURE 5—FUNCTIONAL CIRCUIT DIAGRAM

If the base of Q1 is less positive than the base of Q2, Q2 conducts and causes Q4, Q5, Q7, Q8, and the output transistor, Q9, to conduct. Transistors Q2 and Q5 share the current in emitter resistor R1. Since Q1 does not conduct, Q3 and Q6 do not conduct. There is no base current in Q1, and therefore no current required from the input source. A very high input impedance therefore exists. Since Q2 is conducting, a small voltage drop exists across R3 due to Q2 base current.

If the input voltage is increased, Q1 does not conduct until the input voltage (base voltage of Q1) approaches the base voltage of Q2. Current is then switched from the emitters of Q2 and Q5 to the emitter of Q1. Conduction in Q1 causes current to flow in Q3 and Q6 which results in additional voltage drop in R3 and therefore a reduction in the base voltage of Q2. This positive feedback accelerates switching action and causes conduction to rapidly cease in Q2, Q4, Q5, Q7, Q8, and the output transistor, Q9. Conduction in Q6 causes the base of Q2 to assume a voltage (approximately 0.6 V) much lower than the original reference voltage (approximately 3 V). This results in hysteresis between the positive-going and negative-going threshold levels.

† SN72560 only

TYPES SN72560, SN72D560
PRECISION LEVEL DETECTORS

TYPICAL APPLICATION DATA

After switching occurs, the base current of Q1 increases to a somewhat higher value than just below threshold because of higher Q1 operating currents. Once the positive-going threshold level (≈ 3 V) has been reached, the input voltage must be reduced to the negative-going threshold level (≈ 0.6 V) before switching back to the original state will occur. Figure 4 illustrates the threshold levels of the SN72560 and SN72D560. Because the input current increases after the positive-going threshold voltage level has been exceeded, the input voltage will be reduced by an amount dependent on the source resistance. If the reduced input voltage is not below the negative-going threshold voltage level, a stable state will exist. If the source resistance is too high, oscillation or periodic switching may occur.

The positive-going threshold voltage level (V_{T+}) is guaranteed to be 3.00 ± 0.20 volts at a V_{CC} of 5 V. It is also approximately 60% of the supply voltage over the supply voltage range of 2.5 V to 7 V. With a resistor-capacitor network as illustrated in Figure 7, a V_{T+}/V_{CC} ratio of 60% results in a timed interval of approximately RC seconds, independent of the V_{CC} level. Since the input current is nominally 2 nA just below the V_{T+} level, very large values of R and/or large values of C may be used to achieve long-timed intervals. The duration of the timed interval may be greatly increased (at the expense of accuracy) by using a P-N-P transistor as shown in Figure 11 in a capacitance-multiplication technique. The timed interval is, however, sensitive to variations in the h_{FE} of the P-N-P transistor. Also for any of the timing applications, very-low-leakage capacitors are necessary for accurate operation.

The low input current (30 nA maximum for I_{T+}) and high output sink current (160 mA maximum) make the SN72560 or SN72D560 excellent in applications of interfacing between low-level systems and TTL systems where precision level detection is required. The output is capable of sinking up to a maximum of 160 mA with a TTL-compatible on-state voltage of 0.4 V maximum guaranteed at a sink current of 48 mA. With an appropriate output pull-up resistor ($R_L \approx 2$ kΩ to 5 V), a fan-out of approximately 30 Series 74 TTL loads can be accomodated.

In addition to applications interfacing with TTL systems, the SN72560 and SN72D560 find application in driving relays, lamps, solenoids, thyristors (SCRs and triacs), and other peripheral devices.

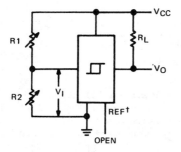

Output turns off when $V_I \geqslant V_{T+}$
Output turns on when $V_I \leqslant V_{T-}$

where $V_I = V_{CC} \dfrac{R2}{R1+R2}$

FIGURE 6—BASIC SENSOR CIRCUIT

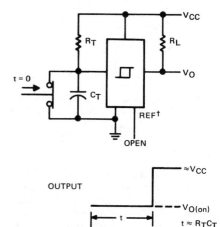

OUTPUT

$t \approx R_T C_T$

FIGURE 7—BASIC TIMED-INTERVAL CIRCUIT

† SN72560 only

TEXAS INSTRUMENTS
INCORPORATED
POST OFFICE BOX 5012 • DALLAS, TEXAS 75222

TYPICAL APPLICATION DATA

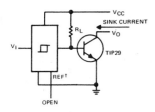

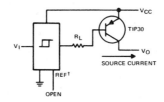

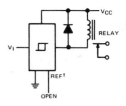

FIGURE 8—EXTERNAL N-P-N TRANSISTOR FOR INCREASING SINK CURRENT

FIGURE 9—EXTERNAL P-N-P TRANSISTOR FOR INCREASING SOURCE CURRENT

FIGURE 10—RELAY DRIVER

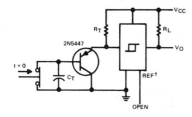

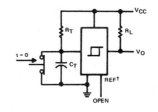

FIGURE 11—LONG-TIMED-INTERVAL CIRCUIT

FIGURE 12—BOUNCELESS SWITCH

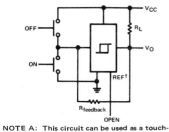

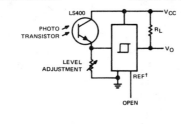

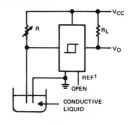

NOTE A: This circuit can be used as a touch-control switch with $R_{feedback} \approx 10 \text{ M}\Omega$.

FIGURE 13—SWITCH WITH TWO STABLE STATES

FIGURE 14—LIGHT-LEVEL SENSOR

FIGURE 15—LIQUID-LEVEL SENSOR

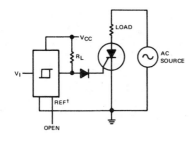

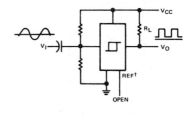

FIGURE 16—THYRISTOR DRIVER CIRCUIT

FIGURE 17—SINE-WAVE-TO-SQUARE-WAVE CONVERTER

†SN72560 only

TEXAS INSTRUMENTS
INCORPORATED
POST OFFICE BOX 5012 • DALLAS, TEXAS 75222

Line Circuits

LINE DRIVERS, DIFFERENTIAL OR SINGLE-ENDED

FEATURES		SN55109 SN75109	SN55110 SN75110	SN55113 SN75113	SN55114 SN75114	SN55183 SN75183	SN55450B SN75450B
Drivers per Package		2	2	2	2	2	2
Party-Line (Data Bus) Operation		Yes	Yes	Yes	No	No	Yes
Type of Output		Current	Current	Voltage	Voltage	Voltage	Voltage
Output Strobe		Yes	Yes	Yes	No	No	No
Input Compatibility		TTL	TTL	TTL	TTL	TTL	TTL
Power Supplies		±5 V	±5 V	+5 V	+5 V	+5 V	+5 V
Package	Series 55	J	J	J, SB	J, SB	J	J, JB
Types	Series 75	J, N	J, N	J, N, SB	J, N, SB	J, N	J, N
Line Length Operating Frequency		See application information on pages 8-4 and 8-5 for information on maximum operating frequency for various line lengths (100 ft to 10,000 ft).					
Application Notes		CA 130: Line Drivers and Receivers CA 146: Data Transmission					CA 150: Peripheral Interface Circuits

LINE DRIVERS, SINGLE-ENDED ONLY

FEATURES		SN55121 SN75121	SN75123	SN75150[†]	SN75188[†]	SN75361A	SN55451B SN75451B
Drivers per Package		2	2	2	4	2	2
Party-Line (Data Bus) Operation		Yes	Yes	No	No	No	Yes
Type of Output		Voltage	Voltage	Voltage	Voltage	Voltage	Voltage
Output Strobe		Yes	Yes	No	No	No	Yes
Input Compatibility		TTL	TTL	TTL	TTL	TTL	TTL
Power Supplies		+5 V	+5 V	±12 V	±12 V	+5 V	+5 V
Package	Series 55	J					JP, L
Types	Series 75	J, N	J, N	J, N, P	J, N	J, N, P	L, P
Line Length Operating Frequency		See application information on pages 8-4 and 8-5 for information on maximum operating frequency for various line lengths (100 ft to 10,000 ft).					
Application Notes							CA 150: Peripheral Interface Circuits

† Satisfies requirements of EIA RS-232-C

8

DIFFERENTIAL LINE RECEIVERS

FEATURES		SN55107A SN55107B SN75107A SN75107B	SN75207	SN55108A SN55108B SN75108A SN75108B	SN75208	SN55115 SN75115	SN75152†	SN55182 SN75182	UNIT
Receivers per Package		2	2	2	2	2	2	2	
Input Sensitivity		±25	±10	±25	±10	±1000	NA	±1000	mV
Input Common-Mode Range		±3	±3	±3	±3	±15	±25	±15	V
Hysteresis (Double Thresholds)		No	No	No	No	No	Yes	No	
Response Control		No	No	No	No	Yes	No	Yes	
Output Strobe		Yes	Yes	Yes	Yes	Yes	Yes	Yes	
TTL Output Configuration		Active Pull-Up	Active Pull-Up	Open-Collector	Open-Collector	Open-Collector with Active Pull-Up Option	Resistor Pull-Up	Active Pull-Up	
Power Supplies		±5	±5	±5	±5	+5	±12	+5	V
Package	Series 55	J		J		J, SB		J	
Types	Series 75	J, N	J, N	J, N	J, N	J, N, SB	J, N	J, N	

SINGLE-ENDED LINE RECEIVERS

FEATURES		SN55122 SN75122	SN75124	SN75140	SN55142* SN75142*	SN75154†	SN75189†	SN75189A†	UNIT
Receivers per Package		3	3	2	2	4	4	4	
Input Sensitivity		NA	NA	±100	±100	NA	NA	NA	mV
Hysteresis (Double Thresholds)		Yes	Yes	No	No	Yes	Yes	Yes	
Response Control		No	No	No	No	No	Yes	Yes	
Output Strobe		Yes	Yes	Yes	Yes	No	No	No	
TTL Output Configuration		Active Pull-Up	Active Pull-Up	Active Pull-Up	Active Pull-Up	Active Pull-Up	Resistor Pull-Up	Resistor Pull-Up	
Power Supplies		+5	+5	+5	+5	+5 or +12	+5	+5	V
Package	Series 55	J			J				
Types	Series 75	J, N	J, N	P	J, N	J, N	J, N	J, N	

NA ≡ Not applicable
* To be announced
† Satisfies requirements of EIA RS-232-C

TEXAS INSTRUMENTS
INCORPORATED
POST OFFICE BOX 5012 • DALLAS, TEXAS 75222

LINE TRANSCEIVERS

FEATURES		SN55138 SN75138	SN55116* SN75116*	SN55117* SN75117*	UNIT
Transceivers per Package		4	1	1	
Type of Operation		Single-Ended	Differential	Differential	
Party-Line (Data Bus) Operation		Yes	Yes	Yes	
Driver Output Type		Voltage (Open-collector)	Voltage (Open-collector with active pull-up option)	Voltage (Active pull-up)	
Driver Output Current Capability		150	40	40	mA
Driver Strobe		Yes	Yes	Yes	
Driver Input Compatibility		TTL	TTL	TTL	
Receiver Input Sensitivity		NA	±1000	±1000	mV
Receiver Strobe		No	Yes	Yes	
Receiver Response Control		No	Yes	No	
Receiver Hysteresis		No	No	No	
Receiver (TTL) Output Configuration		Active Pull-Up	Open-Collector with Active Pull-Up Option	Active Pull-Up	
Receiver Input Common-Mode Range (with Driver Off)		NA	±15	0 to 6	V
Package Types	Series 55	J	J	JP	
	Series 75	J, N	J, N	P	

* To be announced

BASIC DATA TRANSMISSION CATEGORIES

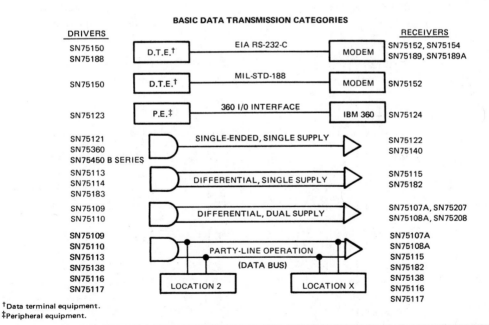

DRIVERS

SN75150
SN75188

SN75150

SN75123

SN75121
SN75360
SN75450 B SERIES

SN75113
SN75114
SN75183

SN75109
SN75110

SN75109
SN75110
SN75113
SN75138
SN75116
SN75117

RECEIVERS

EIA RS-232-C — MODEM — SN75152, SN75154 SN75189, SN75189A

MIL-STD-188 — MODEM — SN75152

360 I/0 INTERFACE — IBM 360 — SN75124

SINGLE-ENDED, SINGLE SUPPLY — SN75122 SN75140

DIFFERENTIAL, SINGLE SUPPLY — SN75115 SN75182

DIFFERENTIAL, DUAL SUPPLY — SN75107A, SN75207 SN75108A, SN75208

PARTY-LINE OPERATION (DATA BUS) — LOCATION 2 — LOCATION X — SN75107A SN75108A SN75115 SN75182 SN75138 SN75116 SN75117

D.T.E.[†]

P.E.[‡]

†Data terminal equipment.
‡Peripheral equipment.

8

LINE CIRCUITS SELECTION GUIDE

TYPICAL APPLICATION DATA

balanced line transmission circuit

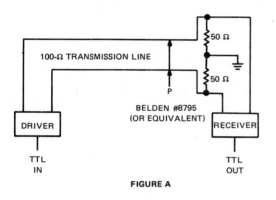

FIGURE A

DRIVER: SN75110
RECEIVER: SN75107
LINE LENGTH CAPABILITY
vs
FREQUENCY

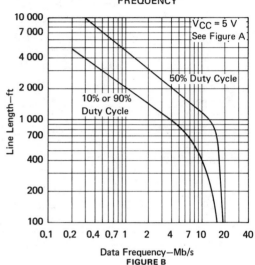

FIGURE B

DRIVER: SN75113/SN75114
RECEIVER: SN75115
LINE LENGTH CAPABILITY
vs
FREQUENCY

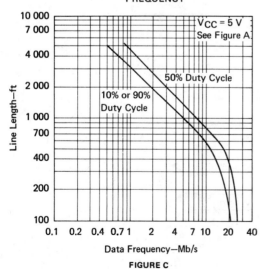

FIGURE C

DRIVER: SN75183
RECEIVER: SN75182
LINE LENGTH CAPABILITY
vs
FREQUENCY

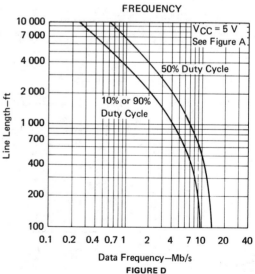

FIGURE D

TEXAS INSTRUMENTS
INCORPORATED
POST OFFICE BOX 5012 • DALLAS, TEXAS 75222

TYPICAL APPLICATION DATA

single-ended line transmission circuits

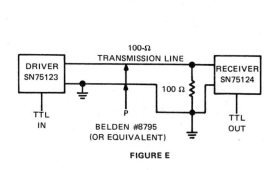

FIGURE E

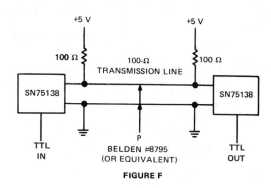

FIGURE F

DRIVER: SN75123
RECEIVER: SN75124
LINE LENGTH CAPABILITY
vs
FREQUENCY

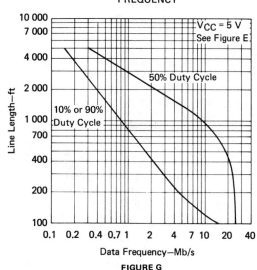

FIGURE G

TRANSCEIVERS: SN75138
LINE LENGTH CAPABILITY
vs
FREQUENCY

FIGURE H

TEXAS INSTRUMENTS
INCORPORATED
POST OFFICE BOX 5012 • DALLAS, TEXAS 75222

SYSTEMS
INTERFACE CIRCUITS

**TYPES SN55107A, SN55108A, SN55109, SN55110,
SN75107A, SN75108A, SN75109, SN75110
DUAL LINE RECEIVERS AND DRIVERS**
BULLETIN NO. DL-S 7111224, FEBRUARY 1971

SERIES 55/75107A LINE CIRCUITS
featuring

• High Speed • Standard Supply Voltages • Dual Channels

additional features of line receivers

- high common-mode rejection ratio
- high input impedance
- high input sensitivity
- differential input common-mode voltage range of ± 3 V
- differential input common-mode voltage range of more than ±15 V using external attenuator
- strobe inputs for receiver selection
- gate inputs for logic versatility
- TTL or DTL drive capability
- high d-c noise margins

−55°C to 125°C J Package	0°C to 70°C J or N Package	CIRCUIT FUNCTION	OUTPUT FUNCTION
SN55107A	SN75107A	Dual Line Receiver	Active Pull-Up
SN55108A	SN55108A	Dual Line Receiver	Open Collector
SN55109	SN75109	Dual Line Driver	6-mA Current Switch
SN55110	SN75110	Dual Line Driver	12-mA Current Switch

additional features of line drivers

- TTL input compatibility
- current-mode output (6 mA or 12 mA typical)
- high output impedance
- high common-mode output voltage range (–3 V to 10 V)
- inhibitor available for driver selection

description

The Series 55/75107 circuits are TTL/DTL compatible high-speed line receivers and drivers. Each is a monolithic dual circuit featuring two independent channels.

The SN55107A, SN55108A, SN75107A, and SN75108A line receivers are designed for general use as well as such specific applications as data comparators and balanced, unbalanced, and party-line transmission systems. These devices are unilaterally interchangeable with and replace SN55107, SN55108, SN75107, and SN75108, respectively, but offer diode-clamped inputs to simplify circuit design.

The SN55109, SN55110, SN75109, and SN75110 line drivers are designed to be used in many categories of applications in balanced, unbalanced, and party-line systems and as level converters.

The SN55107A, SN55108A, SN55109, and SN55110 are characterized for operation over the full military temperature range of −55°C to 125°C, and are available in the ceramic dual-in-line (J) package. The SN75107A, SN75108A, SN75109, and SN75110 are characterized for operation from 0°C to 70°C and are available either in the ceramic dual-in-line (J) package or in the plastic dual-in-line (N) package.

271

8-6

TEXAS INSTRUMENTS
INCORPORATED
POST OFFICE BOX 5012 • DALLAS, TEXAS 75222

design characteristics

Series 55/75107A Line Circuits are TTL-compatible dual circuits intended for use in high-speed data-transmission systems. The drivers are designed to drive balanced, terminated transmission lines, such as twisted-pair, at normal line impedances without high power dissipation. The receivers are designed to detect low-level differential signals in the presence of common-mode noise and variations of temperature and supplies. Either driver may be used with either receiver. Specifications reflect worst-case conditions of temperature, supply voltages, and input voltages.

line receivers - SN55/75107A, SN55/75108A

The SN55/75107A and SN55/75108A are dual line receivers featuring independent channels with common voltage supply and ground terminals. The SN55/75107A circuit features a TTL-compatible active pull-up (totempole) output. The SN55/75108A circuit is also TTL-compatible, but features an open-collector output configuration that permits the wired-AND logic connection with similar outputs (such as the SN54/7401 TTL gate or other SN55/75108A line receivers). This permits a level of logic to be implemented without extra delay. All other features of the line receivers are identical.

The SN55/75107A and SN55/75108A line circuits are designed to detect input signals of 25 millivolts (or greater) amplitude and convert the polarity of the signal into appropriate TTL-compatible output logic levels.

The SN55/75107A and SN55/75108A feature high input impedance and low input currents which induce very little loading on the transmission line. This makes these devices especially useful in party-line systems. The excellent input sensitivity (3 millivolts typical) is particularly important when data is to be detected at the end of a long transmission line and the amplitude of the data has been deteriorated due to cable losses.

The receiver input common-mode voltage range is ±3 volts. This is adequate for application in most systems. In systems with requirements for greater common-mode voltage range, input attenuators may be used to decrease the noise to an acceptable level at the receiver input terminals.

The receivers feature individual strobe inputs for each channel and a strobe input common to both channels for logic versatility. The strobe inputs are tested to guarantee 400 millivolts of d-c noise margin when interfaced with Series 54/74 TTL.

line drivers - SN55/75109, SN55/75110

The SN55/75109 and SN55/75110 are dual line drivers featuring independent channels with common voltage supply and ground terminals. The significant difference between the two drivers is in the output-current specification. The driver circuits feature a constant output current that is switched to either of two output terminals by the appropriate logic levels at the input terminals. The output current can be switched off (inhibited) by appropriate logic levels on the inhibit inputs. The output current is nominally 6 milliamperes for the SN55/75109 and 12 milliamperes for the SN55/75110. System design determines which driver is best suited to a particular application.

The inhibit feature is provided so the circuits can be used in party-line or data-bus applications. A strobe or inhibitor, common to both drivers, is included for increased driver-logic versatility. The output current in the inhibited mode, $I_{O(off)}$ is specified so that minimum line loading is induced when the driver is used in a party-line system with other drivers. The output impedance of the driver in the inhibited mode is very high—the output impedance of a transistor biased to cutoff.

The driver outputs have a common-mode voltage range of −3 volts to +10 volts, allowing common-mode voltage on the line without affecting driver performance.

The logic and inhibit inputs of the drivers are designed to satisfy TTL-system requirements. The logic inputs are tested at 2.0 volts for high-logic-level conditions and 0.8 volt for low-logic-level conditions. These tests guarantee 400 millivolts of noise margin when interfaced with Series 54/74 TTL.

8

TYPES SN55107A, SN55108A, SN75107A, SN75108A
DUAL LINE RECEIVERS

logic

TRUTH TABLE

DIFFERENTIAL INPUTS A-B	STROBES		OUTPUT Y
	G	S	
$V_{ID} \geqslant 25$ mV	L or H	L or H	H
−25 mV $< V_{ID} <$ 25 mV	L or H	L	H
	L	L or H	H
	H	H	INDETERMINATE
$V_{ID} \leqslant$ −25 mV	L or H	L	H
	L	L or H	H
	H	H	L

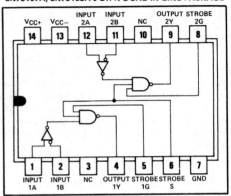

SN55107A, SN55108A J DUAL-IN-LINE PACKAGE
SN75107A, SN75108A J OR N DUAL-IN-LINE PACKAGE

NC—No internal connection

absolute maximum ratings over operating free-air temperature range (unless otherwise noted)

Supply voltage V_{CC+} (See Note 1) . . . . 7 V
Supply voltage V_{CC-} (See Note 1) . . . . −7 V
Differential input voltage (See Note 2) . . . . ±6 V
Common-mode input voltage (See Note 1) . . . . ±5 V
Strobe input voltage (See Note 1) . . . . 5.5 V
Operating free-air temperature range, Series 55 . . . . −55°C to 125°C
Series 75 . . . . 0°C to 70°C
Storage temperature range, ceramic dual-in-line (J) package . . . . −65°C to 150°C
plastic dual-in-line (N) package . . . . −55°C to 150°C

recommended operating conditions (see note 3)

	SN55107A, SN55108A			SN75107A, SN75108A			UNIT
	MIN	NOM	MAX	MIN	NOM	MAX	
Supply voltage V_{CC+} (See Note 1)	4.5	5	5.5	4.75	5	5.25	V
Supply voltage V_{CC-} (See Note 1)	−4.5	−5	−5.5	−4.75	−5	−5.25	V
Output sink current			−16			−16	mA
Differential input voltage (See Notes 2 and 4)	−5†		5	−5†		5	V
Common−mode input voltage (See Notes 1 and 4)	−3†		3	−3†		3	V
Input voltage range, any differential input to ground (See Note 4)	−5†		3	−5†		3	V
Operating free-air temperature	−55		125	0		70	°C

NOTES: 1. These voltage values are with respect to network ground terminal.
2. These voltage values are at the noninverting (A) terminal with respect to the inverting (B) terminal.
3. When using only one channel of the line receiver, the inputs of the other channel should be grounded.
4. The recommended combinations of input voltages fall within the shaded area of the figure at the right.

RECOMMENDED COMBINATIONS OF INPUT VOLTAGES FOR LINE RECEIVERS

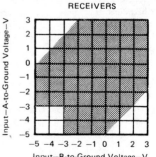

†The algebraic convention where the most-positive (least-negative) limit is designated as maximum is used in this data sheet for logic voltage levels only.

TEXAS INSTRUMENTS
INCORPORATED
POST OFFICE BOX 5012 • DALLAS, TEXAS 75222

TYPES SN55107A, SN55108A, SN75107A, SN75108A
DUAL LINE RECEIVERS

definition of input logic levels†

	TEST FIGURE	MIN	MAX	UNIT
V_{IDH} High-level input voltage between differential inputs	1	0.025	5	V
V_{IDL} Low-level input voltage between differential inputs	1	−5	−0.025	V
$V_{IH(S)}$ High-level input voltage at strobe inputs	3	2	5.5	V
$V_{IL(S)}$ Low-level input voltage at strobe inputs	3	0	0.8	V

†The algebraic convention where the most-positive (least-negative) limit is designated as maximum is used in this data sheet for logic voltage levels only.

electrical characteristics over recommended operating free-air temperature range (unless otherwise noted)

PARAMETER		TEST FIGURE	TEST CONDITIONS‡		SN55107A, SN75107A			SN55108A, SN75108A			UNIT
					MIN	TYP§	MAX	MIN	TYP§	MAX	
I_{IH}	High-level input current into 1A or 2A	2	V_{CC+} = MAX, V_{ID} = 0.5 V,	V_{CC-} = MAX, V_{IC} = −3 V to 3 V	30	75		30	75		µA
I_{IL}	Low-level input current into 1A or 2A	2	V_{CC+} = MAX, V_{ID} = −2 V,	V_{CC-} = MAX, V_{IC} = −3 V to 3 V		−10			−10		µA
I_{IH}	High-level input current into 1G or 2G	4	V_{CC+} = MAX, $V_{IH(S)}$ = 2.4 V	V_{CC-} = MAX,		40			40		µA
			V_{CC+} = MAX, $V_{IH(S)}$ = MAX V_{CC+}	V_{CC-} = MAX,		1			1		mA
I_{IL}	Low-level input current into 1G or 2G	4	V_{CC+} = MAX, $V_{IL(S)}$ = 0.4 V	V_{CC-} = MAX,		−1.6			−1.6		mA
I_{IH}	High-level input current into S	4	V_{CC+} = MAX, $V_{IH(S)}$ = 2.4 V	V_{CC-} = MAX,		80			80		µA
			V_{CC+} = MAX, $V_{IH(S)}$ = MAX V_{CC+}	V_{CC-} = MAX,		2			2		mA
I_{IL}	Low-level input current into S	4	V_{CC+} = MAX, $V_{IL(S)}$ = 0.4 V	V_{CC-} = MAX,		−3.2			−3.2		mA
V_{OH}	High-level output voltage	3	V_{CC+} = MIN, I_{load} = −400 µA,	V_{CC-} = MIN, V_{IC} = −3 V to 3 V	2.4						V
V_{OL}	Low-level output voltage	3	V_{CC+} = MIN, I_{sink} = 16 mA,	V_{CC-} = MIN, V_{IC} = −3 V to 3 V			0.4			0.4	V
I_{OH}	High-level output current	3	V_{CC+} = MIN, V_{OH} = MAX V_{CC+}	V_{CC-} = MIN,			250				µA
I_{OS}	Short-circuit output current ¶	5	V_{CC+} = MAX,	V_{CC-} = MAX	−18	−70					mA
I_{CCH+}	High-logic-level supply current from V_{CC+}	6	V_{CC+} = MAX, V_{ID} = 25 mV,	V_{CC-} = MAX, T_A = 25°C	18	30		18	30		mA
I_{CCH-}	High-logic-level supply current from V_{CC-}	6	V_{CC+} = MAX, V_{ID} = 25 mV,	V_{CC-} = MAX, T_A = 25°C	−8.4	−15		−8.4	−15		mA

‡ For conditions shown as MIN or MAX, use the appropriate value specified under recommended operating conditions.

§ All typical values are at V_{CC+} = 5 V, V_{CC-} = −5 V, T_A = 25°C.

¶ Not more than one output should be shorted at a time.

switching characteristics, V_{CC+} = 5 V, V_{CC-} = −5 V, T_A = 25°C

PARAMETER		TEST FIGURE	TEST CONDITIONS		SN55107A, SN75107A			SN55108A, SN75108A			UNIT
					MIN	TYP	MAX	MIN	TYP	MAX	
$t_{PLH(D)}$	Propagation delay time, low-to-high level, from differential inputs A and B to output	7	R_L = 390 Ω,	C_L = 50 pF		17	25				ns
			R_L = 390 Ω,	C_L = 15 pF					19	25	
$t_{PHL(D)}$	Propagation delay time, high-to-low level, from differential inputs A and B to output	7	R_L = 390 Ω,	C_L = 50 pF		17	25				ns
			R_L = 390 Ω,	C_L = 15 pF					19	25	
$t_{PLH(S)}$	Propagation delay time, low-to-high level, from strobe input G or S to output	7	R_L = 390 Ω,	C_L = 50 pF		10	15				ns
			R_L = 390 Ω,	C_L = 15 pF					13	20	
$t_{PHL(S)}$	Propagation delay time, high-to-low level, from strobe input G or S to output	7	R_L = 390 Ω,	C_L = 50 pF		8	15				ns
			R_L = 390 Ω,	C_L = 15 pF					13	20	

8

TEXAS INSTRUMENTS
INCORPORATED
POST OFFICE BOX 5012 • DALLAS, TEXAS 75222

schematic

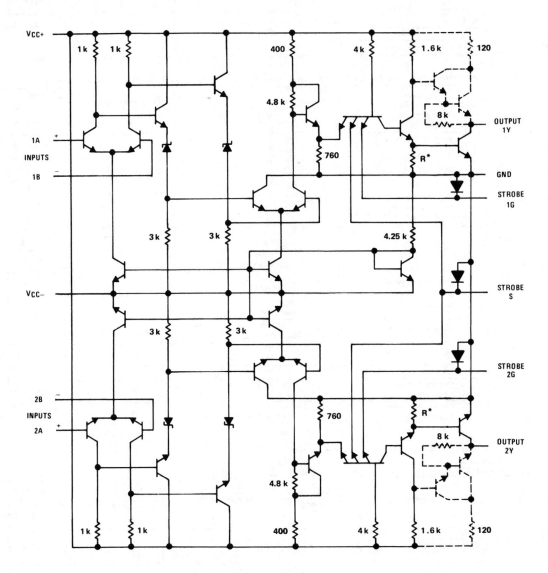

R* = 1 kΩ for SN55107A and SN75107A, 750 Ω for SN55108A and SN75108A.

NOTES: 1. Component values shown are nominal.

2. Resistance values are in ohms.

3. Components shown with dashed lines are applicable to the SN55107A and SN75107A only.

TEXAS INSTRUMENTS
INCORPORATED
POST OFFICE BOX 5012 • DALLAS, TEXAS 75222

PARAMETER MEASUREMENT INFORMATION

d-c test circuits†

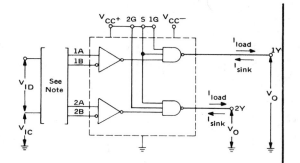

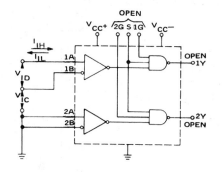

NOTE: When testing one channel, the inputs of the other channel are grounded.

FIGURE 1 – V_{IDH} and V_{IDL}

NOTE: Each pair of differential inputs is tested separately. The inputs of the other pair are grounded.

FIGURE 2 – I_{IH} and I_{IL}

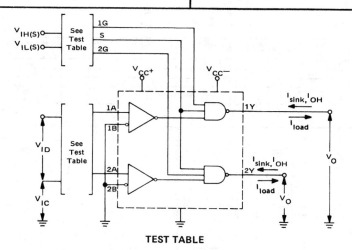

TEST TABLE

SN55107A SN75107A	SN55108A SN75108A	V_{ID}	STROBE 1G or 2G	STROBE S
TEST			APPLY	
V_{OH}	I_{OH}	+25 mV	$V_{IH(S)}$	$V_{IH(S)}$
V_{OH}	I_{OH}	−25 mV	$V_{IL(S)}$	$V_{IH(S)}$
V_{OH}	I_{OH}	−25 mV	$V_{IH(S)}$	$V_{IL(S)}$
V_{OL}	V_{OL}	−25 mV	$V_{IH(S)}$	$V_{IH(S)}$

NOTES: 1. V_{IC} = −3 V to 3 V.
2. When testing one channel, the inputs of the other channel should be grounded.

FIGURE 3 – $V_{IH(S)}$, $V_{IL(S)}$, V_{OH}, V_{OL}, and I_{OH}

† Arrows indicate actual direction of current flow. Current into a terminal is a positive value.

TYPES SN55107A, SN55108A, SN75107A, SN75108A
DUAL LINE RECEIVERS

PARAMETER MEASUREMENT INFORMATION

d-c test circuits† (continued)

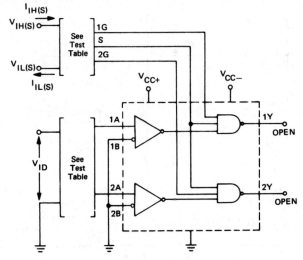

TEST	INPUT 1A	INPUT 2A	STROBE 1G	STROBE S	STROBE 2G
I_{IH} at Strobe 1G	+25 mV	Gnd	$V_{IH(S)}$	Gnd	Gnd
I_{IH} at Strobe 2G	Gnd	+25 mV	Gnd	Gnd	$V_{IH(S)}$
I_{IH} at Strobe S	+25 mV	+25 mV	Gnd	$V_{IH(S)}$	Gnd
I_{IL} at Strobe 1G	−25 mV	Gnd	$V_{IL(S)}$	4.5 V	Gnd
I_{IL} at Strobe 2G	Gnd	−25 mV	Gnd	4.5 V	$V_{IL(S)}$
I_{IL} at Strobe S	−25 mV	−25 mV	4.5 V	$V_{IL(S)}$	4.5 V

FIGURE 4 – $I_{IH(G)}$, $I_{IL(G)}$, $I_{IH(S)}$, and $I_{IL(S)}$

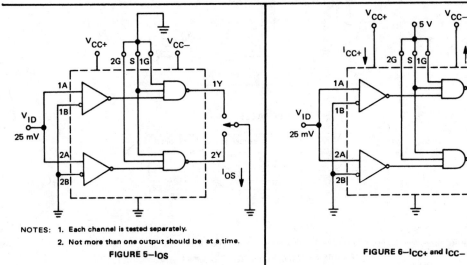

NOTES: 1. Each channel is tested separately.
2. Not more than one output should be at a time.

FIGURE 5 – I_{OS}

FIGURE 6 – I_{CC+} and $I_{CC−}$

† Arrows indicate actual direction of current flow. Current into a terminal is a positive value.

8-12

TYPES SN55107A, SN55108A, SN75107A, SN75108A
DUAL LINE RECEIVERS

PARAMETER MEASUREMENT INFORMATION

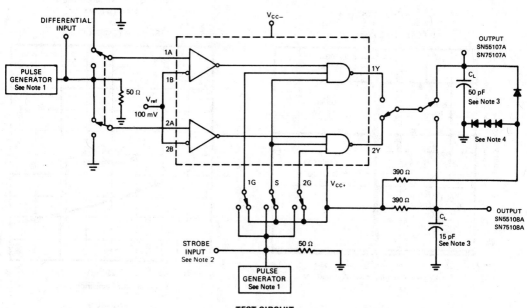

TEST CIRCUIT

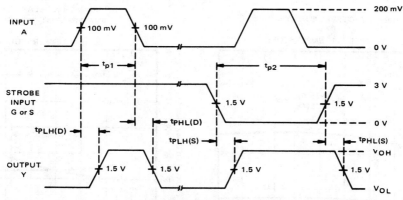

VOLTAGE WAVEFORMS

NOTES: 1. The pulse generators have the following characteristics: $Z_{out} = 50 \ \Omega$, $t_r = t_f = 10 \pm 5$ ns, $t_{p1} = 500$ ns, PRR = 1 MHz, $t_{p2} = 1$ ms, PRR = 500 kHz.
2. Strobe input pulse is applied to Strobe 1G when inputs 1A-1B are being tested, to Strobe S when inputs 1A-1B or 2A-2B are being tested, and to Strobe 2G when inputs 2A-2B are being tested.
3. C_L includes probe and jig capacitance.
4. All diodes are 1N916.

FIGURE 7—PROPAGATION DELAY TIMES

TYPICAL CHARACTERISTICS

OUTPUT VOLTAGE
vs
DIFFERENTIAL INPUT VOLTAGE

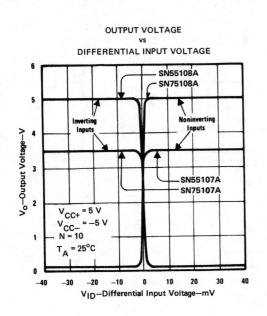

FIGURE 8

HIGH-LEVEL INPUT CURRENT
INTO 1A or 2A
vs
FREE-AIR TEMPERATURE

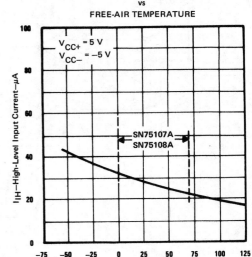

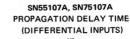

FIGURE 9

HIGH-LOGIC-LEVEL SUPPLY CURRENT
vs
FREE-AIR TEMPERATURE

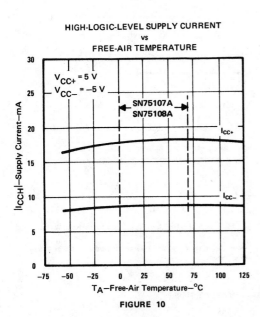

FIGURE 10

SN55107A, SN75107A
PROPAGATION DELAY TIME
(DIFFERENTIAL INPUTS)
vs
FREE-AIR TEMPERATURE

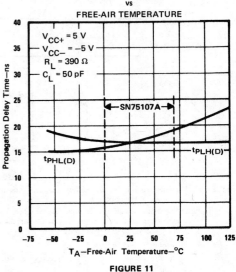

FIGURE 11

8-14

TEXAS INSTRUMENTS
INCORPORATED
POST OFFICE BOX 5012 • DALLAS, TEXAS 75222

TYPICAL CHARACTERISTICS

SN55108A, SN75108A
PROPAGATION DELAY TIME
LOW-TO-HIGH LEVEL
(DIFFERENTIAL INPUTS)
vs
FREE-AIR TEMPERATURE

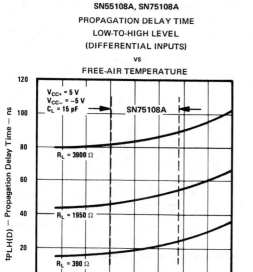

FIGURE 12

SN55108A, SN75108A
PROPAGATION DELAY TIME
HIGH-TO-LOW LEVEL
(DIFFERENTIAL INPUTS)
vs
FREE-AIR TEMPERATURE

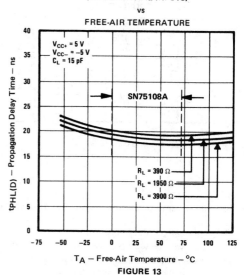

FIGURE 13

SN55107A, SN75107A
PROPAGATION DELAY TIME
(STROBE INPUTS)
vs
FREE-AIR TEMPERATURE

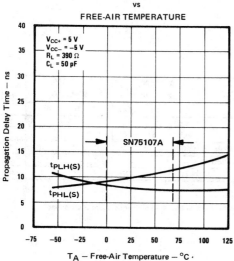

FIGURE 14

SN55108A, SN75108A
PROPAGATION DELAY TIME
(STROBE INPUTS)
vs
FREE-AIR TEMPERATURE

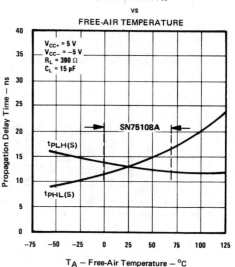

FIGURE 15

TEXAS INSTRUMENTS
INCORPORATED
POST OFFICE BOX 5012 • DALLAS, TEXAS 75222

TYPES SN55109, SN55110, SN75109, SN75110
DUAL LINE DRIVERS

logic

SN55109, SN55110 J DUAL-IN-LINE PACKAGE
SN75109, SN75110 J OR N DUAL-IN-LINE PACKAGE

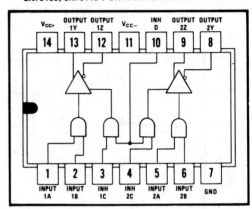

TRUTH TABLE

LOGIC INPUTS		INHIBITOR INPUTS		OUTPUTS	
A	B	C	D	Y	Z
L or H	L or H	L	L or H	H	H
L or H	L or H	L or H	L	H	H
L	L or H	H	H	L	H
L or H	L	H	H	L	H
H	H	H	H	H	L

Low output represents the on state

High output represents the off state

absolute maximum ratings (over operating free-air temperature range unless otherwise noted)

Supply voltage V_{CC+} (See Note 1) . . . . 7 V
Supply voltage V_{CC-} (See Note 1) . . . . −7 V
Logic and inhibitor input voltages (See Note 1) . . . . 5.5 V
Common-mode output voltage (See Note 1) . . . . −5 to 12 V
Operating free-air temperature range, Series 55 . . . . −55°C to 125°C
                                                                                         Series 75 . . . . 0°C to 70°C
Storage temperature range, ceramic dual-in-line (J) package . . . . −65°C to 150°C
                                                       plastic dual-in-line (N) package . . . . −55°C to 150°C

recommended operating conditions (see note 2)

	SN55109, SN55110			SN75109, SN75110			UNIT
	MIN	NOM	MAX	MIN	NOM	MAX	
Supply voltage V_{CC+} (See Note 1)	4.5	5	5.5	4.75	5	5.25	V
Supply voltage V_{CC-} (See Note 1)	−4.5	−5	−5.5	−4.75	−5	−5.25	V
Positive common-mode output voltage (See Note 1)	0		10	0		10	V
Negative common-mode output voltage (See Note 1)	0		−3	0		−3	V
Operating free-air temperature range	−55		125	0		70	°C

NOTES: 1. These voltage values are with respect to the network ground terminal.
       2. When using only one channel of the line drivers, the other channel should be inhibited and/or its outputs grounded.

TEXAS INSTRUMENTS
INCORPORATED
POST OFFICE BOX 5012 • DALLAS, TEXAS 75222

definition of input logic levels[†]

		TEST FIGURE	MIN	MAX	UNIT
V_{IH}	High-level input voltage at any input	16, 17	2	5.5	V
V_{IL}	Low-level input voltage at any input	16, 17	0	0.8	V

[†]The algebraic convention where the most-positive (least-negative) limit is designated as maximum is used in this data sheet for logic voltage levels only.

electrical characteristics over recommended operating free-air temperature range (unless otherwise noted)

PARAMETER		TEST FIGURE	TEST CONDITIONS[‡]		SN55109, SN75109 MIN	TYP[§]	MAX	SN55110, SN75110 MIN	TYP[§]	MAX	UNIT
$I_{IH(L)}$	High-level input current into 1A, 1B, 2A or 2B	16	V_{CC+} = MAX, V_{CC-} = MAX, $V_{IH(L)}$ = 2.4 V				40			40	μA
			V_{CC+} = MAX, V_{CC-} = MAX, $V_{IH(L)}$ = MAX V_{CC+}				1			1	mA
$I_{IL(L)}$	Low-level input current into 1A, 1B, 2A or 2B	16	V_{CC+} = MAX, V_{CC-} = MAX, $V_{IL(L)}$ = 0.4 V				−3			−3	mA
$I_{IH(I)}$	High-level input current into 1C or 2C	17	V_{CC+} = MAX, V_{CC-} = MAX, $V_{IH(I)}$ = 2.4 V				40			40	μA
			V_{CC+} = MAX, V_{CC-} = MAX, $V_{IH(I)}$ = MAX V_{CC+}				1			1	mA
$I_{IL(I)}$	Low-level input current into 1C or 2C	17	V_{CC+} = MAX, V_{CC-} = MAX, $V_{IL(I)}$ = 0.4 V				−3			−3	mA
$I_{IH(I)}$	High-level input current into D	17	V_{CC+} = MAX, V_{CC-} = MAX, $V_{IH(I)}$ = 2.4 V				80			80	μA
			V_{CC+} = MAX, V_{CC-} = MAX, $V_{IH(I)}$ = MAX V_{CC+}				2			2	mA
$I_{IL(I)}$	Low-level input current into D	17	V_{CC+} = MAX, V_{CC-} = MAX, $V_{IL(I)}$ = 0.4 V				−6			−6	mA
$I_{O(on)}$	On-state output current	18	V_{CC+} = MAX, V_{CC-} = MAX			7				15	mA
			V_{CC+} = MIN, V_{CC-} = MAX		3.5			6.5			mA
$I_{O(off)}$	Off-state output current	18	V_{CC+} = MIN, V_{CC-} = MIN				100			100	μA
$I_{CC+(on)}$	Supply current from V_{CC+} with driver enabled	19	$V_{IL(L)}$ = 0.4 V, $V_{IH(I)}$ = 2 V		18	30		23	35		mA
$I_{CC-(on)}$	Supply current from V_{CC-} with driver enabled	19	$V_{IL(L)}$ = 0.4 V, $V_{IH(I)}$ = 2 V		−18	−30		−34	−50		mA
$I_{CC+(off)}$	Supply current from V_{CC+} with driver inhibited	19	$V_{IL(L)}$ = 0.4 V, $V_{IL(I)}$ = 0.4 V		18			21			mA
$I_{CC-(off)}$	Supply current from V_{CC-} with driver inhibited	19	$V_{IL(L)}$ = 0.4 V, $V_{IL(I)}$ = 0.4 V		−10			−17			mA

[‡]For conditions shown as MIN or MAX, use appropriate value specified under recommended operating conditions.

[§]All typical values are at V_{CC+} = 5 V, V_{CC-} = −5 V, T_A = 25°C.

switching characteristics, V_{CC+} = 5 V, V_{CC-} = 5 V, T_A = 25°C

PARAMETER		TEST FIGURE	TEST CONDITIONS		MIN	TYP	MAX	UNIT
$t_{PLH(L)}$	Propagation delay time, low-to-high level, from logic input A or B to output Y or Z	20	R_L = 50 Ω,	C_L = 40 pF		9	15	ns
$t_{PHL(L)}$	Propagation delay time, high-to-low level, from logic input A or B to output Y or Z	20	R_L = 50 Ω,	C_L = 40 pF		9	15	ns
$t_{PLH(I)}$	Propagation delay time, low-to-high level, from inhibitor input C or D to output Y or Z	20	R_L = 50 Ω,	C_L = 40 pF		16	25	ns
$t_{PHL(I)}$	Propagation delay time, high-to-low level, from inhibitor input C or D to output Y or Z	20	R_L = 50 Ω,	C_L = 40 pF		13	25	ns

8

TEXAS INSTRUMENTS
INCORPORATED
POST OFFICE BOX 5012 • DALLAS, TEXAS 75222

schematic

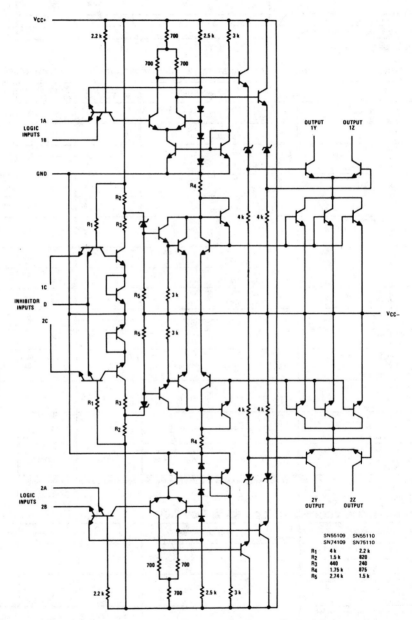

NOTES: 1. Component values shown are nominal.

2. Resistance values are in ohms.

TEXAS INSTRUMENTS
INCORPORATED
POST OFFICE BOX 5012 • DALLAS, TEXAS 75222

PARAMETER MEASUREMENT INFORMATION

d-c test circuits †

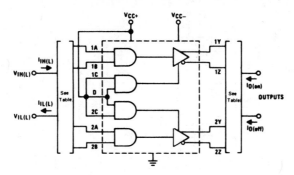

TEST TABLE

TEST AT ANY LOGIC INPUT	LOGIC INPUTS NOT UNDER TEST	ALL INHIBITOR INPUTS	OUTPUT 1Y or 2Y	OUTPUT 1Z or 2Z
$V_{IH(L)}$	Open	$V_{IH(I)}$	H (See Note 1)	L (See Note 1)
$V_{IL(L)}$	V_{CC+}	$V_{IH(I)}$	L (See Note 1)	H (See Note 1)
$I_{IH(L)}$	4.5 V	$V_{IH(I)}$	Gnd	Gnd
$I_{IL(L)}$	Gnd	$V_{IH(I)}$	Gnd	Gnd

NOTES: 1. Low output represents the on state, high output represents the off state.
2. Each input is tested separately.

FIGURE 16 – $V_{IH(L)}$, $V_{IL(L)}$, $I_{IH(L)}$, and $I_{IL(L)}$

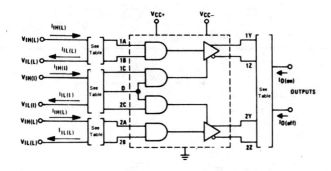

TEST TABLE

TEST AT ANY INHIBITOR INPUT	ALL LOGIC INPUTS	INHIBITOR INPUTS NOT UNDER TEST	OUTPUT 1Y or 2Y	OUTPUT 1Z or 2Z
$V_{IH(I)}$	$V_{IH(L)}$	Open	H (See Note 1)	L (See Note 1)
	$V_{IL(L)}$	Open	L (See Note 1)	H (See Note 1)
$V_{IL(I)}$	$V_{IH(L)}$	V_{CC+}	H (See Note 1)	H (See Note 1)
	$V_{IL(L)}$	V_{CC+}	H (See Note 1)	H (See Note 1)
$I_{IH(I)}$	Gnd	4.5 V	Gnd	Gnd
$I_{IL(I)}$	Gnd	Gnd	Gnd	Gnd

NOTES: 1. Low output represents the on state, high output represents the off state.
2. Each input is tested separately.

FIGURE 17 – $V_{IH(I)}$, $V_{IL(I)}$, $I_{IH(I)}$, $I_{IL(I)}$

† Arrows indicate actual direction of current flow. Current into a terminal is a positive value.

PARAMETER MEASUREMENT INFORMATION

d-c test circuits† (continued)

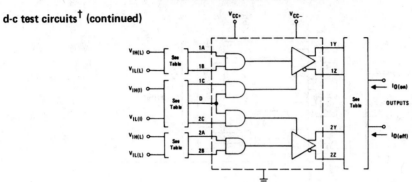

TEST TABLE

TEST		LOGIC INPUTS		INHIBITOR INPUTS	
		1A or 2A	1B or 2B	1C or 2C	D
$I_{O(on)}$	at output 1Y or 2Y	$V_{IL(L)}$ / $V_{IL(L)}$ / $V_{IH(L)}$	$V_{IL(L)}$ / $V_{IH(L)}$ / $V_{IL(L)}$	$V_{IH(I)}$	$V_{IH(I)}$
$I_{O(on)}$	at output 1Z or 2Z	$V_{IH(L)}$	$V_{IH(L)}$	$V_{IH(I)}$	$V_{IH(I)}$
$I_{O(off)}$	at output 1Y or 2Y	$V_{IH(L)}$	$V_{IH(L)}$	$V_{IH(I)}$	$V_{IH(I)}$
$I_{O(off)}$	at output 1Z or 2Z	$V_{IL(L)}$ / $V_{IL(L)}$ / $V_{IH(L)}$	$V_{IL(L)}$ / $V_{IH(L)}$ / $V_{IL(L)}$	$V_{IH(I)}$	$V_{IH(I)}$
$I_{O(off)}$	at output 1Y, 2Y, 1Z, or 2Z	Either state	Either state	$V_{IL(I)}$ / $V_{IL(I)}$ / $V_{IH(I)}$	$V_{IL(I)}$ / $V_{IH(I)}$ / $V_{IL(I)}$

FIGURE 18 — $I_{O(on)}$ and $I_{O(off)}$

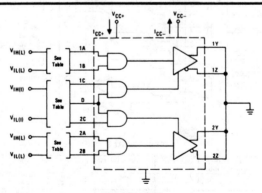

TEST TABLE

TEST		ALL LOGIC INPUTS	ALL INHIBITOR INPUTS
$I_{CC+(on)}$	Driver enabled	$V_{IL(L)}$	$V_{IH(I)}$
$I_{CC-(on)}$	Driver enabled	$V_{IL(L)}$	$V_{IH(I)}$
$I_{CC+(off)}$	Driver inhibited	$V_{IL(L)}$	$V_{IL(I)}$
$I_{CC-(off)}$	Driver inhibited	$V_{IL(L)}$	$V_{IL(I)}$

FIGURE 19 — I_{CC+} and I_{CC-}

† Arrows indicate actual direction of current flow. Current into a terminal is a positive value.

8

TEXAS INSTRUMENTS
INCORPORATED
POST OFFICE BOX 5012 • DALLAS, TEXAS 75222

PARAMETER MEASUREMENT INFORMATION

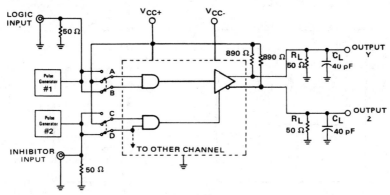

TEST CIRCUIT

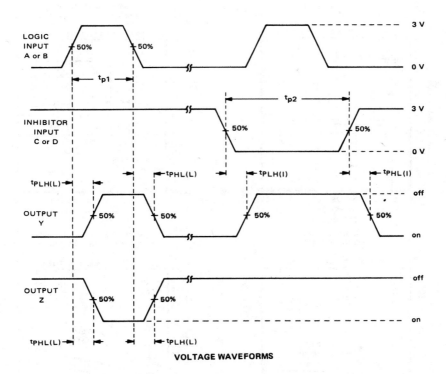

VOLTAGE WAVEFORMS

NOTES: 1. The pulse generators have the following characteristics: Z_{out} = 50 Ω, t_r = t_f = 10 ± 5 ns, t_{p1} = 500 ns, PRR = 1 MHz, t_{p2} = 1 ms, PRR = 500 kHz.

2. C_L includes probe and jig capacitance.

3. For simplicity, only one channel and the inhibitor connections are shown.

FIGURE 20—PROPAGATION DELAY TIMES

TYPES SN55109, SN55110, SN75109, SN75110
DUAL LINE DRIVERS

TYPICAL CHARACTERISTICS

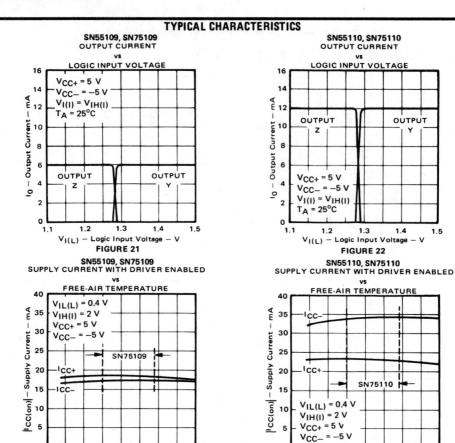

SN55109, SN75109
OUTPUT CURRENT
vs
LOGIC INPUT VOLTAGE

FIGURE 21

SN55110, SN75110
OUTPUT CURRENT
vs
LOGIC INPUT VOLTAGE

FIGURE 22

SN55109, SN75109
SUPPLY CURRENT WITH DRIVER ENABLED
vs
FREE-AIR TEMPERATURE

FIGURE 23

SN55110, SN75110
SUPPLY CURRENT WITH DRIVER ENABLED
vs
FREE-AIR TEMPERATURE

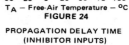

FIGURE 24

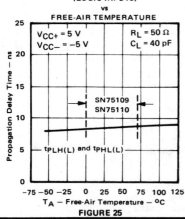

PROPAGATION DELAY TIME
(LOGIC INPUTS)
vs
FREE-AIR TEMPERATURE

FIGURE 25

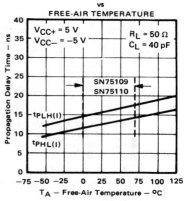

PROPAGATION DELAY TIME
(INHIBITOR INPUTS)
vs
FREE-AIR TEMPERATURE

FIGURE 26

8

TEXAS INSTRUMENTS
INCORPORATED
POST OFFICE BOX 5012 • DALLAS, TEXAS 75222

TYPICAL APPLICATION DATA

BASIC BALANCED-LINE TRANSMISSION SYSTEM

Series 55/75107A dual line circuits are designed specifically for use in high-speed data transmission systems that utilize balanced, terminated transmission lines such as twisted-pair lines. The system operates in the balanced mode, so that noise induced on one line is also induced on the other. The noise appears common-mode at the receiver input terminals where it is rejected. The ground connection between the line driver and receiver is not part of the signal circuit so that system performance is not affected by circulating ground currents.

The unique driver-output circuit allows terminated transmission lines to be driven at normal line impedances. High-speed system operation is ensured since line reflections are virtually eliminated when terminated lines are used. Cross-talk is minimized by low signal amplitudes and low line impedances.

The typical data delay in a system is approximately

(30 + 1.3 L) nanoseconds, where L is the distance in feet separating the driver and receiver. This delay includes one gate delay in both the driver and receiver.

Data is impressed on the balanced-line system by unbalancing the line voltages with the driver output current. The driven line is selected by appropriate driver-input logic levels. The voltage difference is approximately:

$$V_{DIFF} \simeq 1/2 \ I_{O(on)} \cdot R_T$$

High series line resistance will cause degradation of the signal. The receivers, however, will detect signals as low as 25 mV (or less). For normal line resistances, data may be recovered from lines of several thousand feet in length.

Line-termination resistors (R_T) are required only at the extreme ends of the line. For short lines, termination resistors at the receiver only may prove adequate. The signal amplitude will then be approximately:

$$V_{DIFF} \simeq I_{O(on)} \cdot R_T$$

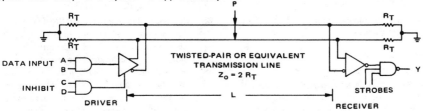

DATA-BUS OR PARTY-LINE SYSTEM

The strobe feature of the receivers and the inhibit feature of the drivers allow the Series 55/75107A dual line circuits to be used in data-bus or party-line systems. In these applications, several drivers and receivers may share a common transmission line. An enabled driver transmits data to all enabled receivers on the line while other drivers and

receivers are disabled. Data is thus time-multiplexed on the transmission line. Series 55/75107A device specifications allow widely varying thermal and electrical environments at the various driver and receiver locations. The data-bus system offers maximum performance at minimum cost.

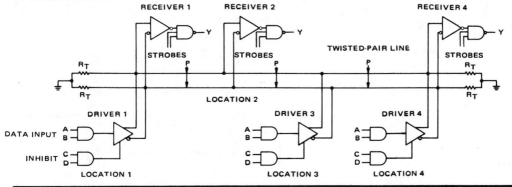

73

TYPES SN55107A, SN55108A, SN55109, SN55110, SN75107A, SN75108A, SN75109, SN75110 DUAL LINE RECEIVERS AND DRIVERS

TYPICAL APPLICATION DATA

UNBALANCED OR SINGLE-LINE SYSTEMS

Series 55/75107A dual line circuits may also be used in unbalanced or single-line systems. Although these systems do not offer the same performance as balanced systems for long lines, they are adequate for very short lines where environmental noise is not severe.

The receiver threshold level is established by applying a d-c reference voltage to one receiver input terminal. The signal from the transmission line is applied to the remaining input. The reference voltage should be optimized so that signal swing is symmetrical about it for maximum

noise margin. The reference voltage should be in the range of −3 volts to +3 volts. It can be provided by a voltage supply or by a voltage divider from an available supply voltage.

A single-ended output from a driver may be used in single-line systems. Coaxial or shielded line is preferred for minimum noise and cross-talk problems. For large signal swings, the high output current (12 mA) of the SN55/75110 is recommended. Drivers may be paralleled for higher current. The unused driver output must be tied to ground.

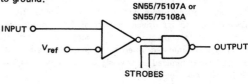

PRECAUTIONS IN THE USE OF SERIES 55/75107A LINE CIRCUITS

The following precautions should be observed when using or testing Series 55/75107A line circuits:

(1) **Drivers, SN55/75109 and SN55/75110**
     When only one driver in a package is being used, the outputs of the other driver must either be grounded or inhibited in order to prevent excess power dissipation.

(2) **Receivers, SN55/75107A and SN55/75108A**
     When only one receiver in a package is being used, at least one of the differential inputs of the unused receiver should be terminated at some voltage between −3 volts and +3 volts, preferably at ground. Failure to do so will cause improper operation of the unit being used because of common bias circuitry for the current sources of the two receivers.

INCREASING COMMON-MODE INPUT VOLTAGE RANGE OF RECEIVER

The SN55/75107A and SN55/75108A line receivers feature a common-mode input voltage range of ±3 volts. This satisfies the requirements for all but the noisiest system applications. For these severe noise environments, the common-mode range can be extended by the use of external input attenuators. Common-mode input voltages can in this way be reduced to ±3 volts at the receiver input terminals. Differential data signals will be reduced proportionately. Input sensitivity, input impedance, and delay times will be adversely affected.

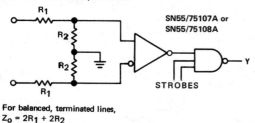

For balanced, terminated lines,
$Z_0 = 2R_1 + 2R_2$

SN55/75108A DOT-AND OUTPUT CONNECTIONS

The SN55/75108A line receivers feature an open-collector-output circuit that can be connected in the DOT-AND logic configuration with other SN55/75108A outputs, SN5401/7401 outputs, or other similar outputs. This allows a level of logic to be implemented without additional logic delay.

For rules for such DOT-AND connections, refer to the SN5401 or SN7401 data sheet.

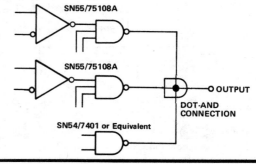

TEXAS INSTRUMENTS
INCORPORATED
POST OFFICE BOX 5012 • DALLAS, TEXAS 75222

8

- Diode-Protected Input Stage for Power-Off Condition
- Plug-In Replacement for SN55107A/SN75107A and SN55108A/SN75108A
- "B" Versions Available Only Upon Request

description

The essential difference between the "A" and "B" versions is shown in the following schematics of the input stage:

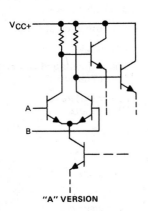

"A" VERSION

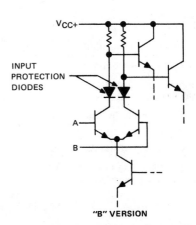

"B" VERSION

The input-protection diodes are useful in certain "party-line" systems which may have multiple V_{CC+} power supplies and, in which case, may be operated with some of the V_{CC+} supplies turned off. In such a system, if a supply is turned off and allowed to go to ground, the equivalent input circuit connected to that supply would be as follows:

"A" VERSION

"B" VERSION

This would be a problem in specific systems which might possibly have the transmission lines biased to some potential greater than 1.4 volts. Since this is not a widespread application problem, both the "A" and "B" versions will be available. The ratings and characteristic specifications of the "B" versions are the same as those of the "A" versions. The "B" versions will only be supplied upon request.

> It is necessary to use this data sheet in conjunction with the data sheet for
> SN55107A, SN55108A, SN75107A, and SN75108A dated February 1971.

8

TEXAS INSTRUMENTS
INCORPORATED
POST OFFICE BOX 5012 • DALLAS, TEXAS 75222

LINE CIRCUITS
featuring

- Each Circuit Offers Choice of Open-Collector or Active Pull-Up (Totem-Pole) Outputs

- Single 5-V Supply

- Differential Line Operation

- Dual Channels

- TTL/DTL Compatibility

additional features of SN55113 and SN75113 line drivers with three-state outputs

- High-Impedance Output State for Party-Line Applications

- Short-Circuit Protection

- High-Current Outputs

- Single-Ended or Differential AND/NAND Outputs

- Common and Individual Output Controls

- Clamp Diodes at Inputs

- Easily Adaptable to SN55114 and SN75114 Applications

additional features of SN55114 and SN75114 line drivers

- Designed to be Interchangeable with Fairchild 9614 Line Drivers

- Short-Circuit Protection of Outputs

- High-Current Outputs

- Clamp Diodes at Inputs and Outputs to Terminate Line Transients

- Single-Ended or Differential AND/NAND Outputs

- Triple Inputs

additional features of SN55115 and SN75115 line receivers

- Designed to be interchangeable with Fairchild 9615 Line Receivers

- ±15 V Common-Mode Input Voltage Range

- Optional-Use Built-In 130-Ω Line-Terminating Resistor

- Individual Frequency Response Controls

- Individual Channel Strobes

CONTENTS

8

TEXAS INSTRUMENTS
INCORPORATED
POST OFFICE BOX 5012 • DALLAS, TEXAS 75222

description

The SN55113 and SN75113 dual differential line drivers with three-state outputs are designed to provide all the features of the SN55114 and SN75114 line drivers with the added feature of driver output controls. There are individual controls for each output pair, as well as a common control for both output pairs. When an output control is low, the associated output is in a high-impedance state and the output can neither drive nor load the bus. This permits many devices to be connected together on the same transmission line for party-line applications.

The output stages are similar to TTL totem-pole outputs, but with the sink outputs, YS and ZS, and the corresponding active pull-up terminals, YP and ZP, available on adjacent package pins.

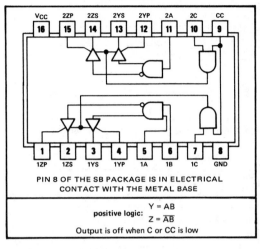

J OR N DUAL-IN-LINE PACKAGE
SB FLAT PACKAGE
(TOP VIEW)

PIN 8 OF THE SB PACKAGE IS IN ELECTRICAL
CONTACT WITH THE METAL BASE

positive logic: $Y = AB$
$Z = \overline{AB}$

Output is off when C or CC is low

FUNCTION TABLE

INPUTS				OUTPUTS	
OUTPUT CONTROL		DATA		AND	NAND
C	CC	A	B[†]	Y	Z
L	X	X	X	Z	Z
X	L	X	X	Z	Z
H	H	L	X	L	H
H	H	X	L	L	H
H	H	H	H	H	L

H = high level, L = low level, X = irrelevant, Z = high impedance (off)
[†]B input and 4th line of function table applicable only to driver number 1.

schematic

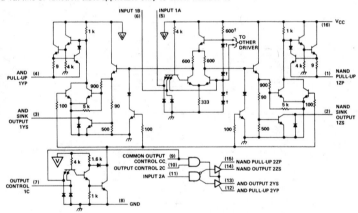

INPUT 1B (6) INPUT 1A (5)

1 k 4 k 600[†] 1 k (16) V_{CC}

TO OTHER DRIVER

AND PULL-UP 1YP (4)   9 4 k   600 600   4 k 9   (1) NAND PULL-UP 1ZP

900 90 900

100 5 k 90 333 90 5 k 100

AND SINK OUTPUT 1YS (3) 500 100 100 500   (2) NAND SINK OUTPUT 1ZS

COMMON OUTPUT CONTROL CC (9)   (15) NAND PULL-UP 2ZP
OUTPUT CONTROL 2C (10)   (14) NAND OUTPUT 2ZS
INPUT 2A (11)
4 k 1.6 k   (13) AND OUTPUT 2YS
OUTPUT CONTROL 1C (7) 1 k   (12) AND PULL-UP 2YP

(8) GND

▽ ... V_{CC} bus
Resistor values shown are nominal and in ohms.

[†]These components common to both drivers.

absolute maximum ratings over operating free-air temperature (unless otherwise noted)

Supply voltage, V_{CC} (see Note 1) . . . . 7 V
Input voltage . . . . 5.5 V
Off-state voltage applied to open-collector outputs . . . . 12 V
Continuous total dissipation at (or below) 70°C free-air temperature (see Note 2) . . . . 600 mW
Operating free-air temperature range: SN55113 . . . . −55°C to 125°C
                                      SN75113 . . . . 0°C to 70°C
Storage temperature range . . . . −65°C to 150°C
Lead temperature 1/16 inch from case for 60 seconds: J or SB package . . . . 300°C
Lead temperature 1/16 inch from case for 10 seconds: N package . . . . 260°C

NOTES: 1. All voltage values are with respect to network ground terminal.
       2. For operation of SN55113 above 70°C free-air temperature, refer to Dissipation Derating Curve, Figure 43.

8

TEXAS INSTRUMENTS
INCORPORATED
POST OFFICE BOX 5012 • DALLAS, TEXAS 75222

recommended operating conditions

	SN55113 MIN	NOM	MAX	SN75113 MIN	NOM	MAX	UNIT
Supply voltage, V_{CC}	4.5	5	5.5	4.75	5	5.25	V
High-level output current, I_{OH}			−40			−40	mA
Low-level output current, I_{OL}			40			40	mA
Operating free-air temperature, T_A	−55		125	0		70	°C

electrical characteristics over recommended operating free-air temperature range (unless otherwise noted)

PARAMETER		TEST CONDITIONS†	SN55113 MIN	TYP‡	MAX	SN75113 MIN	TYP‡	MAX	UNIT
V_{IH}	High-level input voltage		2			2			V
V_{IL}	Low-level input voltage				0.8			0.8	V
V_I	Input clamp voltage	V_{CC} = MIN, I_I = −12 mA		−0.9	−1.5		−0.9	−1.5	V
V_{OH}	High-level output voltage	V_{CC} = MIN, $V_{IH} = V_{IH}$ min, $V_{IL} = V_{IL}$ max, I_{OH} = −10 mA	2.4	3.4		2.4	3.4		V
		I_{OH} = −40 mA	2	3.0		2	3.0		
V_{OL}	Low-level output voltage	V_{CC} = MIN, $V_{IH} = V_{IH}$ min, $V_{IL} = V_{IL}$ max, I_{OL} = 40 mA		0.23	0.4		0.23	0.4	V
V_O	Output clamp voltage	V_{CC} = MAX, I_O = −40 mA		−1.1	−1.5		−1.1	−1.5	V
$I_{O(off)}$	Off-state open-collector output current	V_{CC} = MAX, V_{OH} = 12 V, T_A = 25°C		1	10				µA
		T_A = 125°C			200				
		V_{OH} = 5.25 V, T_A = 25°C					1	10	
		T_A = 70°C						20	
I_{OZ}	Off-state (high-impedance-state) output current	V_{CC} = MAX, Output controls at V_{IL} max, T_A = 25°C, V_O = 0 to V_{CC}			±10			±10	µA
		T_A = MAX, V_O = 0			−150			−20	
		V_O = 0.4 V			±80			±20	
		V_O = 2.4 V			±80			±20	
		$V_O = V_{CC}$			80			20	
I_I	Input current at maximum input voltage — A, B, C	V_{CC} = MAX, V_I = 5.5 V			1			1	mA
	CC				2			2	
I_{IH}	High-level input current — A, B, C	V_{CC} = MAX, V_I = 2.4 V			40			40	µA
	CC				80			80	
I_{IL}	Low-level input current — A, B, C	V_{CC} = MAX, V_I = 0.4 V			−1.6			−1.6	mA
	CC				−3.2			−3.2	
I_{OS}	Short-circuit output current§	V_{CC} = MAX, V_O = 0	−40	−90	−120	−40	−90	−120	mA
I_{CC}	Supply current (both drivers)	All inputs at 0 V, No load, T_A = 25°C, V_{CC} = MAX		47	65		47	65	mA
		V_{CC} = 7 V		65	85		65	85	

†All parameters with the exception of off-state open-collector output current, are measured with the active pull-up connected to the sink output.
‡All typical values are at T_A = 25°C and V_{CC} = 5 V, with the exception of I_{CC} at 7 V.
§Only one output should be shorted at a time.

TEXAS INSTRUMENTS
INCORPORATED
POST OFFICE BOX 5012 • DALLAS, TEXAS 75222

DUAL DIFFERENTIAL LINE DRIVERS WITH 3-STATE OUTPUTS

switching characteristics, $V_{CC} = 5$ V, $C_L = 30$ pF, $T_A = 25°C$

PARAMETER		TEST CONDITIONS	SN55113			SN75113			UNIT
			MIN	TYP	MAX	MIN	TYP	MAX	
t_{PLH}	Propagation delay time, low-to-high-level output	See Figure 1		13	20		13	30	ns
t_{PHL}	Propagation delay time, high-to-low-level output			12	20		12	30	ns
t_{ZH}	Output enable time to high level	$R_L = 180$ Ω, See Figure 2		7	15		7	20	ns
t_{ZL}	Output enable time to low level	$R_L = 250$ Ω, See Figure 3		14	30		14	40	ns
t_{HZ}	Output disable time from high level	$R_L = 180$ Ω, See Figure 2		10	20		10	30	ns
t_{LZ}	Output disable time from low level	$R_L = 250$ Ω, See Figure 3		17	35		17	35	ns

PARAMETER MEASUREMENT INFORMATION

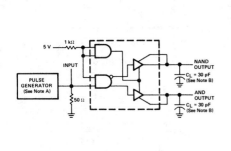

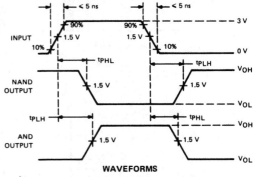

TEST CIRCUIT   **WAVEFORMS**

FIGURE 1—t_{PLH} and t_{PHL}

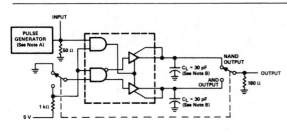

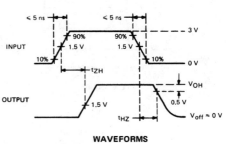

TEST CIRCUIT   **WAVEFORMS**

FIGURE 2—t_{ZH} and t_{HZ}

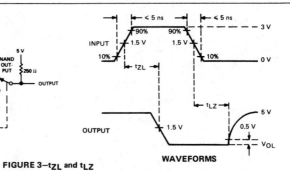

TEST CIRCUIT   **WAVEFORMS**

FIGURE 3—t_{ZL} and t_{LZ}

NOTES: A. The pulse generator has the following characteristics: $Z_{out} = 50$ Ω, PRR = 500 kHz, $t_w = 100$ ns.
   B. C_L includes probe and jig capacitance.

TYPES SN55113, SN75113
DUAL DIFFERENTIAL LINE DRIVERS WITH 3-STATE OUTPUTS

TYPICAL CHARACTERISTICS†

OUTPUT VOLTAGE
vs
DATA INPUT VOLTAGE

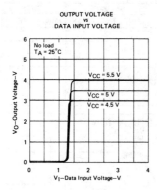

FIGURE 4

OUTPUT VOLTAGE
vs
DATA INPUT VOLTAGE

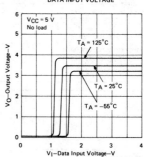

FIGURE 5

OUTPUT VOLTAGE
vs
OUTPUT CONTROL VOLTAGE

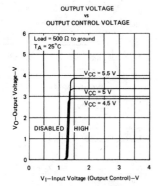

FIGURE 6

OUTPUT VOLTAGE
vs
OUTPUT CONTROL VOLTAGE

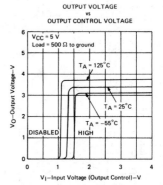

FIGURE 7

OUTPUT VOLTAGE
vs
OUTPUT CONTROL VOLTAGE

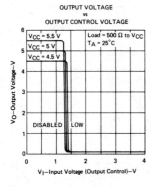

FIGURE 8

OUTPUT VOLTAGE
vs
OUTPUT CONTROL VOLTAGE

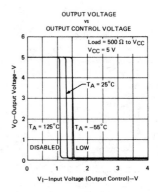

FIGURE 9

†Data for temperatures below 0°C and above 70°C and for supply voltages below 4.75 V and above 5.25 V are applicable to SN55113 circuits only. These parameters were measured with the active pull-up connected to the sink output.

TEXAS INSTRUMENTS
INCORPORATED
POST OFFICE BOX 5012 • DALLAS, TEXAS 75222

97

TYPICAL CHARACTERISTICS†

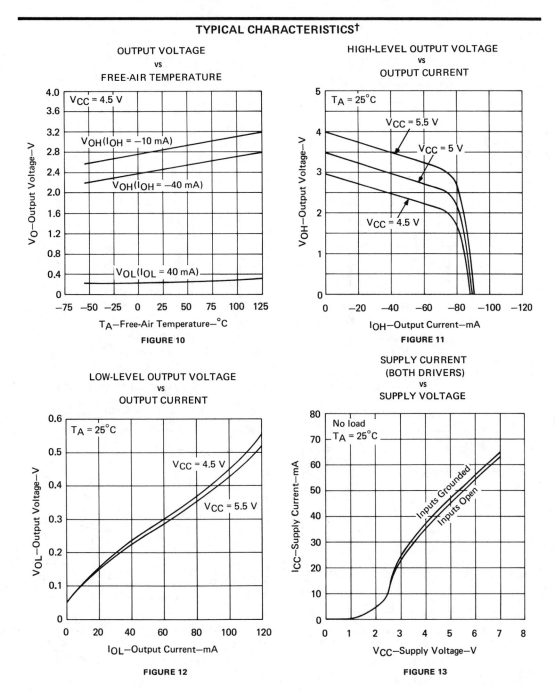

OUTPUT VOLTAGE
vs
FREE-AIR TEMPERATURE

FIGURE 10

HIGH-LEVEL OUTPUT VOLTAGE
vs
OUTPUT CURRENT

FIGURE 11

LOW-LEVEL OUTPUT VOLTAGE
vs
OUTPUT CURRENT

FIGURE 12

SUPPLY CURRENT
(BOTH DRIVERS)
vs
SUPPLY VOLTAGE

FIGURE 13

†Data for temperature below 0°C and above 70°C and for supply voltages below 4.75 V and above 5.25 V are applicable to SN55113 circuits only. These parameters were measured with the active pull-up connected to the sink output.

TYPICAL CHARACTERISTICS†

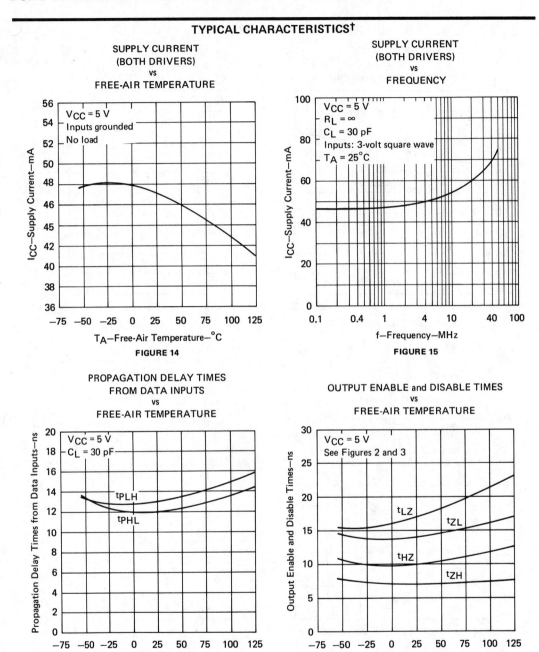

SUPPLY CURRENT
(BOTH DRIVERS)
vs
FREE-AIR TEMPERATURE

$V_{CC} = 5$ V
Inputs grounded
No load

FIGURE 14

SUPPLY CURRENT
(BOTH DRIVERS)
vs
FREQUENCY

$V_{CC} = 5$ V
$R_L = \infty$
$C_L = 30$ pF
Inputs: 3-volt square wave
$T_A = 25°C$

FIGURE 15

PROPAGATION DELAY TIMES
FROM DATA INPUTS
vs
FREE-AIR TEMPERATURE

$V_{CC} = 5$ V
$C_L = 30$ pF

t_{PLH}
t_{PHL}

FIGURE 16

OUTPUT ENABLE and DISABLE TIMES
vs
FREE-AIR TEMPERATURE

$V_{CC} = 5$ V
See Figures 2 and 3

t_{LZ}
t_{ZL}
t_{HZ}
t_{ZH}

FIGURE 17

†Data for temperature below 0°C and above 70°C and for supply voltages below 4.75 V and above 5.25 V are applicable to SN55113 circuits only. These parameters were measured with the active pull-up connected to the sink output.

TEXAS INSTRUMENTS
INCORPORATED
POST OFFICE BOX 5012 • DALLAS, TEXAS 75222

description

The SN55114 and SN75114 dual differential line drivers are designed to provide differential output signals with high current capability for driving balanced lines, such as twisted-pair at normal line impedances, without high power dissipation. The output stages are similar to TTL totem-pole outputs, but with the sink outputs, YS and ZS, and the corresponding active pull-up terminals, YP and ZP, available on adjacent package pins. Since the output stages provide TTL compatible output levels, these devices may also be used as TTL expanders or phase splitters.

FUNCTION TABLE

INPUTS			OUTPUTS	
A	B	C	Y	Z
H	H	H	H	L
ALL OTHER INPUT COMBINATIONS			L	H

H = high level, L = low level

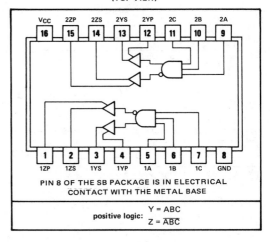

J OR N DUAL-IN-LINE PACKAGE
SB FLAT PACKAGE
(TOP VIEW)

PIN 8 OF THE SB PACKAGE IS IN ELECTRICAL CONTACT WITH THE METAL BASE

positive logic: $Y = ABC$
$Z = \overline{ABC}$

schematic (each driver)

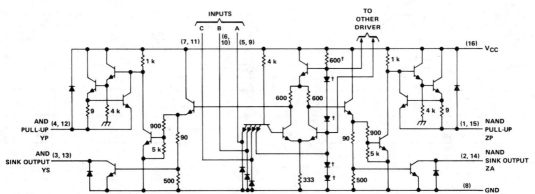

† These components common to both drivers.
Resistor values shown are nominal and in ohms.

absolute maximum ratings over operating free-air temperature range (unless otherwise noted)

Supply voltage, V_{CC} (see Note 1) . . . . 7 V
Input voltage . . . . 5.5 V
Off-state voltage applied to open-collector outputs . . . . 12 V
Continuous total dissipation at (or below) 70°C free-air temperature (see Note 2) . . . . 600 mW
Operating free-air temperature range: SN55114 . . . . -55°C to 125°C
　　　　　　　　　　　　　　　　　SN75114 . . . . 0°C to 70°C
Storage temperature range . . . . -65°C to 150°C
Lead temperature 1/16 inch from case for 60 seconds: J or SB package . . . . 300°C
Lead temperature 1/16 inch from case for 10 seconds: N package . . . . 260°C

NOTES: 1. All voltage values are with respect to network ground terminal.
　　　　2. For operation of SN55114 above 70°C free-air temperature, refer to Dissipation Derating Curve, Figure 43.

recommended operating conditions

	SN55114			SN75114			UNIT
	MIN	NOM	MAX	MIN	NOM	MAX	
Supply voltage, V_{CC}	4.5	5	5.5	4.75	5	5.25	V
High-level output current, I_{OH}			−40			−40	mA
Low-level output current, I_{OL}			40			40	mA
Operating free-air temperature, T_A	−55		125	0		70	°C

electrical characteristics over recommended operating free-air temperature range (unless otherwise noted)

PARAMETER		TEST CONDITIONS[†]			SN55114			SN75114			UNIT
					MIN	TYP[‡]	MAX	MIN	TYP[‡]	MAX	
V_{IH}	High-level input voltage				2			2			V
V_{IL}	Low-level input voltage						0.8			0.8	
V_I	Input clamp voltage	V_{CC} = MIN,	I_I = −12 mA			−0.9	−1.5		−0.9	−1.5	V
V_{OH}	High-level output voltage	V_{CC} = MIN, $V_{IH} = V_{IH}$ min,	I_{OH} = −10 mA		2.4	3.4		2.4	3.4		V
		$V_{IL} = V_{IL}$ max	I_{OH} = −40 mA		2	3.0		2	3.0		
V_{OL}	Low-level output voltage	V_{CC} = MIN, $V_{IH} = V_{IH}$ min, $V_{IL} = V_{IL}$ max, I_{OL} = 40 mA				0.2	0.4		0.2	0.45	V
V_O	Output clamp voltage	V_{CC} = 5 V,	I_O = 40 mA,	$T_A = 25°C$		6.1	6.5		6.1	6.5	V
		V_{CC} = MAX,	I_O = −40 mA,	$T_A = 25°C$		−1.1	−1.5		−1.1	−1.5	
$I_{O(off)}$	Off-state open-collector output current	V_{CC} = MAX	V_{OH} = 12 V	$T_A = 25°C$		1	100				µA
				$T_A = 125°C$			200				
			V_{OH} = 5.25 V	$T_A = 25°C$					1	100	
				$T_A = 70°C$						200	
I_I	Input current at maximum input voltage	V_{CC} = MAX,	V_I = 5.5 V				1			1	mA
I_{IH}	High-level input current	V_{CC} = MAX,	V_I = 2.4 V				40			40	µA
I_{IL}	Low-level input current	V_{CC} = MAX,	V_I = 0.4 V			−1.1	−1.6		−1.1	−1.6	mA
I_{OS}	Short-circuit output current[§]	V_{CC} = MAX,	V_O = 0		−40	−90	−120	−40	−90	−120	mA
I_{CC}	Supply current (both drivers)	Inputs grounded, No load, $T_A = 25°C$	V_{CC} = MAX			37	50		37	50	mA
			V_{CC} = 7 V			47	65		47	70	

[†]All parameters, with the exception of off-state open-collector output current, are measured with the active pull-up connected to the sink output.

[‡]All typical values are at $T_A = 25°C$ and V_{CC} = 5 V, with the exception of I_{CC} at 7 V.

[§]Only one output should be shorted at a time.

switching characteristics, V_{CC} = 5 V, $T_A = 25°C$

PARAMETER		TEST CONDITIONS	SN55114			SN75114			UNIT
			MIN	TYP	MAX	MIN	TYP	MAX	
t_{PLH}	Propagation delay time, low-to-high-level output	C_L = 30 pF, See Figure 18		15	20		15	30	ns
t_{PHL}	Propagation delay time, high-to-low-level output			11	20		11	30	ns

TEXAS INSTRUMENTS
INCORPORATED

POST OFFICE BOX 5012 • DALLAS, TEXAS 75222

PARAMETER MEASUREMENT INFORMATION

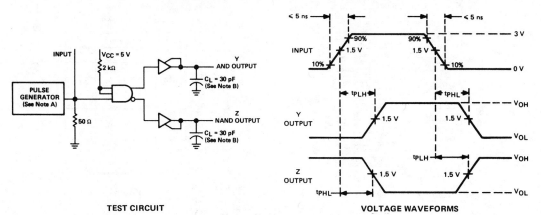

TEST CIRCUIT

VOLTAGE WAVEFORMS

NOTES: A. The pulse generator has the following characteristics: Z_{out} = 50 Ω, t_w = 100 ns, PRR = 500 kHz.
       B. C_L includes probe and jig capacitance.

FIGURE 18—PROPAGATION DELAY TIMES

TYPICAL CHARACTERISTICS†

OUTPUT VOLTAGE
vs
DATA INPUT VOLTAGE

FIGURE 19

OUTPUT VOLTAGE
vs
DATA INPUT VOLTAGE

FIGURE 20

HIGH-LEVEL OUTPUT VOLTAGE
vs
OUTPUT CURRENT

FIGURE 21

LOW-LEVEL OUTPUT VOLTAGE
vs
OUTPUT CURRENT

FIGURE 22

†Data for temperatures below 0°C and above 70°C and for supply voltages below 4.75 V and above 5.25 V are applicable to SN55114 circuits only. These parameters were measured with the active pull-up connected to the sink output.

TYPES SN55114, SN75114
DUAL DIFFERENTIAL LINE DRIVERS

TYPICAL CHARACTERISTICS[†]

OUTPUT VOLTAGE
vs
FREE-AIR TEMPERATURE

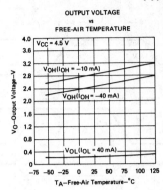

FIGURE 23

PROPAGATION DELAY TIMES
vs
FREE-AIR TEMPERATURE

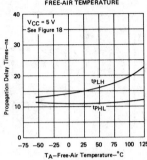

FIGURE 24

SUPPLY CURRENT
(BOTH DRIVERS)
vs
SUPPLY VOLTAGE

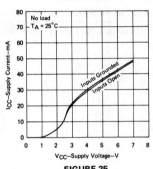

FIGURE 25

SUPPLY CURRENT
(BOTH DRIVERS)
vs
FREE-AIR TEMPERATURE

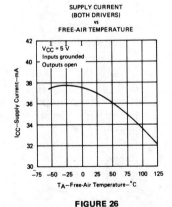

FIGURE 26

SUPPLY CURRENT
(BOTH DRIVERS)
vs
FREQUENCY

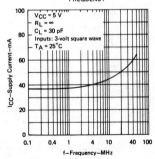

FIGURE 27

[†]Data for temperatures below 0°C and above 70°C are applicable to SN55114 circuits only. These parameters were measured with the active pull-up connected to the sink output.

TEXAS INSTRUMENTS
INCORPORATED
POST OFFICE BOX 5012 • DALLAS, TEXAS 75222

description

The SN55115 and SN75115 dual differential line receivers are designed to sense small differential signals in the presence of large common-mode noise. These devices give TTL-compatible output signals as a function of the polarity of the differential input voltage. The open-collector output configuration permits the wire-AND connection with similar outputs (such as SN5401/SN7401 TTL gates or other SN55115/SN75115 line receivers). This permits a level of logic to be implemented without extra delay. The output stages are similar to TTL totem-pole outputs, but with the sink outputs, 1YS and 2YS, and the corresponding active pull-up terminals, 1YP and 2YP, available on adjacent package pins. The frequency response of each channel may be easily controlled by a single external capacitor to provide immunity to differential noise spikes. A strobe input is provided for each channel. With the strobe in the low level, the receiver is disabled and the outputs are forced to a high level.

J OR N DUAL-IN-LINE PACKAGE
SB FLAT PACKAGE
(TOP VIEW)

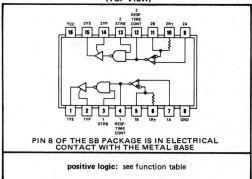

PIN 8 OF THE SB PACKAGE IS IN ELECTRICAL
CONTACT WITH THE METAL BASE

positive logic: see function table

FUNCTION TABLE

STROBE	DIFF INPUT	OUTPUT
L	X	H
H	L	H
H	H	L

H = $V_I \geqslant V_{IH}$ min or V_{ID} more positive than V_{TH} max
L = $V_I \leqslant V_{IL}$ max or V_{ID} more negative than V_{TL} max
X = irrelevant

schematic (each receiver)

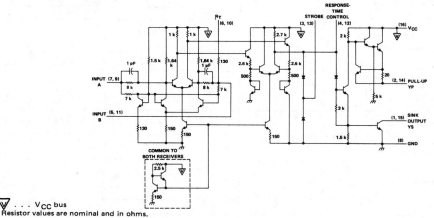

∇ ... V_{CC} bus
Resistor values are nominal and in ohms.

absolute maximum ratings over operating free-air temperature range (unless otherwise noted)

Supply voltage, V_{CC} (see Note 1)	7 V
Input voltage at A, B, and R_T inputs	±25 V
Input voltage at strobe input	5.5 V
Off-state voltage applied to open-collector outputs	14 V
Continuous total dissipation at (or below 70°C free-air temperature (see Note 2)	600 mW
Operating free-air temperature range: SN55115	−55°C to 125°C
SN75115	0°C to 70°C
Storage temperature range	−65°C to 150°C
Lead temperature 1/16 inch from case for 60 seconds: J or SB package	300°C
Lead temperature 1/16 inch from case for 10 seconds: N package	260°C

NOTES: 1. All voltage values, except differential input voltage, are with respect to network ground terminal.
2. For operation of SN55115 above 70°C free-air temperature refer to Dissipation Derating Curve, Figure 43.

TEXAS INSTRUMENTS
INCORPORATED
POST OFFICE BOX 5012 • DALLAS, TEXAS 75222

recommended operating conditions

	SN55115			SN75115			UNIT
	MIN	NOM	MAX	MIN	NOM	MAX	
Supply voltage, V_{CC}	4.5	5	5.5	4.75	5	5.25	V
High-level output current, I_{OH}			−5			−5	mA
Low-level output current, I_{OL}			15			15	mA
Operating free-air temperature, T_A	−55		125	0		70	°C

electrical characteristics over recommended operating free-air temperature range (unless otherwise noted)

PARAMETER		TEST CONDITIONS[†]		SN55115			SN75115			UNIT
				MIN	TYP[‡]	MAX	MIN	TYP[‡]	MAX	
V_{TH}[§]	Differential input high-threshold voltage	$V_O = 0.4$ V, $I_{OL} = 15$ mA, $V_{IC} = 0$				500			500	mV
V_{TL}[§]	Differential input low-threshold voltage	$V_O = 2.4$ V, $I_{OH} = -5$ mA, $V_{IC} = 0$				−500			−500	mV
V_{ICR}	Common-mode input voltage range	$V_{ID} = \pm 1$ V		+15 to −15	+24 to −19		+15 to −15	+24 to −19		V
$V_{IH(strobe)}$	High-level strobe input voltage			2.4			2.4			V
$V_{IL(strobe)}$	Low-level strobe input voltage					0.4			0.4	V
V_{OH}	High-level output voltage	$V_{CC} = $ MIN, $V_{ID} = -0.5$ V, $I_{OH} = -5$ mA	$T_A = $ MIN	2.2			2.4			V
			$T_A = 25°C$	2.4	3.4		2.4	3.4		
			$T_A = $ MAX	2.4			2.4			
V_{OL}	Low-level output voltage	$V_{CC} = $ MIN, $V_{ID} = 0.5$ V, $I_{OL} = 15$ mA			0.22	0.4		0.22	0.45	V
I_{IL}	Low-level input current	$V_{CC} = $ MAX, $V_I = 0.4$ V, Other Input at 5.5 V	$T_A = $ MIN			−0.9			−0.9	mA
			$T_A = 25°C$		−0.5	−0.7		−0.5	−0.7	
			$T_A = $ MAX			−0.7			−0.7	
I_{SH}	High-level strobe current	$V_{CC} = $ MIN, $V_{ID} = -0.5$ V, $V_{strobe} = 4.5$ V	$T_A = 25°C$		2	5		2	5	µA
			$T_A = $ MAX			5			10	
I_{SL}	Low-level strobe current	$V_{CC} = $ MAX, $V_{ID} = 0.5$ V, $V_{strobe} = 0.4$ V	$T_A = 25°C$		−1.15	−2.4		−1.15	−2.4	mA
I_4, I_{12}	Response-time-control current (Pin 4 or Pin 12)	$V_{CC} = $ MAX, $V_{ID} = 0.5$ V, $V_{RC} = 0$	$T_A = 25°C$	−1.2	−3.4		−1.2	−3.4		mA
$I_{O(off)}$	Off-state open-collector output current	$V_{CC} = $ MIN, $V_{OH} = 12$ V, $V_{ID} = -4.5$ V	$T_A = 25°C$			100				µA
			$T_A = $ MAX			200				
		$V_{CC} = $ MIN, $V_{OH} = 5.25$ V, $V_{ID} = -4.75$ V	$T_A = 25°C$						100	
			$T_A = $ MAX						200	
R_T	Line-terminating resistance	$V_{CC} = 5$ V	$T_A = 25°C$	77	130	167	74	130	179	Ω
I_{OS}	Short-circuit output current	$V_{CC} = $ MAX, $V_O = 0$, $V_{ID} = -0.5$ V	$T_A = 25°C$	−15	−40	−80	−14	−40	−100	mA
I_{CC}	Supply current (both receivers)	$V_{CC} = $ MAX, $V_{ID} = 0.5$ V, $V_{IC} = 0$	$T_A = 25°C$		32	50		32	50	mA

[†] Unless otherwise noted $V_{strobe} = 2.4$ V. All parameters with the exception of off-state open-collector output current are measured with the active pull-up connected to the sink output.
[‡] All typical values are at $V_{CC} = 5$ V, $T_A = 25°C$, and $V_{IC} = 0$.
[§] Differential voltages are at the B input terminal with respect to the A input terminal.

8

TEXAS INSTRUMENTS
INCORPORATED
POST OFFICE BOX 5012 • DALLAS, TEXAS 75222

switching characteristics, V_{CC} = 5 V, C_L = 30 pF, T_A = 25°C

PARAMETER	TEST CONDITIONS	SN55115			SN75115			UNIT
		MIN	TYP	MAX	MIN	TYP	MAX	
t_{PLH} Propagation delay time, low-to-high-level output	R_L = 3.9 kΩ, See Figure 28		18	50		18	75	ns
t_{PHL} Propagation delay time, high-to-low-level output	R_L = 390 Ω, See Figure 28		20	50		20	75	ns

PARAMETER MEASUREMENT INFORMATION

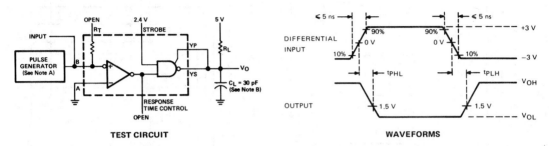

TEST CIRCUIT　　　　　　　　**WAVEFORMS**

NOTES: A. The pulse generator has the following characteristics: Z_{out} = 50 Ω, PRR = 500 kHz, t_w = 100 ns.
　　　　B. C_L includes probe and jig capacitance.

FIGURE 28—PROPAGATION DELAY TIMES

TYPICAL CHARACTERISTICS[†]

INPUT CURRENT
vs
INPUT VOLTAGE

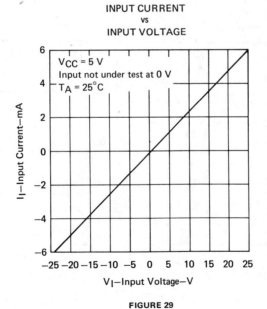

FIGURE 29

[†]Data for temperatures below 0°C and above 70°C and for supply voltages below 4.75 V and above 5.25 V are applicable to SN55115 circuits only.

TYPICAL CHARACTERISTICS[†]

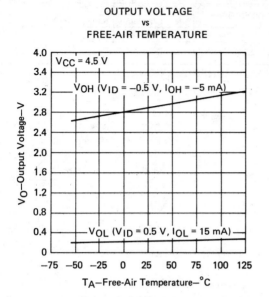

OUTPUT VOLTAGE
vs
FREE-AIR TEMPERATURE

FIGURE 30

OUTPUT VOLTAGE
vs
COMMON-MODE INPUT VOLTAGE

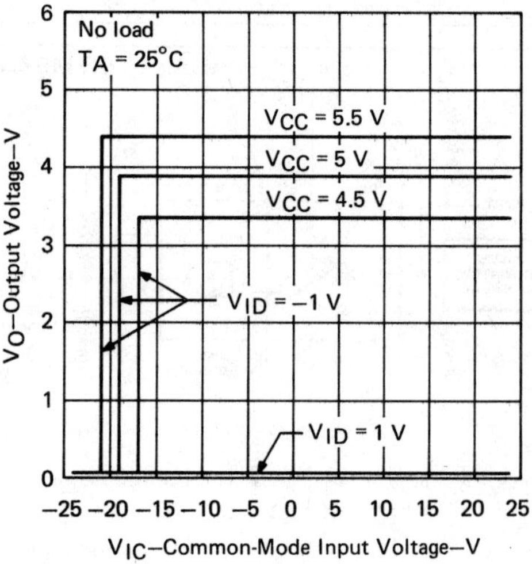

FIGURE 31

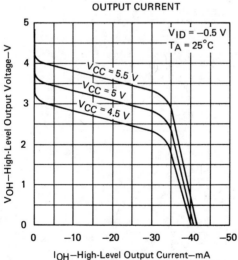

HIGH-LEVEL OUTPUT VOLTAGE
vs
OUTPUT CURRENT

FIGURE 32

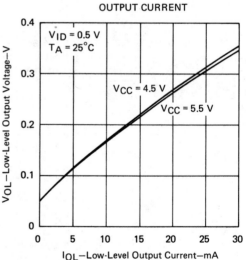

LOW-LEVEL OUTPUT VOLTAGE
vs
OUTPUT CURRENT

FIGURE 33

[†]Data for temperatures below 0°C and above 70°C and for supply voltages below 4.75 V and above 5.25 V are applicable to SN55115 circuits only. These parameters were measured with the active pull-up connected to the sink output.

TEXAS INSTRUMENTS
INCORPORATED
POST OFFICE BOX 5012 • DALLAS, TEXAS 75222

TYPICAL CHARACTERISTICS[†]

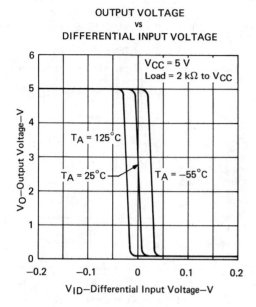

OUTPUT VOLTAGE
vs
DIFFERENTIAL INPUT VOLTAGE

FIGURE 34

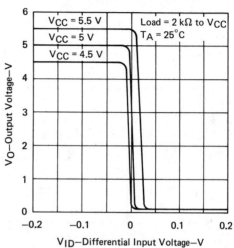

OUTPUT VOLTAGE
vs
DIFFERENTIAL INPUT VOLTAGE

FIGURE 35

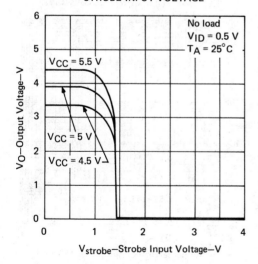

OUTPUT VOLTAGE
vs
STROBE INPUT VOLTAGE

FIGURE 36

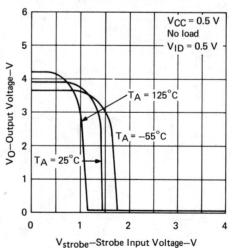

OUTPUT VOLTAGE
vs
STROBE INPUT VOLTAGE

FIGURE 37

[†]Data for temperatures below $0°C$ and above $70°C$ and for supply voltages below 4.75 V and above 5.25 V are applicable to SN55115 circuits only. These parameters were measured with the active pull-up connected to the sink output.

TYPICAL CHARACTERISTICS[†]

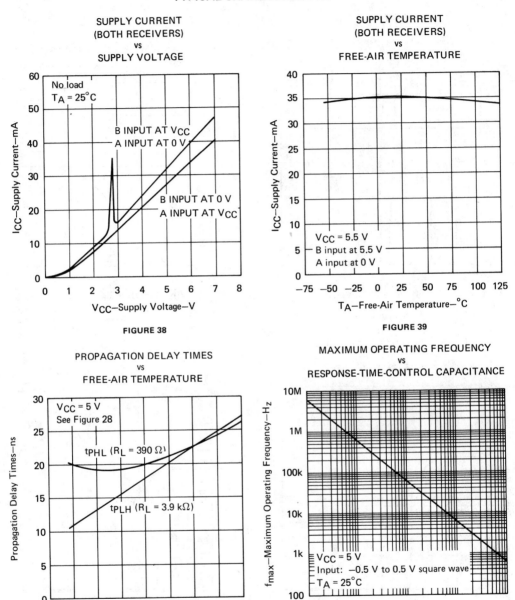

SUPPLY CURRENT
(BOTH RECEIVERS)
vs
SUPPLY VOLTAGE

FIGURE 38

SUPPLY CURRENT
(BOTH RECEIVERS)
vs
FREE-AIR TEMPERATURE

FIGURE 39

PROPAGATION DELAY TIMES
vs
FREE-AIR TEMPERATURE

FIGURE 40

MAXIMUM OPERATING FREQUENCY
vs
RESPONSE-TIME-CONTROL CAPACITANCE

FIGURE 41

[†]Data for temperatures below 0°C and above 70°C and for supply voltages below 4.75 V and above 5.25 V are applicable to SN55115 circuits only. These parameters were measured with the active pull-up connected to the sink output.

TEXAS INSTRUMENTS
INCORPORATED
POST OFFICE BOX 5012 • DALLAS, TEXAS 75222

TYPICAL APPLICATION DATA

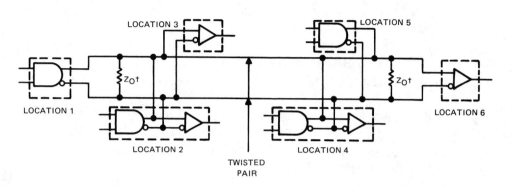

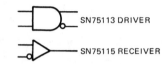

SN75113 DRIVER

SN75115 RECEIVER

† A capacitor may be connected in series with Z_O to reduce power dissipation.

FIGURE 42—BASIC PARTY-LINE OR DATA-BUS DIFFERENTIAL DATA TRANSMISSION

THERMAL INFORMATION

SN55113, SN55114, SN55115
DISSIPATION DERATING CURVE

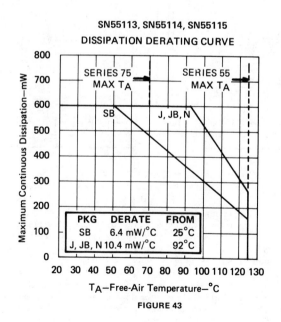

PKG	DERATE	FROM
SB	6.4 mW/°C	25°C
J, JB, N	10.4 mW/°C	92°C

T_A—Free-Air Temperature—°C

FIGURE 43

TEXAS INSTRUMENTS
INCORPORATED
POST OFFICE BOX 5012 • DALLAS, TEXAS 75222

LINE CIRCUITS

- Designed for Digital Data Transmission over Coaxial Cable, Strip Line, or Twisted Pair
- Designed for Operation with 50-Ω to 500-Ω Transmission Lines
- TTL Compatible with Single 5-V Supply

additional features of SN55121, SN75121 line drivers

- Plug-In Replacement for Signetics 8T13
- 2.4-V Output at I_{OH} = −75 mA
- Uncommitted Emitter-Follower Output Structure for Party-Line Operation
- Short-Circuit Protection
- AND-OR Logic Configuration
- High Speed . . . Maximum Propagation Delay Time = 20 ns

additional features of SN55122, SN75122 line receivers

- Plug-In Replacement for Signetics 8T14
- Built-In Input Threshold Hysteresis
- High Speed . . . Typical Propagation Delay Time = 20 ns
- Independent Channel Strobes
- Input Gating Increases Application Flexibility
- Fanout to 10 Series 54/74 Standard Loads

SN55121, SN75121
J OR N
DUAL-IN-LINE PACKAGE (TOP VIEW)

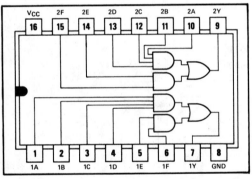

SN55122, SN75122
J OR N
DUAL-IN-LINE PACKAGE (TOP VIEW)

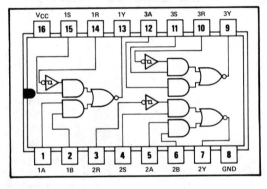

description

The SN55121, SN75121 dual line drivers and the SN55122, SN75122 triple line receivers are designed for digital data transmission over lines having impedances from 50 to 500 ohms. They are also compatible with standard TTL logic and supply voltage levels.

The low-impedance emitter-follower outputs of the SN55121, SN75121 will drive terminated lines such as coaxial cable or twisted pair. Having the outputs uncommitted allows wired-OR logic to be performed in party-line applications. Output short-circuit protection is provided by an internal clamping network which turns on when the output voltage drops below approximately 1.5 volts. All of the inputs are in conventional TTL configuration and the gating can be used during power-up and power-down sequences to ensure that no noise is introduced to the line.

The SN55122, SN75122 have receiver inputs with built-in hysteresis to provide increased noise margin for single-ended systems. The high impedance of this input presents a minimum load to the driver and allows termination of the transmission line in its characteristic impedance to minimize line reflection. An open line will affect the receiver input as would a low-level input voltage and the receiver input can withstand a level of −0.15 volt with power on or off. The other inputs are in TTL configuration. The S input must be high to enable the receiver input. Two of the line receivers have A and B inputs which, if both are high, will hold the output low. The third receiver has only an A input which, if high, will hold the output low.

TEXAS INSTRUMENTS
INCORPORATED
POST OFFICE BOX 5012 • DALLAS, TEXAS 75222

SN55121, SN75121 FUNCTION TABLE

INPUTS						OUTPUT
A	B	C	D	E	F	Y
H	H	H	H	X	X	H
X	X	X	X	H	H	H
ALL OTHER INPUT COMBINATIONS						L

H = high level
L = low level
X = irrelevant

SN55122, SN75122 FUNCTION TABLE

INPUTS				OUTPUT
A	B†	R	S	Y
H	H	X	X	L
X	X	L	H	L
L	X	H	X	H
L	X	X	L	H
X	L	H	X	H
X	L	X	L	H

†B input and last two lines of the function table are applicable to receivers 1 and 2 only.

SN55121, SN75121 schematic (each driver)

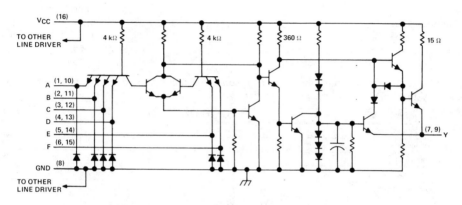

SN55122, SN75122 schematic (each receiver)

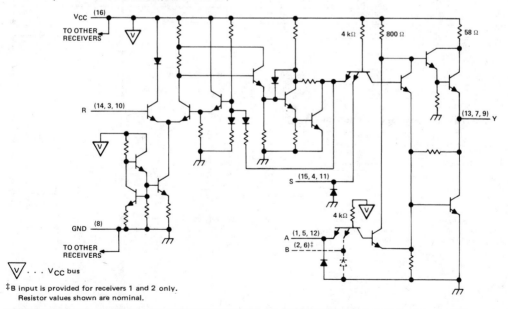

▽ . . . V_CC bus

‡B input is provided for receivers 1 and 2 only.
  Resistor values shown are nominal.

TEXAS INSTRUMENTS
INCORPORATED
POST OFFICE BOX 5012 • DALLAS, TEXAS 75222

SN55121, SN75121 absolute maximum ratings over operating free-air temperature range (unless otherwise noted)

Supply voltage, V_{CC} (see Note 1) . . . . 6 V
Input voltage . . . . 6 V
Output voltage . . . . 6 V
Continuous total dissipation at (or below) 25°C free-air temperature (see Note 2) . . . . 800 mW
Operating free-air temperature range: SN55121 . . . . −55°C to 125°C
SN75121 . . . . 0°C to 75°C
Lead temperature 1/16 inch from case for 60 seconds: J package . . . . 300°C
Lead temperature 1/16 inch from case for 10 seconds: N package . . . . 260°C

SN55121, SN75121 recommended operating conditions

	MIN	NOM	MAX	UNIT
Supply voltage, V_{CC}	4.75	5	5.25	V
High-level output current, I_{OH}			−75	mA
Operating free-air temperature, T_A: SN55121	−55		125	°C
SN75121	0		75	°C

SN55121, SN75121 electrical characteristics over recommended operating free-air temperature range, V_{CC} = 4.75 V to 5.25 V (unless otherwise noted)

PARAMETER		TEST CONDITIONS			MIN	MAX	UNIT
V_{IH}	High-level input voltage				2		V
V_{IL}	Low-level input voltage					0.8	V
V_I	Input clamp voltage	V_{CC} = 5 V,	I_I = −12 mA			−1.5	V
$V_{(BR)I}$	Input breakdown voltage	V_{CC} = 5 V,	I_I = 10 mA		5.5		V
V_{OH}	High-level output voltage	V_{IH} = 2 V,	I_{OH} = −75 mA,	See Note 3	2.4		V
I_{OH}	High-level output current	V_{CC} = 5 V, T_A = 25°C,	V_{IH} = 4.5 V, See Note 3	V_{OH} = 2 V,	−100	−250	mA
I_{OL}	Low-level output current	V_{IL} = 0.8 V,	V_{OL} = 0.4 V,	See Note 3		−800	μA
$I_{O(off)}$	Off-state output current	V_{CC} = 0,	V_O = 3 V			500	μA
I_{IH}	High-level input current	V_I = 4.5 V				40	μA
I_{IL}	Low-level input current	V_I = 0.4 V			−0.1	−1.6	mA
I_{OS}	Short-circuit output current	V_{CC} = 5 V,	T_A = 25°C			−30	mA
I_{CCH}	Supply current, outputs high	V_{CC} = 5.25 V,	All inputs at 2 V,	Outputs open		28	mA
I_{CCL}	Supply current, outputs low	V_{CC} = 5.25 V,	All inputs at 0.8 V, Outputs open			60	mA

SN55121, SN75121 switching characteristics, V_{CC} = 5 V, T_A = 25°C

PARAMETER		TEST CONDITIONS	MIN	TYP	MAX	UNIT
t_{PLH}	Propagation delay time, low-to-high-level output	R_L = 37 Ω, C_L = 15 pF,		11	20	ns
t_{PHL}	Propagation delay time, high-to-low-level output	See Figure 1		8	20	
t_{PLH}	Propagation delay time, low-to-high-level output	R_L = 37 Ω, C_L = 1000 pF,		22	50	ns
t_{PHL}	Propagation delay time, high-to-low-level output	See Figure 1		20	50	

NOTES: 1. Voltage values are with respect to network ground terminal.
2. For operation above 25°C free-air temperature, refer to Dissipation Derating Curve, Figure 3.
3. The output voltage and current limits are guaranteed for any appropriate combination of high and low inputs specified by the function table for the desired output.

TEXAS INSTRUMENTS
INCORPORATED
POST OFFICE BOX 5012 • DALLAS, TEXAS 75222

SN55122, SN75122 absolute maximum ratings over operating free-air temperature range (unless otherwise noted)

Supply voltage, V_{CC} (see Note 1)	6 V
Input voltage: R input	6 V
A, B, or S input	5.5 V
Output voltage	6 V
Output current	±100 mA
Continuous total dissipation at (or below) 25°C free-air temperature (see Note 2)	800 mW
Operating free-air temperature range: SN55122	−55°C to 125°C
SN75122	0°C to 75°C
Storage temperature range	−65°C to 150°C
Lead temperature 1/16 inch from case for 60 seconds: J package	300°C
Lead temperature 1/16 inch from case for 10 seconds: N package	260°C

SN55122, SN75122 recommended operating conditions

	MIN	NOM	MAX	UNIT
Supply voltage, V_{CC}	4.75	5	5.25	V
High-level output current, I_{OH}			−500	μA
Low-level output current, I_{OL}			16	mA
Operating free-air temperature, T_A: SN55122	−55		125	°C
SN75122	0		75	°C

SN55122, SN75122 electrical characteristics over recommended operating free-air temperature range, $V_{CC} = 4.75$ V to 5.25 V (unless otherwise noted)

	PARAMETER		TEST CONDITIONS		MIN	TYP	MAX	UNIT
V_{IH}	High-level input voltage	A,B,R, or S			2			V
V_{IL}	Low-level input voltage	A,B,R, or S					0.8	V
$V_{T+}-V_{T-}$	Hysteresis[†]	R	$V_{CC} = 5$ V,	$T_A = 25°C$	0.3	0.6		V
V_I	Input clamp voltage	A,B, or S	$V_{CC} = 5$ V,	$I_I = -12$ mA			−1.5	V
$V_{(BR)I}$	Input breakdown voltage	A,B, or S	$V_{CC} = 5$ V,	$I_I = 10$ mA	5.5			V
V_{OH}	High-level output voltage		$V_{IH} = 0$ V, $V_{IL} = 0.8$ V, $I_{OH} = -500$ μA, See Note 3		2.6			V
			$V_{I(A)} = 0$ V, $V_{I(B)} = 0$ V, $V_{I(S)} = 2$ V, $V_{I(R)} = 1.45$ V (See Note 4), $I_{OH} = -500$ μA		2.6			
V_{OL}	Low-level output voltage		$V_{IH} = 2$ V, $V_{IL} = 0.8$ V, $I_{OL} = 16$ mA, See Note 3				0.4	V
			$V_{I(A)} = 0$ V, $V_{I(B)} = 0$ V, $V_{I(S)} = 2$ V, $V_{I(R)} = 1.45$ V (See Note 5), $I_{OL} = 16$ mA				0.4	
I_{IH}	High-level input current	A,B, or S	$V_I = 4.5$ V				40	μA
		R	$V_I = 3.8$ V				170	
I_{IL}	Low-level input current	A,B, or S	$V_I = 0.4$ V		−0.1		−1.6	mA
I_{OS}	Short-circuit output current[‡]		$V_{CC} = 5$ V,	$T_A = 25°C$	−50		−100	mA
I_{CC}	Supply current		$V_{CC} = 5.25$ V				72	mA

[†]Hysteresis is the difference between the positive-going input threshold voltage, V_{T+}, and the negative-going input threshold voltage, V_{T-}. See Figure 5.

[‡]Not more than one output should be shorted at a time.

NOTES: 1. Voltage values are with respect to network ground terminal.
2. For operation above 25°C free-air temperature, refer to Dissipation Derating Curve, Figure 3.
3. The output voltage limits are guaranteed for any appropriate combination of high and low inputs specified by the function table for the desired output.
4. Receiver input was at a high level immediately before being reduced to 1.45 V.
5. Receiver input was at a low level immediately before being raised to 1.45 V.

8

TYPES SN55121, SN55122, SN75121, SN75122
DUAL LINE DRIVERS AND TRIPLE LINE RECEIVERS

SN55122, SN75122 switching characteristics, V_{CC} = 5 V, T_A = 25°C

PARAMETER	TEST CONDITIONS	MIN	TYP	MAX	UNIT
t_{PLH} Propagation delay time, low-to-high-level output from R input	See Figure 2		20	30	ns
t_{PHL} Propagation delay time, high-to-low-level output from R input			20	30	

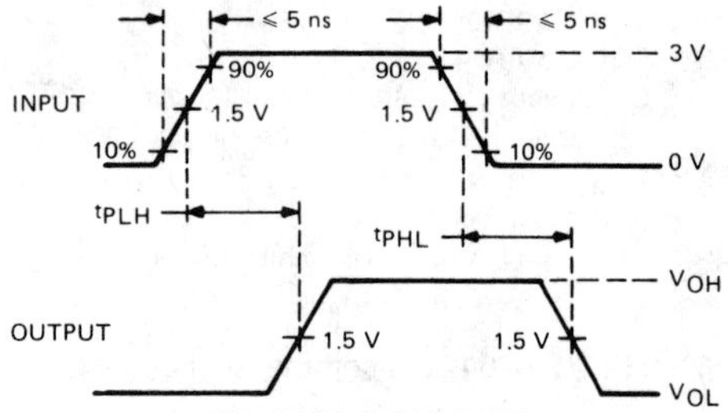

PARAMETER MEASUREMENT INFORMATION

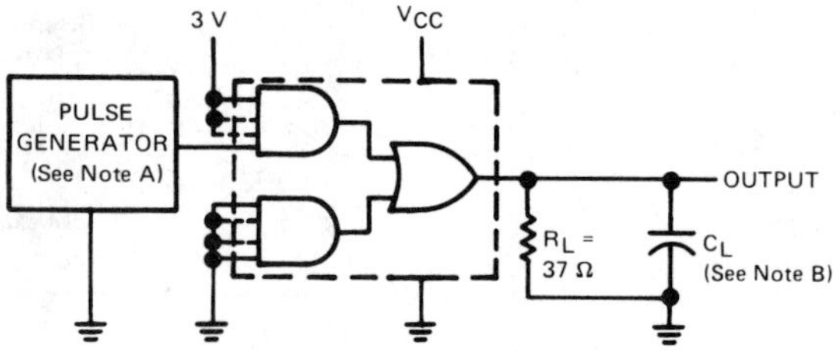

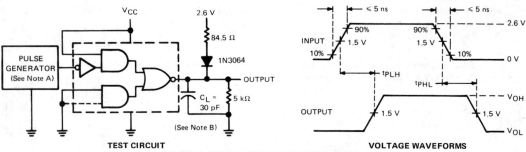

FIGURE 1—SN55121, SN75121 SWITCHING TIMES

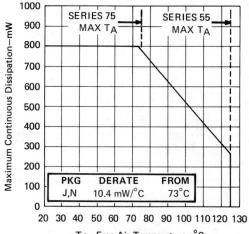

FIGURE 2—SN55122, SN75122 SWITCHING TIMES

NOTES: A. The pulse generators have the following characteristics: $Z_{out} \approx 50\ \Omega$, t_w = 200 ns, duty cycle = 50%.
B. C_L includes probe and jig capacitance.

THERMAL INFORMATION
DISSIPATION DERATING CURVE

PKG	DERATE	FROM
J,N	10.4 mW/°C	73°C

T_A—Free-Air Temperature—°C

FIGURE 3

TEXAS INSTRUMENTS
INCORPORATED
POST OFFICE BOX 5012 • DALLAS, TEXAS 75222

TYPICAL CHARACTERISTICS

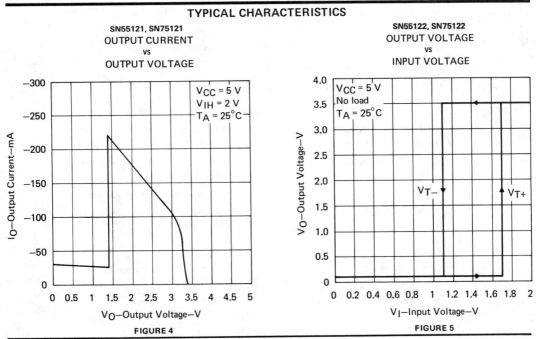

SN55121, SN75121
OUTPUT CURRENT
vs
OUTPUT VOLTAGE

FIGURE 4

SN55122, SN75122
OUTPUT VOLTAGE
vs
INPUT VOLTAGE

FIGURE 5

TYPICAL APPLICATION DATA

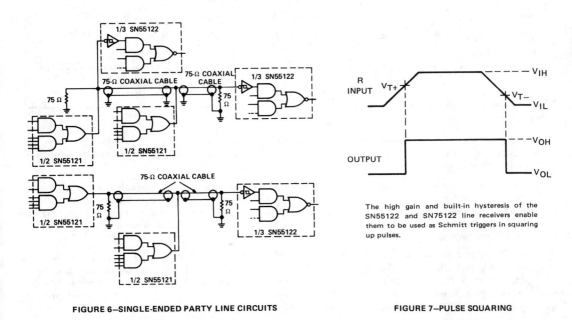

The high gain and built-in hysteresis of the SN55122 and SN75122 line receivers enable them to be used as Schmitt triggers in squaring up pulses.

FIGURE 6—SINGLE-ENDED PARTY LINE CIRCUITS

FIGURE 7—PULSE SQUARING

TEXAS INSTRUMENTS
INCORPORATED
POST OFFICE BOX 5012 • DALLAS, TEXAS 75222

LINE CIRCUITS

- Meet IBM System 360 Input/Output Interface Specifications
- Operate from Single 5-V Supply
- TTL Compatible

additional features of SN75123 line driver

- Plug-In Replacement for Signetics 8T23
- 3.11-V Output at I_{OH} = −59.3 mA
- Uncommitted Emitter-Follower Output Structure for Party-Line Operation
- Short-Circuit Protection
- AND-OR Logic Configuration

additional features of SN75124 line receiver

- Plug-In Replacement for Signetics 8T24
- Built-In Input Threshold Hysteresis
- High Speed . . . Typical Propagation Delay Time = 20 ns
- Independent Channel Strobes
- Input Gating Increases Application Flexibility

SN75123
J OR N
DUAL-IN-LINE PACKAGE (TOP VIEW)

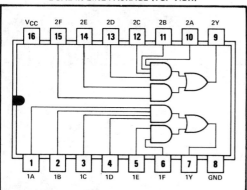

SN75124
J OR N
DUAL-IN-LINE PACKAGE (TOP VIEW)

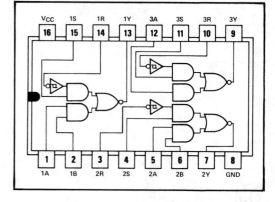

description

The SN75123 dual line driver and the SN75124 triple line receiver are both specifically designed to meet the input/output interface specifications for IBM System 360. They are also compatible with standard TTL logic and supply voltage levels.

The low-impedance emitter-follower outputs of the SN75123 will drive terminated lines such as coaxial cable or twisted pair. Having the outputs uncommitted allows wired-OR logic to be performed in party-line applications. Output short-circuit protection is provided by an internal clamping network which turns on when the output voltage drops below approximately 1.5 volts. All of the inputs are in conventional TTL configuration and the gating can be used during power-up and power-down sequences to ensure that no noise is introduced to the line.

The SN75124 has receiver inputs with built-in hysteresis to provide increased noise margin for single-ended systems. An open line will affect the receiver input as would a low-level input voltage and the receiver input can withstand a level of −0.15 volt with power on or off. The other inputs are in TTL configuration. The S input must be high to enable the receiver input. Two of the line receivers have A and B inputs which, if both are high, will hold the output low. The third receiver has only an A input which, if high, will hold the output low.

TEXAS INSTRUMENTS
INCORPORATED
POST OFFICE BOX 5012 • DALLAS, TEXAS 75222

SN75123 FUNCTION TABLE

INPUTS						OUTPUT
A	B	C	D	E	F	Y
H	H	H	H	X	X	H
X	X	X	X	H	H	H
ALL OTHER INPUT COMBINATIONS						L

H = high level
L = low level
X = irrelevant

SN75124 FUNCTION TABLE

INPUTS				OUTPUT
A	B†	R	S	Y
H	H	X	X	L
X	X	L	H	L
L	X	H	X	H
L	X	X	L	H
X	L	H	X	H
X	L	X	L	H

†B input and last two lines of the function table are applicable to receivers 1 and 2 only.

SN75123 schematic (each driver)

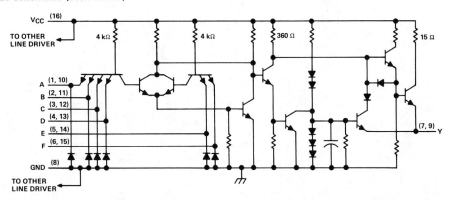

SN75124 schematic (each receiver)

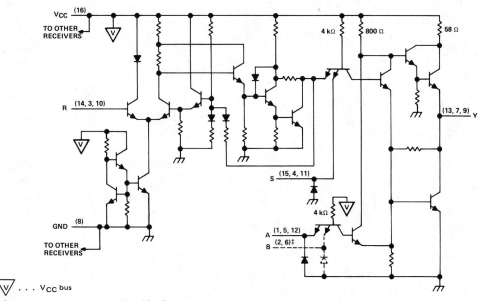

▽ . . . V_{CC} bus

‡B input is provided on receivers 1 and 2 only
Resistor values shown are nominal

TYPES SN75123, SN75124
DUAL LINE DRIVER AND TRIPLE LINE RECEIVER

SN75123 absolute maximum ratings over operating free-air temperature range (unless otherwise noted)

Supply voltage, V_{CC} (see Note 1) . . . . 7 V
Input voltage . . . . 5.5 V
Output voltage . . . . 7 V
Continuous total dissipation . . . . 800 mW
Operating free-air temperature range . . . . 0°C to 75°C
Storage temperature range . . . . −65°C to 150°C
Lead temperature 1/16 inch from case for 60 seconds: J package . . . . 300°C
Lead temperature 1/16 inch from case for 10 seconds: N package . . . . 260°C

SN75123 recommended operating conditions

	MIN	NOM	MAX	UNIT
Supply voltage, V_{CC}	4.75	5	5.25	V
High-level output current, I_{OH}			−100	mA
Operating free-air temperature, T_A	0		75	°C

SN75123 electrical characteristics, V_{CC} = 4.75 V to 5.25 V, T_A = 0°C to 75°C (unless otherwise noted)

PARAMETER		TEST CONDITIONS			MIN	TYP	MAX	UNIT
V_{IH}	High-level input voltage				2			V
V_{IL}	Low-level input voltage						0.8	V
V_I	Input clamp voltage	V_{CC} = 5 V,	I_I = −12 mA				−1.5	V
$V_{(BR)I}$	Input breakdown voltage	V_{CC} = 5 V,	I_I = 10 mA		5.5			V
V_{OH}	High-level output voltage	V_{CC} = 5 V,	V_{IH} = 2 V,	T_A = 25°C	3.11			V
		I_{OH} = −59.3 mA, See Note 2		T_A = 0°C to 75°C	2.9			
I_{OH}	High-level output current	V_{CC} = 5 V,	V_{IH} = 4.5 V,	V_{OH} = 2 V,	−100		−250	mA
		T_A = 25°C,	See Note 2					
V_{OL}	Low-level output voltage	V_{IL} = 0.8 V,	I_{OL} = −240 μA, See Note 2				0.15	V
$I_{O(off)}$	Off-state output current	V_{CC} = 0,	V_O = 3 V				40	μA
I_{IH}	High-level input current	V_I = 4.5 V					40	μA
I_{IL}	Low-level input current	V_I = 0.4 V			−0.1		−1.6	mA
I_{OS}	Short-circuit output current	V_{CC} = 5 V,	T_A = 25°C				−30	mA
I_{CCH}	Supply current, outputs high	V_{CC} = 5.25 V,	All inputs at 2 V,				28	mA
		Outputs open						
I_{CCL}	Supply current, outputs low	V_{CC} = 5.25 V,	All inputs at 0.8 V,				60	mA
		Outputs open						

SN75123 switching characteristics, V_{CC} = 5 V, T_A = 25°C

PARAMETER		TEST CONDITIONS	MIN	TYP	MAX	UNIT
t_{PLH}	Propagation delay time, low-to-high-level output	R_L = 50 Ω, C_L = 15 pF,		12	20	ns
t_{PHL}	Propagation delay time, high-to-low-level output	See Figure 1		12	20	
t_{PLH}	Propagation delay time, low-to-high-level output	R_L = 50 Ω, C_L = 100 pF,		20	35	ns
t_{PHL}	Propagation delay time, high-to-low-level output	See Figure 1		15	25	

NOTES: 1. Voltage values are with respect to network ground terminal.
2. The output voltage and current limits are guaranteed for any appropriate combination of high and low inputs specified by the function table for the desired output.

8

TEXAS INSTRUMENTS
INCORPORATED
POST OFFICE BOX 5012 • DALLAS, TEXAS 75222

SN75124 absolute maximum ratings over operating free-air temperature range (unless otherwise noted)

Supply voltage, V_{CC} (see Note 1) . . . . 7 V
Input voltage: R input with V_{CC} applied . . . . 7 V
              R input with V_{CC} not applied . . . . 6 V
              A, B, or S input . . . . 5.5 V
Output voltage . . . . 7 V
Output current . . . . ±100 mA
Continuous total dissipation . . . . 800 mW
Operating free-air temperature range . . . . 0°C to 75°C
Storage temperature range . . . . −65°C to 150°C
Lead temperature 1/16 inch from case for 60 seconds: J package . . . . 300°C
Lead temperature 1/16 inch from case for 10 seconds: N package . . . . 260°C

SN75124 recommended operating conditions

	MIN	NOM	MAX	UNIT
Supply voltage, V_{CC}	4.75	5	5.25	V
High-level output current, I_{OH}			−800	μA
Low-level output current, I_{OL}			16	mA
Operating free-air temperature, T_A	0		75	°C

SN75124 electrical characteristics, V_{CC} = 4.75 V to 5.25 V, T_A = 0°C to 75°C (unless otherwise noted)

PARAMETER		TEST CONDITIONS	MIN	TYP	MAX	UNIT
V_{IH} High-level input voltage	A,B, or S		2			V
	R		1.7			
V_{IL} Low-level input voltage	A,B, or S				0.8	V
	R				0.7	
$V_{T+}-V_{T-}$ Hysteresis[†]	R	V_{CC} = 5 V, T_A = 25°C	0.2	0.4		V
V_I Input clamp voltage	A,B, or S	V_{CC} = 5 V, I_I = −12 mA			−1.5	V
$V_{(BR)I}$ Input breakdown voltage	A,B, or S	V_{CC} = 5 V, I_I = 10 mA	5.5			V
V_{OH} High-level output voltage		V_{IH} = V_{IH} min, V_{IL} = V_{IL}max, I_{OH} = −800 μA, See Note 2	2.6			V
V_{OL} Low-level output voltage		V_{IH} = V_{IH} min, V_{IL} = V_{IL}max, I_{OL} = 16 mA, See Note 2			0.4	V
I_I Input current at maximum input voltage	R	V_I = 7 V			5	mA
	R	V_I = 6 V, V_{CC} = 0			5	
I_{IH} High-level input current	A,B, or S	V_I = 4.5 V			40	μA
	R	V_I = 3.11 V			170	
I_{IL} Low-level input current	A,B, or S	V_I = 0.4 V	−0.1		−1.6	mA
I_{OS} Short-circuit output current[‡]		V_{CC} = 5 V, T_A = 25°C	−50		−100	mA
I_{CC} Supply current		V_{CC} = 5.25 V			72	mA

[†]Hysteresis is the difference between the positive-going input threshold voltage, V_{T+}, and the negative-going input threshold voltage, V_{T-}. See Figure 4.
[‡]Not more than one output should be shorted at a time.

SN75124 switching characteristics, V_{CC} = 5 V, T_A = 25°C

PARAMETER	TEST CONDITIONS	MIN	TYP	MAX	UNIT
t_{PLH} Propagation delay time, low-to-high-level output from R input	See Figure 2		20	30	ns
t_{PHL} Propagation delay time, high-to-low-level output from R input			20	30	

NOTES: 1. Voltage values are with respect to network ground terminal.
      2. The output voltage and current limits are guaranteed for any appropriate combination of high and low inputs specified by the function table for the desired output.

TYPES SN75123, SN75124
DUAL LINE DRIVER AND TRIPLE LINE RECEIVER

PARAMETER MEASUREMENT INFORMATION

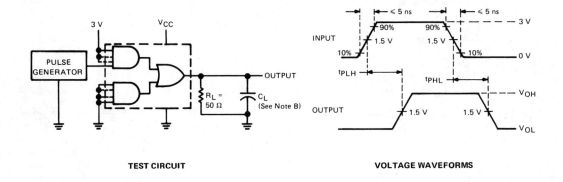

TEST CIRCUIT

VOLTAGE WAVEFORMS

FIGURE 1—SN75123 SWITCHING TIMES

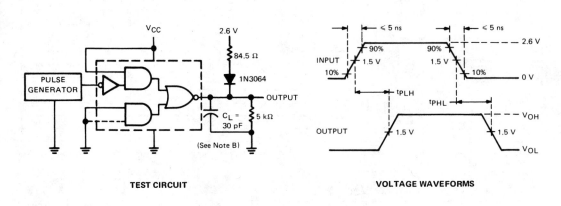

TEST CIRCUIT

VOLTAGE WAVEFORMS

FIGURE 2—SN75124 SWITCHING TIMES

NOTES: A. The pulse generator has the following characterisitcs: $Z_{out} \approx 50\ \Omega$, $t_w = 200$ ns, duty cycle = 50%.
B. C_L includes probe and jig capabitance.

TEXAS INSTRUMENTS
INCORPORATED
POST OFFICE BOX 5012 • DALLAS, TEXAS 75222

TYPICAL CHARACTERISTICS

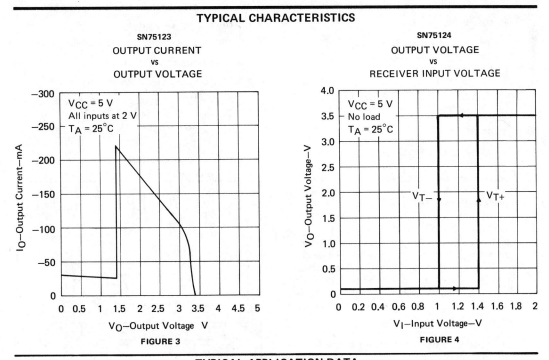

SN75123
OUTPUT CURRENT
vs
OUTPUT VOLTAGE

FIGURE 3

SN75124
OUTPUT VOLTAGE
vs
RECEIVER INPUT VOLTAGE

FIGURE 4

TYPICAL APPLICATION DATA

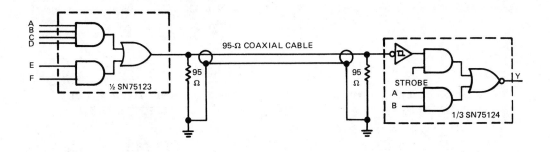

FIGURE 5

TEXAS INSTRUMENTS
INCORPORATED
POST OFFICE BOX 5012 • DALLAS, TEXAS 75222

- Single 5-V Supply
- High-Input-Impedance, High-Threshold Receivers
- Common Driver Strobe
- TTL/DTL Compatible Driver and Strobe Inputs with Clamp Diodes

- High-Speed Operation
- 100-mA Open-Collector Driver Outputs
- Four Independent Channels
- TTL Compatible Receiver Output
- Available in Plastic or Ceramic 16-Pin Dual-In-Line Packages

description

The SN55138 and SN75138 quad bus transceivers are designed for two-way data communication over single-ended transmission lines. Each of the four identical channels consists of a driver with TTL inputs and a receiver with a TTL output. The driver output is of the open-collector type, and is designed to handle loads of up to 100 milliamperes (50 ohms to 5 volts). The receiver input is internally connected to the driver output, and has a high impedance to minimize loading of the transmission line. Because of the high driver-output current and the high receiver-input impedance, a very large number (typically hundreds) of transceivers may be connected to a single data bus.

The receiver design also features a threshold of 2.3 volts (typical), providing a wider noise margin than would be possible with a receiver having the usual TTL threshold. A strobe turns off all drivers (high impedance) but does not affect receiver operation. These circuits are designed for operation from a single five-volt supply and include a provision to minimize loading of the data bus when the power-supply voltage is zero. The SN55138 is characterized for operation over the full military temperature range of −55°C to 125°C; the SN75138 is characterized for operation from 0°C to 70°C.

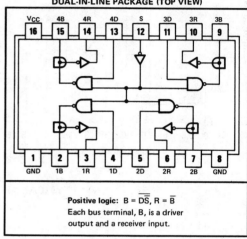

J OR N
DUAL-IN-LINE PACKAGE (TOP VIEW)

Positive logic: B = $\overline{DS}$, R = $\overline{B}$
Each bus terminal, B, is a driver output and a receiver input.

FUNCTION TABLE (TRANSMITTING)

INPUTS		OUTPUTS	
S	D	B	R
L	H	L	H
L	L	H	L

FUNCTION TABLE (RECEIVING)

INPUTS			OUTPUT
S	B	D	R
H	H	X	L
H	L	X	H

H = high level, L = low level, X = irrelevant

TEXAS INSTRUMENTS
INCORPORATED
POST OFFICE BOX 5012 • DALLAS, TEXAS 75222

absolute maximum ratings over operating free-air temperature range (unless otherwise noted)

Supply voltage, V_{CC} (see Note 1) . . . . 7 V
Input voltage . . . . 5.5 V
Low-level output current into the driver output . . . . 150 mA
Operating free-air temperature range: SN55138 . . . . −55°C to 125°C
                                SN75138 . . . . 0°C to 70°C
Storage temperature range . . . . −65°C to 150°C

NOTE 1: Voltage values are with respect to both ground terminals connected in parallel.

recommended operating conditions

		SN55138			SN75138			UNIT
		MIN	NOM	MAX	MIN	NOM	MAX	
Supply voltage, V_{CC}		4.5	5	5.5	4.75	5	5.25	V
Low-level output current, I_{OL}	Driver output			100			100	mA
	Receiver output			16			16	
High-level output current, I_{OH}	Receiver output			−400			−400	µA
Operating free-air temperature, T_A		−55		125	0		70	°C

electrical characteristics over recommended operating free-air temperature range (unless otherwise noted)

PARAMETER			TEST CONDITIONS†		SN55138			SN75138			UNIT
					MIN	TYP‡	MAX	MIN	TYP‡	MAX	
V_{IH}	High-level input voltage	Driver or strobe			2			2			V
		Receiver			3.2			2.9			
V_{IL}	Low-level input voltage	Driver or strobe					0.8			0.8	V
		Receiver					1.5			1.8	
V_I	Input clamp voltage	Driver or strobe	V_{CC} = MIN,	I_I = −12 mA			−1.5			−1.5	V
V_{OH}	High-level output voltage	Receiver	V_{CC} = MIN, $V_{IL(R)}$ = V_{IL} max,	$V_{IH(S)}$ = 2 V, I_{OH} = −400 µA	2.4	3.5		2.4	3.5		V
V_{OL}	Low-level output voltage	Driver	V_{CC} = MIN, $V_{IL(S)}$ = 0.8 V,	$V_{IH(D)}$ = 2 V, I_{OL} = 100 mA			0.45			0.45	V
		Receiver	V_{CC} = MIN, $V_{IH(S)}$ = 2 V,	$V_{IH(R)}$ = V_{IH} min, I_{OL} = 16 mA			0.4			0.4	
I_I	Input current at maximum input voltage	Driver or strobe	V_{CC} = MAX,	V_I = V_{CC}			1			1	mA
I_{IH}	High-level input current	Driver or strobe	V_{CC} = MAX,	V_I = 2.4 V			40			40	µA
		Receiver	V_{CC} = 5 V, $V_{I(S)}$ = 2 V	$V_{I(R)}$ = 4.5 V,		25	300		25	300	
I_{IL}	Low-level input current	Driver or strobe	V_{CC} = MAX,	V_I = 0.4 V		−1	−1.6		−1	−1.6	mA
		Receiver	V_{CC} = MAX, $V_{I(S)}$ = 2 V	$V_{I(R)}$ = 0.45 V,			−50			−50	µA
	Input current with power off	Receiver	V_{CC} = 0,	V_I = 4.5 V		1.1	1.5		1.1	1.5	mA
I_{OS}	Short-circuit output current§	Receiver	V_{CC} = MAX		−20		−55	−18		−55	mA
I_{CC}	Supply current	All driver outputs low	V_{CC} = MAX, $V_{I(S)}$ = 0.8 V	$V_{I(D)}$ = 2 V,		50	65		50	65	mA
		All driver outputs high	V_{CC} = MAX, $V_{I(S)}$ = 2 V, Receiver output open	$V_{I(R)}$ = 3.5 V,		42	55		42	55	

†For conditions shown as MIN or MAX, use the appropriate value specified under recommended operating conditions. Parenthetical letters D, R, and S used with V_I refer to the driver input, receiver input, and strobe input, respectively.
‡All typical values are at V_{CC} = 5 V, T_A = 25°C.
§Not more than one output should be shorted at a time.

8

TEXAS INSTRUMENTS
INCORPORATED
POST OFFICE BOX 5012 • DALLAS, TEXAS 75222

switching characteristics, V_{CC} = 5 V, T_A = 25°C

PARAMETER¶	FROM (INPUT)	TO (OUTPUT)	TEST CONDITIONS		MIN	TYP	MAX	UNIT
t_{PLH}	Driver	Driver	C_L = 50 pF,	R_L = 50 Ω,		15	24	ns
t_{PHL}	Driver	Driver	See Figure 1			14	24	ns
t_{PLH}	Strobe	Driver				18	28	ns
t_{PHL}	Strobe	Driver				22	32	ns
t_{PLH}	Receiver	Receiver	C_L = 15 pF,	R_L = 400 Ω,		7	15	ns
t_{PHL}	Receiver	Receiver	See Figure 2			8	15	ns

¶ t_{PLH} ≡ propagation delay time, low-to-high-level output
t_{PHL} ≡ propagation delay time, high-to-low-level output

schematics of inputs and outputs

EQUIVALENT OF EACH STROBE AND DRIVER INPUT	EQUIVALENT OF EACH RECEIVER INPUT	TYPICAL OF ALL DRIVER OUTPUTS	TYPICAL OF ALL RECEIVER OUTPUTS
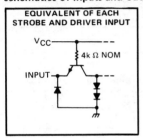	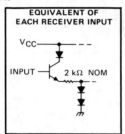	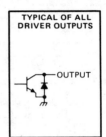	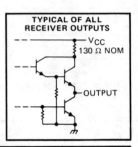

PARAMETER MEASUREMENT INFORMATION

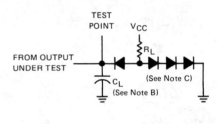

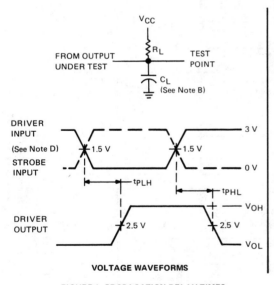

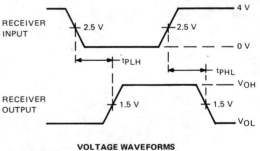

VOLTAGE WAVEFORMS

FIGURE 1–PROPAGATION DELAY TIMES FROM DATA AND STROBE INPUTS

VOLTAGE WAVEFORMS

FIGURE 2–PROPAGATION DELAY TIMES FROM RECEIVER INPUT

NOTES: A. Input pulses are supplied by generators having the following characteristics: t_w = 100 ns, PRR = 1 MHz, t_r ≤10 ns, t_f ≤10 ns, Z_{out} ≈ 50 Ω.
 B. C_L includes probe and jig capacitance.
 C. All diodes are 1N916 or 1N3064.
 D. When testing driver input (solid line) strobe must be low; when testing strobe input (dashed line) driver input must be high.

TEXAS INSTRUMENTS
INCORPORATED
POST OFFICE BOX 5012 • DALLAS, TEXAS 75222

TYPICAL APPLICATION DATA

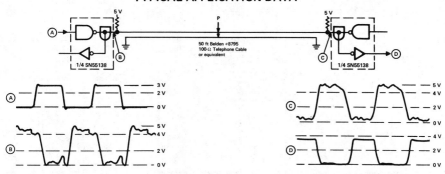

TYPICAL VOLTAGE WAVEFORMS

FIGURE 3—POINT-TO-POINT COMMUNICATION OVER 50 FEET OF TWISTED PAIR AT 5 MHz

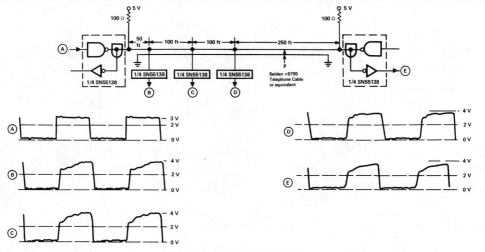

TYPICAL VOLTAGE WAVEFORMS

FIGURE 4—PARTY-LINE COMMUNICATION ON 500 FEET OF TWISTED PAIR AT 1 MHz

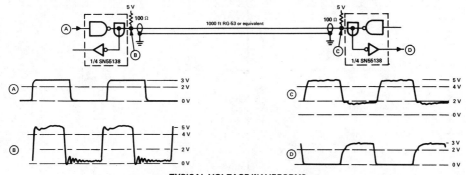

TYPICAL VOLTAGE WAVEFORMS

FIGURE 5—POINT-TO-POINT COMMUNICATION OVER 1000 FEET OF COAX AT 1 MHz

TYPICAL CHARACTERISTICS†

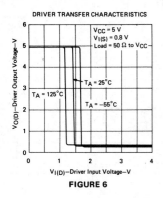

FIGURE 6

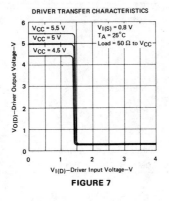

FIGURE 7

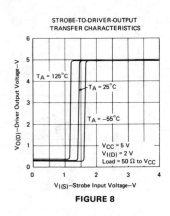

FIGURE 8

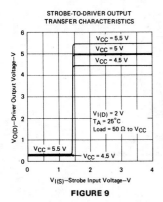

FIGURE 9

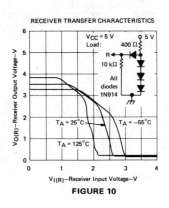

FIGURE 10

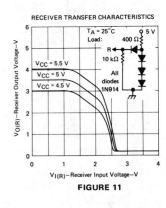

FIGURE 11

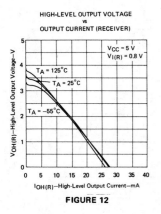

FIGURE 12

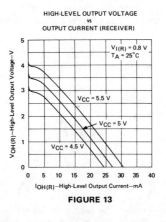

FIGURE 13

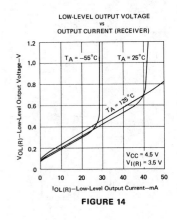

FIGURE 14

†Data for temperatures below 0°C and above 70°C is applicable to SN55138 circuits only.

TEXAS INSTRUMENTS
INCORPORATED
POST OFFICE BOX 5012 • DALLAS, TEXAS 75222

TYPICAL CHARACTERISTICS†

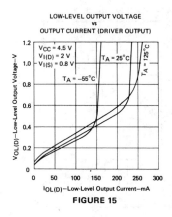

LOW-LEVEL OUTPUT VOLTAGE
vs
OUTPUT CURRENT (DRIVER OUTPUT)

FIGURE 15

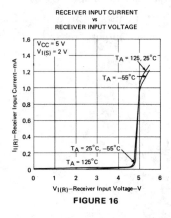

RECEIVER INPUT CURRENT
vs
RECEIVER INPUT VOLTAGE

FIGURE 16

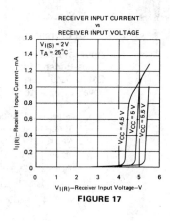

RECEIVER INPUT CURRENT
vs
RECEIVER INPUT VOLTAGE

FIGURE 17

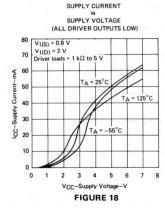

SUPPLY CURRENT
vs
SUPPLY VOLTAGE
(ALL DRIVER OUTPUTS LOW)

FIGURE 18

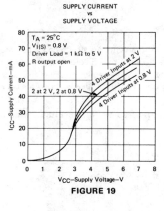

SUPPLY CURRENT
vs
SUPPLY VOLTAGE

FIGURE 19

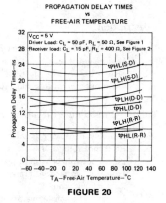

PROPAGATION DELAY TIMES
vs
FREE-AIR TEMPERATURE

FIGURE 20

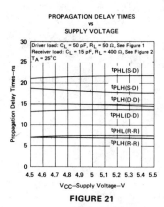

PROPAGATION DELAY TIMES
vs
SUPPLY VOLTAGE

FIGURE 21

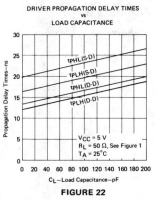

DRIVER PROPAGATION DELAY TIMES
vs
LOAD CAPACITANCE

FIGURE 22

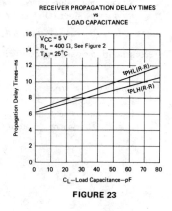

RECEIVER PROPAGATION DELAY TIMES
vs
LOAD CAPACITANCE

FIGURE 23

†Data for temperatures below 0°C and above 70°C is applicable to SN55138 circuits only.

TEXAS INSTRUMENTS
INCORPORATED
POST OFFICE BOX 5012 • DALLAS, TEXAS 75222

- Single 5-V Supply
- Adjustable Reference Voltage
- ± 100 mV Sensitivity
- TTL Outputs
- Low Input Current
- Common Output Strobe
- For Applications As:
  Single-Ended Line Receiver
  Gated Oscillator
  Level Comparator

P
DUAL-IN-LINE PACKAGE (TOP VIEW)

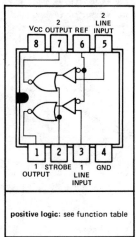

positive logic: see function table

FUNCTION TABLE
(EACH RECEIVER)

LINE INPUT	STROBE	OUTPUT
$V_{ref} - 100$ mV	L	H
$V_{ref} + 100$ mV	X	L
X	H	L

H = high level, L = low level, X = irrelevant

description

The SN75140 is a dual line receiver with a common strobe and a common reference. The reference voltage is applied externally and can be adjusted from 1.5 volts to 3.5 volts, making it possible to optimize noise immunity for a given system design. The SN75140 operates as a single-ended receiver and is particularly useful in TTL systems. Due to its low input current (less than 100 microamperes), it is ideally suited for party-line (bus-organized) systems.

absolute maximum ratings over operating free-air temperature range (unless otherwise noted)

Supply voltage, V_{CC} (see Note 1)	7 V
Reference voltage, V_{ref}	5.5 V
Line input voltage with respect to ground	-2 V to 5.5 V
Line input voltage with respect to V_{ref}	±5 V
Strobe input voltage	5.5 V
Operating free-air temperature range	$0°C$ to $70°C$
Storage temperature range	$-65°C$ to $150°C$
Lead temperature 1/16 inch from case for 10 seconds	$260°C$

NOTE 1: Unless otherwise specified, voltage values are with respect to network ground terminal.

recommended operating conditions

	MIN	NOM	MAX	UNIT
Supply voltage, V_{CC}	4.5	5	5.5	V
Reference voltage, V_{ref}	1.5		3.5	V
Input voltage, line or strobe, V_I	0		5.5	V
Operating free-air temperature, T_A	0		70	$°C$

TEXAS INSTRUMENTS
INCORPORATED
POST OFFICE BOX 5012 • DALLAS, TEXAS 75222

electrical characteristics over recommended operating free-air temperature range,
V_{CC} = 5 V ± 10%, V_{ref} = 1.5 V to 3.5 V (unless otherwise noted)

	PARAMETER		TEST CONDITIONS		MIN	TYP[†]	MAX	UNIT
$V_{IH(L)}$	High-level line input voltage				V_{ref} + 100			mV
$V_{IL(L)}$	Low-level line input voltage						V_{ref} − 100	mV
$V_{IH(S)}$	High-level strobe input voltage				2			V
$V_{IL(S)}$	Low-level strobe input voltage						0.8	V
V_{OH}	High-level output voltage		$V_{IL(L)} = V_{ref} − 100$ mV, $V_{IL(S)} = 0.8$ V, $I_{OH} = −400 \mu A$		2.4			V
V_{OL}	Low-level output voltage		$V_{IH(L)} = V_{ref} + 100$ mV, $V_{IL(S)} = 0.8$ V, $I_{OL} = 16$ mA				0.4	V
			$V_{IL(L)} = V_{ref} − 100$ mV, $V_{IH(S)} = 2$ V, $I_{OL} = 16$ mA				0.4	
$V_{I(S)}$	Strobe input clamp voltage		$I_{I(S)} = −12$ mA				−1.5	V
$I_{I(S)}$	Strobe input current at maximum input voltage		$V_{I(S)} = 5.5$ V				2	mA
I_{IH}	High-level input current	Strobe	$V_{I(S)} = 2.4$ V				80	μA
		Line	$V_{I(L)} = V_{CC}$,	$V_{ref} = 1.5$ V		35	100	
		Reference	$V_{ref} = 3.5$ V,	$V_{I(L)} = 1.5$ V		70	200	
I_{IL}	Low-level input current	Strobe	$V_{I(S)} = 0.4$ V				−3.2	mA
		Line	$V_{I(L)} = 0$ V,	$V_{ref} = 1.5$ V			−10	μA
		Reference	$V_{ref} = 0$ V,	$V_{I(L)} = 1.5$ V			−20	μA
I_{OS}	Short-circuit output current‡		$V_{CC} = 5.5$ V		−18		−55	mA
I_{CCH}	Supply current, output high		$V_{I(S)} = 0$ V,	$V_{I(L)} = V_{ref} − 100$ mV		18	30	mA
I_{CCL}	Supply current, output low		$V_{I(S)} = 0$ V,	$V_{I(L)} = V_{ref} + 100$ mV		20	35	mA

[†] All typical values are at V_{CC} = 5 V, $T_A = 25°C$.
‡Only one output should be shorted at a time.

switching characteristics, V_{CC} = 5 V, V_{ref} = 2.5 V, $T_A = 25°C$

	PARAMETER	TEST CONDITIONS	MIN	TYP	MAX	UNIT
$t_{PLH(L)}$	Propagation delay time, low-to-high-level output from line input			22	35	ns
$t_{PHL(L)}$	Propagation delay time, high-to-low-level output from line input	$C_L = 15$ pF, $R_L = 400 \Omega$, See Figure 1		22	30	
$t_{PLH(S)}$	Propagation delay time, low-to-high-level output from strobe input			12	22	ns
$t_{PHL(S)}$	Propagation delay time, high-to-low-level output from strobe input			8	15	

8

TYPE SN75140
DUAL LINE RECEIVER

schematic (each receiver)

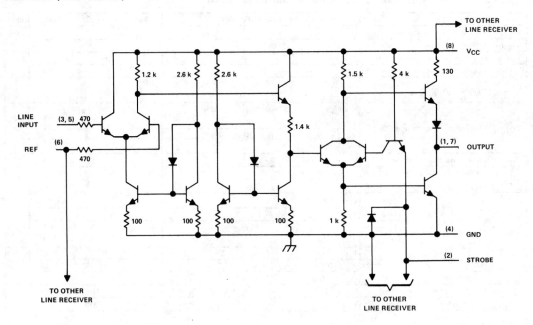

Resistor values shown are nominal in ohms.

PARAMETER MEASUREMENT INFORMATION

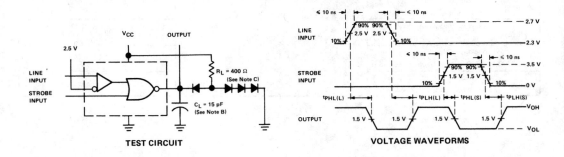

TEST CIRCUIT

VOLTAGE WAVEFORMS

NOTES: A. Input pulses are supplied by generators having the following characteristics: PRR = 1 MHz, duty cycle ≤ 50%, $Z_{out} \approx 50\ \Omega$.
   B. C_L includes probe and jig capacitance.
   C. All diodes are 1N3064.

FIGURE 1

TEXAS INSTRUMENTS
INCORPORATED
POST OFFICE BOX 5012 • DALLAS, TEXAS 75222

TYPICAL CHARACTERISTICS

OUTPUT VOLTAGE
vs
LINE INPUT VOLTAGE

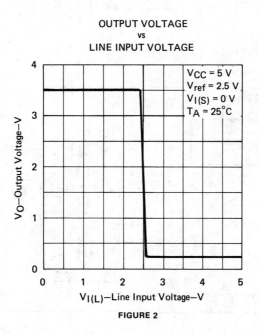

FIGURE 2

TYPE SN75140
DUAL LINE RECEIVER

TYPICAL APPLICATION DATA

line receiver

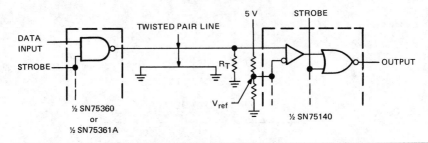

high fan-out from standard TTL gate

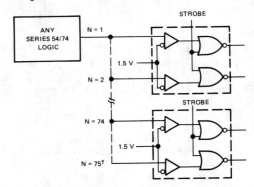

†Although most Series 54/74 circuits have a guaranteed 2.4-V output at 400 μA, they are typically capable of maintaining a 2.4-V output level under a load of 7.5 mA.

dual bus transceiver

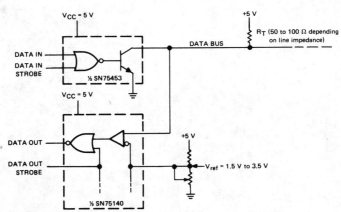

Using this arrangement, as many as 100 transceivers can be connected to a single data bus. The adjustable reference voltage feature allows the noise margin to be optimized for a given system. The complete dual bus transceiver can be assembled in the space required by a single 16-pin package, and only one power supply is required (+5 V). Data In and Data Out terminals are TTL compatible.

TEXAS INSTRUMENTS
INCORPORATED
POST OFFICE BOX 5012 • DALLAS, TEXAS 75222

TYPICAL APPLICATION DATA

schmitt trigger

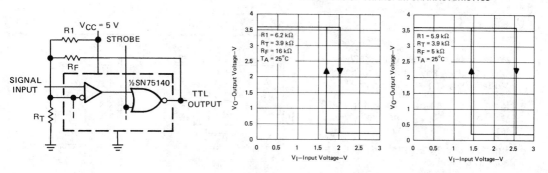

EXAMPLES OF TRANSFER CHARACTERISTICS

Slowly changing input levels from data lines, optical detectors, and other types of transducers may be converted to standard TTL signals with this Schmitt trigger circuit. R1, R_F and R_T may be adjusted for the desired hysteresis and trigger levels.

gated oscillator

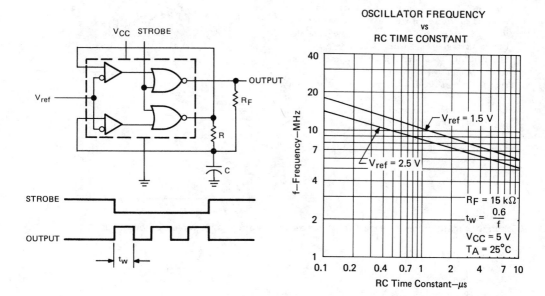

PRINTED IN U.S.A.

TI cannot assume any responsibility for any circuits shown
or represent that they are free from patent infringement.

TEXAS INSTRUMENTS RESERVES THE RIGHT TO MAKE CHANGES AT ANY TIME
IN ORDER TO IMPROVE DESIGN AND TO SUPPLY THE BEST PRODUCT POSSIBLE.

TEXAS INSTRUMENTS
INCORPORATED
POST OFFICE BOX 5012 • DALLAS, TEXAS 75222

SATISFIES REQUIREMENTS OF EIA STANDARD RS-232-C

- **Withstands Sustained Output Short-Circuit to any Low-Impedance Voltage between −25 V and 25 V**

- **2 μs Max Transition Time through the +3 V to −3 V Transition Region under Full 2500-pF Load**

- **Inputs Compatible with Most TTL and DTL Families**

- **Common Strobe Input**

- **Inverting Output**

- **Slew Rate can be Controlled with an External Capacitor at the Output**

- **Standard Supply Voltages . . . ±12 V**

J OR N
DUAL-IN-LINE PACKAGE
(TOP VIEW)

	OUTPUT	OUTPUT				
NC	VCC+	1Y	2Y	VCC−	NC	NC
14	13	12	11	10	9	8
1	2	3	4	5	6	7
NC	STROBE S	INPUT 1A	INPUT 2A	GND	NC	NC

P
DUAL-IN-LINE PACKAGE
(TOP VIEW)

	OUTPUT	OUTPUT	
VCC+	1Y	2Y	VCC−
8	7	6	5
1	2	3	4
STROBE S	INPUT 1A	INPUT 2A	GND

positive logic: Y = $\overline{AS}$

NC—No internal connection

description

The SN75150 is a monolithic dual line driver designed to satisfy the requirements of the standard interface between data terminal equipment and data communication equipment as defined by EIA Standard RS-232-C. A rate of 20,000 bits per second can be transmitted with a full 2500-pF load. Other applications are in data-transmission systems using relatively short single lines, in level translators, and for driving MOS devices. The logic input is compatible with most TTL and DTL families. Operation is from +12-volt and −12-volt power supplies. The SN75150 is characterized for operation from 0°C to 70°C.

schematic (each line driver)

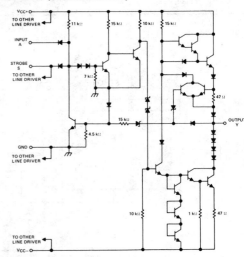

Component values shown are nominal.

absolute maximum ratings over operating free-air temperature range (unless otherwise noted)

Supply voltage V_{CC+} (see Note 1) . . . . 15 V
Supply voltage $V_{CC−}$ (see Note 1) . . . . −15 V
Input voltage (see Note 1) . . . . 15 V
Applied output voltage (see Note 1) . . . . ±25 V
Operating free-air temperature range . . . . 0°C to 70°C
Storage temperature range . . . . −65°C to 150°C

NOTE 1: Voltage values are with respect to network ground terminal.

TEXAS INSTRUMENTS
INCORPORATED
POST OFFICE BOX 5012 • DALLAS, TEXAS 75222

recommended operating conditions

	MIN	NOM	MAX	UNIT
Supply voltage V_{CC+}	10.8	12	13.2	V
Supply voltage V_{CC-}	−10.8	−12	−13.2	V
Input voltage, V_I	0		5.5	V
Applied output voltage, V_O			±15	V
Operating free-air temperature, T_A	0		70	°C

electrical characteristics over recommended operating free-air temperature range (unless otherwise noted)

PARAMETER		TEST FIGURE	TEST CONDITIONS		MIN	TYP† (SEE NOTE 2)	MAX	UNIT
V_{IH}	High-level input voltage	1			2			V
V_{IL}	Low-level input voltage	2					0.8	V
V_{OH}	High-level output voltage	2	$V_{CC+} = 10.8$ V, $V_{CC-} = -13.2$ V, $V_{IL} = 0.8$ V, $R_L = 3$ kΩ to 7 kΩ		5	8		V
V_{OL}	Low-level output voltage	1	$V_{CC+} = 10.8$ V, $V_{CC-} = -10.8$ V, $V_{IH} = 2$ V, $R_L = 3$ kΩ to 7 kΩ			−8	−5	V
I_{IH}	High-level input current	3	$V_{CC+} = 13.2$ V, $V_{CC-} = -13.2$ V, $V_I = 2.4$ V	Data input		1	10	μA
				Strobe input		2	20	
I_{IL}	Low-level input current	3	$V_{CC+} = 13.2$ V, $V_{CC-} = -13.2$ V, $V_I = 0.4$ V	Data input		−1	−1.6	mA
				Strobe input		−2	−3.2	
I_{OS}	Short-circuit output current	4	$V_{CC+} = 13.2$ V, $V_{CC-} = -13.2$ V	$V_O = 25$ V		2		mA
				$V_O = -25$ V		−3		
				$V_O = 0$ V, $V_I = 3$ V		15		
				$V_O = 0$ V, $V_I = 0$ V		−15		
I_{CCH+}	Supply current from V_{CC+}, high-level output	5	$V_{CC+} = 13.2$ V, $V_{CC-} = -13.2$ V, $V_I = 0$ V, $R_L = 3$ kΩ, $T_A = 25$°C			10	22	mA
I_{CCH-}	Supply current from V_{CC-}, high-level output					−1	−10	mA
I_{CCL+}	Supply current from V_{CC+}, low-level output	5	$V_{CC+} = 13.2$ V, $V_{CC-} = -13.2$ V, $V_I = 3$ V, $R_L = 3$ kΩ, $T_A = 25$°C			8	17	mA
I_{CCL-}	Supply current from V_{CC-}, low-level output					−9	−20	mA

NOTE 2: The algebraic convention where the most-positive (least-negative) limit is designated as maximum is used in this data sheet for logic levels only, e.g., when −5 V is the maximum, the typical value is a more-negative voltage.

† All typical values are at $V_{CC+} = 12$ V, $V_{CC-} = -12$ V, $T_A = 25$°C.

switching characteristics, $V_{CC+} = 12$ V, $V_{CC-} = -12$ V, $T_A = 25$°C

PARAMETER		TEST FIGURE	TEST CONDITIONS	MIN	TYP	MAX	UNIT
t_{TLH}	Transition time, low-to-high-level output	6	$C_L = 2500$ pF, $R_L = 3$ kΩ to 7 kΩ	0.2	1.4	2	μs
t_{THL}	Transition time, high-to-low-level output			0.2	1.5	2	μs
t_{TLH}	Transition time, low-to-high-level output	6	$C_L = 15$ pF, $R_L = 7$ kΩ		40		ns
t_{THL}	Transition time, high-to-low-level output				20		ns
t_{PLH}	Propagation delay time, low-to-high-level output	6	$C_L = 15$ pF, $R_L = 7$ kΩ		60		ns
t_{PHL}	Propagation delay time, high-to-low-level output				45		ns

8

PARAMETER MEASUREMENT INFORMATION

d-c test circuits‡

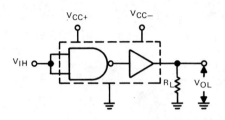

FIGURE 1–V_{IH}, V_{OL}

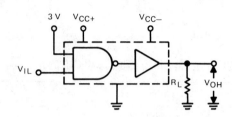

Each input is tested separately.

FIGURE 2–V_{IL}, V_{OH}

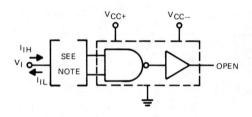

NOTE: When testing I_{IH}, the other input is at 3 V; when testing I_{IL}, the other input is open.

FIGURE 3–I_{IH}, I_{IL}

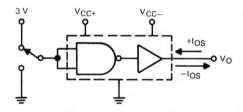

I_{OS} is tested for both input conditions at each of the specified output conditions.

FIGURE 4–I_{OS}

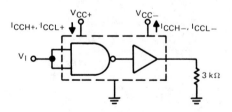

FIGURE 5–I_{CCH+}, I_{CCH-}, I_{CCL+}, I_{CCL-}

‡Arrows indicate actual direction of current flow. Current into a terminal is a positive value.

TEXAS INSTRUMENTS
INCORPORATED
POST OFFICE BOX 5012 • DALLAS, TEXAS 75222

PARAMETER MEASUREMENT INFORMATION

switching characteristics

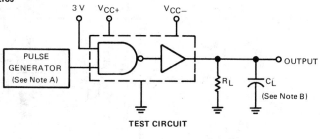

TEST CIRCUIT

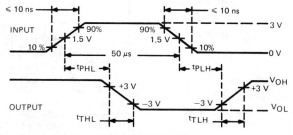

VOLTAGE WAVEFORMS

NOTES: A. The pulse generator has the following characteristics: duty cycle $\leqslant$ 50%, $Z_{out} \approx 50\ \Omega$.
   B. C_L includes probe and jig capacitance.

FIGURE 6—SWITCHING CHARACTERISTICS

TYPICAL CHARACTERISTICS

OUTPUT CURRENT

vs

APPLIED OUTPUT VOLTAGE

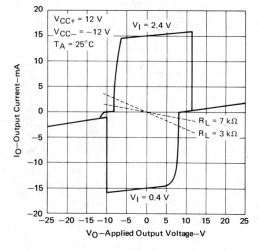

FIGURE 7

TEXAS INSTRUMENTS
INCORPORATED
POST OFFICE BOX 5012 • DALLAS, TEXAS 75222

- Meets Specifications of EIA RS-232-C or MIL-STD-188C[†]
- Dual Differential Receiver with Independent Strobes
- Common-Mode Input Voltage Range . . . ±25 V
- Differential Input Capability with One Input Grounded . . . ±25 V
- Continuously Adjustable Hysteresis with External Resistors
- Standard Supply Voltages . . . +12 V and −12 V
- Input Hysteresis (Double Thresholds) Remain Approximately Fixed for Power Supply and/or Temperature Variations

J OR N
DUAL-IN-LINE PACKAGE (TOP VIEW)

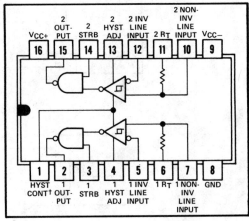

[†]To meet the specifications of EIA Standard RS-232-C, connect Hysteresis Control (Pin 1) to V_{CC-} (Pin 9). Also, connect pin 6 to pin 5 and pin 11 to pin 12. To meet the specifications of MIL-STD-188, leave Hysteresis Control (pin 1) and termination resistors (pin 6 and 11) open.

description

The SN75152 is a dual differential line receiver designed to meet the requirements of EIA standard RS-232-C or MIL-STD-188 interfaces. A single control (pin 1) sets the input hysteresis for the required operation. An added feature is the capability of adjusting the hysteresis to any voltage between ± 0.3 volt typical and ± 5 volts typical by means of the hysteresis adjust terminals (pin 4 and 13) making the SN75152 useful for a wide variety of line receiver and Schmitt trigger applications. The large common-mode input voltage range and differential input voltage (± 25 volts) give the circuit added versatility. The SN75152 is designed for operation from standard ± 12-volt supplies with ± 10% variation. Each receiver has an output strobe that is TTL compatible.

FUNCTION TABLE
(EACH RECEIVER)

LINE INPUT	STROBE	OUTPUT
H	H	H
L	H	L
X	L	H

Definition of logic levels:

For the strobe: H (high) is any voltage between V_{IH} min and V_{CC}.
L (low) is any voltage between ground and V_{IL} max.

For the line input: H (high) is any differential input voltage (V_{ID})[‡] more positive than V_{T-}, once the level of V_{T+} has been reached.
L (low) is any differential input voltage (V_{ID})[‡] more negative than V_{T+}, once the level of V_{T-} has been reached.
X (irrelevant) is any input voltage permitted by maximum ratings.

[‡]Differential input voltages $(V_T$ and $V_{ID})$ are at the noninverting input terminal with respect to the inverting input terminal.

TEXAS INSTRUMENTS
INCORPORATED
POST OFFICE BOX 5012 • DALLAS, TEXAS 75222

absolute maximum ratings over operating free-air temperature range (unless otherwise noted)

Supply voltage V_{CC+} (see Note 1)	15 V
Supply voltage V_{CC-} (see Note 1)	−15 V
Voltage at any line input with respect to other line input, ground, or R_T terminal	±25 V
R_T terminal voltage (see Note 1)	±25 V
Strobe input voltage (see Note 1)	5.5 V
Operating free-air temperature range	0°C to 70°C
Storage temperature range	−65°C to 150°C
Lead temperature 1/16 inch from case for 60 seconds: J package	300°C
Lead temperature 1/16 inch from case for 10 seconds: N package	260°C

NOTE 1: These voltage values are with respect to network ground terminal.

electrical characteristics over operating free-air temperature range, V_{CC+} = 12 V ± 10%, V_{CC-} = −12 V ± 10% (unless otherwise noted)

PARAMETER		TEST FIGURE	TEST CONDITIONS‡	MIN	TYP§ (SEE NOTE 2)	MAX	UNIT
V_{T+}	Positive-going threshold voltage	See Figure 8	1	MIL-STD-188 Conditions	0.1	0.3	0.5	V
V_{T-}	Negative-going threshold voltage				−0.5	−0.3	−0.1	
V_{T+}	Positive-going threshold voltage		2	EIA RS-232-C Conditions	1.5	2.2	3	V
V_{T-}	Negative-going threshold voltage				−3	−2.2	−1.5	
V_{IH}	High-level input voltage at strobe		1		2			V
V_{IL}	Low-level input voltage at strobe		1				0.8	V
V_{OH}	High-level output voltage		1 and 2	V_{ID} = V_{T+} max, $V_{I(strobe)}$ = 2 V, I_{OH} = −500 µA	3	4.1	6	V
			1 and 2	V_{ID} = V_{T-} min, $V_{I(strobe)}$ = 0.8 V, I_{OH} = −500 µA	3	4.1	6	
V_{OL}	Low level output voltage		1 and 2	V_{ID} = V_{T-} min, $V_{I(strobe)}$ = 2 V, I_{OL} = 6.4 mA	0	0.15	0.4	V
I_I	Input current into strobe at maximum strobe voltage		3	$V_{I(strobe)}$ = 5.5 V		0.1	1	mA
I_{IH}	High-level strobe current		3	$V_{I(strobe)}$ = 2.4 V		30	80	µA
I_{IL}	Low-level strobe current		3	$V_{I(strobe)}$ = 0.4 V		−0.5	−1.5	mA
r_I	Input resistance	MIL-STD-188	4	$|V_{ID}|$ = 0 V to 25 V, R_T open	6	9		kΩ
		EIA RS-232-C	4	$|V_{ID}|$ = 3 V to 25 V, R_T connected to inverting line input	3	5	7	
$V_{I(open)}$	Open-circuit input voltage		5			+1	±2	V
I_{OS}	Short-circuit output current		6	V_{ID} = 3 V		−1.9	−4	mA
I_{CC+}	Supply current from V_{CC+}		1	V_{ID} = −3 V, $V_{I(strobe)}$ = 2.4 V		10	16	mA
I_{CC-}	Supply current from V_{CC-}		1	V_{ID} = −3 V, $V_{I(strobe)}$ = 2.4 V		−7	−13	mA

‡Differential input voltages (V_T and V_{ID}) are at the noninverting line input terminal with respect to the inverting line input terminal.

§Typical values are at V_{CC+} = 12 V, V_{CC-} = −12 V, T_A = 25°C.

NOTE 2: The algebraic convention where the most-positive (least-negative) limit is designated as maximum is used in this data sheet for threshold levels only, e.g., when −0.1 V is the maximum, the minimum limit is a more-negative voltage.

switching characteristics, V_{CC+} = 12 V, V_{CC-} = −12 V, T_A = 25°C

PARAMETER		TEST FIGURE	TEST CONDITIONS	MIN	TYP	MAX	UNIT
t_{PLH}	Propagation delay time, low-to-high-level output	7	C_L = 15 pF		40		ns
t_{PHL}	Propagation delay time, high-to-low-level output				60		ns

8

TYPE SN75152
DUAL LINE RECEIVER

PARAMETER MEASUREMENT INFORMATION

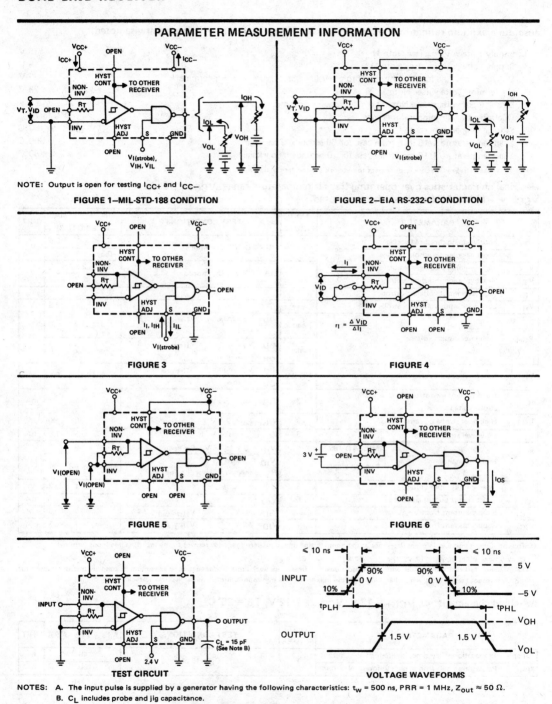

NOTE: Output is open for testing I_{CC+} and I_{CC-}

FIGURE 1—MIL-STD-188 CONDITION

FIGURE 2—EIA RS-232-C CONDITION

FIGURE 3

$$r_I = \frac{\Delta V_{ID}}{\Delta I_I}$$

FIGURE 4

FIGURE 5

FIGURE 6

TEST CIRCUIT

VOLTAGE WAVEFORMS

NOTES: A. The input pulse is supplied by a generator having the following characteristics: t_w = 500 ns, PRR = 1 MHz, Z_{out} ≈ 50 Ω.

B. C_L includes probe and jig capacitance.

FIGURE 7—PROPAGATION DELAY TIMES

TEXAS INSTRUMENTS
INCORPORATED
POST OFFICE BOX 5012 • DALLAS, TEXAS 75222

TYPICAL CHARACTERISTICS

OUTPUT VOLTAGE
vs
DIFFERENTIAL INPUT VOLTAGE

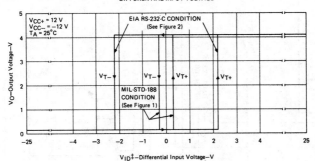

FIGURE 8

THRESHOLD VOLTAGE VARIATION
vs
POSITIVE SUPPLY VOLTAGE

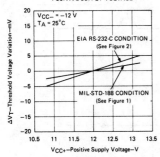

FIGURE 9

THRESHOLD VOLTAGE VARIATION
vs
NEGATIVE POWER SUPPLY

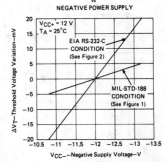

FIGURE 10

THRESHOLD VOLTAGE
vs
HYSTERESIS ADJUST RESISTANCE

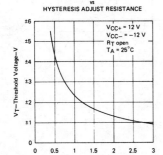

FIGURE 11

PROPAGATION DELAY TIME
vs
FREE-AIR TEMPERATURE

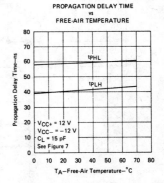

FIGURE 12

‡Differential input voltages (V_T and V_{ID}) are at the noninverting input terminal with respect to the inverting input terminal.
¶R_{adj} is connected between Hysteresis Adjust terminal and V_{CC-}.

TEXAS INSTRUMENTS
INCORPORATED
POST OFFICE BOX 5012 • DALLAS, TEXAS 75222

TYPE SN75152
DUAL LINE RECEIVER

schematic (each receiver)

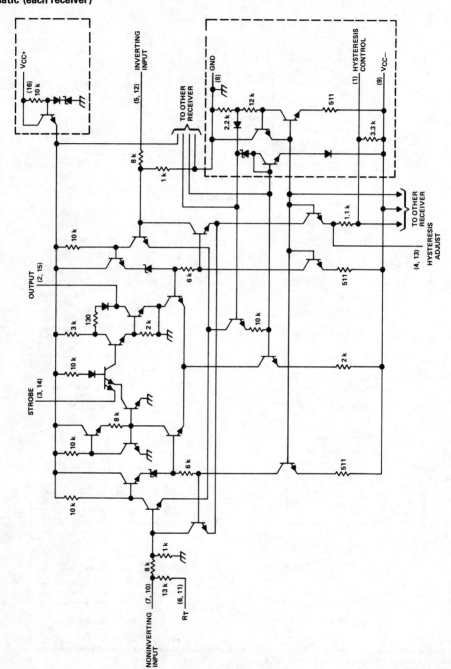

Portions of circuit within dashed lines are common to both receivers.
Resistor values shown are nominal and in ohms.

TEXAS INSTRUMENTS
INCORPORATED
POST OFFICE BOX 5012 • DALLAS, TEXAS 75222

TYPICAL APPLICATIONS

Some typical applications of the SN75152 are as follows:

- MIL-STD-188 Interface Receiver
- EIA RS-232-C Interface Receiver
- Single-Ended Line Receiver
- Differential Line Receiver
- High-Noise-Immunity Line Receiver
- Schmitt Trigger
- High-Voltage-Logic-to-TTL Translator
- MOS to TTL Converter
- Pulse Generator
- Threshold detector
- Pulse Shaper

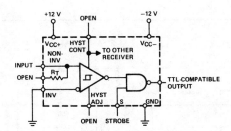

MIL-STD-188 SINGLE-ENDED LINE RECEIVER

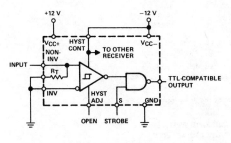

NORMAL OPERATION

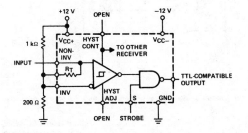

FAIL-SAFE OPERATION

EIA RS-232-C SINGLE-ENDED LINE RECEIVER

TEXAS INSTRUMENTS
INCORPORATED
POST OFFICE BOX 5012 • DALLAS, TEXAS 75222

TYPE SN75152
DUAL LINE RECEIVER

TYPICAL APPLICATIONS

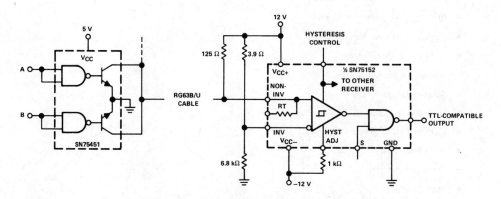

**SINGLE-ENDED TRANSMISSION WITH DRIVER "OR" CAPABILITY AND
RECEIVER WITH ADJUSTABLE NOISE IMMUNITY**

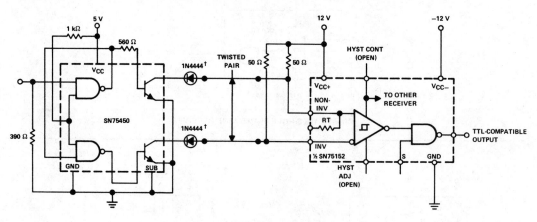

Frequency to 0.5 MHz
Common-Mode Voltage . . . −12 V to +10 V

†The 1N4444 diodes are required only for negative common-mode protection at the driver outputs.

**BALANCED LINE TRANSMISSION WITH
HIGH COMMON-MODE-VOLTAGE CAPABILITY**

TEXAS INSTRUMENTS
INCORPORATED
POST OFFICE BOX 5012 • DALLAS, TEXAS 75222

SATISFIES REQUIREMENTS OF EIA STANDARD RS-232-C

- **Input Resistance . . . 3 kΩ to 7 kΩ over Full RS-232-C Voltage Range**

- **Input Threshold Adjustable to Meet "Fail-Safe" Requirements Without Using External Components**

- **Built-In Hysteresis for Increased Noise Immunity**

- **Inverting Output Compatible with DTL or TTL**

- **Output with Active Pull-Up for Symmetrical Switching Speeds**

- **Standard Supply Voltages . . . 5 V or 12 V**

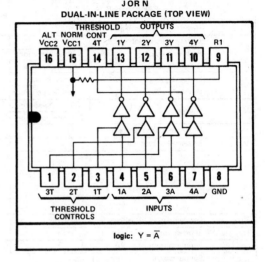

description

The SN75154 is a monolithic quadruple line receiver designed to satisfy the requirements of the standard interface between data terminal equipment and data communication equipment as defined by EIA Standard RS-232C. Other applications are for relatively short, single-line, point-to-point data transmission and for level translators. Operation is normally from a single five-volt supply; however, a built-in option allows operation from a 12-volt supply without the use of additional components. The output is compatible with most TTL and DTL circuits when either supply voltage is used.

In normal operation, the threshold-control terminals are connected to the V_{CC1} terminal, pin 15, even if power is being supplied via the alternate V_{CC2} terminal, pin 16. This provides a wide hysteresis loop which is the difference between the positive-going and negative-going threshold voltages. See typical characteristics. In this mode of operation, if the input voltage goes to zero, the output voltage will remain at the low or high level as determined by the previous input.

For fail-safe operation, the threshold-control terminals are open. This reduces the hysteresis loop by causing the negative-going threshold voltage to be above zero. The positive-going threshold voltage remains above zero as it is unaffected by the disposition of the threshold terminals. In the fail-safe mode, if the input voltage goes to zero or an open-circuit condition, the output will go to the high level regardless of the previous input condition.

The SN75154 is characterized for operation from 0°C to 70°C.

absolute maximum ratings over operating free-air temperature range (unless otherwise noted)

Normal supply voltage (pin 15), V_{CC1} (see Note 1)	7 V
Alternate supply voltage (pin 16), V_{CC2} (see Note 1)	14 V
Input voltage (see Note 1)	±25 V
Operating free-air temperature range	0°C to 70°C
Storage temperature range	−65°C to 150°C

NOTE 1: Voltage values are with respect to the network ground terminal.

recommended operating conditions

	MIN	NOM	MAX	UNIT
Normal supply voltage (pin 15), V_{CC1}	4.5	5	5.5	V
Alternate supply voltage (pin 16), V_{CC2}	10.8	12	13.2	V
Input voltage			±15	V
Normalized fan-out from each output, N			10	
Operating free-air temperature, T_A	0		70	°C

TEXAS INSTRUMENTS
INCORPORATED
POST OFFICE BOX 5012 • DALLAS, TEXAS 75222

TYPE SN75154
QUADRUPLE LINE RECEIVER

electrical characteristics over recommended operating free-air temperature range (unless otherwise noted)

	PARAMETER		TEST FIGURE	TEST CONDITIONS	MIN	TYP‡ (SEE NOTE 2)	MAX	UNIT
V_{IH}	High-level input voltage		1		3			V
V_{IL}	Low-level input voltage		1				−3	V
V_{T+}	Positive-going threshold voltage	Normal operation	1		0.8	2.2	3	V
		Fail-safe operation			0.8	2.2	3	
V_{T-}	Negative-going threshold voltage	Normal operation	1		−3	−1.1	0	V
		Fail-safe operation			0.8	1.4	3	
$V_{T+}-V_{T-}$	Hysteresis	Normal operation	1		0.8	3.3	6	V
		Fail-safe operation			0	0.8	2.2	
V_{OH}	High-level output voltage		1	$I_{OH} = -400 \mu A$	2.4	3.5		V
V_{OL}	Low-level output voltage		1	$I_{OL} = 16 mA$		0.23	0.4	V
r_I	Input resistance		2	$\Delta V_I = -25 V$ to $-14 V$	3	5	7	kΩ
				$\Delta V_I = -14 V$ to $-3 V$	3	5	7	
				$\Delta V_I = -3 V$ to $3 V$	3	6		
				$\Delta V_I = 3 V$ to $14 V$	3	5	7	
				$\Delta V_I = 14 V$ to $25 V$	3	5	7	
$V_{I(open)}$	Open-circuit input voltage		3	$I_I = 0$	0	0.2	2	V
I_{OS}	Short-circuit output current†		4	$V_{CC1} = 5.5 V$, $V_I = -5 V$	−10	−20	−40	mA
I_{CC1}	Supply current from V_{CC1}		5	$V_{CC1} = 5.5 V$, $T_A = 25°C$		20	35	mA
I_{CC2}	Supply current from V_{CC2}			$V_{CC2} = 13.2 V$, $T_A = 25°C$		23	40	

†Not more than one output should be shorted at a time.

‡ All typical values are at $V_{CC1} = 5$ V, $T_A = 25°C$.

NOTE 2: The algebraic convention where the most-positive (least-negative) limit is designated as maximum is used in this data sheet for logic and threshold levels only, e.g., when −3 V is the maximum, the minimum limit is a more-negative voltage.

switching characteristics, $V_{CC1} = 5$ V, $T_A = 25°C$, N = 10

	PARAMETER	TEST FIGURE	TEST CONDITIONS	MIN	TYP	MAX	UNIT
t_{PLH}	Propagation delay time, low-to-high-level output	6	$C_L = 50 pF$, $R_L = 390 \Omega$		22		ns
t_{PHL}	Propagation delay time, high-to-low-level output				20		ns
t_{TLH}	Transition time, low-to-high-level output				9		ns
t_{THL}	Transition time, high-to-low-level output				6		ns

TYPICAL CHARACTERISTICS

OUTPUT VOLTAGE vs INPUT VOLTAGE

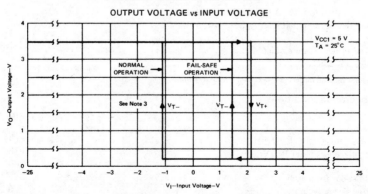

NOTE 3: For normal operation, the threshold controls are connected to V_{CC1}, pin 15. For fail-safe operation, the threshold controls are open.

TEXAS INSTRUMENTS
INCORPORATED
POST OFFICE BOX 5012 • DALLAS, TEXAS 75222

schematic

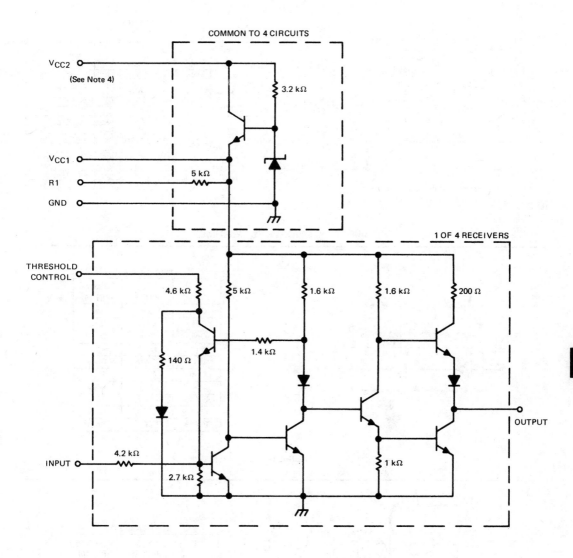

Component values shown are nominal

⊥ . . . Substrate

NOTE 4: When using V_{CC1}(pin 15), V_{CC2}(pin 16) may be left open or shorted to V_{CC1}. When using V_{CC2}, V_{CC1} must be left open or connected to the threshold control pins.

TEXAS INSTRUMENTS
INCORPORATED

POST OFFICE BOX 5012 • DALLAS, TEXAS 75222

PARAMETER MEASUREMENT INFORMATION

d-c test circuits†

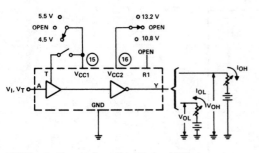

TEST TABLE

TEST	MEASURE	A	T	Y	V_{CC1} (PIN 15)	V_{CC2} (PIN 16)
Open-circuit input (fail safe)	V_{OH}	Open	Open	I_{OH}	4.5 V	Open
	V_{OH}	Open	Open	I_{OH}	Open	10.8 V
V_{T+} min, V_{T-} min (fail safe)	V_{OH}	0.8 V	Open	I_{OH}	5.5 V	Open
	V_{OH}	0.8 V	Open	I_{OH}	Open	13.2 V
V_{T+} min (normal)	V_{OH}	Note A	Pin 15	I_{OH}	5.5 V and T	Open
	V_{OH}	Note A	Pin 15	I_{OH}	T	13.2 V
V_{IL} max, V_{T-} min (normal)	V_{OH}	−3 V	Pin 15	I_{OH}	5.5 V and T	Open
	V_{OH}	−3 V	Pin 15	I_{OH}	T	13.2 V
V_{IH} min, V_{T+} max, V_{T-} max (fail safe)	V_{OL}	3 V	Open	I_{OL}	4.5 V	Open
	V_{OL}	3 V	Open	I_{OL}	Open	10.8 V
V_{IH} min, V_{T+} max (normal)	V_{OL}	3 V	Pin 15	I_{OL}	4.5 V and T	Open
	V_{OL}	3 V	Pin 15	I_{OL}	T	10.8 V
V_{T-} max (normal)	V_{OL}	Note B	Pin 15	I_{OL}	5.5 V and T	Open
	V_{OL}	Note B	Pin 15	I_{OL}	T	13.2 V

NOTES: A. Momentarily apply −5 V, then 0.8 V.
B. Momentarily apply 5 V, then ground.

FIGURE 1 – V_{IH}, V_{IL}, V_{T+}, V_{T-}, V_{OH}, V_{OL}.

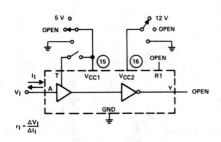

TEST TABLE

T	V_{CC1} (PIN 15)	V_{CC2} (PIN 16)
Open	5 V	Open
Open	GND	Open
Open	Open	Open
Pin 15	T and 5 V	Open
GND	GND	Open
Open	Open	12 V
Open	Open	GND
Pin 15	T	12 V
Pin 15	T	GND
Pin 15	T	Open

$r_I = \dfrac{\Delta V_I}{\Delta I_I}$

FIGURE 2 – r_I

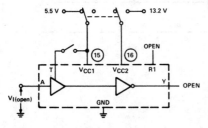

TEST TABLE

T	V_{CC1} (PIN 15)	V_{CC2} (PIN 16)
Open	5.5 V	Open
Pin 15	5.5 V	Open
Open	Open	13.2 V
Pin 15	T	13.2 V

FIGURE 3 – $V_{I(open)}$

† Arrows indicate actual direction of current flow. Current into a terminal is a positive value.

TEXAS INSTRUMENTS
INCORPORATED
POST OFFICE BOX 5012 • DALLAS, TEXAS 75222

1170

PARAMETER MEASUREMENT INFORMATION

d-c test circuits† (continued)

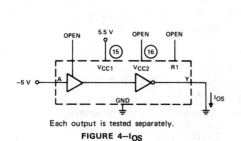

Each output is tested separately.

FIGURE 4—I$_{OS}$

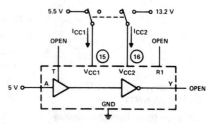

All four line receivers are tested simultaneously.

FIGURE 5—I$_{CC}$

†Arrows indicate actual direction of current flow. Current into a terminal is a positive value.

switching characteristics

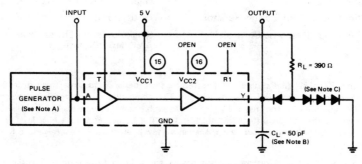

TEST CIRCUIT

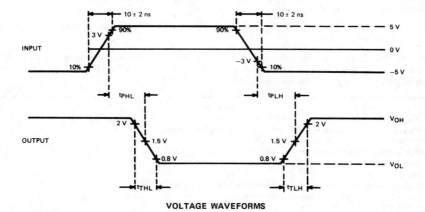

VOLTAGE WAVEFORMS

NOTES: A. The pulse generator has the following characteristics: Z_{out} = 50 Ω, t_w = 200 ns, duty cycle ⩽ 20%.
   B. C_L includes probe and jig capacitance.
   C. All diodes are 1N3064.

FIGURE 6—SWITCHING TIMES

TEXAS INSTRUMENTS
INCORPORATED
POST OFFICE BOX 5012 • DALLAS, TEXAS 75222

SYSTEMS INTERFACE CIRCUITS

TYPES SN55182, SN75182, SN55183, SN75183
DUAL DIFFERENTIAL RECEIVERS AND DRIVERS
BULLETIN NO. DL-S 7311767, OCTOBER 1972 — REVISED SEPTEMBER 1973

LINE CIRCUITS
featuring

- Single 5-V Supply
- Differential Line Operation
- Dual Channels
- TTL/DTL Compatibility

additional features of SN55182 and SN75182 line receivers

- Designed to be Interchangeable with National Semiconductor DM7820A and DM8820A
- ±15 V Common-Mode Input Voltage Range
- ±15 V Differential Input Voltage Range
- Individual Channel Strobes
- Built-In Optional Line-Termination Resistor
- Individual Frequency Response Controls

additional features of SN55183 and SN75183 line drivers

- Designed to be Interchangeable with National Semiconductor DM7830 and DM8830
- Short-circuit Protection of Outputs
- Output Clamp Diodes to Terminate Line Transients
- High-Current Outputs
- Quad Inputs
- Single-Ended or Differential AND/NAND Outputs

description

The SN55182 and SN75182 dual differential line receivers are designed to sense small differential signals in the presence of large common-mode noise. These devices give TTL compatible output signals as a function of the polarity of the differential input voltage. The frequency response of each channel may be easily controlled by a single external capacitor to provide immunity to differential noise spikes. The output goes to a high level when the inputs are open-circuited. A strobe input is provided which, when in the low level, disables the receiver and forces the output to a high level.

The SN55183 and SN75183 dual differential line drivers are designed to provide differential output signals with high-current capability for driving balanced lines, such as twisted-pair, at normal line impedances without high power dissipation. These devices may be used as TTL expander/phase splitters as the output stages are similar to TTL totem-pole outputs.

Both the driver and receiver are of monolithic single-chip construction, and both halves of the dual circuits use common power supply and ground terminals.

The SN55182 and SN55183 are characterized for operation over the full military temperature range of −55°C to 125°C and the SN75182 and SN75183 are characterized for operation from 0°C to 70°C. Both devices are available in either the ceramic (J) or plastic (N) dual-in-line package.

8

TEXAS INSTRUMENTS
INCORPORATED
POST OFFICE BOX 5012 • DALLAS, TEXAS 75222

schematic (each receiver)

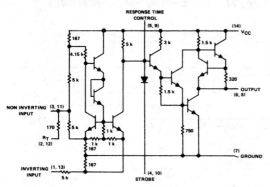

Resistor values shown are nominal and in ohms.

J OR N DUAL-IN-LINE PACKAGE

(TOP VIEW)

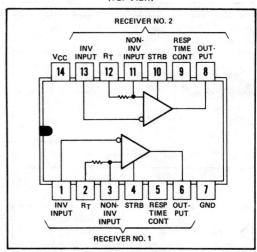

logic

FUNCTION TABLE

STROBE	DIFF INPUT	OUTPUT
L	X	H
H	H	H
H	L	L

$H = V_I \geqslant V_{IH}$ min or V_{ID} more positive than V_{TH} max
$L = V_I \leqslant V_{IL}$ max or V_{ID} more negative than V_{TL} max
X = irrelevant

absolute maximum ratings over operating free-air temperature range (unless otherwise noted)

Supply voltage, V_{CC} (see Note 1) . . . . 8 V
Common-mode input voltage . . . . ±20 V
Differential input voltage (see Note 2) . . . . ±20 V
Strobe input voltage . . . . 8 V
Output sink current . . . . 50 mA
Continuous total dissipation at (or below) 70°C free-air temperature (see Note 3) . . . . 600 mW
Operating free-air temperature range: SN55182 . . . . −55°C to 125°C
　　　　　　　　　　　　　　　　　　　SN75182 . . . . 0°C to 70°C
Storage temperature range . . . . −65°C to 150°C
Lead temperature 1/16 inch from case for 60 seconds: J package . . . . 300°C
Lead temperature 1/16 inch from case for 10 seconds: N package . . . . 260°C

NOTES: 1. All voltage values, except differential voltages, are with respect to the network ground terminal.
　　　　2. Differential voltage values are at the noninverting terminal with respect to the inverting terminal.
　　　　3. For operation of SN55182 above 70°C free-air temperature, refer to Dissipation Derating Curve, Figure 22.

recommended operating conditions

	SN55182			SN75182			UNIT
	MIN	NOM	MAX	MIN	NOM	MAX	
Supply voltage, V_{CC}	4.5	5	5.5	4.5	5	5.5	V
Common-mode input voltage, V_{IC}			±15			±15	
High-level output current, I_{OH}			−400			−400	µA
Low-level output current, I_{OL}			16			16	mA
Operating free-air temperature, T_A	−55		125	0		70	°C

TEXAS INSTRUMENTS
INCORPORATED
POST OFFICE BOX 5012 • DALLAS, TEXAS 75222

electrical characteristics over recommended ranges of V_{CC}, V_{IC}, and operating free-air temperature (unless otherwise noted)

	PARAMETER		TEST CONDITIONS†		MIN	TYP‡	MAX	UNIT
V_{TH}	Differential input high-threshold voltage		$V_O = 2.5$ V,	$V_{IC} = -3$ V to 3 V			0.5	V
			$I_{OH} = -400$ μA	$V_{IC} = -15$ V to 15 V			1	
V_{TL}	Differential input low-threshold voltage		$V_O = 0.4$ V,	$V_{IC} = -3$ V to 3 V			-0.5	V
			$I_{OL} = 16$ mA,	$V_{IC} = -15$ V to 15 V			-1	
$V_{IH(strobe)}$	High-level strobe input voltage				2.1		5.5	V
$V_{IL(strobe)}$	Low-level strobe input voltage				0		0.9	V
V_{OH}	High-level output voltage		$V_{ID} = 1$ V, $\quad$ $V_{strobe} = 2.1$ V, $I_{OH} = -400$ μA		2.5	4.2	5.5	V
			$V_{ID} = -1$ V, $\quad$ $V_{strobe} = 0.4$ V, $I_{OH} = -400$ μA		2.5	4.2	5.5	
V_{OL}	Low-level output voltage		$V_{ID} = -1$ V, $\quad$ $V_{strobe} = 2.1$ V, $I_{OL} = 16$ mA			0.25	0.4	V
I_I	Input current	Inverting input	$V_{IC} = 15$ V			3	4.2	mA
			$V_{IC} = 0$ V			0	0.5	
			$V_{IC} = -15$ V			-3	-4.2	
		Noninverting input	$V_{IC} = 15$ V			5	7	mA
			$V_{IC} = 0$ V			-1	-1.4	
			$V_{IC} = -15$ V			-7	-9.8	
I_{SH}	High-level strobe current		$V_{strobe} = 5.5$ V				5	μA
I_{SL}	Low-level strobe current		$V_{strobe} = 0$			-1	-1.4	mA
r_i	Input resistance	Inverting input				3.6	5	kΩ
		Noninverting input				1.8	2.5	kΩ
R_T	Line terminating resistance		$T_A = 25°C$		120	170	250	Ω
I_{OS}	Short-circuit output current		$V_{CC} = 5.5$ V, $\quad$ $V_O = 0$		-2.8	-4.5	-6.7	mA
I_{CC}	Supply current (average per receiver)		$V_{IC} = 15$ V, $\quad$ $V_{ID} = -1$ V			4.2	6	mA
			$V_{IC} = 0$, $\quad$ $V_{ID} = -0.5$ V			6.8	10.2	
			$V_{IC} = -15$ V, $\quad$ $V_{ID} = -1$ V			9.4	14	

†Unless otherwise noted, $V_{strobe} \geqslant 2.1$ V or open.

‡All typical values are at $V_{CC} = 5$ V, $T_A = 25°C$, and $V_{IC} = 0$.

switching characteristics, $V_{CC} = 5$ V, $T_A = 25°C$

	PARAMETER	TEST CONDITIONS	MIN	TYP	MAX	UNIT
$t_{PLH(D)}$	Propagation delay time, low-to-high-level output from differential input			18	40	ns
$t_{PHL(D)}$	Propagation delay time, high-to-low-level output from differential input	$R_L = 400$ Ω, $C_L = 15$ pF, See Figure 1		31	45	ns
$t_{PLH(S)}$	Propagation delay time, low-to-high-level output from strobe input			9	30	ns
$t_{PHL(S)}$	Propagation delay time, high-to-low-level output from strobe input			15	25	ns

8

TEXAS INSTRUMENTS
INCORPORATED
POST OFFICE BOX 5012 • DALLAS, TEXAS 75222

PARAMETER MEASUREMENT INFORMATION

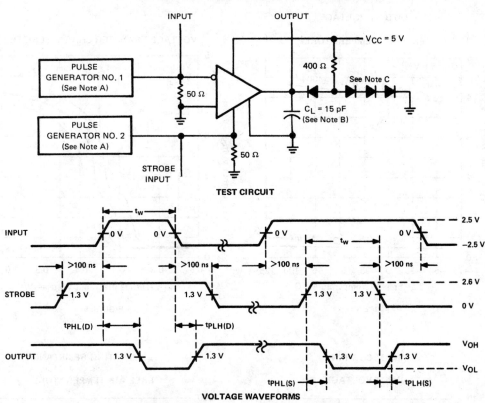

TEST CIRCUIT

VOLTAGE WAVEFORMS

NOTES: A. The pulse generators have the following characteristics: Z_O = 50 Ω, t_r = 10 ns, t_f = 10 ns, t_w = 0.5 ± 0.1 μs, PRR = 1 MHz.
       B. C_L includes probe and jig capacitance.
       C. All diodes are 1N3064 or equivalent.

FIGURE 1—PROPAGATION DELAY TIMES

TYPICAL CHARACTERISTICS

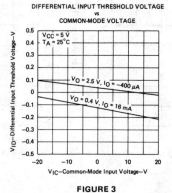

DIFFERENTIAL INPUT THRESHOLD VOLTAGE
vs
SUPPLY VOLTAGE

DIFFERENTIAL INPUT THRESHOLD VOLTAGE
vs
COMMON-MODE VOLTAGE

FIGURE 2

FIGURE 3

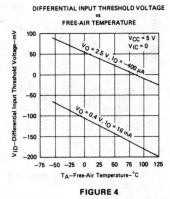

DIFFERENTIAL INPUT THRESHOLD VOLTAGE
vs
FREE-AIR TEMPERATURE

FIGURE 4

8

973

TYPICAL CHARACTERISTICS

OUTPUT VOLTAGE
vs
FREE-AIR TEMPERATURE

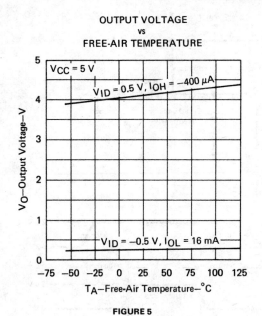

FIGURE 5

VOLTAGE TRANSFER CHARACTERISTICS

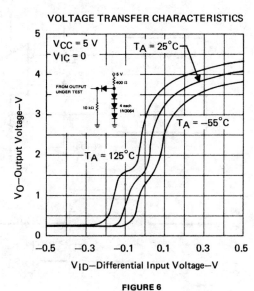

FIGURE 6

INPUT CURRENT
vs
INPUT VOLTAGE

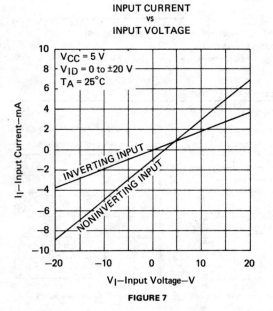

FIGURE 7

TERMINATING RESISTANCE
vs
FREE-AIR TEMPERATURE

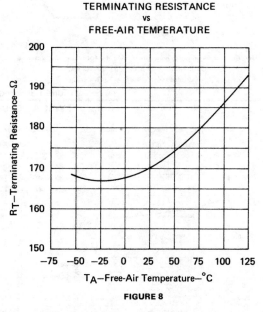

FIGURE 8

TEXAS INSTRUMENTS
INCORPORATED
POST OFFICE BOX 5012 • DALLAS, TEXAS 75222

TYPICAL CHARACTERISTICS

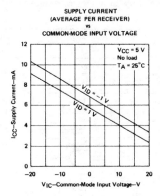

SUPPLY CURRENT
(AVERAGE PER RECEIVER)
vs
COMMON-MODE INPUT VOLTAGE

FIGURE 9

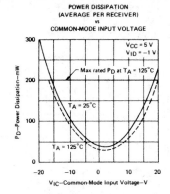

POWER DISSIPATION
(AVERAGE PER RECEIVER)
vs
COMMON-MODE INPUT VOLTAGE

FIGURE 10

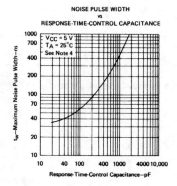

NOISE PULSE WIDTH
vs
RESPONSE-TIME-CONTROL CAPACITANCE

FIGURE 11

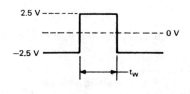

INPUT PULSE FOR FIGURE 11

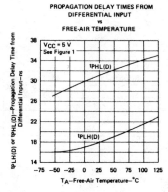

PROPAGATION DELAY TIMES FROM
DIFFERENTIAL INPUT
vs
FREE-AIR TEMPERATURE

FIGURE 12

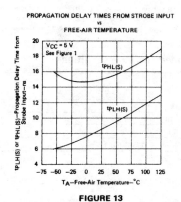

PROPAGATION DELAY TIMES FROM STROBE INPUT
vs
FREE-AIR TEMPERATURE

FIGURE 13

NOTE 4: Figure 11 shows the maximum width of the illustrated pulse that can be applied differentially without the output changing from the low to high level.

TEXAS INSTRUMENTS
INCORPORATED
POST OFFICE BOX 5012 • DALLAS, TEXAS 75222

schematic (each driver)

Resistor values shown are nominal and in ohms.

▽ . . . V$_{CC}$ bus

J OR N DUAL-IN-LINE PACKAGE

(TOP VIEW)

DRIVER NO. 2

V$_{CC}$	D	C	B	A	Y	Z
14	13	12	11	10	9	8

1	2	3	4	5	6	7
A	B	C	D	Y	Z	GND

DRIVER NO. 1

positive logic: Y = ABCD
                 Z = $\overline{ABCD}$

absolute maximum ratings over operating free-air temperature range (unless otherwise noted)

Supply voltage, V$_{CC}$ (see Note 1) . . . . 7 V

Input voltage . . . . 5.5 V

Duration of output short-circuit (see Note 2) . . . . 1 s

Continuous total power dissipation at (or below) 70°C free-air temperature (see Note 3) . . . . 600 mW

Operating free-air temperature range, SN55183 . . . . −55°C to 125°C

SN75183 . . . . 0°C to 70°C

Storage temperature range . . . . −65°C to 150°C

Lead temperature 1/16 inch from case for 60 seconds: J package . . . . 300°C

Lead temperature 1/16 inch from case for 10 seconds: N package . . . . 260°C

NOTES: 1. All voltage values, except differential voltages, are with respect to network ground terminal.
2. Not more than one output should be shorted to ground at a time.
3. For operation of SN55183 above 70°C free-air temperature, refer to Dissipation Derating Curve, Figure 22.

recommended operating conditions

	SN55183			SN75183			UNIT
	MIN	NOM	MAX	MIN	NOM	MAX	
Supply voltage, V$_{CC}$	4.5	5	5.5	4.75	5	5.25	V
High-level output current, I$_{OH}$			−40			−40	mA
Low-level output current, I$_{OL}$			40			40	mA
Operating free-air temperature, T$_A$	−55		125	0		70	°C

TEXAS INSTRUMENTS
INCORPORATED
POST OFFICE BOX 5012 • DALLAS, TEXAS 75222

97

electrical characteristics over recommended ranges of V_{CC} and operating free-air temperature (unless otherwise noted)

PARAMETER			TEST CONDITIONS		MIN	TYP[†]	MAX	UNIT
V_{IH}	High-level input voltage				2			V
V_{IL}	Low-level input voltage						0.8	V
V_{OH}	High-level output voltage	Y (AND) OUTPUT	V_{IH} = 2 V,	I_{OH} = −0.8 mA	2.4			V
			V_{IH} = 2 V,	I_{OH} = −40 mA	1.8	3.3		
V_{OL}	Low-level output voltage		V_{IL} = 0.8 V,	I_{OL} = 32 mA		0.2		V
			V_{IL} = 0.8 V,	I_{OL} = 40 mA		0.22	0.4	
V_{OH}	High-level output voltage	Z (NAND) OUTPUT	V_{IL} = 0.8 V,	I_{OH} = −0.8 mA	2.4			V
			V_{IL} = 0.8 V,	I_{OH} = −40 mA	1.8	3.3		
V_{OL}	Low-level output voltage		V_{IH} = 2 V,	I_{OL} = 32 mA		0.2		V
			V_{IH} = 2 V,	I_{OL} = 40 mA		0.22	0.4	
I_{IH}	High-level input current		V_{IH} = 2.4 V				120	µA
I_I	Input current at maximum input voltage		V_{IH} = 5.5 V				2	mA
I_{IL}	Low-level input current		V_{IL} = 0.4 V				−4.8	mA
I_{OS}	Short-circuit output current§		V_{CC} = 5 V,	T_A = 125°C	−40	−100	−120	mA
I_{CC}	Supply current (average per driver)		V_{CC} = 5 V, All inputs at 5 V, No load			10	18	mA

†All typical values are at V_{CC} = 5 V, T_A = 25°C.
§Not more than one output should be shorted to ground at a time.

switching characteristics, V_{CC} = 5 V, T_A = 25°C

PARAMETER			TEST CONDITIONS	MIN	TYP	MAX	UNIT
t_{PLH}	Propagation delay time, low-to-high-level Y output	AND gates	C_L = 15 pF, See Figure 14(a)		8	12	ns
t_{PHL}	Propagation delay time, high-to-low-level Y output				12	18	ns
t_{PLH}	Propagation delay time, low-to-high-level Z output	NAND gates			6	12	ns
t_{PHL}	Propagation delay time, high-to-low-level Z output				6	8	ns
t_{PLH}	Propagation delay time, low-to-high-level differential output	Y output with respect to Z output	Z_L = 100 Ω in series with 500 pF, See Figure 14(b)		9	16	ns
t_{PHL}	Propagation delay time high-to-low-level differential output				8	16	ns

8

TEXAS INSTRUMENTS
INCORPORATED
POST OFFICE BOX 5012 • DALLAS, TEXAS 75222

TYPES SN55183, SN75183
DUAL DIFFERENTIAL LINE DRIVERS

PARAMETER MEASUREMENT INFORMATION

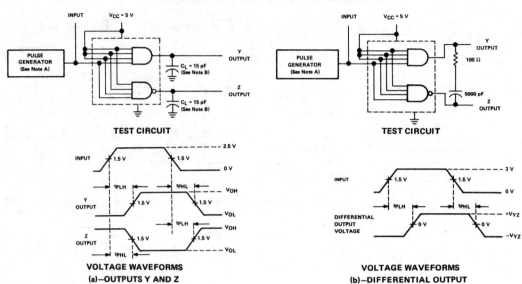

TEST CIRCUIT

VOLTAGE WAVEFORMS
(a)—OUTPUTS Y AND Z

VOLTAGE WAVEFORMS
(b)—DIFFERENTIAL OUTPUT

NOTES: A. The pulse generator has the following characteristics: $Z_O = 50\ \Omega$, $t_r = 10$ ns, $t_f = 10$ ns, $t_w = 0.5\ \mu s$, PRR = 1 MHz.
B. C_L includes probe and jig capacitance.
C. Waveforms are monitored on an oscilloscope with $R_{in} \geqslant 1$ MΩ.

FIGURE 14—PROPAGATION DELAY TIMES

TYPICAL CHARACTERISTICS

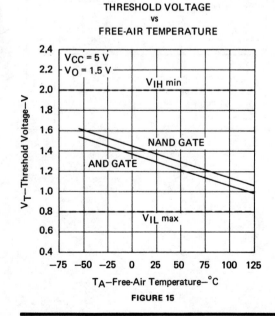

THRESHOLD VOLTAGE
vs
FREE-AIR TEMPERATURE

FIGURE 15

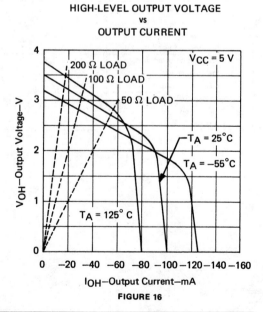

HIGH-LEVEL OUTPUT VOLTAGE
vs
OUTPUT CURRENT

FIGURE 16

TEXAS INSTRUMENTS
INCORPORATED
POST OFFICE BOX 5012 • DALLAS, TEXAS 75222

973

TYPICAL CHARACTERISTICS

DIFFERENTIAL OUTPUT VOLTAGE
vs
DIFFERENTIAL OUTPUT CURRENT

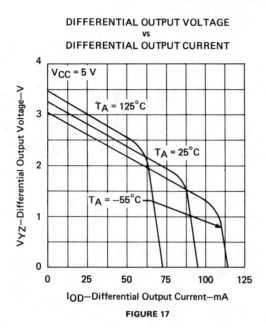

FIGURE 17

LOW-LEVEL OUTPUT VOLTAGE
vs
OUTPUT CURRENT

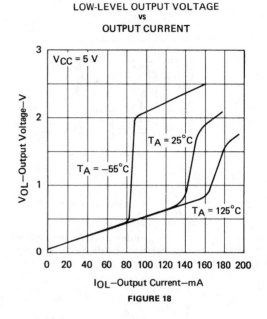

FIGURE 18

PROPAGATION DELAY TIME OF
DIFFERENTIAL OUTPUT
vs
FREE-AIR TEMPERATURE

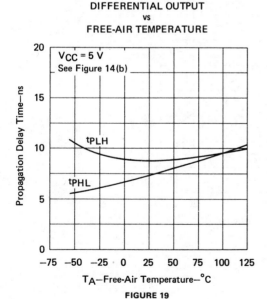

FIGURE 19

TOTAL POWER DISSIPATION
(BOTH DRIVERS)
vs
FREQUENCY

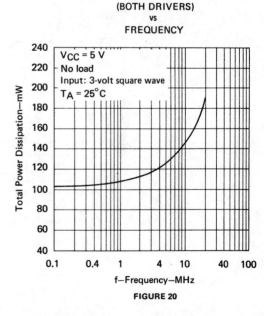

FIGURE 20

8

1072

TEXAS INSTRUMENTS
INCORPORATED
POST OFFICE BOX 5012 • DALLAS, TEXAS 75222

TYPES SN55182, SN75182, SN55183, SN75183
DUAL DIFFERENTIAL RECEIVERS AND DRIVERS

TYPICAL APPLICATION DATA

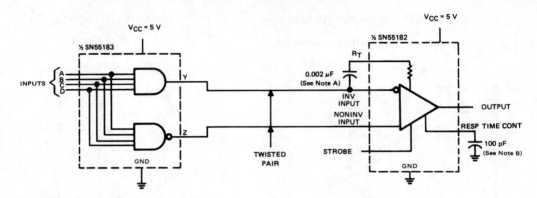

NOTES: A. A capacitor may be used for dc isolation of the line terminating resistor. The exact value of this capacitor depends on the data transmission rate.
B. Use of this capacitor to control response time is optional.

FIGURE 21—TRANSMISSION OF DIGITAL DATA OVER TWISTED—PAIR LINE

THERMAL INFORMATION

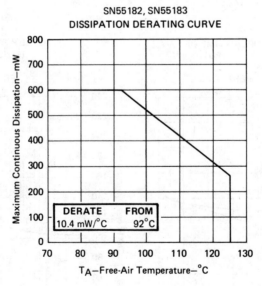

SN55182, SN55183
DISSIPATION DERATING CURVE

DERATE 10.4 mW/°C FROM 92°C

FIGURE 22

TEXAS INSTRUMENTS
INCORPORATED
POST OFFICE BOX 5012 • DALLAS, TEXAS 75222

- Meets Specifications of EIA RS-232C
- Designed to be Interchangeable with Motorola MC1488L
- Current-Limited Output . . . 10 mA Typical
- Power-Off Output Impedance . . . 300 Ω Min
- Slew Rate Control by Load Capacitor
- Flexible Supply Voltage Range
- Input Compatible with Most TTL and DTL Circuits

description

The SN75188 is a monolithic quadruple line driver designed to interface data terminal equipment with data communications equipment in conformance with the specifications of EIA Standard RS-232C. The device is characterized for operation from 0°C to 75°C.

**J OR N
DUAL-IN-LINE PACKAGE
(TOP VIEW)**

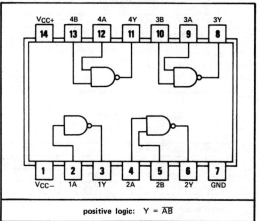

positive logic: $Y = \overline{AB}$

schematic (each driver)

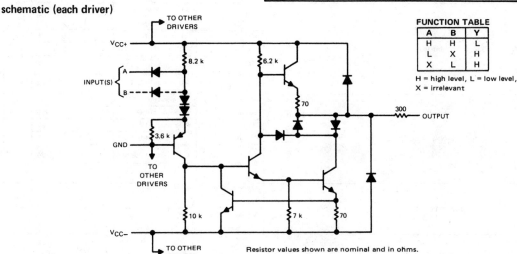

Resistor values shown are nominal and in ohms.

FUNCTION TABLE

A	B	Y
H	H	L
L	X	H
X	L	H

H = high level, L = low level,
X = irrelevant

absolute maximum ratings over operating free-air temperature range (unless otherwise noted)

Supply voltage V_{CC+} at (or below) 25°C free-air temperature (see Notes 1 and 2) . . . . 15 V
Supply voltage V_{CC-} at (or below) 25°C free-air temperature (see Notes 1 and 2) . . . . −15 V
Input voltage range . . . . −15 V to 7 V
Output voltage range . . . . −15 V to 15 V
Continuous total dissipation at (or below) 54°C free-air temperature (see Note 3) . . . . 1 W
Operating free-air temperature range . . . . 0°C to 75°C
Storage temperature range . . . . −65°C to 175°C
Lead temperature 1/16 inch from case for 60 seconds: J package . . . . 300°C
Lead temperature 1/16 inch from case for 10 seconds: N package . . . . 260°C

NOTES: 1. All voltage values are with respect to the network ground terminal.
2. For operation above 25°C free-air temperature, refer to the Maximum Supply Voltage Curve, Figure 6.
3. Derate linearly to 780 mW at 75°C free-air temperature at the rate of 10.4 mW/°C.

TYPE SN75188
QUADRUPLE LINE DRIVER

electrical characteristics over operating free-air temperature range, V_{CC+} = 9 V, V_{CC-} = −9 V (unless otherwise noted)

PARAMETER		TEST CONDITIONS		MIN	TYP† (SEE NOTE 4)	MAX	UNIT
V_{IH}	High-level input voltage			1.9			V
V_{IL}	Low-level input voltage					0.8	V
V_{OH}	High-level output voltage	V_{IL} = 0.8 V, R_L = 3 kΩ	V_{CC+} = 9 V, V_{CC-} = −9 V	6	7		V
			V_{CC+} = 13.2 V, V_{CC-} = −13.2 V	9	10.5		
V_{OL}	Low-level output voltage	V_{IH} = 1.9 V, R_L = 3 kΩ	V_{CC+} = 9 V, V_{CC-} = −9 V		−7	−6	V
			V_{CC+} = 13.2 V, V_{CC-} = −13.2 V		−10.5	−9	
I_{IH}	High-level input current	V_I = 5 V				10	μA
I_{IL}	Low-level input current	V_I = 0			−1	−1.6	mA
$I_{OS(H)}$	Short-circuit output current at high level	V_I = 0.8 V, V_O = 0		−6	−10	−12	mA
$I_{OS(L)}$	Short-circuit output current at low level	V_I = 1.9 V, V_O = 0		6	10	12	mA
r_o	Output resistance, power off	V_{CC+} = 0, V_{CC-} = 0, V_O = −2 V to 2 V		300			Ω
I_{CC+}	Supply current from V_{CC+}	V_{CC+} = 9 V, No load	All inputs at 1.9 V		15	20	mA
			All inputs at 0.8 V		4.5	6	
		V_{CC+} = 12 V, No load	All inputs at 1.9 V		19	25	
			All inputs at 0.8 V		5.5	7	
		V_{CC+} = 15 V, No load, T_A = 25°C	All inputs at 1.9 V			34	
			All inputs at 0.8 V			12	
I_{CC-}	Supply current from V_{CC-}	V_{CC-} = −9 V, No load	All inputs at 1.9 V		−13	−17	mA
			All inputs at 0.8 V			−0.015	
		V_{CC-} = −12 V, No load	All inputs at 1.9 V		−18	−23	
			All inputs at 0.8 V			−0.015	
		V_{CC-} = −15 V, No load, T_A = 25°C	All inputs at 1.9 V			−34	
			All inputs at 0.8 V			−2.5	
P_D	Total power dissipation	V_{CC+} = 9 V, V_{CC-} = −9 V, No load				333	mW
		V_{CC+} = 12 V, V_{CC-} = −12 V, No load				576	

†All typical values are at T_A = 25°C.

NOTE 4: The algebraic convention where the most-positive (least-negative) limit is designated as maximum is used in this data sheet for logic voltage levels only, e.g., if −6 V is a maximum, the typical value is a more-negative voltage.

switching characteristics, V_{CC+} = 9 V, V_{CC-} = −9 V, T_A = 25°C

	PARAMETER	TEST CONDITIONS		MIN	TYP	MAX	UNIT
t_{PLH}	Propagation delay time, low-to-high-level output	R_L = 3 kΩ,	C_L = 15 pF,		220	375	ns
t_{PHL}	Propagation delay time, high-to-low-level output	See Figure 1			100	175	ns
t_{TLH}	Transition time, low-to-high-level output‡				55	100	ns
t_{THL}	Transition time, high-to-low-level output‡				45	75	ns
t_{TLH}	Transition time, low-to-high-level output§	R_L = 3 kΩ to 7 kΩ, C_L = 2500 pF,			2.5		μs
t_{THL}	Transition time, high-to-low-level output§	See Figure 1			3.0		μs

‡Measured between 10% and 90% points of output waveform.
§Measured between +3 V and −3 V points of output waveform (EIA RS-232C conditions).

TEXAS INSTRUMENTS
INCORPORATED
POST OFFICE BOX 5012 • DALLAS, TEXAS 75222

8

PARAMETER MEASUREMENT INFORMATION

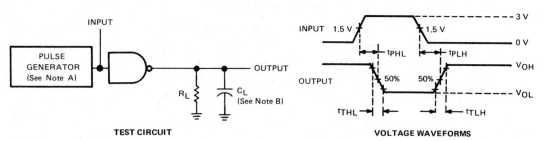

TEST CIRCUIT

VOLTAGE WAVEFORMS

NOTE: A. The pulse generator has the following characteristics: $t_w = 0.5 \ \mu s$, PRR = 1 MHz, $Z_O = 50 \ \Omega$.
B. C_L includes probe and jig capacitance.

FIGURE 1—PROPAGATION AND TRANSITION TIMES

TYPICAL CHARACTERISTICS

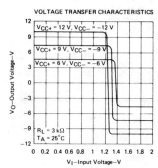

VOLTAGE TRANSFER CHARACTERISTICS

FIGURE 2

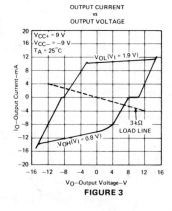

OUTPUT CURRENT
vs
OUTPUT VOLTAGE

FIGURE 3

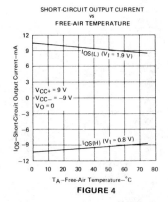

SHORT-CIRCUIT OUTPUT CURRENT
vs
FREE-AIR TEMPERATURE

FIGURE 4

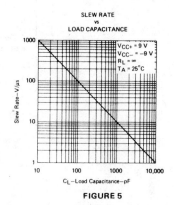

SLEW RATE
vs
LOAD CAPACITANCE

FIGURE 5

8

TEXAS INSTRUMENTS
INCORPORATED
POST OFFICE BOX 5012 • DALLAS, TEXAS 75222

TYPE SN75188
QUADRUPLE LINE DRIVER

THERMAL INFORMATION

MAXIMUM SUPPLY VOLTAGE
vs
FREE-AIR TEMPERATURE

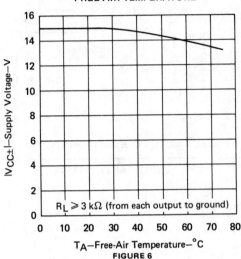

FIGURE 6

TYPICAL APPLICATION DATA

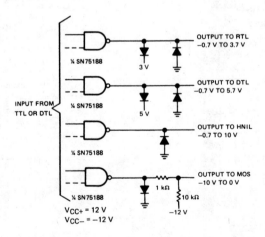

FIGURE 7—LOGIC TRANSLATOR APPLICATIONS

TEXAS INSTRUMENTS
INCORPORATED
POST OFFICE BOX 5012 • DALLAS, TEXAS 75222

- Input Resistance . . . 3 kΩ to 7 kΩ
- Input Signal Range . . . ±30 V
- Fully Interchangeable with Mototola MC1489, MC1489A
- Operates From Single 5-V Supply

- Built-in Input Hysteresis (Double Thresholds)
- Response Control Provides:
  Input Threshold Shifting
  Input Noise Filtering
- Satisfies Requirements of EIA RS-232-C

schematic (each receiver)

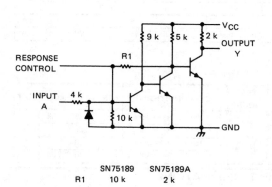

R1	SN75189	SN75189A
	10 k	2 k

Resistor values shown are nominal and in ohms.

J OR N
DUAL-IN-LINE PACKAGE (TOP VIEW)

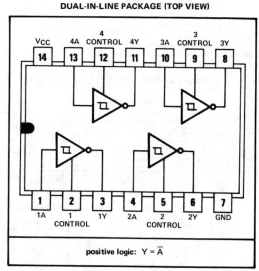

positive logic: Y = $\overline{A}$

description

The SN75189 and SN75189A are monolithic quadruple line receivers designed to satisfy the requirements of the standard interface between data terminal equipment and data communication equipment as defined by EIA Standard RS-232C. A separate response control terminal is provided for each receiver. A resistor or a resistor and bias voltage can be connected between this terminal and ground to shift the input threshold voltage levels. An external capacitor can be connected from this terminal to ground to provide input noise filtering.

absolute maximum ratings at 25°C free-air temperature (unless otherwise noted)

Supply voltage, V_{CC} (see Note 1) . . . . 10 V
Input voltage . . . . ±30 V
Output current . . . . 20 mA
Continuous total dissipation at (or below) 25°C free-air temperature (see Note 2) . . . . 1 W
Operating free-air temperature range . . . . 0°C to 75°C
Storage temperature range . . . . −65°C to 175°C
Lead temperature 1/16 inch from case for 60 seconds: J package . . . . 300°C
Lead temperature 1/16 inch from case for 10 seconds: N package . . . . 260°C

NOTES: 1. Voltage values are with respect to the network ground terminal.
2. For operation above 25°C free-air temperature, refer to Dissipation Derating Curve, Figure 12.

8

electrical characteristics over operating free-air temperature range, V_{CC} = 5V ± 1%, (unless otherwise noted)

PARAMETER		TEST FIGURE	TEST CONDITIONS†		SN75189			SN75189A			UNIT
					MIN	TYP‡	MAX	MIN	TYP‡	MAX	
V_{T+}	Positive-going threshold voltage	1				1	1.5	1.75	1.9	2.25	V
V_{T-}	Negative-going threshold voltage	1				0.75	1.25	0.75	0.97	1.25	V
V_{OH}	High-level output voltage	1	V_I = 0.75 V,	I_{OH} = −0.5 mA	2.6	4	5	2.6	4	5	V
			Input open,	I_{OH} = −0.5 mA	2.6	4	5	2.6	4	5	
V_{OL}	Low-level output voltage	1	V_I = 3 V,	I_{OL} = 10 mA		0.2	0.45		0.2	0.45	V
I_{IH}	High-level input current	2	V_I = 25 V		3.6		8.3	3.6		8.3	mA
			V_I = 3 V		0.43			0.43			
I_{IL}	Low-level input current	2	V_I = −25 V		−3.6		−8.3	−3.6		−8.3	mA
			V_I = −3 V		−0.43			−0.43			
I_{OS}	Short-circuit output current	3				−3			−3		mA
I_{CC}	Supply current	2	V_I = 5 V,	Outputs open		20	26		20	26	mA

†All characteristics are measured with the response control terminal open.
‡All typical values are at V_{CC} = 5 V, T_A = 25°C.

switching characteristics, V_{CC} = 5 V, T_A = 25°C

PARAMETER		TEST FIGURE	TEST CONDITIONS†	MIN	TYP	MAX	UNIT
t_{PLH}	Propagation delay time, low-to-high-level output	4	C_L = 15 pF, R_L = 3.9 kΩ		25	85	ns
t_{PHL}	Propagation delay time, high-to-low-level output		C_L = 15 pF, R_L = 390 Ω		25	50	
t_{TLH}	Transition time, low-to-high-level output		C_L = 15 pF, R_L = 3.9 kΩ		120	175	ns
t_{THL}	Transition time, high-to-low-level output		C_L = 15 pF, R_L = 390 Ω		10	20	

PARAMETER MEASUREMENT INFORMATION§

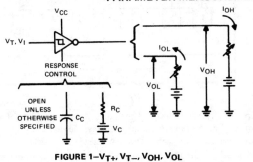

FIGURE 1−V_{T+}, V_{T-}, V_{OH}, V_{OL}

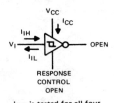

I_{CC} is tested for all four receivers simultaneously

FIGURE 2−I_{IH}, I_{IL}, I_{CC}

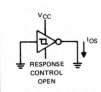

FIGURE 3−I_{OS}

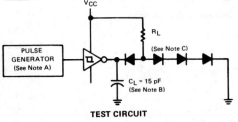

TEST CIRCUIT

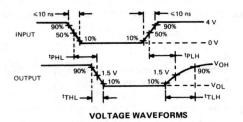

VOLTAGE WAVEFORMS

NOTES: A. The pulse generator has the following characteristics: Z_{out} ≈ 50 Ω, t_w = 500 ns.
B. C_L includes probe and jig capacitance.
C. All diodes are 1N3064 or equivalent.

FIGURE 4−SWITCHING TIMES

§ Arrows indicate actual direction of current flow. Current into a terminal is a positive value.

TEXAS INSTRUMENTS
INCORPORATED
POST OFFICE BOX 5012 • DALLAS, TEXAS 75222

TYPICAL CHARACTERISTICS

SN75189
OUTPUT VOLTAGE vs INPUT VOLTAGE

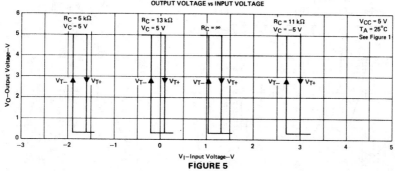

FIGURE 5

SN75189A
OUTPUT VOLTAGE vs INPUT VOLTAGE

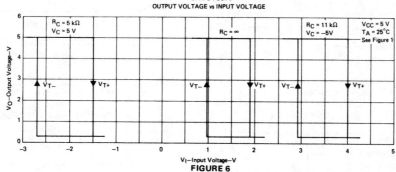

FIGURE 6

INPUT THRESHOLD VOLTAGE
vs
FREE-AIR TEMPERATURE

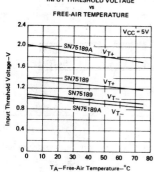

FIGURE 7

INPUT THRESHOLD VOLTAGE
vs
SUPPLY VOLTAGE

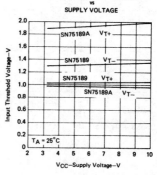

FIGURE 8

8

TEXAS INSTRUMENTS
INCORPORATED
POST OFFICE BOX 5012 • DALLAS, TEXAS 75222

TYPICAL CHARACTERISTICS

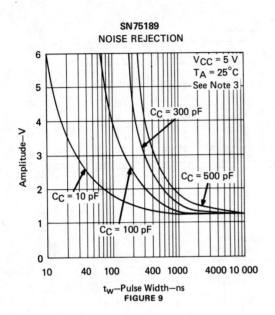

SN75189
NOISE REJECTION

$V_{CC} = 5$ V
$T_A = 25°C$
See Note 3

$C_C = 300$ pF
$C_C = 500$ pF
$C_C = 10$ pF
$C_C = 100$ pF

Amplitude—V

t_w—Pulse Width—ns
FIGURE 9

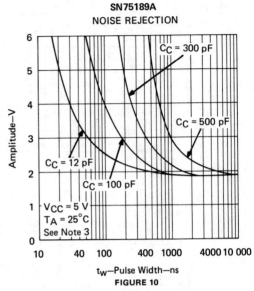

SN75189A
NOISE REJECTION

$C_C = 300$ pF
$C_C = 500$ pF
$C_C = 12$ pF
$C_C = 100$ pF

$V_{CC} = 5$ V
$T_A = 25°C$
See Note 3

Amplitude—V

t_w—Pulse Width—ns
FIGURE 10

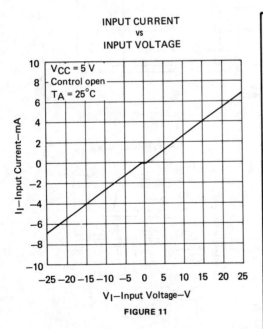

INPUT CURRENT
vs
INPUT VOLTAGE

$V_{CC} = 5$ V
Control open
$T_A = 25°C$

I_I—Input Current—mA

V_I—Input Voltage—V
FIGURE 11

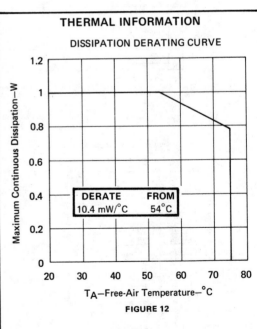

THERMAL INFORMATION

DISSIPATION DERATING CURVE

Maximum Continuous Dissipation—W

DERATE	FROM
10.4 mW/°C	54°C

T_A—Free-Air Temperature—°C
FIGURE 12

NOTE 3: This figure shows the maximum amplitude of a positive-going pulse that, starting from zero volts, will not cause a change of the output level.

PRINTED IN U.S.A.

TI cannot assume any responsibility for any circuits shown
or represent that they are free from patent infringement.

TEXAS INSTRUMENTS
INCORPORATED
POST OFFICE BOX 5012 • DALLAS, TEXAS 75222

TEXAS INSTRUMENTS RESERVES THE RIGHT TO MAKE CHANGES AT ANY TIME
IN ORDER TO IMPROVE DESIGN AND TO SUPPLY THE BEST PRODUCT POSSIBLE

MOS Memory
Interface Circuits

MOS MEMORY INTERFACE CIRCUITS SELECTION GUIDE

FEATURE		SN75361A	SN75362*	SN75365	SN55367* SN75367*	SN75368*	SN75369*	SN75370	UNIT
Function		Dual TTL-MOS Driver	Dual TTL-MOS Driver	Quad TTL-MOS Driver	Quad TTL-CMOS Driver	Dual ECL 10K-MOS Driver	Dual Current Input-MOS Driver	Dual Read/Write Amplifier for TMS4062	
Power Supplies Required		$V_{CC1} = 5$ $V_{CC2} = 20$	$V_{CC1} = 5$ $V_{CC2} = 20$ $V_{CC3} = 24$	$V_{CC1} = 5$ $V_{CC2} = 20$ $V_{CC3} = 24$	$V_{CC1} = 5$ $V_{CC2} = 12$	$V_{CC1} = 5$ $V_{CC2} = 20$ $V_{CC3} = 24$ $V_{EE} = -5.2$	$V_{CC} = V_{EE}+20$	$V_{SS} = 20$ $V_{REF} = 7$	V
Output Voltages	V_{OH} min	$V_{CC2}-1$	$V_{CC2}-0.3$	$V_{CC2}-0.3$	$V_{CC2}-2$	$V_{CC2}-0.3$	$V_{CC}-1$	See Data Sheet	V
	V_{OL} max	0.3	0.3	0.3	0.3	0.3	0.3		
Propagation Delay Times	t_{PLH} typ	36	30	31	30	30	30	See Data Sheet	ns
	t_{PHL} typ	31	30	30	30	30	30		
Package Types		J, N, P	P	J, N	J, JB, N, SB	J, N	J, N, P	JB, N	
Special Features			V_{CC3} pull-up	V_{CC3} pull-up	Three-State outputs, Short-circuit protection	V_{CC3} pull-up	Series resistor input	Variable supply voltages	

*To be announced

9

- Output Compatible with All MOS Devices
- Inputs Fully Compatible with Most TTL and DTL Circuits
- Designed to be Interchangeable with National Semiconductor DM7800 and DM8800

- Standard 5 V Logic Supply Voltage
- Variable V_{CC2} and V_{CC3} Supply Voltages
- 31-Volt Maximum Output Swing
- 1 mW Dissipation with Output at High Level

schematic

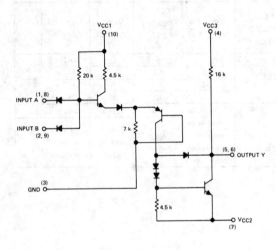

Resistor values shown are nominal and in ohms.

L
PLUG-IN PACKAGE (TOP VIEW)

```
            VCC1
             (10)
INPUT 1A  (1)      (9)  INPUT 2B
INPUT 1B  (2)      (8)  INPUT 2A
GND       (3)      (7)  VCC2
VCC3      (4)      (6)  OUTPUT 2Y
             (5)
          OUTPUT 1Y
```

PIN 7 IS IN ELECTRICAL CONTACT WITH THE CASE

positive logic: $Y = \overline{AB}$

description

The SN55180 and SN75180 are dual voltage-level converters designed for interfacing between TTL or DTL voltage levels and those levels associated with high-impedance junction or MOS FET-type devices. These devices offer the system designer the flexibility of tailoring the output voltage swing to his application. This can be accomplished by varying the V_{CC2} and V_{CC3} supply voltage within the ranges shown in Figure 1. Typical applications include interfacing with MOS shift registers and analog gates.

The SN55180 is characterized for operation over the full military temperature range of -55°C to 125°C; the SN75180 is characterized for operation from 0°C to 70°C.

absolute maximum ratings over operating free-air temperature range (unless otherwise noted)

Supply voltage V_{CC1} (see Note 1)	7 V
Supply voltage V_{CC2} (see Note 1)	-30 V
Supply voltage V_{CC3} (see Note 1)	30 V
V_{CC3} to V_{CC2} voltage differential	40 V
Input voltage (see Note 1)	5.5 V
Continuous total dissipation at (or below) 70°C free-air temperature (see Note 2)	300 mW
Operating free-air temperature range: SN55180 Circuits	-55°C to 125°C
SN75180 Circuits	0°C to 70°C
Storage temperature range	-65°C to 150°C
Lead temperature 1/16 inch from case for 60 seconds	300°C

NOTES: 1. Voltage values are with respect to network ground terminal.
2. For operation of the SN55180 above 70°C free-air temperature, refer to Dissipation Derating Curve, Figure 6.

9

recommended operating conditions

	SN55180			SN75180			UNIT
	MIN	NOM	MAX	MIN	NOM	MAX	
Supply voltage, V_{CC1}	4.5	5	5.5	4.75	5	5.25	V
Supply voltage, V_{CC2} (See Figure 1)	−8		−25	−8		−25	V
Supply voltage, V_{CC3} (See Figure 1)			+25			+25	V
			−20			−20	
Operating free-air temperature, T_A	−55		125	0		70	°C

Figure 1 shows the boundary conditions within which it is recommended that the SN55180 and SN75180 be operated for proper functioning of these converters. The range of operation for supply V_{CC2} is shown on the horizontal axis. V_{CC2} must be between −25 V and −8 V. The allowable range for V_{CC3} is governed by V_{CC2}. After a value for V_{CC2} has been chosen, V_{CC3} may be selected as any value along a vertical line passing through the V_{CC2} value and terminated by the boundaries of the recommended operating region. A voltage difference between supplies of at least 5 volts should be maintained for adequate output voltage swing.

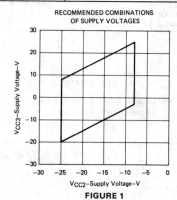

RECOMMENDED COMBINATIONS
OF SUPPLY VOLTAGES

V_{CC3}—Supply Voltage—V

V_{CC2}—Supply Voltage—V

FIGURE 1

electrical characteristics over recommended operating free-air temperature range (unless otherwise noted) (see note 3)

	PARAMETER	TEST CONDITIONS†	MIN	TYP‡	MAX	UNIT
V_{IH}	High-level input voltage		2			V
V_{IL}	Low-level input voltage				0.8	V
V_{OH}	High-level output voltage	V_{CC1} = MIN, V_I = 0.8 V, I_{OH} = 0	V_{CC3}−0.2			V
V_{OL}	Low-level output voltage	V_{CC1} = MIN, V_I = 2 V			V_{CC2}+2	V
$R_{pull-up}$	Output pull-up resistor (internal)	T_A = 25°C	11.5	16	20	kΩ
I_{IH}	High-level input current	V_{CC1} = MAX, V_I = 2.4 V			5	µA
I_I	Input current at maximum input voltage	V_{CC1} = MAX, V_I = 5.5 V			1	mA
I_{IL}	Low-level input current	V_{CC1} = MAX, V_I = 0.4 V		0.2	0.4	mA
$I_{CC1(H)}$	Supply current from V_{CC1}, outputs high (both converters)	V_{CC1} = MAX, all inputs at 0 V, outputs open		440	820	µA
$I_{CC1(L)}$	Supply current from V_{CC1}, outputs low (both converters)	V_{CC1} = MAX, all inputs at 4.5 V, outputs open		1.7	3.2	mA
$I_{CC3(H)}$	Supply current from V_{CC3}, outputs high (both converters)	V_{CC3} = MAX, all inputs at 0.8 V, outputs open			20	µA

NOTE 3: Minimum and maximum limits apply for all allowable values of V_{CC2} and V_{CC3}.

†For conditions shown as MIN or MAX, use appropriate value specified under recommended operating conditions for the applicable device type.

switching characteristics

	PARAMETER	TEST FIGURE	TEST CONDITIONS	MIN	TYP‡	MAX	UNIT
t_{PLH}	Propagation delay time, low-to-high-level output	2	C_L = 15 pF, See Figure 2		85		ns
t_{PHL}	Propagation delay time, high-to-low-level output		C_L = 15 pF, See Figure 2		85		ns

‡All typical values are at V_{CC1} = 5 V, V_{CC2} = −22 V, V_{CC3} = 8 V, T_A = 25°C.

9

TEXAS INSTRUMENTS
INCORPORATED
POST OFFICE BOX 5012 • DALLAS, TEXAS 75222

TYPES SN55180, SN75180
DUAL TTL-TO-MOS LEVEL CONVERTERS

PARAMETER MEASUREMENT INFORMATION

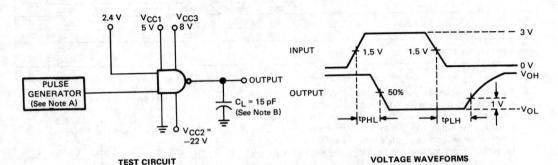

TEST CIRCUIT

VOLTAGE WAVEFORMS

NOTES: A. The pulse generator has the following characteristics: Z_{out} = 50 Ω, t_r = 10 ns, t_f = 10 ns, PRR = 500 kHz, t_w = 500 ns.
B. C_L includes probe and jig capacitance.

FIGURE 2

TYPICAL CHARACTERISTICS†

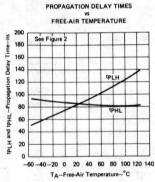

PROPAGATION DELAY TIMES
vs
FREE-AIR TEMPERATURE

FIGURE 3

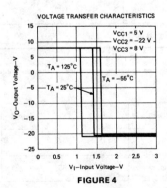

VOLTAGE TRANSFER CHARACTERISTICS

FIGURE 4

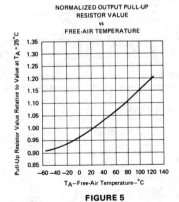

NORMALIZED OUTPUT PULL-UP
RESISTOR VALUE
vs
FREE-AIR TEMPERATURE

FIGURE 5

†Data for temperatures below 0°C and above 70°C is applicable to SN55180 circuits only.

TEXAS INSTRUMENTS
INCORPORATED
POST OFFICE BOX 5012 • DALLAS, TEXAS 75222

THERMAL INFORMATION

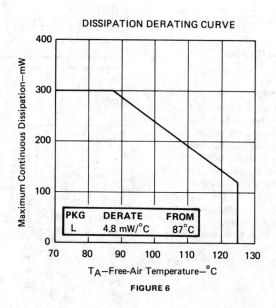

DISSIPATION DERATING CURVE

PKG	DERATE	FROM
L	4.8 mW/°C	87°C

FIGURE 6

9

TEXAS INSTRUMENTS
INCORPORATED
POST OFFICE BOX 5012 • DALLAS, TEXAS 75222

features

- Plug-in Replacement for SN75107A, SN75108A with Improved Characteristics
- ±10 mV Guaranteed Input Sensitivity
- TTL Compatible
- Standard Supply Voltages . . . ±5 V
- Differential Input Common-Mode Voltage Range of ±3 V
- Strobe Inputs for Channel Selection

applications

- Sense Amplifier for MOS Memories
- Dual Comparator
- High-Sensitivity Line Receiver

description

The SN75207 and SN75208 are pin-for-pin replacements for the SN75107A and SN75108A, respectively. The improved input sensitivity makes them more suitable for MOS memory sense amplifiers and can result in faster memory cycles. Improved sensitivity also makes them more useful in line receiver applications by allowing use of longer transmission line lengths. The SN75207 features a TTL-compatible active-pull-up output. The SN75208 features an open-collector output that permits wired-AND logic connections with similar output configurations. Both devices are designed for operation from 0°C to 70°C and are available in the ceramic dual-in-line (J) package or in the plastic dual-in-line (N) package.

J OR N
DUAL-IN-LINE PACKAGE

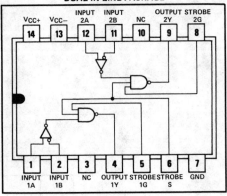

NC—No internal connection

schematic

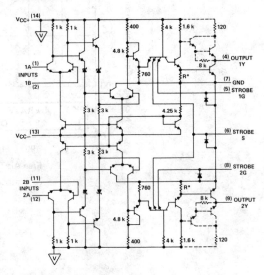

NOTES: A. R* = 1 kΩ for SN75207 and 750 Ω for SN75208.
B. Resistor values shown are nominal and in ohms.
C. Components shown with dashed lines are applicable to the SN75207 only.

▽ . . . V_{CC} bus

FUNCTION TABLE

DIFFERENTIAL INPUTS A-B	STROBES		OUTPUT
	G	S	Y
$V_{ID} \geqslant 10$ mV	X	X	H
	X	L	H
-10 mV $< V_{ID} < 10$ mV	L	X	H
	H	H	INDETERMINATE
	X	L	H
$V_{ID} \leqslant -10$ mV	L	X	H
	H	H	L

H = high level, L = low level, X = irrelevant

TEXAS INSTRUMENTS
INCORPORATED
POST OFFICE BOX 5012 • DALLAS, TEXAS 75222

973

absolute maximum ratings over operating operating free-air temperature range (unless otherwise noted)

Supply voltage V_{CC+} (see Note 1) . . . . 7 V
Supply voltage V_{CC-} (see Note 1) . . . . −7 V
Differential input voltage (see Note 2) . . . . ±6 V
Common-mode input voltage (see Note 1) . . . . ±5 V
Strobe input voltage (see Note 1) . . . . 5.5 V
Operating free-air temperature range . . . . 0°C to 70°C
Storage temperature range . . . . −65°C to 150°C

recommended operating conditions (see note 3)

	SN75207, SN75208			UNIT
	MIN	NOM	MAX	
Supply voltage V_{CC+} (see Note 1)	4.75	5	5.25	V
Supply voltage V_{CC-} (see Note 1)	−4.75	−5	−5.25	V
Output sink current			−16	mA
Differential input voltage (see Notes 2 and 4)	−5†		5	V
Common-mode input voltage (see Notes 1 and 4)	−3†		3	V
Input voltage range, any differential input to ground (see Note 4)	−5†		3	V
Operating free-air temperature	0		70	°C

NOTES: 1. All voltage values, except differential voltages, are with respect to network ground terminal.
       2. Differential voltage values are at the noninverting (A) terminal with respect to the inverting (B) terminal.
       3. When using only one channel of the line receiver, the inputs of the other channel should be grounded.
       4. The recommended combinations of input voltage fall within the shaded area of the figure below.

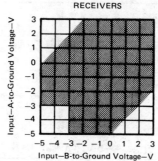

RECOMMENDED COMBINATIONS OF
INPUT VOLTAGES FOR LINE
RECEIVERS

definition of input logic levels†

		TEST FIGURE	MIN	MAX	UNIT
V_{IDH}	High-level input voltage between differential inputs	1	0.01	5	V
V_{IDL}	Low-level input voltage between differential inputs	1	−5	−0.01	V
$V_{IH(S)}$	High-level input voltage at strobe inputs	3	2	5.5	V
$V_{IL(S)}$	Low-level input voltage at strobe inputs	3	0	0.8	V

†The algebraic convention, where the most-positive (least-negative) limit is designated maximum, is used in this data sheet with logic input voltage levels only.

9

electrical characteristics over operating free-air temperature range (unless otherwise noted)

PARAMETER		TEST FIGURE	TEST CONDITIONS‡			SN75207 MIN	SN75207 TYP§	SN75207 MAX	SN75208 MIN	SN75208 TYP§	SN75208 MAX	UNIT
I_I	Input current into 1A or 2A	2	V_{CC+} = MAX, V_{IC} = −3 V to 3 V	$V_{CC−}$ = MAX,	V_{ID} = 0.5 V	30		75	30		75	μA
					V_{ID} = −2 V			−10			−10	
I_I	Input current into 1B or 2B	2	V_{CC+} = MAX, V_{IC} = −3 V to 3 V	$V_{CC−}$ = MAX,	V_{ID} = −0.5 V	30		75	30		75	μA
					V_{ID} = 2 V			−10			−10	
I_{IH}	High-level input current into 1G or 2G	4	V_{CC+} = MAX, $V_{IH(S)}$ = 2.4 V	$V_{CC−}$ = MAX,				40			40	μA
			V_{CC+} = MAX, $V_{IH(S)}$ = MAX V_{CC+}	$V_{CC−}$ = MAX,				1			1	mA
I_{IL}	Low-level input current into 1G or 2G	4	V_{CC+} = MAX, $V_{IL(S)}$ = 0.4 V	$V_{CC−}$ = MAX,				−1.6			−1.6	mA
I_{IH}	High-level input current into S	4	V_{CC+} = MAX, $V_{IH(S)}$ = 2.4 V	$V_{CC−}$ = MAX,				80			80	μA
			V_{CC+} = MAX, $V_{IH(S)}$ = MAX V_{CC+}	$V_{CC−}$ = MAX,				2			2	mA
I_{IL}	Low-level input current into S	4	V_{CC+} = MAX, $V_{IL(S)}$ = 0.4 V	$V_{CC−}$ = MAX,				−3.2			−3.2	mA
V_{OH}	High-level output voltage	3	V_{CC+} = MIN, I_{OH} = −400 μA,	$V_{CC−}$ = MIN, V_{IC} = −3 V to 3 V		2.4						V
V_{OL}	Low-level output voltage	3	V_{CC+} = MIN, I_{OL} = 16 mA,	$V_{CC−}$ = MIN, V_{IC} = −3 V to 3 V				0.4			0.4	V
I_{OH}	High-level output current	3	V_{CC+} = MIN, V_{OH} = MAX V_{CC+}	$V_{CC−}$ = MIN,							250	μA
I_{OS}	Short-circuit output current¶	5	V_{CC+} = MAX	$V_{CC−}$ = MAX		−18		−70				mA
I_{CCH+}	Supply current from V_{CC+}, output high	6	V_{CC+} = MAX, T_A = 25°C	$V_{CC−}$ = MAX,			18	30		18	30	mA
$I_{CCH−}$	Supply current from $V_{CC−}$, output high	6	V_{CC+} = MAX, T_A = 25°C	$V_{CC−}$ = MAX,			−8.4	−15		−8.4	−15	mA

‡For conditions shown as MIN or MAX, use the appropriate value specified under recommended operating conditions for the applicable device type.
§All typical values are at V_{CC+} = 5 V, $V_{CC−}$ = −5 V, T_A = 25°C.
¶Not more than one output should be shorted at a time.

switching characteristics, V_{CC+} = 5 V, $V_{CC−}$ = −5 V, T_A = 25°C

PARAMETER		TEST FIGURE	TEST CONDITIONS	SN75207 MIN	SN75207 TYP	SN75207 MAX	SN75208 MIN	SN75208 TYP	SN75208 MAX	UNIT
$t_{PLH(D)}$	Propagation delay time, low-to-high-level output from differential inputs A and B	7	R_L = 470 Ω, C_L = 15 pF			35			35	ns
$t_{PHL(D)}$	Propagation delay time, high-to-low-level output from differential inputs A and B					20			20	ns
$t_{PLH(S)}$	Propagation delay time, low-to-high-level output from strobe input G or S					17			17	ns
$t_{PHL(S)}$	Propagation delay time, high-to-low-level output from strobe input G or S					17			17	ns

9

TEXAS INSTRUMENTS
INCORPORATED
POST OFFICE BOX 5012 • DALLAS, TEXAS 75222

PARAMETER MEASUREMENT INFORMATION

d-c test circuits†

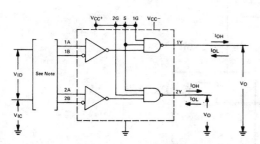

NOTE: When testing one channel, the inputs of the other channel are grounded.

FIGURE 1—V_{IDH} and V_{IDL}

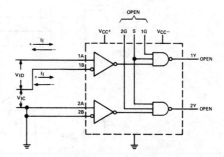

NOTE: Each pair of differential inputs is tested separately. The other pair of inputs are grounded.

FIGURE 2—I_{IH} and I_{IL}

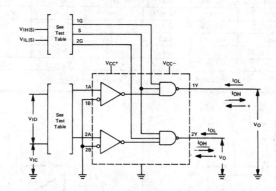

TEST TABLE

SN75207	SN75208	V_{ID}	STROBE 1G or 2G	STROBE S
TEST			APPLY	
V_{OH}	I_{OH}	+10 mV	$V_{IH(S)}$	$V_{IH(S)}$
V_{OH}	I_{OH}	−10 mV	$V_{IL(S)}$	$V_{IH(S)}$
V_{OH}	I_{OH}	−10 mV	$V_{IH(S)}$	$V_{IL(S)}$
V_{OL}	V_{OL}	−10 mV	$V_{IH(S)}$	$V_{IH(S)}$

NOTES: 1. V_{IC} = −3 V to 3 V.
2. When testing one channel, the inputs of the other channel should be grounded.

FIGURE 3—$V_{IH(S)}$, $V_{IL(S)}$, V_{OH}, V_{OL}, and I_{OH}

†Arrows indicate actual direction of current flow. Current into a terminal is a positive value.

PARAMETER MEASUREMENT INFORMATION

d-c test circuits† (continued)

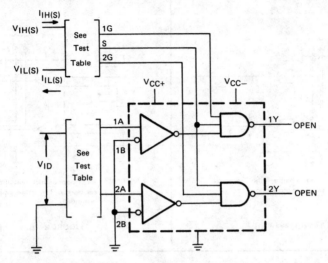

TEST	INPUT 1A	INPUT 2A	STROBE 1G	STROBE S	STROBE 2G
I_{IH} at Strobe 1G	+10 mV	Gnd	$V_{IH(S)}$	Gnd	Gnd
I_{IH} at Strobe 2G	Gnd	+10 mV	Gnd	Gnd	$V_{IH(S)}$
I_{IH} at Strobe S	+10 mV	+10 mV	Gnd	$V_{IH(S)}$	Gnd
I_{IL} at Strobe 1G	−10 mV	Gnd	$V_{IL(S)}$	4.5 V	Gnd
I_{IL} at Strobe 2G	Gnd	−10 mV	Gnd	4.5 V	$V_{IL(S)}$
I_{IL} at Strobe S	−10 mV	−10 mV	4.5 V	$V_{IL(S)}$	4.5 V

FIGURE 4—$I_{IH(G)}$, $I_{IL(G)}$, $I_{IH(S)}$, and $I_{IL(S)}$

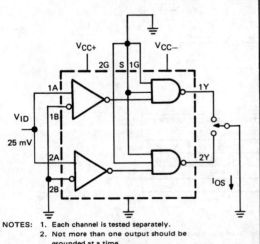

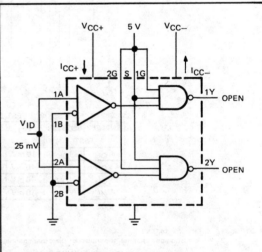

NOTES: 1. Each channel is tested separately.
2. Not more than one output should be grounded at a time.

FIGURE 5—I_{OS}

FIGURE 6—I_{CC+} and $I_{CC−}$

†Arrows indicate actual direction of current flow. Current into a terminal is a positive value.

TEXAS INSTRUMENTS
INCORPORATED
POST OFFICE BOX 5012 • DALLAS, TEXAS 75222

PARAMETER MEASUREMENT INFORMATION

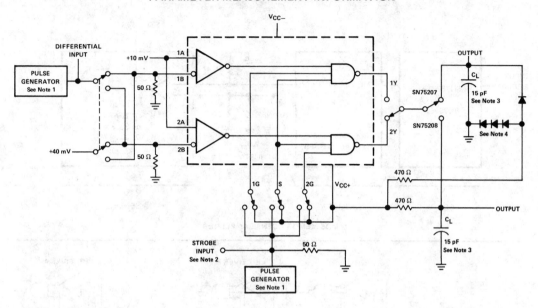

TEST CIRCUIT

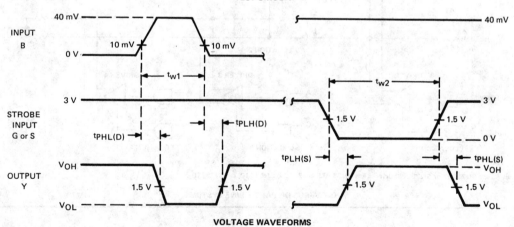

VOLTAGE WAVEFORMS

NOTES: 1. The pulse generators have the following characteristics: $Z_{out} = 50\ \Omega$, $t_r \leqslant 5$ ns, $t_f \leqslant 5$ ns, $t_{w1} = 500$ ns with PRR = 1 MHz, $t_{w2} = 1$ ms with PRR = 500 kHz.
2. Strobe input pulse is applied to Strobe 1G when inputs 1A-1B are being tested, to Strobe S when inputs 1A-1B or 2A-2B are being tested, and to Strobe 2G when inputs 2A-2B are being tested.
3. C_L includes probe and jig capacitance.
4. All diodes are 1N916.

FIGURE 7—PROPAGATION DELAY TIMES

TYPES SN75207, SN75208
DUAL SENSE AMPLIFIERS FOR MOS MEMORIES

TYPICAL APPLICATION DATA

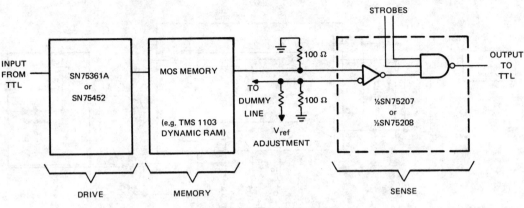

MOS MEMORY SENSE AMPLIFIER

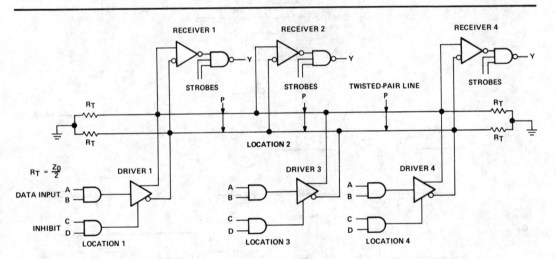

Receivers are SN75207 or SN75208; drivers are SN55109, SN75109, SN55110, or SN75110

DATA-BUS OR PARTY-LINE SYSTEM

PRECAUTIONS: When only one receiver in a package is being used, at least one of the differential inputs of the unused receiver should be terminated at some voltage between −3 volts and +3 volts, preferably at ground. Failure to do so will cause improper operation of the unit being used because of common bias circuitry for the current sources of the two receivers.

TEXAS INSTRUMENTS
INCORPORATED
POST OFFICE BOX 5012 • DALLAS, TEXAS 75222

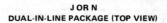
schematic (each driver)

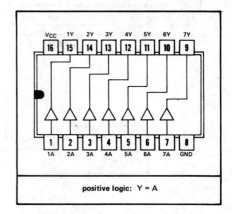

**J OR N
DUAL-IN-LINE PACKAGE (TOP VIEW)**

positive logic: Y = A

Resistor values are nominal and in ohms.

absolute maximum ratings over operating free-air temperature range (unless otherwise noted)

Supply voltage, V_{CC} (see Note 1)	7 V
Input current	4 mA
Continuous total dissipation	800 mW
Operating free-air temperature range	0°C to 70°C
Storage temperature range	−65°C to 150°C
Lead temperature 1/16 inch from case for 60 seconds: J package	300°C
Lead temperature 1/16 inch from case for 10 seconds: N package	260°C

recommended operating conditions

	MIN	NOM	MAX	UNIT
Supply voltage, V_{CC}	4.75	5	5.25	V
High-level input current, I_{IH}	0.5		2	mA
Low-level input current, I_{IL}	0		0.1	mA
Operating free-air temperature, T_A	0		70	°C

electrical characteristics over recommended operating free-air temperature range

PARAMETER	TEST CONDITIONS	MIN	TYP	MAX	UNIT
V_{OH} High-level output voltage	V_{CC} = 4.75 V, I_{IH} = 500 µA, I_{OH} = −80 µA	2.4			V
V_{OL} Low-level output voltage	V_{CC} = 4.75 V, I_{IL} = 100 µA, I_{OL} = 3.2 mA			0.4	V
I_{OH} High-level output current	V_{CC} = 4.75 V, I_{IH} = 500 µA, V_O = 1 V	−5			mA
	V_{CC} = 5.25 V, I_{IH} = 500 µA, V_O = 0.25 V			−15	
I_{CCL} Total supply current, all outputs low	V_{CC} = 5 V, I_{IL} = 100 µA, I_O = 0		20	35	mA

NOTE 1: Voltage values are with respect to network ground terminal.

switching characteristics, $T_A = 25°C$

PARAMETER		TEST CONDITIONS		MIN	TYP	MAX	UNIT
t_{PLH}	Propagation delay time, low-to-high-level output	$V_{CC} = 5$ V,	$C_L = 15$ pF,		30		ns
t_{PHL}	Propagation delay time, high-to-low-level output	$R_L = 1.5$ kΩ,	See Figure 1		8		ns

PARAMETER MEASUREMENT INFORMATION

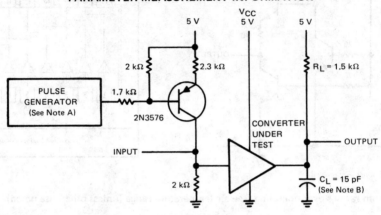

NOTES: A. The pulse generator has the following characteristics: $Z_{out} = 50$ Ω, $t_r \leqslant 10$ ns, $t_f \leqslant 10$ ns, PRR = 500 kHz, $t_w = 500$ ns.
B. C_L includes probe and jig capacitance.

TEST CIRCUIT

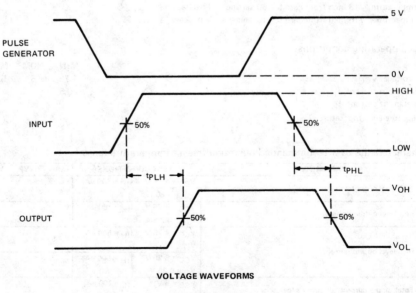

VOLTAGE WAVEFORMS

FIGURE 1

TEXAS INSTRUMENTS
INCORPORATED
POST OFFICE BOX 5012 • DALLAS, TEXAS 75222

MOS MEMORY INTERFACE

- Dual Positive-Logic NAND TTL-to-MOS Driver

- Versatile Interface Circuit for Use between TTL and High-Current, High-Voltage Systems

- Capable of Driving High-Capacitance Loads

- Compatible with Many Popular MOS RAMs

- V_{CC2} Supply Voltage Variable over Wide Range to 24 Volts Maximum

- TTL and DTL Compatible Diode-Clamped Inputs

- Operates from Standard Bipolar and MOS Supply Voltages

- High-Speed Switching

- Transient Overdrive Minimizes Power Dissipation

- Low Standby Power Dissipation

**J OR N
DUAL-IN-LINE PACKAGE (TOP VIEW)**

V_{CC1}	NC	1Y	NC	2Y	NC	V_{CC2}
14	13	12	11	10	9	8
1	2	3	4	5	6	7
NC	NC	1A	E	2A	NC	GND

positive logic: Y = $\overline{AE}$

NC—No internal connection

description

The SN75361A is a monolithic integrated dual TTL-to-MOS driver and interface circuit. The device accepts standard TTL and DTL input signals and provides high-current and high-voltage output levels suitable for driving MOS circuits. Specifically, it may be used to drive address, control, and timing inputs for several types of MOS RAMs including the '1103 and TMS4062.

The SN75361A operates from the TTL 5-volt supply and the MOS V_{SS} supply in many applications. This device has been optimized for operation with V_{CC2} supply voltage from 16 volts to 20 volts; however, it is designed so as to be useable over a much wider range of V_{CC2}.

The SN75361A is characterized for operation from $0°C$ to $70°C$.

**P
DUAL-IN-LINE PACKAGE (TOP VIEW)**

V_{CC1}	1Y	2Y	V_{CC2}
8	7	6	5
1	2	3	4
1A	E	2A	GND

positive logic: Y = $\overline{AE}$

schematic (each driver)

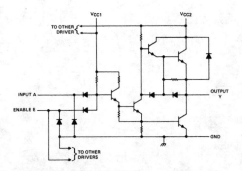

TYPE SN75361A
DUAL TTL-TO-MOS DRIVER

absolute maximum ratings over operating free-air temperature range (unless otherwise noted)

Supply voltage range of V_{CC1} (see Note 1) . . . . −0.5 V to 7 V
Supply voltage range of V_{CC2} . . . . −0.5 V to 25 V
Input voltage . . . . 5.5 V
Inter-input voltage (see Note 2) . . . . 5.5 V
Continuous total dissipation at (or below) 25°C free-air temperature (see Note 3):
   J or N package . . . . 1300 mW
   P package . . . . 1000 mW
Operating free-air temperature range . . . . 0°C to 70°C
Storage temperature range . . . . −65°C to 150°C
Lead temperature 1/16 inch from case for 60 seconds: J package . . . . 300°C
Lead temperature 1/16 inch from case for 10 seconds: N or P package . . . . 260°C

NOTES: 1. Voltage values are with respect to network ground terminal.
       2. This rating applies between the A input of either driver and the common E input.
       3. For operation above 25°C free-air temperature, refer to Dissipation Derating Curve, Figure 17.

recommended operating conditions

	MIN	NOM	MAX	UNIT
Supply voltage, V_{CC1}	4.75	5	5.25	V
Supply voltage, V_{CC2}	4.75	20	24	V
Operating free-air temperature, T_A	0		70	°C

TEXAS INSTRUMENTS
INCORPORATED
POST OFFICE BOX 5012 • DALLAS, TEXAS 75222

electrical characteristics over recommended ranges of V$_{CC1}$, V$_{CC2}$, and operating free-air temperature (unless otherwise noted)

	PARAMETER	TEST CONDITIONS		MIN	TYP†	MAX	UNIT
V$_{IH}$	High-level input voltage			2			V
V$_{IL}$	Low-level input voltage					0.8	V
V$_I$	Input clamp voltage	I$_I$ = −12 mA				−1.5	V
V$_{OH}$	High-level output voltage	V$_{IL}$ = 0.8 V,	I$_{OH}$ = −50 µA	V$_{CC2}$−1	V$_{CC2}$−0.7		V
		V$_{IL}$ = 0.8 V,	I$_{OH}$ = −10 mA	V$_{CC2}$−2.3	V$_{CC2}$−1.8		
V$_{OL}$	Low-level output voltage	V$_{IH}$ = 2 V,	I$_{OL}$ = 10 mA		0.15	0.3	V
		V$_{CC2}$ = 15 V to 24 V, V$_{IH}$ = 2 V, I$_{OL}$ = 40 mA			0.25	0.5	V
V$_O$	Output clamp voltage	V$_I$ = 0 V,	I$_{OH}$ = 20 mA			V$_{CC2}$+1.5	V
I$_I$	Input current at maximum input voltage	V$_I$ = 5.5 V				1	mA
I$_{IH}$	High-level input current	V$_I$ = 2.4 V	A inputs			40	µA
			E input			80	
I$_{IL}$	Low-level input current	V$_I$ = 0.4 V	A inputs		−1	−1.6	mA
			E input		−2	−3.2	
I$_{CC1(H)}$	Supply current from V$_{CC1}$, both outputs high	V$_{CC1}$ = 5.25 V,	V$_{CC2}$ = 24 V,		2	4	mA
I$_{CC2(H)}$	Supply current from V$_{CC2}$, both outputs high	All inputs at 0 V,	No load			0.5	
I$_{CC1(L)}$	Supply current from V$_{CC1}$, both outputs low	V$_{CC1}$ = 5.25 V,	V$_{CC2}$ = 24 V,		16	24	mA
I$_{CC2(L)}$	Supply current from V$_{CC2}$, both outputs low	All inputs at 5 V,	No load		7	11	
I$_{CC2(S)}$	Supply current from V$_{CC2}$, stand-by condition	V$_{CC1}$ = 0 V, V$_{CC2}$ = 24 V, All inputs at 5 V, No load				0.5	mA

†All typical values are at V$_{CC1}$ = 5 V, V$_{CC2}$ = 20 V, and T$_A$ = 25°C.

switching characteristics, V$_{CC1}$ = 5 V, V$_{CC2}$ = 20 V, T$_A$ = 25°C

	PARAMETER	TEST CONDITIONS	MIN	TYP	MAX	UNIT
t$_{DLH}$	Delay time, low-to-high-level output			11	20	ns
t$_{DHL}$	Delay time, high-to-low-level output	C$_L$ = 390 pF, R$_D$ = 10 Ω, See Figure 1		10	18	ns
t$_{TLH}$	Transition time, low-to-high-level output			25	40	ns
t$_{THL}$	Transition time, high-to-low-level output			21	35	ns
t$_{PLH}$	Propagation delay time, low-to-high-level output		10	36	55	ns
t$_{PHL}$	Propagation delay time, high-to-low-level output		10	31	47	ns

9

TEXAS INSTRUMENTS
INCORPORATED
POST OFFICE BOX 5012 • DALLAS, TEXAS 75222

PARAMETER MEASUREMENT INFORMATION

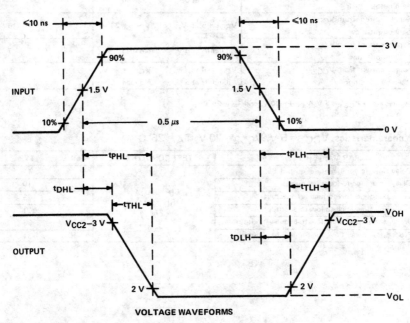

TEST CIRCUIT

VOLTAGE WAVEFORMS

NOTES: A. The pulse generator has the following characteristics: PRR = 1 MHz, $Z_{out} \approx 50\ \Omega$.
   B. C_L includes probe and jig capacitance.

FIGURE 1—SWITCHING TIMES, EACH DRIVER

973

TEXAS INSTRUMENTS
INCORPORATED
POST OFFICE BOX 5012 • DALLAS, TEXAS 75222

9

TYPICAL CHARACTERISTICS

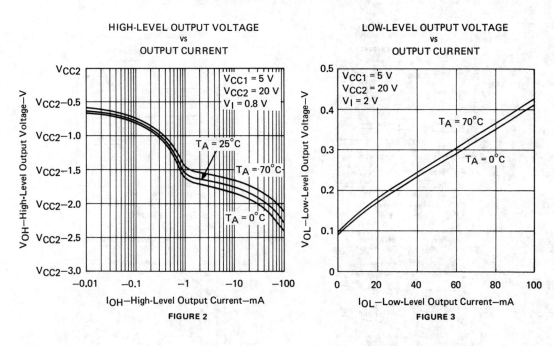

HIGH-LEVEL OUTPUT VOLTAGE
vs
OUTPUT CURRENT

V_{CC1} = 5 V
V_{CC2} = 20 V
V_I = 0.8 V

T_A = 25°C
T_A = 70°C
T_A = 0°C

V_{OH}–High-Level Output Voltage–V

I_{OH}–High-Level Output Current–mA

FIGURE 2

LOW-LEVEL OUTPUT VOLTAGE
vs
OUTPUT CURRENT

V_{CC1} = 5 V
V_{CC2} = 20 V
V_I = 2 V

T_A = 70°C
T_A = 0°C

V_{OL}–Low-Level Output Voltage–V

I_{OL}–Low-Level Output Current–mA

FIGURE 3

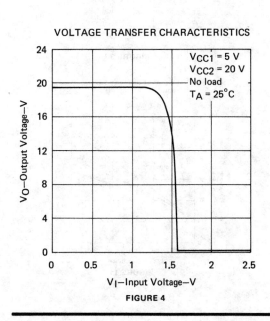

VOLTAGE TRANSFER CHARACTERISTICS

V_{CC1} = 5 V
V_{CC2} = 20 V
No load
T_A = 25°C

V_O–Output Voltage–V

V_I–Input Voltage–V

FIGURE 4

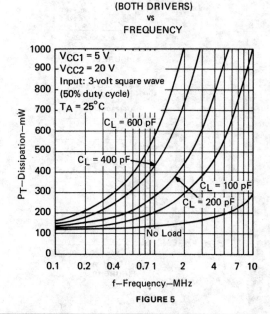

TOTAL DISSIPATION
(BOTH DRIVERS)
vs
FREQUENCY

V_{CC1} = 5 V
V_{CC2} = 20 V
Input: 3-volt square wave
(50% duty cycle)
T_A = 25°C

C_L = 600 pF
C_L = 400 pF
C_L = 100 pF
C_L = 200 pF
No Load

P_T–Dissipation–mW

f–Frequency–MHz

FIGURE 5

9

TYPICAL CHARACTERISTICS

PROPAGATION DELAY TIME,
LOW-TO-HIGH-LEVEL OUTPUT
vs
FREE-AIR TEMPERATURE

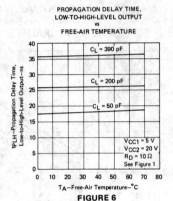

FIGURE 6

PROPAGATION DELAY TIME,
HIGH-TO-LOW-LEVEL OUTPUT
vs
FREE-AIR TEMPERATURE

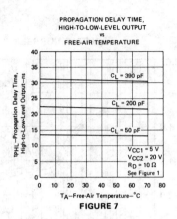

FIGURE 7

PROPAGATION DELAY TIME,
LOW-TO-HIGH-LEVEL OUTPUT
vs
V_{CC2} SUPPLY VOLTAGE

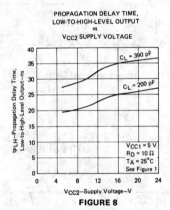

FIGURE 8

PROPAGATION DELAY TIME,
HIGH-TO-LOW-LEVEL OUTPUT
vs
V_{CC2} SUPPLY VOLTAGE

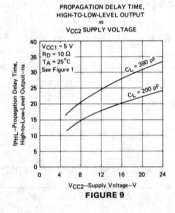

FIGURE 9

PROPAGATION DELAY TIME,
LOW-TO-HIGH-LEVEL OUTPUT
vs
LOAD CAPACITANCE

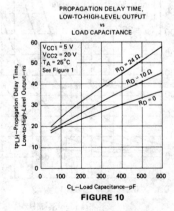

FIGURE 10

PROPAGATION DELAY TIME,
HIGH-TO-LOW-LEVEL OUTPUT
vs
LOAD CAPACITANCE

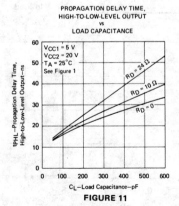

FIGURE 11

9

TEXAS INSTRUMENTS
INCORPORATED
POST OFFICE BOX 5012 • DALLAS, TEXAS 75222

TYPICAL APPLICATION DATA

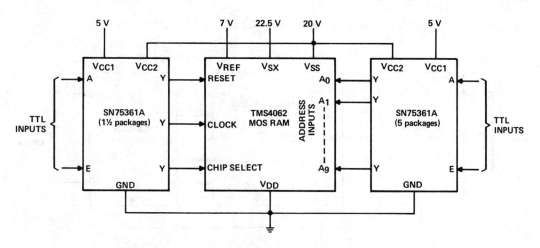

FIGURE 12—INTERCONNECTION OF SN75361A DEVICES WITH TMS4062-TYPE P-CHANNEL MOS RAM

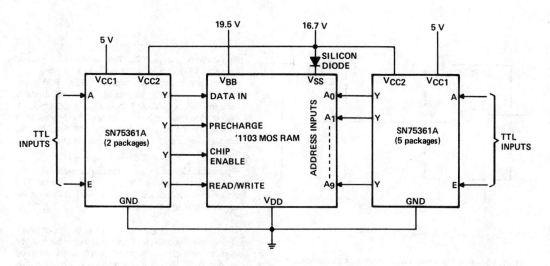

FIGURE 13—INTERCONNECTION OF SN75361A DEVICES WITH '1103-TYPE SILICON-GATE MOS RAM

9

TEXAS INSTRUMENTS
INCORPORATED
POST OFFICE BOX 5012 • DALLAS, TEXAS 75222

TYPE SN75361A
DUAL TTL-TO-MOS DRIVER

TYPICAL APPLICATION DATA

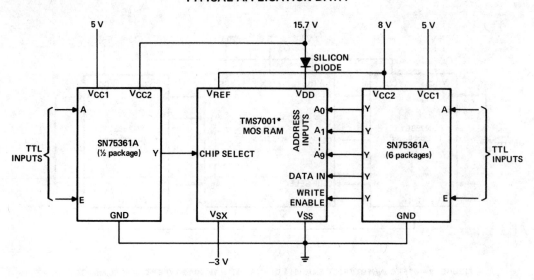

FIGURE 14—INTERCONNECTION OF SN75361A DEVICES WITH TMS7001-TYPE N-CHANNEL MOS RAM

*To be announced

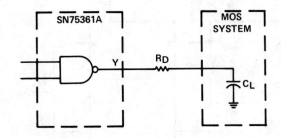

NOTE: $R_D \approx 10\,\Omega$ to $30\,\Omega$ (optional).

FIGURE 15—USE OF DAMPING RESISTOR TO REDUCE OR
ELIMINATE OUTPUT TRANSIENT OVERSHOOT IN
CERTAIN SN75361A APPLICATIONS

Applications using SN75361A as interface devices between TTL inputs and the address, control, and timing inputs for three types of MOS RAMs are shown in Figures 12, 13, and 14. A silicon diode is used in Figures 13 and 14 to increase the SN75361A high-level output voltage to obtain the desired high-level input voltage required by these MOS RAMs. An extra power supply could be used in place of the diode.

Figures 12, 13, and 14 show the use of the SN75361A over a wide range of V_{CC2} supply voltages. The device may even be used as a TTL gate, if desired, by connecting V_{CC2} to 5 volts.

The fast switching speeds of this device may produce undesirable output transient overshoot because of load or wiring inductance. A small series damping resistor may be used to reduce or eliminate this output transient overshoot. The optimum value of the damping resistor to use depends on the specific load characteristics and switching speed. A typical value would be between $10\,\Omega$ and $30\,\Omega$. See Figure 15.

TEXAS INSTRUMENTS
INCORPORATED
POST OFFICE BOX 5012 • DALLAS, TEXAS 75222

THERMAL INFORMATION

power dissipation precautions

Significant power may be dissipated in the SN75361A driver when charging and discharging high-capacitance loads over a wide voltage range at high frequencies. Figure 5 shows the power dissipated in a typical SN75361A as a function of load capacitance and frequency. Average power dissipated by this driver can be broken into three components:

$$P_{T(AV)} = P_{DC(AV)} + P_{C(AV)} + P_{S(AV)}$$

where $P_{DC(AV)}$ is the steady-state power dissipation with the output high or low, $P_{C(AV)}$ is the power level during charging or discharging of the load capacitance, and $P_{S(AV)}$ is the power dissipation during switching between the low and high levels. None of these include energy transferred to the load and all are averaged over a full cycle.

The power components per driver channel are:

$$P_{DC(AV)} = \frac{p_L t_L + p_H t_H}{T}$$

$$P_{C(AV)} \approx C\, V_C^2\, f$$

$$P_{S(AV)} = \frac{p_{LH} t_{LH} + p_{HL} t_{HL}}{T}$$

where the times are as defined in Figure 16.

p_L, p_H, p_{LH}, and p_{HL} are the respective instantaneous levels of power dissipation and C is load capacitance.

The SN75361A is so designed that P_S is a negligible portion of P_T in most applications. Except at very high frequencies, $t_L + t_H \gg t_{LH} + t_{HL}$ so that P_S can be neglected. Figure 5 for no load demonstrates this point. The power dissipation contributions from both channels are then added together to obtain total device power.

The following example illustrates this power calculation technique. Assume both channels are operating identically with C = 200 pF, f = 2 MHz, V_{CC1} = 5 V, V_{CC2} = 20 V, and duty cycle = 60% outputs high ($t_H/T = 0.6$). Also, assume V_{OH} = 19.3 V, V_{OL} = 0.1 V, P_S is negligible, and that the current from V_{CC2} is negligible when the output is high.

On a per-channel basis using data sheet values:

$$P_{DC(AV)} = \left[(5\text{ V}) \left(\frac{2\text{ mA}}{2} \right) + (20\text{ V}) \left(\frac{0\text{ mA}}{2} \right) \right] (0.6) + \left[(5\text{ V}) \left(\frac{16\text{ mA}}{2} \right) + (20\text{ V}) \left(\frac{7\text{ mA}}{2} \right) \right] (0.4)$$

$P_{DC(AV)}$ = 47 mW per channel

$P_{C(AV)} \approx (200\text{ pF})\ (19.2\text{ V})^2\ (2\text{ MHz})$

$P_{C(AV)} \approx 148$ mW per channel.

For the total device dissipation of the two channels:

$P_{T(AV)} \approx 2\ (47 + 148)$

$P_{T(AV)} \approx 390$ mW typical for total package.

9

TEXAS INSTRUMENTS
INCORPORATED
POST OFFICE BOX 5012 • DALLAS, TEXAS 75222

THERMAL INFORMATION

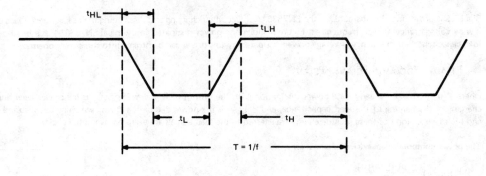

FIGURE 16—OUTPUT VOLTAGE WAVEFORM

DISSIPATION DERATING CURVE

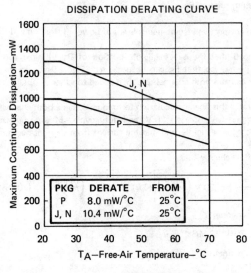

PKG	DERATE	FROM
P	8.0 mW/°C	25°C
J, N	10.4 mW/°C	25°C

FIGURE 17

TEXAS INSTRUMENTS
INCORPORATED
POST OFFICE BOX 5012 • DALLAS, TEXAS 75222

PRINTED IN U.S.A.   97

TI cannot assume any responsibility for any circuits shown
or represent that they are free from patent infringement.

TEXAS INSTRUMENTS RESERVES THE RIGHT TO MAKE CHANGES AT ANY TIME
IN ORDER TO IMPROVE DESIGN AND TO SUPPLY THE BEST PRODUCT POSSIBLE.

9

MOS MEMORY INTERFACE

- Quad Positive-Logic NAND TTL-to-MOS Driver
- Versatile Interface Circuit for Use between TTL and High-Current, High-Voltage Systems
- Capable of Driving High-Capacitance Loads
- Compatible with Many Popular MOS RAMs
- Designed to be Interchangeable with Intel 3207
- V_{CC2} Supply Voltage Variable over Wide Range to 24 Volts Maximum
- V_{CC3} Supply Voltage Pin Available
- V_{CC3} Pin Can Be Connected to V_{CC2} Pin in Some Applications
- TTL and DTL Compatible Diode-Clamped Inputs
- Operates from Standard Bipolar and MOS Supply Voltages
- Two Common Enable Inputs per Gate-Pair
- High-Speed Switching
- Transient Overdrive Minimizes Power Dissipation
- Low Standby Power Dissipation

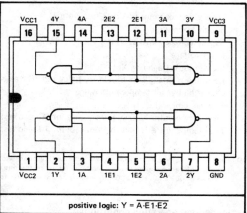

J OR N
DUAL-IN-LINE PACKAGE (TOP VIEW)

positive logic: $Y = \overline{A \cdot E1 \cdot E2}$

description

The SN75365 is a monolithic integrated quad TTL-to-MOS driver and interface circuit. The device accepts standard TTL and DTL input signals and provides high-current and high-voltage output levels suitable for driving MOS circuits. Specifically, it may be used to drive address, control, and timing inputs for several types of MOS RAMs including the '1103 and TMS4062.

The SN75365 operates from the TTL 5-volt supply and the MOS V_{SS} and V_{BB} supplies in many applications. This device has been optimized for operation with V_{CC2} supply voltage from 16 volts to 20 volts, and with nominal V_{CC3} supply voltage from 3 volts to 4 volts higher than V_{CC2}. However, it is designed so as to be useable over a much wider range of V_{CC2} and V_{CC3}. In some applications the V_{CC3} power supply can be eliminated by connecting the V_{CC3} pin to the V_{CC2} pin.

The SN75365 is characterized for operation from $0°C$ to $70°C$.

schematic (each driver)

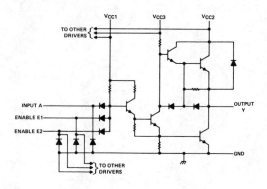

9

TEXAS INSTRUMENTS
INCORPORATED
POST OFFICE BOX 5012 • DALLAS, TEXAS 75222

TYPE SN75365
QUAD TTL-TO-MOS DRIVER

absolute maximum ratings over operating free-air temperature range (unless otherwise noted)

Supply voltage range of V_{CC1} (see Note 1) . . . . −0.5 V to 7 V

Supply voltage range of V_{CC2} . . . . −0.5 V to 25 V

Supply voltage range of V_{CC3} . . . . −0.5 V to 30 V

Input voltage . . . . 5.5 V

Inter-input voltage (see Note 2) . . . . 5.5 V

Continuous total dissipation at (or below) 25°C free-air temperature (see Note 3) . . . . 1300 mW

Operating free-air temperature range . . . . 0°C to 70°C

Storage temperature range . . . . −65°C to 150°C

Lead temperature 1/16 inch from case for 60 seconds: J package . . . . 300°C

Lead temperature 1/16 inch from case for 10 seconds: N package . . . . 260°C

NOTES: 1. Voltage values are with respect to network ground terminal unless otherwise noted.
2. This rating applies between any two inputs of any one of the gates.
3. For operation above 25°C free-air temperature, refer to Dissipation Derating Curve, Figure 18.

recommended operating conditions

	MIN	NOM	MAX	UNIT
Supply voltage, V_{CC1}	4.75	5	5.25	V
Supply voltage, V_{CC2}	4.75	20	24	V
Supply voltage, V_{CC3}	V_{CC2}	24	28	V
Voltage difference between supply voltages: $V_{CC3}-V_{CC2}$	0	4	10	V
Operating free-air temperature, T_A	0		70	°C

TEXAS INSTRUMENTS
INCORPORATED
POST OFFICE BOX 5012 • DALLAS, TEXAS 75222

electrical characteristics over recommended ranges of V_{CC1}, V_{CC2}, V_{CC3} and operating free-air temperature (unless otherwise noted)

	PARAMETER	TEST CONDITIONS	MIN	TYP†	MAX	UNIT
V_{IH}	High-level input voltage		2			V
V_{IL}	Low-level input voltage				0.8	V
V_I	Input clamp voltage	$I_I = -12$ mA			-1.5	V
V_{OH}	High-level output voltage	$V_{CC3} = V_{CC2}+3$ V, $V_{IL} = 0.8$ V, $I_{OH} = -100$ µA		$V_{CC2}-0.3$	$V_{CC2}-0.1$	V
		$V_{CC3} = V_{CC2}+3$ V, $V_{IL} = 0.8$ V, $I_{OH} = -10$ mA		$V_{CC2}-1.2$	$V_{CC2}-0.9$	
		$V_{CC3} = V_{CC2}$, $V_{IL} = 0.8$ V, $I_{OH} = -50$ µA		$V_{CC2}-1$	$V_{CC2}-0.7$	
		$V_{CC3} = V_{CC2}$, $V_{IL} = 0.8$ V, $I_{OH} = -10$ mA		$V_{CC2}-2.3$	$V_{CC2}-1.8$	
V_{OL}	Low-level output voltage	$V_{IH} = 2$ V, $I_{OL} = 10$ mA			0.15	0.3	V
		$V_{CC3} = 15$ V to 28 V, $V_{IH} = 2$ V, $I_{OL} = 40$ mA		0.25	0.5	
V_O	Output clamp voltage	$V_I = 0$ V, $I_{OH} = 20$ mA			$V_{CC2}+1.5$	V
I_I	Input current at maximum input voltage	$V_I = 5.5$ V			1	mA
I_{IH}	High-level input current	$V_I = 2.4$ V A inputs			40	µA
		$V_I = 2.4$ V E1 and E2 inputs			80	
I_{IL}	Low-level input current	$V_I = 0.4$ V A inputs		-1	-1.6	mA
		$V_I = 0.4$ V E1 and E2 inputs		-2	-3.2	
$I_{CC1(H)}$	Supply current from V_{CC1}, all outputs high	$V_{CC1} = 5.25$ V, $V_{CC2} = 24$ V, $V_{CC3} = 28$ V, All inputs at 0 V, No load		4	8	mA
$I_{CC2(H)}$	Supply current from V_{CC2}, all outputs high			-2.2	$+0.25$ / -3.2	
$I_{CC3(H)}$	Supply current from V_{CC3}, all outputs high			2.2	3.5	
$I_{CC1(L)}$	Supply current from V_{CC1}, all outputs low	$V_{CC1} = 5.25$ V, $V_{CC2} = 24$ V, $V_{CC3} = 28$ V, All inputs at 5 V, No load		31	47	mA
$I_{CC2(L)}$	Supply current from V_{CC2}, all outputs low				0.25	
$I_{CC3(L)}$	Supply current from V_{CC3}, all outputs low			16	25	
$I_{CC2(H)}$	Supply current from V_{CC2}, all outputs high	$V_{CC1} = 5.25$ V, $V_{CC2} = 24$ V, $V_{CC3} = 24$ V, All inputs at 0 V, No load			0.25	mA
$I_{CC3(H)}$	Supply current from V_{CC3}, all outputs high				0.5	
$I_{CC2(S)}$	Supply current from V_{CC2}, stand-by condition	$V_{CC1} = 0$ V, $V_{CC2} = 24$ V, $V_{CC3} = 24$ V, All inputs at 5 V, No load			0.25	mA
$I_{CC3(S)}$	Supply current from V_{CC3}, standby condition				0.5	

†All typical values are at $V_{CC1} = 5$ V, $V_{CC2} = 20$ V, $V_{CC3} = 24$ V, and $T_A = 25°$C.

switching characteristics, $V_{CC1} = 5$ V, $V_{CC2} = 20$ V, $V_{CC3} = 24$ V, $T_A = 25°$C

	PARAMETER	TEST CONDITIONS	MIN	TYP	MAX	UNIT
t_{DLH}	Delay time, low-to-high-level output	$C_L = 200$ pF, $R_D = 24$ Ω, See Figure 1		11	20	ns
t_{DHL}	Delay time, high-to-low-level output			10	18	ns
t_{TLH}	Transition time, low-to-high-level output			20	33	ns
t_{THL}	Transition time, high-to-low-level output			20	33	ns
t_{PLH}	Propagation delay time, low-to-high-level output		10	31	48	ns
t_{PHL}	Propagation delay time, high-to-low-level output		10	30	46	ns

9

TYPE SN75365
QUAD TTL-TO-MOS DRIVER

PARAMETER MEASUREMENT INFORMATION

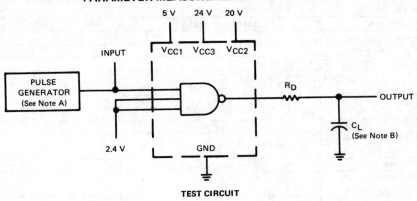

TEST CIRCUIT

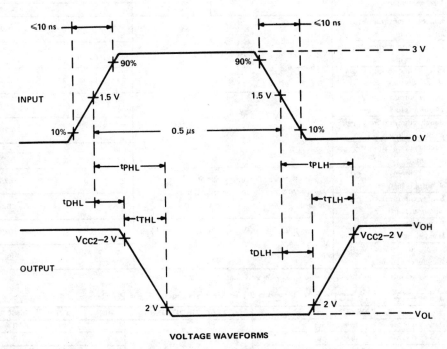

VOLTAGE WAVEFORMS

NOTES: A. The pulse generator has the following characteristics: PRR = 1 MHz, $Z_{out} \approx 50 \ \Omega$.
B. C_L includes probe and jig capacitance.

FIGURE 1—SWITCHING TIMES, EACH DRIVER

TEXAS INSTRUMENTS
INCORPORATED
POST OFFICE BOX 5012 • DALLAS, TEXAS 75222

TYPICAL CHARACTERISTICS

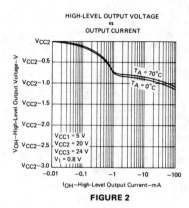

HIGH-LEVEL OUTPUT VOLTAGE
vs
OUTPUT CURRENT

FIGURE 2

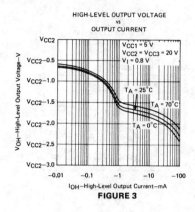

HIGH-LEVEL OUTPUT VOLTAGE
vs
OUTPUT CURRENT

FIGURE 3

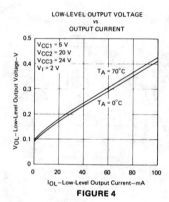

LOW-LEVEL OUTPUT VOLTAGE
vs
OUTPUT CURRENT

FIGURE 4

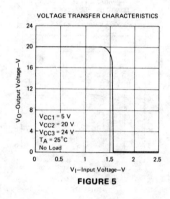

VOLTAGE TRANSFER CHARACTERISTICS

FIGURE 5

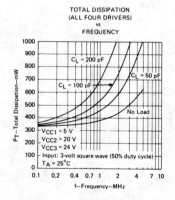

TOTAL DISSIPATION
(ALL FOUR DRIVERS)
vs
FREQUENCY

FIGURE 6

TEXAS INSTRUMENTS
INCORPORATED
POST OFFICE BOX 5012 • DALLAS, TEXAS 75222

TYPE SN75365
QUAD TTL-TO-MOS DRIVER

TYPICAL CHARACTERISTICS

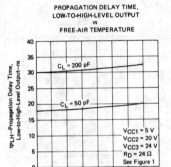

PROPAGATION DELAY TIME,
LOW-TO-HIGH-LEVEL OUTPUT
vs
FREE-AIR TEMPERATURE

FIGURE 7

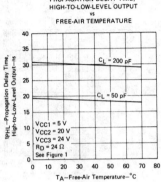

PROPAGATION DELAY TIME,
HIGH-TO-LOW-LEVEL OUTPUT
vs
FREE-AIR TEMPERATURE

FIGURE 8

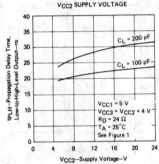

PROPAGATION DELAY TIME,
LOW-TO-HIGH-LEVEL OUTPUT
vs
V_{CC2} SUPPLY VOLTAGE

FIGURE 9

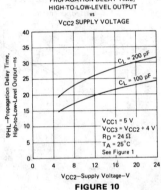

PROPAGATION DELAY TIME,
HIGH-TO-LOW-LEVEL OUTPUT
vs
V_{CC2} SUPPLY VOLTAGE

FIGURE 10

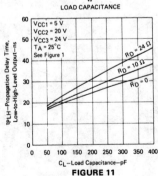

PROPAGATION DELAY TIME,
LOW-TO-HIGH-LEVEL OUTPUT
vs
LOAD CAPACITANCE

FIGURE 11

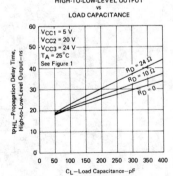

PROPAGATION DELAY TIME,
HIGH-TO-LOW-LEVEL OUTPUT
vs
LOAD CAPACITANCE

FIGURE 12

9

TEXAS INSTRUMENTS
INCORPORATED
POST OFFICE BOX 5012 • DALLAS, TEXAS 75222

TYPICAL APPLICATION DATA

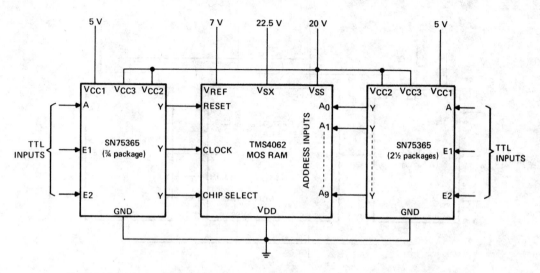

FIGURE 13—INTERCONNECTION OF SN75365 DEVICES WITH TMS4062-TYPE P-CHANNEL MOS RAM

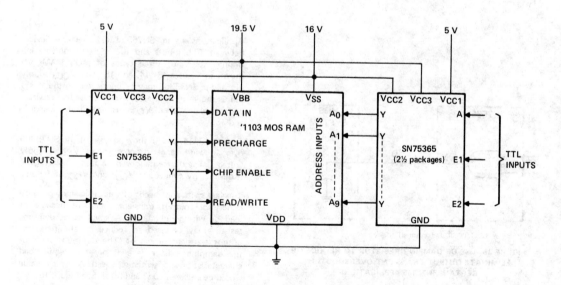

FIGURE 14—INTERCONNECTION OF SN75365 DEVICES WITH '1103-TYPE SILICON-GATE MOS RAM

TYPE SN75365
QUAD TTL-TO-MOS DRIVER

TYPICAL APPLICATION DATA

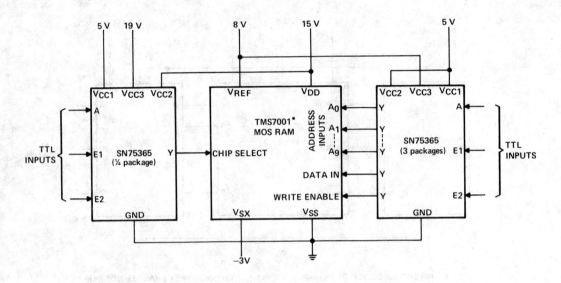

FIGURE 15—INTERCONNECTION OF SN75365 DEVICES WITH TMS7001-TYPE N-CHANNEL MOS RAM

*To be announced

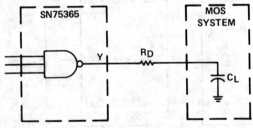

NOTE: $R_D \approx 10\ \Omega$ TO $30\ \Omega$ (optional).

FIGURE 16—USE OF DAMPING RESISTOR TO REDUCE OR
ELIMINATE OUTPUT TRANSIENT OVERSHOOT IN
CERTAIN SN75365 APPLICATIONS

Applications using SN75365 as interface devices between TTL inputs and the address, control, and timing inputs for three types of MOS RAMs are shown in Figures 13, 14, and 15. The V_{CC3} supply pin of the SN75365 may be connected to the V_{CC2} pin as shown in Figure 13 or connected to a separate voltage higher than V_{CC2} as shown in Figures 14 and 15.

Figures 13, 14, and 15 show the use of the SN75365 over a wide range of V_{CC2} and V_{CC3} supply voltages. The device may even be used as a TTL gate, if desired, by connecting V_{CC2} and V_{CC3} to 5 volts.

The fast switching speeds of this device may produce undesirable output transient overshoot because of load or wiring inductance. A small series damping resistor may be used to reduce or eliminate this output transient overshoot. The optimum value of the damping resistor depends on the specific load characteristics and switching speed. A typical value would be between $10\ \Omega$ and $30\ \Omega$. See Figure 16.

TEXAS INSTRUMENTS
INCORPORATED
POST OFFICE BOX 5012 • DALLAS, TEXAS 75222

THERMAL INFORMATION

power dissipation precautions

Significant power may be dissipated in the SN75365 driver when charging and discharging high capacitance loads over a wide voltage range at high-frequencies. Figure 6 shows the power dissipated in a typical SN75365 as a function of frequency and load capacitance. Average power dissipated by this driver can be broken into three components:

$$P_{T(AV)} = P_{DC(AV)} + P_{C(AV)} + P_{S(AV)}$$

where $P_{DC(AV)}$ is the steady-state power dissipation with the output high or low, $P_{C(AV)}$ is the power level during charging or discharging of the load capacitance, and $P_{S(AV)}$ is the power dissipation during switching between the low and high levels. None of these include energy transferred to the load and all are averaged over a full cycle.

The power components per driver channel are:

$$P_{DC(AV)} = \frac{P_L t_L + P_H t_H}{T}$$

$$P_{C(AV)} \approx C V_C^2 f$$

$$P_{S(AV)} = \frac{P_{LH} t_{LH} + P_{HL} t_{HL}}{T}$$

where the times are as defined in Figure 17.

P_L, P_H, P_{LH}, and P_{HL} are the respective instantaneous levels of power dissipation and C is load capacitance.

The SN75365 is so designed that P_S is a negligible portion of P_T in most applications. Except at very high frequencies, $t_L + t_H \gg t_{LH} + t_{HL}$ so that P_S can be neglected. Figure 6 for no load demonstrates this point. The power dissipation contributions from all four channels are then added together to obtain total device power.

The following example illustrates this power calculation technique. Assume all four channels are operating identically with $C = 100$ pF, $f = 2$ MHz, $V_{CC1} = 5$ V, $V_{CC2} = 20$ V, $V_{CC3} = 24$ V and duty cycle = 60% outputs high ($t_H/T = 0.6$). Also, assume $V_{OH} = 20$ V, $V_{OL} = 0.1$ V, P_S is negligible, and that the current from V_{CC2} is negligible when the output is low.

On a per-channel basis using data sheet values:

$$P_{DC(AV)} = \left[(5\text{ V})\left(\frac{4\text{ mA}}{4}\right) + (20\text{ V})\left(\frac{-2.2\text{ mA}}{4}\right) + (24\text{ V})\left(\frac{2.2\text{ mA}}{4}\right)\right](0.6) +$$

$$\left[(5\text{ V})\left(\frac{31\text{ mA}}{4}\right) + (20\text{ V})\left(\frac{0\text{ mA}}{4}\right) + (24\text{ V})\left(\frac{16\text{ mA}}{4}\right)\right](0.4)$$

$P_{DC(AV)} = 58$ mW per channel

$P_{C(AV)} \approx (100\text{ pF})(19.9\text{ V})^2(2\text{ MHz})$

$P_{C(AV)} \approx 79$ mW per channel.

For the total device dissipation of the four channels:

$P_{T(AV)} \approx 4(58 + 79)$

$P_{T(AV)} \approx 548$ mW typical for total package.

9

THERMAL INFORMATION

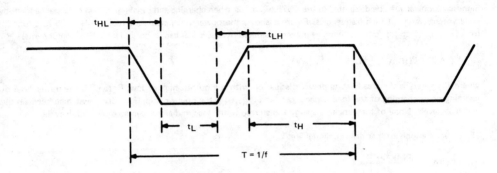

FIGURE 17—OUTPUT VOLTAGE WAVEFORM

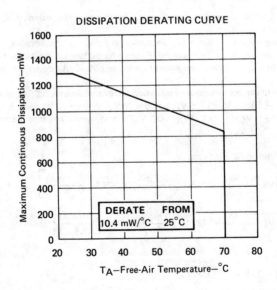

DISSIPATION DERATING CURVE

FIGURE 18

TEXAS INSTRUMENTS
INCORPORATED
POST OFFICE BOX 5012 • DALLAS, TEXAS 75222

DUAL READ/WRITE AMPLIFIER FOR INTERFACING BETWEEN TTL AND TMS4062-TYPE MOS RANDOM-ACCESS MEMORY (RAM)

performance features

- Node Terminals Connect Directly to I/O Terminals of TMS4062 (AMS6002) and Similar MOS RAMs

- In Write Mode, Write Driver Provides Complementary High-Voltage Outputs at Node Terminals

- In Read Mode, Read Amplifier Responds to Small Differential-Input Current in Node Terminals

ease of design features

- TTL and DTL Compatible Diode-Clamped Inputs

- TTL and DTL Compatible Data Outputs

- 50-mA Data Output Sink-Current Capability

- Data Outputs May Be Wire-AND Connected

- Operates Over Wide Range of Supply Voltages

- Minimizes or Eliminates External Components

description

The SN75370 is a monolithic integrated circuit read/write amplifier that is designed to interface the Input/Output (I/O) terminals of the TMS4062 (AMS6002) and similar type MOS RAMs with TTL.

The device contains two separate channels. Each channel consists of a write driver and a read amplifier, which are common at the input/output node (N) terminals. These terminals are outputs for the write driver and inputs for the read amplifier. In the write mode, the write driver circuit is designed to write MOS-level binary information into the MOS RAM under control of TTL inputs. In the read mode, the read amplifier is designed to read MOS-level binary information from the MOS RAM and convert it to TTL levels at the data output. This is controlled by TTL inputs also.

Data outputs are constructed so that they may be wire-AND connected to other outputs and/or be connected to an external pull-up resistor, if desired. The device has a chip-enable input common to both channels which can be used to enable the entire device. Internal voltage regulators permit circuit operation over a wide range of supply voltages.

functional block diagram (each channel)

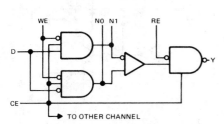

JB OR N
DUAL-IN-LINE PACKAGE (TOP VIEW)

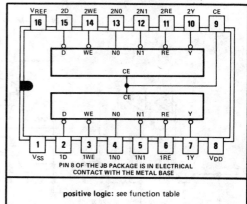

PIN 8 OF THE JB PACKAGE IS IN ELECTRICAL CONTACT WITH THE METAL BASE

positive logic: see function table

FUNCTION TABLE

MODE	VOLTAGE INPUTS				VOLTAGE OUTPUTS		DIFFERENTIAL CURRENT INPUT	OUTPUT
	CE	WE	RE	D	N0	N1	N1–N0	Y
Write 0	H	L	H	L	H	L	X	H
Write 1	H	L	H	H	L	H	X	H
Read 0	H	H	L	X	L	L	L	L
Read 1	H	H	L	X	L	L	H	H
Standby	H	H	H	X	L	L	X	H
Disabled	L	X	X	X	L	L	X	Off

H = high level (voltage or current), L = low level (voltage or current), X = irrelevant
Input levels at CE, WE, RE, and D, and output levels at Y are TTL-compatible.
Voltage output levels at N fall between V_{SS} and V_{REF}.

TEXAS INSTRUMENTS
INCORPORATED
POST OFFICE BOX 5012 • DALLAS, TEXAS 75222

schematic

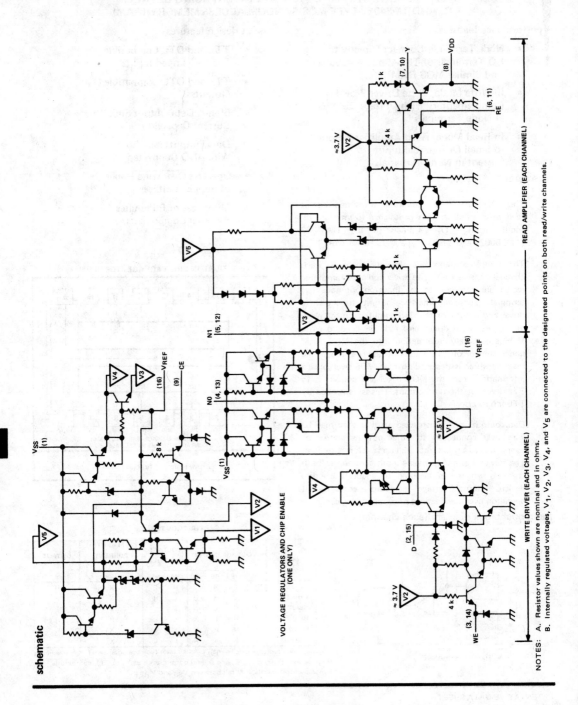

VOLTAGE REGULATORS AND CHIP ENABLE
(ONE ONLY)

WRITE DRIVER (EACH CHANNEL)

READ AMPLIFIER (EACH CHANNEL)

NOTES: A. Resistor values shown are nominal and in ohms.
        B. Internally regulated voltages, V_1, V_2, V_3, V_4, and V_5 are connected to the designated points on both read/write channels.

TEXAS INSTRUMENTS
INCORPORATED
POST OFFICE BOX 5012 • DALLAS, TEXAS 75222

absolute maximum ratings over operating free-air temperature range (unless otherwise noted)

Supply voltage range, V_{SS} (see Note 1)	−0.5 V to 25 V
Supply voltage range, V_{REF}	−0.5 V to 15 V
Voltage-difference range between supply voltages, $V_{SS}-V_{REF}$	−0.5 V to 20 V
Input voltage at CE, WE, RE, or D	5.5 V
Output voltage at Y	7 V
Continuous output current into Y	50 mA
Continuous current into any node terminal	±40 mA
Continuous total dissipation at (or below) 25°C free-air temperature (see Note 2)	1300 mW
Operating free-air temperature range	0°C to 70°C
Storage temperature range	−65°C to 150°C
Lead temperature 1/16 inch from case for 60 seconds: JB package	300°C
Lead temperature 1/16 inch from case for 10 seconds: N package	260°C

NOTES: 1. Voltage values are with respect to the V_{DD} terminal unless otherwise noted.
2. For operation above 25°C free-air temperature, refer to Dissipation Derating Curve, Figure 35.

recommended operating conditions

	MIN	NOM	MAX	UNIT
Supply voltage, V_{SS}	17	20	22	V
Supply voltage, V_{REF}	4.5	7	10	V
Voltage difference between supply voltages, $V_{SS}-V_{REF}$	8	13	16	V
Operating free-air temperature, T_A	0		70	°C

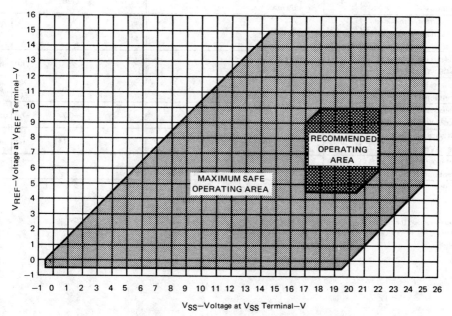

FIGURE 1—MAXIMUM SAFE OPERATING AREA AND RECOMMENDED OPERATING AREA

TEXAS INSTRUMENTS
INCORPORATED
POST OFFICE BOX 5012 • DALLAS, TEXAS 75222

definition of input logic levels

PARAMETER		B (LEAST POSITIVE)	A (MOST POSITIVE)	UNIT
V_{IH}	High-level input voltage at CE, WE, RE, or D	2		V
V_{IL}	Low-level input voltage at CE, WE, RE, or D		0.8	V
I_{IDH}	High-level differential input current in node terminals (see Note 3)	50		μA
I_{IHL}	Low-level differential input current in node terminals (see Note 3)		−50	μA

NOTE 3: $I_{ID} = I_{N1} - I_{N0}$ with current into a terminal being a positive value.

electrical characteristics over recommended ranges of V_{SS}, V_{REF}, and operating free-air temperature (unless otherwise noted)

PARAMETER		TEST FIGURE	TEST CONDITIONS		MIN	TYP[†]	MAX	UNIT
V_I	Input clamp voltage at CE, WE, RE, or D	2	$I_I = -12$ mA				−1.5	V
V_{ONH}	High-level output voltage at node terminals	3	$V_{IH} = 2$ V, $V_{IL} = 0.8$ V, $I_{NH} = 0$		$V_{SS}-2$	$V_{SS}-1.6$		V
			$V_{IH} = 2$ V, $V_{IL} = 0.8$ V, $I_{NH} = -40$ mA		$V_{SS}-3$	$V_{SS}-2$		
V_{ONL}	Low-level output voltage at node terminals	3	$V_{IH} = 2$ V, $V_{IL} = 0.8$ V, $I_{NL} = 0$		V_{REF}	$V_{REF}+0.2$	$V_{REF}+1$	V
			$V_{IH} = 2$ V, $V_{IL} = 0.8$ V, $I_{NL} = 20$ mA		V_{REF}	$V_{REF}+1.2$	$V_{REF}+2$	
I_{OH}	High-level output current into output Y	4	$V_{IH} = 2$ V, $V_{IL} = 0.8$ V, $I_{IDH} = 50$ μA, $V_{OH} = 5.5$ V				100	μA
V_{OH}	High-level output voltage at output Y	4	$V_{IH} = 2$ V, $V_{IL} = 0.8$ V, $I_{IDH} = 50$ μA, $I_{OH} = -200$ μA		2.2	2.8	4.5	V
V_{OL}	Low-level output voltage at output Y	4	$V_{IH} = 2$ V, $V_{IL} = 0.8$ V, $I_{IDL} = -50$ μA, $I_{OL} = 50$ mA			0.25	0.4	V
I_I	Input current at maximum input voltage into CE, WE, RE, or D	5	$V_I = 5.5$ V				1	mA
I_{IH}	High-level input current into CE, WE, or RE	5	$V_I = 2.4$ V				40	μA
I_{IH}	High-level input current into D	5	$V_I = 2.4$ V			−150	+80 −600	μA
I_{IL}	Low-level input current into CE, WE, RE, or D	2	$V_I = 0.4$ V			−0.7	−1.6	mA
r_N	Resistance from any node to V_{REF}	6	V_{SS} open, $V_{REF} = 0$, $I_N = 500$ μA, $T_A = 25°C$		0.7	1[‡]	1.3	kΩ
I_{OS}	Short-circuit output current into D	7	$V_O = 0$ V	CE at 2 V		−3.2	−4.5	mA
				CE at 0.8 V			−1	

See next page for supply current and dissipation.

[†]All typical values, except for r_N and $I_{REF(D, O)}$, are at $V_{SS} = 20$ V, $V_{REF} = 7$ V, $T_A = 25°C$.
[‡]Typical value of r_N is with V_{SS} open, $V_{REF} = 0$ V, $T_A = 25°C$.

9

TEXAS INSTRUMENTS
INCORPORATED
POST OFFICE BOX 5012 • DALLAS, TEXAS 75222

supply current and dissipation over operating free-air temperature range (unless otherwise noted)

PARAMETER		MODE	TEST FIGURE	TEST CONDITIONS	MIN	TYP[†]	MAX	UNIT
$I_{SS(D)}$	Current from V_{SS}	Disabled	8	V_{SS} = 20 V, V_{REF} = 7 V		27	35	mA
$I_{REF(D)}$	Current from V_{REF}					−20	−25	mA
P_D	Dissipation					410	500	mW
$I_{SS(SB)}$	Current from V_{SS}	Standby	8	V_{SS} = 20 V, V_{REF} = 7 V		31	39	mA
$I_{REF(SB)}$	Current from V_{REF}					−12	−18	mA
P_{SB}	Dissipation					540	690	mW
$I_{SS(R1)}$	Current from V_{SS}	Read-1	8	V_{SS} = 20 V, V_{REF} = 7 V, I_{N1} = 100 μA		31	39	mA
$I_{REF(R1)}$	Current from V_{REF}					−12	−18	mA
P_{R1}	Dissipation					540	690	mW
$I_{SS(R0)}$	Current from V_{SS}	Read-0	8	V_{SS} = 20 V, V_{REF} = 7 V, I_{N0} = 100 μA		31	39	mA
$I_{REF(R0)}$	Current from V_{REF}					4	10	mA
P_{R0}	Dissipation					640	790	mW
$I_{SS(W)}$	Current from V_{SS}	Write	8	V_{SS} = 20 V, V_{REF} = 7 V, See Note 4		53	66	mA
$I_{REF(W)}$	Current from V_{REF}					−23	−31	mA
P_W	Dissipation					910	1100	mW
$I_{REF(D, O)}$	Current from V_{REF}	Disabled, V_{SS}-open	8	V_{SS} open, V_{REF} = 10 V		2[§]	5	mA

[†]All typical values, except for r_N and $I_{REF(D,O)}$, are at V_{SS} = 20 V, V_{REF} = 7 V, T_A = 25°C.
[§]Typical value of $I_{REF(D,O)}$ is with V_{SS} open, V_{REF} = 7 V, T_A = 25°C.
NOTE 4: Duty cycle in the write mode must be low enough to maintain the average dissipation within the continuous dissipation rated limit when averaged over short intervals.

switching characteristics, V_{SS} = 20 V, V_{REF} = 7 V, $C_{I/O}$ = 40 pF, R_L = 400 Ω, T_A = 25°C

PARAMETER[¶]	FROM (INPUT)	TO (OUTPUT)	TEST FIGURE	TEST CONDITIONS	MIN	TYP	MAX	UNIT
t_{PLH}	WE	N	10			52	80	ns
t_{PHL}						31	47	
t_{PLH}	D	N	11			44	70	ns
t_{PHL}						30	45	
t_{PLH}	CE	N	12			60	95	ns
t_{PHL}						43	65	
t_{PLH}	RE	Y	13	I_{ID} = −100 μA		13	20	ns
t_{PHL}						19	28	
t_{PLH}	CE	Y	14	I_{ID} = −100 μA		25	38	ns
t_{PHL}						32	48	
t_{PLH}	N0	Y	15			25	40	ns
t_{PHL}						25	40	
t_{PLH}	N1	Y	16			25	40	ns
t_{PHL}						25	40	
t_{PLH}	WE	Y	17	I_{N1} = 100 μA		135	190	ns
t_{PHL}				I_{N0} = 100 μA		125	190	

[¶]t_{PLH} ≡ propagation delay time, low-to-high-level output.
t_{PHL} ≡ propagation delay time, high-to-low-level output.

9

TYPE SN75370
DUAL-CHANNEL INTERFACE TO MOS MEMORIES

PARAMETER MEASUREMENT INFORMATION

d-c test circuits†

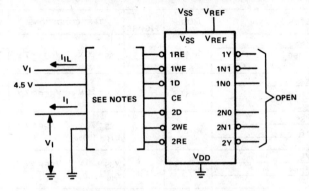

NOTES: A. WE, RE, and D inputs are tested for two conditions of CE: CE at 4.5 V and CE at 0 V.
        B. When WE is low, these parameters must be measured using pulse techniques. t_W = 200 μs, duty cycle ≤ 20%.

FIGURE 2—V_I and I_{IL}

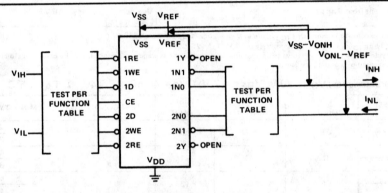

NOTE A: When WE is low, these parameters must be measured using pulse techniques. t_W = 200 μs, duty cycle ≤ 20%.

FIGURE 3—V_{IH}, V_{IL}, V_{ONH}, and V_{ONL}

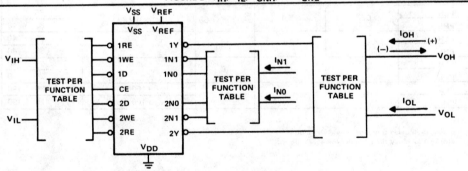

NOTES: A. I/O terminals are used as inputs.
        B. For testing purposes: I_{IDH} = I_{N1} with I_{N0} = 0. (Current into I_{N1} terminal only.)
             $-I_{IDL}$ = I_{N0} with I_{N1} = 0. (Current into I_{N0} terminal only.)
        C. When WE is low, these parameters must be measured using pulse techniques. t_W = 200 μs, duty cycle ≤ 20%.

FIGURE 4—V_{IH}, V_{IL}, I_{IDH}, I_{IDL}, V_{OH}, V_{OL}, I_{OH}

†Arrows indicate actual direction of current flow. Current into a terminal is a positive value.

TEXAS INSTRUMENTS
INCORPORATED
POST OFFICE BOX 5012 • DALLAS, TEXAS 75222

PARAMETER MEASUREMENT INFORMATION

d-c test circuits† (continued)

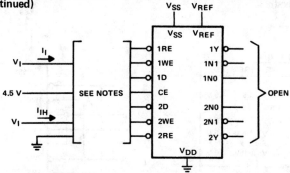

NOTES: A. WE, RE, and D inputs are tested for two conditions of CE: CE at 4.5 V and CE at 0 V.
B. When WE is low, these parameters must be measured using pulse techniques. t_W = 200 μs, duty cycle ⩽ 20%.

FIGURE 5—I_I and I_{IH}

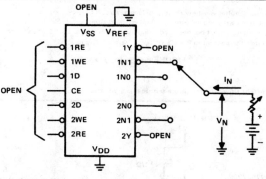

NOTE A: Resistance r_N is calculated using the equation: $r_N = \dfrac{V_N}{I_N}$.

FIGURE 6—r_N

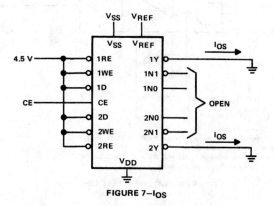

FIGURE 7—I_{OS}

†Arrows indicate actual direction of current flow. Current into a terminal is a positive value.

TEXAS INSTRUMENTS
INCORPORATED
POST OFFICE BOX 5012 • DALLAS, TEXAS 75222

DUAL-CHANNEL INTERFACE TO MOS MEMORIES

PARAMETER MEASUREMENT INFORMATION

d-c test circuits† (continued)

TEST TABLE

MODE	CE	WE	RE	D
Disabled	0 V	0 V	0 V	4.5 V
Standby	4.5 V	4.5 V	4.5 V	4.5 V
Read-1	4.5 V	4.5 V	0 V	4.5 V
Read-0	4.5 V	4.5 V	0 V	0 V
Write	4.5 V	0 V	4.5 V	4.5 V
Disabled, V_{SS}-open	0 V	0 V	0 V	0 V

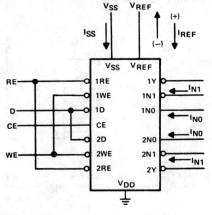

NOTES: A. I_{SS} and I_{REF} are measured simultaneously with both halves of circuit biased identically.
      B. All node terminals are open except as noted otherwise in test conditions.
      C. When WE is low, these parameters must be measured using pulse techniques. t_w = 200 μs, duty cycle ≤ 20%.
      D. Dissipation is calculated using the equation $P = V_{SS} \cdot I_{SS} + V_{REF} \cdot I_{REF}$.

FIGURE 8—I_{SS}, I_{REF}, and P

†Arrows indicate actual direction of current flow. Current into a terminal is a positive value.

switching characteristics

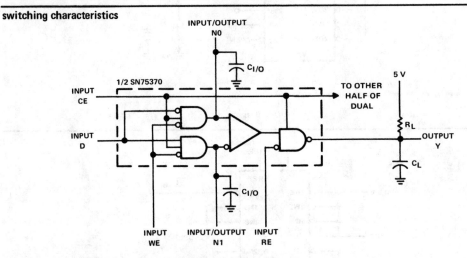

NOTES: A. Refer to this figure and notes for all switching tests.
      B. The pulse generator has the following characteristics: PRR = 1 MHz, Z_{out} ≈ 50 Ω.
      C. C_L and $C_{I/O}$ include probe and jig capacitance.
      D. Input conditions for channel not under test: WE and RE at 2.4 V, D at 0.4 V.
      E. N terminals are connected only to $C_{I/O}$ unless otherwise noted.

FIGURE 9—SWITCHING TEST CIRCUIT

TEXAS INSTRUMENTS
INCORPORATED
POST OFFICE BOX 5012 • DALLAS, TEXAS 75222

PARAMETER MEASUREMENT INFORMATION

switching characteristics (continued)

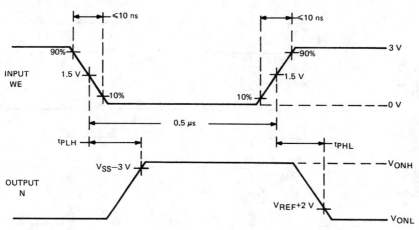

NOTES: A. See Figure 9.
 B. Output N0 is tested with D at 0.4 V and output N1 is tested with D at 2.4 V.
 C. Input conditions for other inputs of channel under test: CE at 2.4 V, RE at 2.4 V.

FIGURE 10—VOLTAGE WAVEFORMS, WE TO N

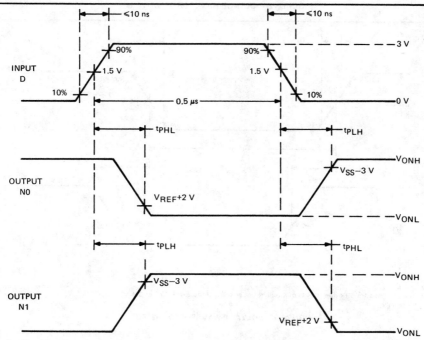

NOTES: A. See Figure 9.
 B. Input conditions for other inputs of channel under test: CE at 2.4 V, WE at 0.4 V, RE at 2.4 V.

FIGURE 11—VOLTAGE WAVEFORMS, D TO N

9

73

TEXAS INSTRUMENTS
INCORPORATED
POST OFFICE BOX 5012 • DALLAS, TEXAS 75222

PARAMETER MEASUREMENT INFORMATION
switching characteristics (continued)

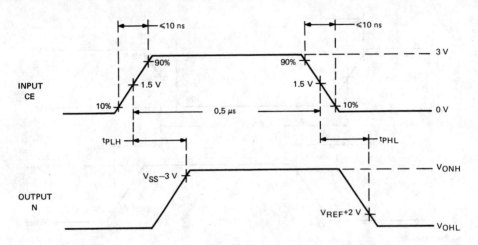

NOTES: A. See Figure 9.
B. Output N0 is tested with D at 0.4 V and output N1 is tested with D at 2.4 V.
C. Input conditions for all other inputs of channel under test: WE at 0.4 V, RE at 2.4 V.

FIGURE 12–VOLTAGE WAVEFORMS, CE TO N

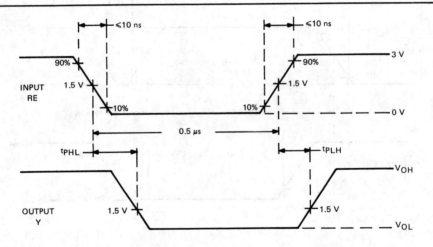

NOTES: A. See Figure 9.
B. Input conditions for all other inputs of channel under test: CE at 2.4 V, WE at 2.4 V, D at 0.4 V.
C. I_{NO} = 100 μA.

FIGURE 13–VOLTAGE WAVEFORMS, RE TO Y

9

TEXAS INSTRUMENTS
INCORPORATED
POST OFFICE BOX 5012 • DALLAS, TEXAS 75222

PARAMETER MEASUREMENT INFORMATION
switching characteristics (continued)

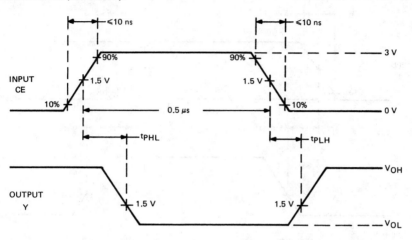

NOTES: A. See Figure 9.
B. Input conditons for all other inputs of channel under test: WE at 2.4 V, RE at 0.4 V, D at 0.4 V.
C. I_{NO} = 100 μA.

FIGURE 14—VOLTAGE WAVEFORMS, CE TO Y

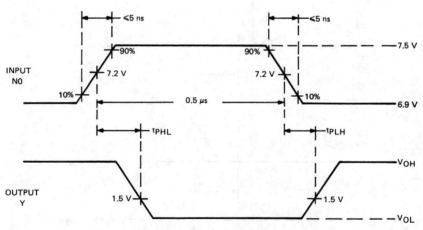

NOTES: A. See Figure 9.
B. Input conditions for all other inputs of channel under test: CE at 2.4 V, WE at 2.4 V, RE at 0.4 V, D at 2.4 V.

FIGURE 15—VOLTAGE WAVEFORMS, N0 TO Y

9

PARAMETER MEASUREMENT INFORMATION
switching characteristics (continued)

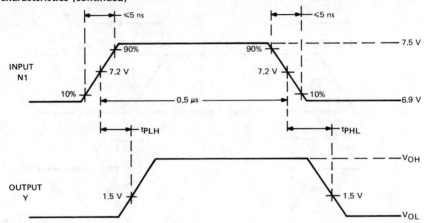

NOTES: A. See Figure 9.
         B. Input conditions for other inputs of channel under test: CE at 2.4 V, WE at 2.4 V, RE at 0.4 V, D at 2.4 V.

FIGURE 16—VOLTAGE WAVEFORMS, N1 TO Y

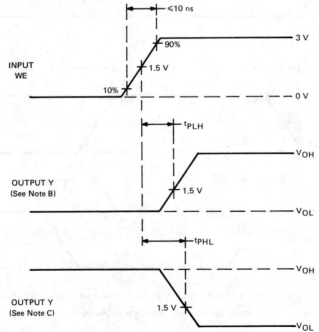

NOTES: A. See Figure 9.
         B. t_{PLH} is tested with I_{N1} = 100 μA, D at 0.4 V, CE at 2.4 V, RE at 0.4 V.
         C. t_{PHL} is tested with I_{N0} = 100 μA, D at 2.4 V, CE at 2.4 V, RE at 0.4 V.
         D. Duty cycle of input WE pulse generator is 50%.

FIGURE 17—VOLTAGE WAVEFORMS, WE TO Y

TEXAS INSTRUMENTS
INCORPORATED
POST OFFICE BOX 5012 • DALLAS, TEXAS 75222

TYPICAL CHARACTERISTICS

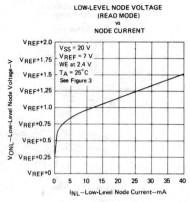

LOW-LEVEL NODE VOLTAGE
(READ MODE)
vs
NODE CURRENT

FIGURE 18

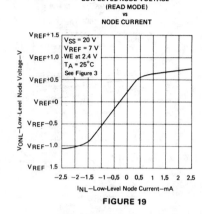

LOW-LEVEL NODE VOLTAGE
(READ MODE)
vs
NODE CURRENT

FIGURE 19

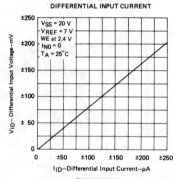

DIFFERENTIAL INPUT VOLTAGE
(READ MODE)
vs
DIFFERENTIAL INPUT CURRENT

FIGURE 20

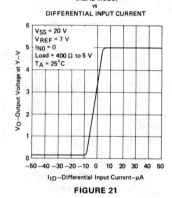

OUTPUT VOLTAGE AT Y
(READ MODE)
vs
DIFFERENTIAL INPUT CURRENT

FIGURE 21

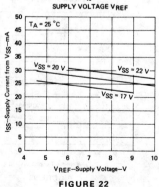

SUPPLY CURRENT FROM V_{SS}
(DISABLED MODE)
vs
SUPPLY VOLTAGE V_{REF}

FIGURE 22

SUPPLY CURRENT FROM V_{REF}
(DISABLED MODE)
vs
SUPPLY VOLTAGE V_{REF}

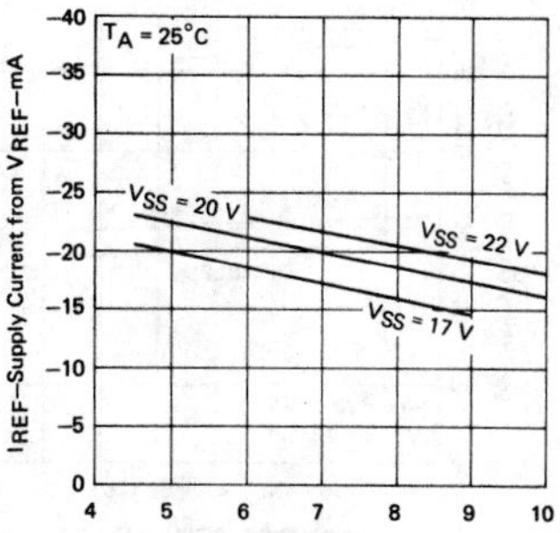

FIGURE 23

TEXAS INSTRUMENTS
INCORPORATED
POST OFFICE BOX 5012 • DALLAS, TEXAS 75222

TYPICAL CHARACTERISTICS

SUPPLY CURRENT FROM V_SS
(READ-1, READ-0, OR STANDBY MODE)
vs
SUPPLY VOLTAGE V_REF

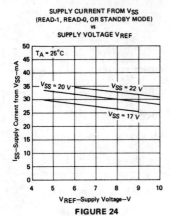

FIGURE 24

SUPPLY CURRENT FROM V_REF
(READ-1, READ-0, OR STANDBY MODE)
vs
SUPPLY VOLTAGE V_REF

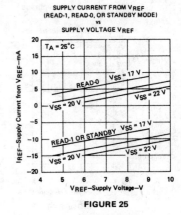

FIGURE 25

SUPPLY CURRENT FROM V_SS
(WRITE MODE)
vs
SUPPLY VOLTAGE V_REF

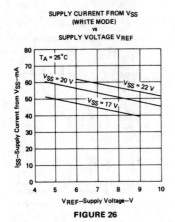

FIGURE 26

SUPPLY CURRENT FROM V_REF
(WRITE MODE)
vs
SUPPLY VOLTAGE V_REF

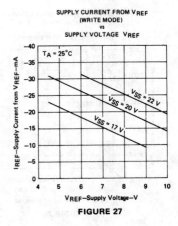

FIGURE 27

SUPPLY CURRENT FROM V_SS
vs
FREE-AIR TEMPERATURE

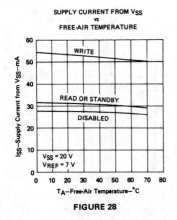

FIGURE 28

SUPPLY VOLTAGE FROM V_REF
vs
FREE-AIR TEMPERATURE

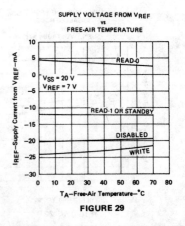

FIGURE 29

9

973

TEXAS INSTRUMENTS
INCORPORATED
POST OFFICE BOX 5012 • DALLAS, TEXAS 75222

TYPICAL APPLICATION DATA

Figure 30 illustrates a typical MOS memory system using SN75370, TMS4062, and SN75361A. All inputs and outputs from this system are TTL-compatible. The SN75361A is a high-speed monolithic dual TTL-to-MOS driver. The address SN75361As select a cell in each of the 72 TMS4062s. In Figure 30 the I/O terminals of the eight TMS4062 RAMs in each row have been connected to the node terminals of the associated SN75370 channel. Time multiplexing of the column of RAMs (M) by the SN75361A Clock/CS and Reset drivers is then used to write into or read from the cells that have been selected by the address SN75361As.

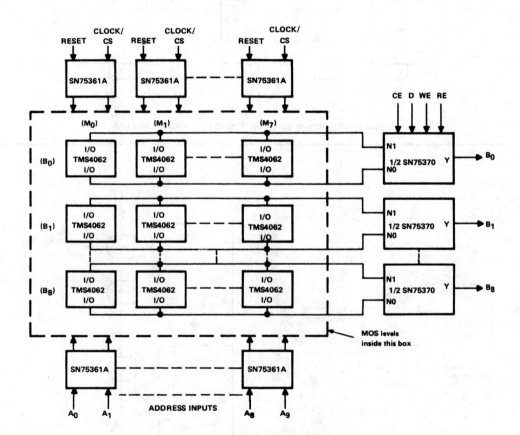

FIGURE 30—BLOCK DIAGRAM OF TOTALLY TTL-COMPATIBLE 8K X 9-BIT MOS-MEMORY SYSTEM USING SN75370, TMS4062, AND SN75361A

9

TEXAS INSTRUMENTS
INCORPORATED
POST OFFICE BOX 5012 • DALLAS, TEXAS 75222

TYPE SN75370
DUAL-CHANNEL INTERFACE TO MOS MEMORIES

TYPICAL APPLICATION DATA

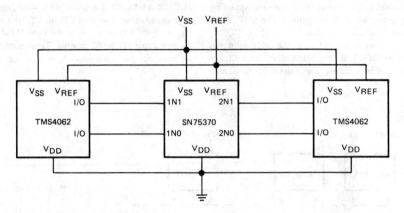

FIGURE 31—INTERCONNECTION OF SN75370 WITH TMS4062 MOS RAM

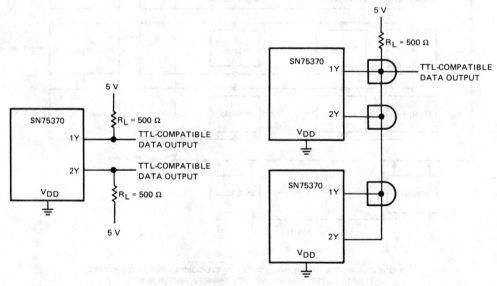

NOTE A: Pull-up resistor R_L is not necessary, but may be desirable for faster low-to-high-level transition of data output and increased TTL high-level noise margin. The value of R_L is determined by the user based upon the constraints of the system.

FIGURE 32—METHODS OF USING DATA OUTPUTS OF SN75370

97

TEXAS INSTRUMENTS
INCORPORATED
POST OFFICE BOX 5012 • DALLAS, TEXAS 75222

TYPICAL APPLICATION DATA

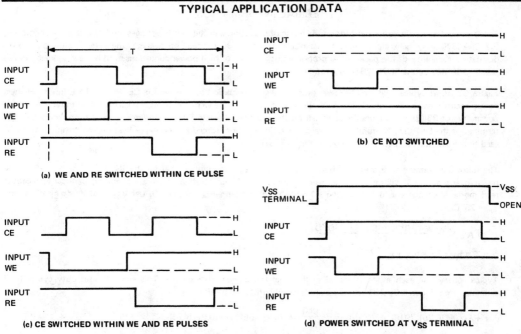

(a) WE AND RE SWITCHED WITHIN CE PULSE

(b) CE NOT SWITCHED

(c) CE SWITCHED WITHIN WE AND RE PULSES

(d) POWER SWITCHED AT V_{SS} TERMINAL

FIGURE 33—TYPICAL OPERATING INPUT VOLTAGE WAVEFORMS FOR SN75370

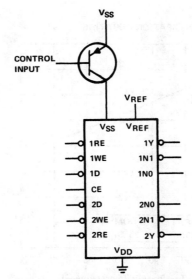

FIGURE 34—SWITCHING POWER TO V_{SS} TERMINAL
OF SN75370 USING P-N-P TRANSISTOR

TEXAS INSTRUMENTS
INCORPORATED
POST OFFICE BOX 5012 • DALLAS, TEXAS 75222

DUAL-CHANNEL INTERFACE TO MOS MEMORIES

THERMAL INFORMATION

Power generated by the device depends on the mode of operation and the supply voltages used. Under some conditions, the SN75370 may generate sufficient instantaneous power to exceed, on average, the rated continuous power dissipation capability of the package. Appropriate duty-cycling of high-power conditions must be used to keep average power generated by the SN75370 within ratings.

Figure 33 shows typical methods to lower average power dissipation by pulsing the CE, WE, and RE inputs. Highest power occurs when both channels are in the write mode. Usually the write mode must be duty-cycled to reduce average power. Figure 33 (d) and Figure 34 demonstrate the use of a discrete P-N-P transistor to switch power to the V_{SS} terminal of the SN75370 to minimize average power. In addition, forced-air cooling or heat-sinking techniques may be used to increase the dissipation capability of the SN75370.

The following example illustrates a method to calculate average d-c supply power for the SN75370. The typical average power over a period T will be calculated using Figure 33(a). Assume both channels are operating identically, except in read mode when one channel is reading a 1 and the other channel is reading a 0. Let $V_{SS} = 20$ V, $V_{REF} = 7$ V and $T_A = 25°C$.

$$P_{AV} = \frac{t_W P_W + t_R P_R + t_{SB} P_{SB} + t_D P_D}{T}$$

$$T = t_W + t_R + t_{SB} + t_D$$

Typical power for each mode is stated in the electrical characteristics table. This example uses duty cycles (t/T) estimated from Figure 33(a). These values are then substituted in order:

$$P_{AV} = (0.25)\ (910) + (0.25)\ (\frac{560+640}{2}) + (0.2)\ (560) + (0.3)\ (410)$$

$$P_{AV} = 613\ mW$$

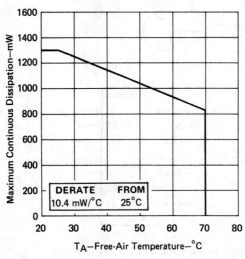

DISSIPATION DERATING CURVE

FIGURE 35

TEXAS INSTRUMENTS
INCORPORATED

POST OFFICE BOX 5012 • DALLAS, TEXAS 75222

QUAD SEGMENT DRIVER AND HEX DIGIT DRIVER FOR INTERFACING BETWEEN MOS AND VISIBLE-LIGHT-EMITTING-DIODE (VLED) DISPLAYS

- 50-mA Source or Sink Capability (SN75491)
- 250-mA Sink Capability (SN75492)
- Low Input Current for MOS Compatability
- Low Standby Power
- High-Gain Darlington Circuits

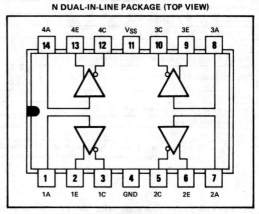

SN75491
N DUAL-IN-LINE PACKAGE (TOP VIEW)

description

The SN75491 and SN75492 are designed to be used together with MOS integrated circuits and with common-cathode VLED's in serially addressed multi-digit displays. This time-multiplexed system, which uses a segment-address-and-digit-scan method of VLED drive, minimizes the number of drivers required.

SN75492
N DUAL-IN-LINE PACKAGE (TOP VIEW)

schematic

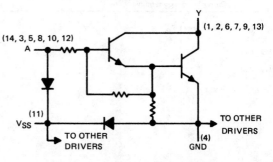

SN75491 (each driver)   SN75492 (each driver)

absolute maximum ratings over operating free-air temperature range (unless otherwise noted)

	SN75491	SN75492	UNIT
Input voltage range (see Note 1)	−5 to V_{SS}	−5 to V_{SS}	V
Collector (output) voltage (see Note 2)	10	10	V
Collector (output)-to-input voltage	10	10	V
Emitter-to-ground voltage ($V_I \geqslant 5$ V)	10		V
Emitter-to-input voltage	5		V
Voltage at V_{SS} terminal with respect to any other device terminal	10	10	V
Collector (output) current — each collector (output)	50	250	mA
Collector (output) current — all collectors (outputs)	200	600	mA
Continuous total dissipation	800	800	mW
Operating free-air temperature range	0 to 70	0 to 70	°C
Storage temperature range	−65 to 150	−65 to 150	°C
Lead temperature 1/16 inch from case for 10 seconds	260	260	°C

NOTES: 1. The input is the only device terminal which may be negative with respect to ground.
2. Voltage values are with respect to network ground terminal unless otherwise noted.

SN75491 electrical characteristics (unless otherwise noted V_{SS} = 10 V, T_A = 0°C to 70°C)

PARAMETER		TEST CONDITIONS		MIN	TYP[†]	MAX	UNIT
$V_{CE(on)}$	On-state collector-emitter voltage	Input = 8.5 V through 1 kΩ, V_E = 5 V, I_C = 50 mA, T_A = 25°C			0.9	1.2	V
		Input = 8.5 V through 1 kΩ, V_E = 5 V, I_C = 50 mA				1.5	
$I_{C(off)}$	Off-state collector current	V_C = 10 V, V_E = 0,	I_I = 40 µA			100	µA
		V_C = 10 V, V_E = 0,	V_I = 0.7 V			100	
I_I	Input current at maximum input voltage	V_I = 10 V, V_E = 0,	I_C = 20 mA	2.2		3.3	mA
I_E	Emitter reverse current	V_I = 0, V_E = 5 V,	I_C = 0			100	µA
I_{SS}	Current into V_{SS} terminal					1	mA

SN75492 electrical characteristics (unless otherwise noted V_{SS} = 10 V, T_A = 0°C to 70°C)

PARAMETER		TEST CONDITIONS		MIN	TYP[†]	MAX	UNIT
V_{OL}	Low-level output voltage	Input = 6.5 V through 1 kΩ, I_{OL} = 250 mA, T_A = 25°C			0.9	1.2	V
		Input = 6.5 V through 1 kΩ, I_{OL} = 250 mA				1.5	
I_{OH}	High-level output current	V_{OH} = 10 V, I_I = 40 µA				200	µA
		V_{OH} = 10 V, V_I = 0.5 V				200	
I_I	Input current at maximum input voltage	V_I = 10 V, I_{OL} = 20 mA		2.2		3.3	mA
I_{SS}	Current into V_{SS} terminal					1	mA

[†] All typical values are at T_A = 25°C

9

TEXAS INSTRUMENTS
INCORPORATED
POST OFFICE BOX 5012 • DALLAS, TEXAS 75222

SN75491 switching characteristics, $V_{SS} = 7.5$ V, $T_A = 25°C$

PARAMETER	TEST CONDITIONS	MIN	TYP	MAX	UNIT
t_{PLH} Propagation delay time, low-to-high-level output (collector)	$V_{IH} = 4.5$ V, $V_E = 0$,		100		ns
t_{PHL} Propagation delay time, high-to-low-level output (collector)	$R_L = 200$ Ω, $C_L = 15$ pF		20		ns

SN75492 switching characteristics, $V_{SS} = 7.5$ V, $T_A = 25°C$

PARAMETER	TEST CONDITIONS	MIN	TYP	MAX	UNIT
t_{PLH} Propagation delay time, low-to-high-level output	$V_{IH} = 7.5$ V, $R_L = 39$ Ω,		300		ns
t_{PHL} Propagation delay time, high-to-low-level output	$C_L = 15$ pF		30		ns

PARAMETER MEASUREMENT INFORMATION

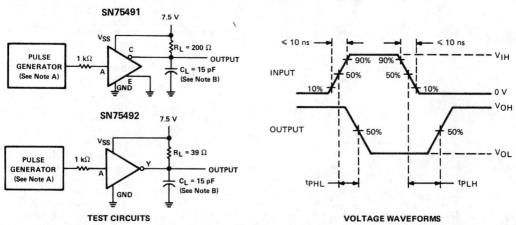

TEST CIRCUITS

VOLTAGE WAVEFORMS

NOTES: A. The pulse generator has the following characteristics: $Z_{out} = 50$ Ω, PRR = 100 kHz, $t_w = 1$ μs.
B. C_L includes probe and jig capacitance.

FIGURE 1—PROPAGATION DELAY TIMES

TYPICAL CHARACTERISTICS

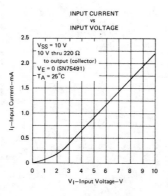

INPUT CURRENT
vs
INPUT VOLTAGE

FIGURE 2

TYPICAL CHARACTERISTICS

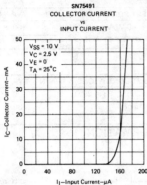

SN75491
COLLECTOR CURRENT
vs
INPUT CURRENT

FIGURE 3

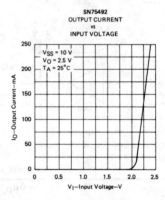

SN75492
OUTPUT CURRENT
vs
INPUT CURRENT

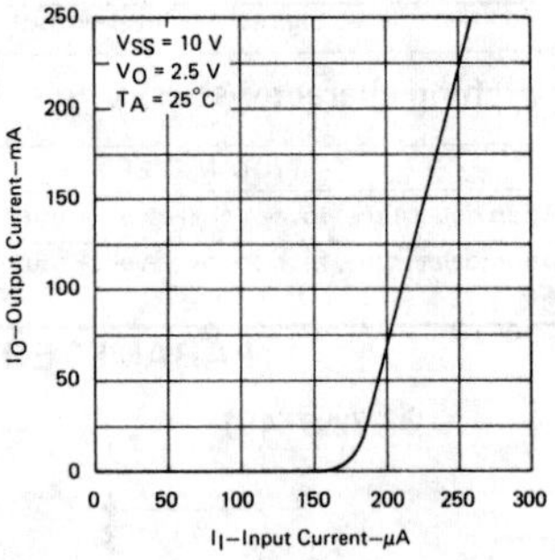

FIGURE 4

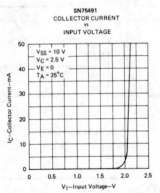

SN75491
COLLECTOR CURRENT
vs
INPUT VOLTAGE

FIGURE 5

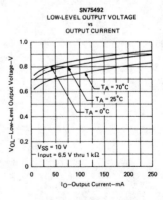

SN75492
OUTPUT CURRENT
vs
INPUT VOLTAGE

FIGURE 6

SN75491
ON-STATE COLLECTOR-EMITTER VOLTAGE
vs
COLLECTOR CURRENT

FIGURE 7

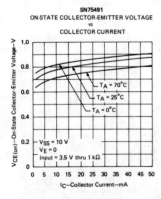

SN75492
LOW-LEVEL OUTPUT VOLTAGE
vs
OUTPUT CURRENT

FIGURE 8

TEXAS INSTRUMENTS
INCORPORATED
POST OFFICE BOX 5012 • DALLAS, TEXAS 75222

TYPICAL APPLICATION DATA

Figure 9 is an example of time multiplexing the individual digits in a visible display to minimize display circuitry. Up to twelve digits, each of which use a seven-segment display with decimal point, may be displayed using only two SN75491 and two SN75492 drivers.

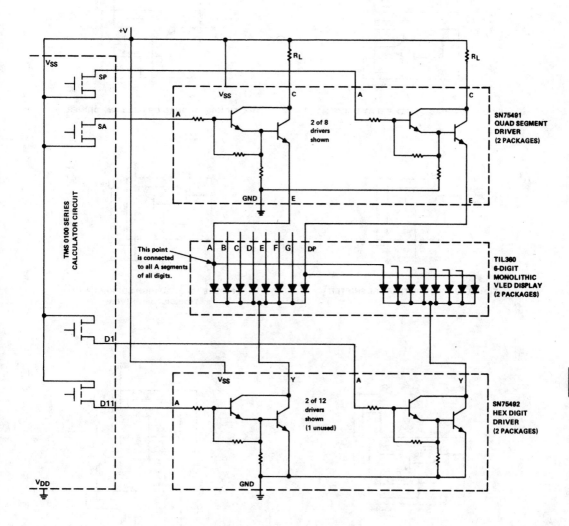

FIGURE 9—INTERFACING BETWEEN MOS CALCULATOR CIRCUIT AND VLED MULTI-DIGIT DISPLAY

TYPICAL APPLICATION DATA

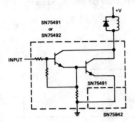

FIGURE 10—QUAD OR HEX RELAY DRIVER

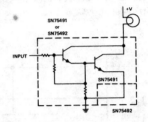

FIGURE 11—QUAD OR HEX LAMP DRIVER

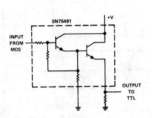

FIGURE 12—MOS-TO-TTL LEVEL SHIFTER

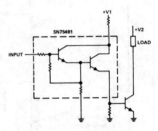

FIGURE 13—QUAD HIGH-CURRENT N-P-N
TRANSISTOR DRIVER

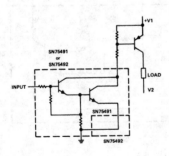

NOTE A: This circuit may be used as a digit driver for common-
anode VLED displays.

FIGURE 14—QUAD OR HEX HIGH-CURRENT
P-N-P TRANSISTOR DRIVER

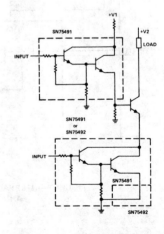

FIGURE 15—BASE/EMITTER SELECT N-P-N
TRANSISTOR DRIVER

TEXAS INSTRUMENTS
INCORPORATED
POST OFFICE BOX 5012 • DALLAS, TEXAS 75222

TYPICAL APPLICATION DATA

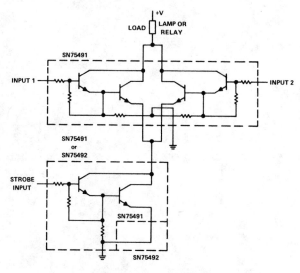

FIGURE 16—STROBED "NOR" DRIVER

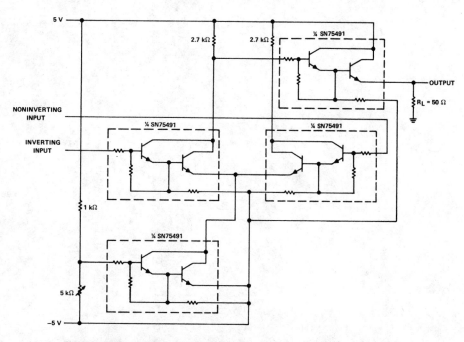

**FIGURE 17—SN75491 USED AS AN INTERFACE CIRCUIT BETWEEN THE BALANCED
30-MHz OUTPUT OF AN RF AMPLIFIER AND A COAXIAL CABLE**

TEXAS INSTRUMENTS
INCORPORATED

POST OFFICE BOX 5012 • DALLAS, TEXAS 75222

Magnetic Memory and Peripheral Drivers

memory drivers

TYPE	SN75303	SN75308	SN75324
Block Diagrams			
Features	• Monolithic Array of Eight 150-mA N-P-N Transistors • $V_{(BR)CBO}$ = 25 V Min • $V_{(BR)CEO}$ = 18 V Min • $V_{CE(sat)}$ = 0.75 V Max at I_C = 150 mA • t_{PHL} = 14 ns Typ • t_{PLH} = 18 ns Typ	• Monolithic Array of Eight 600-mA N-P-N Transistors • $V_{(BR)CBO}$ = 25 V Min • $V_{(BR)CEO}$ = 10 V Min • $V_{CE(sat)}$ = 0.55 V Typ at I_C = 500 mA • t_{on} = 36 ns Typ • t_{off} = 23 ns Typ	• Dual 400-mA Sink/Source Memory Switch • Single 14-V Power Supply • TTL-Compatible Inputs • Internal Decoding and Timing Gates • Source Output Terminals Swing between 14 V and Gnd
Applications	• Core Memories • Read-Only Memories • Plated-Wire Memories	• Core Memories • Read-Only Memories • Plated-Wire Memories	• Core Memories
Package Types	N	J, N	J, N

TYPE	SN55325, SN75325	SN55326, SN75326	SN55327, SN75327
Block Diagrams			
Features	• Dual 600-mA Sink/Source Memory Switch • Inputs Accept TTL Decoder Signals • 5-V Power Supply and V_{CC2} Variable to 24 V Max • Output Sink Collector Clamp Diodes • Source Output Terminals Swing between V_{CC2} and GND	• Quad 600-mA Sink Memory Driver • Inputs Accept TTL Decoder Signals • Single 5-V Power Supply • 24-V Output Capability • Output Collector Clamp Diodes	• Quad 600-mA Memory Switch • Inputs Accept TTL Decoder Signals • 5-V Power Supply and V_{CC2} Variable to 24 V Max • Output Terminals Swing between V_{CC2} and GND
Applications	• Core Memories • Plated-Wire Memories • High-Voltage, High-Current Drivers	• Core Memories • Plated-Wire Memories • Inhibit Drivers • High-Voltage, High-Current Drivers	• Core Memories • Plated-Wire Memories • High-Voltage, High-Current Drivers
Package Types — Series 55	J, JB, N, SB	J, JB, N, SB	J, JB, N, SB
Package Types — Series 75	J, N, SB	J, N, SB	J, N, SB

10

TEXAS INSTRUMENTS
INCORPORATED
POST OFFICE BOX 5012 • DALLAS, TEXAS 75222

peripheral drivers

TYPES	SN55450B SN75450B SN55460 SN75460	SN55451B SN75451B SN55461 SN75461	SN55452B SN75452B SN55462 SN75462	SN55453B SN75453B SN55463 SN75463	SN55454B SN75454B SN55464 SN75464
Block Diagram		Y = AB	Y = $\overline{AB}$	Y = A+B	Y = $\overline{A+B}$
Features	• Positive-AND[†] • Two Uncommitted Output Transistors	• Positive-AND	• Positive-NAND	• Positive-OR	• Positive-NOR
	Two TTL gates and two high-current output transistors on one chip. Each transistor is capable of sinking 300 mA through a resistive load returned to 20 V for Series 55450B/75450B or 30 V for Series 55460/75460.				
Applications		• Lamp Drivers • Relay Drivers • MOS Drivers • Line Drivers • Core Drivers • Power Drivers • Logic Buffers			
Package Types — Series 55	J, JB	JP, L	JP, L	JP, L	JP, L
Package Types — Series 75	J, N	L, P	L, P	L, P	L, P

[†]With output transistor base connected externally to output of gate.

TEXAS INSTRUMENTS
INCORPORATED
POST OFFICE BOX 5012 • DALLAS, TEXAS 75222

150-mA MEMORY DRIVER

- Maximum $V_{CE(sat)}$ of 750 mV at 150 mA I_C

- Maximum V_{BE} of 1.1 V at 150 mA I_C

- Minimum h_{FE} of 15 at 150 mA I_C

description

Each SN75303 is a monolithic array of eight n-p-n transistors designed for use in core, thin-film, and plated-wire memories as a medium-current word-line driver. Selection is by base-emitter activation. The SN75303 is characterized for operation from 0°C to 70°C.

N DUAL-IN-LINE PACKAGE (TOP VIEW)

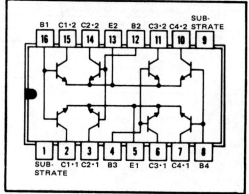

schematic

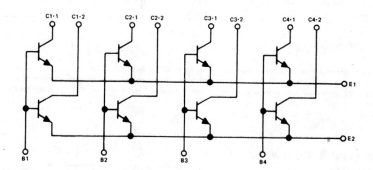

absolute maximum ratings over operating free-air temperature range (unless otherwise noted)

Collector-base voltage . . . . 25 V
Collector-emitter voltage (see Note 1) . . . . 18 V
Emitter-base voltage . . . . 5 V
Continuous collector current . . . . 200 mA
Continuous total package dissipation . . . . 250 mW
Operating free-air temperature range . . . . 0°C to 70°C
Storage temperature range . . . . −65°C to 150°C

NOTE 1: This value applies when the base-emitter diode is open-circuited.

electrical characteristics at 25°C free-air temperature (unless otherwise noted)[†]

PARAMETER		TEST CONDITIONS			MIN	TYP	MAX	UNIT
$V_{(BR)CBO}$	Collector-base breakdown voltage	$I_C = 10\ \mu A$,	$I_E = 0$		25			V
$V_{(BR)CEO}$	Collector-emitter breakdown voltage	$I_C = 10\ mA$,	$I_B = 0$,	See Note 2	18			V
$V_{(BR)CES}$	Collector-emitter breakdown voltage	$I_C = 1\ mA$,	$V_{BE} = 0$		25			V
$V_{(BR)EBO}$	Emitter-base breakdown voltage	$I_E = 10\ \mu A$,	$I_C = 0$		5			V
h_{FE}	Static forward current transfer ratio	$V_{CE} = 2\ V$, $\quad I_C = 30\ mA$			20	35		
		$V_{CE} = 2\ V$, $\quad I_C = 30\ mA$, $T_A = 0°C$		See Note 2	15			
		$V_{CE} = 2\ V$, $\quad I_C = 150\ mA$			15	25		
V_{BE}	Base-emitter voltage	$I_B = 3\ mA$, $\quad I_C = 30\ mA$			0.7	0.8	0.9	V
		$I_B = 3\ mA$, $\quad I_C = 30\ mA$, $T_A = 0°C$ to $70°C$		See Note 2	0.65		0.95	
		$I_B = 15\ mA$, $\quad I_C = 150\ mA$			0.8	1	1.1	
$V_{CE(sat)}$	Collector-emitter saturation voltage	$I_B = 3\ mA$, $\quad I_C = 30\ mA$				0.2	0.4	V
		$I_B = 3\ mA$, $\quad I_C = 30\ mA$, $T_A = 70°C$		See Note 2			0.45	
		$I_B = 15\ mA$, $\quad I_C = 150\ mA$				0.5	0.75	
C_{obo}	Common-base open-circuit output capacitance (1 transistor)	$V_{CB} = 5\ V$, $\quad I_E = 0$, $\quad f = 140\ kHz$, See Note 3				5		pF
C_{ibo}	Common-base open-circuit input capacitance (4 transistors in parallel)	$V_{EB} = 0.5\ V$, $\quad I_C = 0$, $\quad f = 140\ kHz$, See Note 4				40		pF

NOTES: 2. These parameters must be measured using pulse techniques, $t_W = 300\ \mu s$, duty cycle $\leqslant 2\%$.
     3. For measuring C_{obo}, the emitter of the transistor under test and all terminals of the other transistors are open.
     4. For measuring C_{ibo}, the four base terminals are connected in parallel. The emitter terminal of the transistors not under test and all the collector terminals are open.

switching characteristics at 25°C free-air temperature[†]

PARAMETER		TEST CONDITIONS[‡]		MIN	TYP	MAX	UNIT
t_{THL}	Transition time, high-to-low-level output	$I_C = 100\ mA$, $\quad I_{B(1)} = 10\ mA$,			8	12	
		$V_{BE(off)} = 0$, $\quad R_L = 43\ \Omega$,					ns
t_{PHL}	Propagation delay time, high-to-low-level output	$C_L \leqslant 15\ pF$, $\quad$ See Figure 1			14	22	
t_{TLH}	Transition time, low-to-high-level output	$I_C = 100\ mA$, $\quad I_{B(1)} = 10\ mA$,			6	12	
		$I_{B(2)} = -10\ mA$, $\quad R_L = 43\ \Omega$,					ns
t_{PLH}	Propagation delay time, low-to-high-level output	$C_L \leqslant 15\ pF$, $\quad$ See Figure 2			18	30	

[†]Test conditions and limits apply separately to each transistor unless otherwise noted. The terminals of the transistors not under test are open during the measurement of these characteristics.

[‡]Voltage and current values shown are nominal; exact values vary slightly with transistor parameters.

10

TEXAS INSTRUMENTS
INCORPORATED
POST OFFICE BOX 5012 • DALLAS, TEXAS 75222

PARAMETER MEASUREMENT INFORMATION

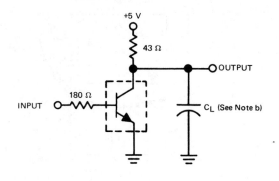

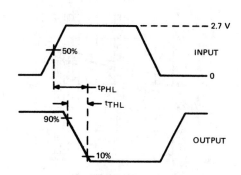

TEST CIRCUIT

VOLTAGE WAVEFORMS

FIGURE 1—t_{THL} and t_{PHL}

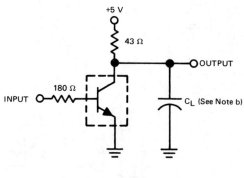

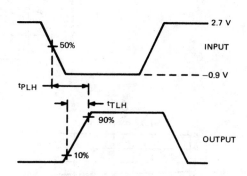

TEST CIRCUIT

VOLTAGE WAVEFORMS

FIGURE 2—t_{TLH} and t_{PLH}

NOTES: a. The input waveforms are supplied by a generator with the following characteristics: $Z_{out} = 50\ \Omega$, $t_r \leqslant 2$ ns, $t_w \approx 70$ ns, duty cycle $\leqslant 2\%$.

b. C_L includes probe and jig capacitance.

10

TYPE SN75303
2-BY-4 TRANSISTOR ARRAY

TYPICAL CHARACTERISTICS

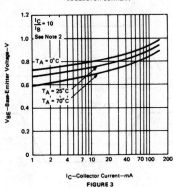

BASE-EMITTER VOLTAGE
vs
COLLECTOR CURRENT

FIGURE 3

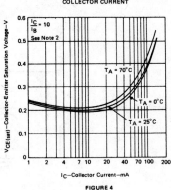

COLLECTOR-EMITTER SATURATION VOLTAGE
vs
COLLECTOR CURRENT

FIGURE 4

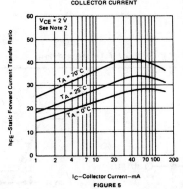

STATIC FORWARD
CURRENT TRANSFER RATIO
vs
COLLECTOR CURRENT

FIGURE 5

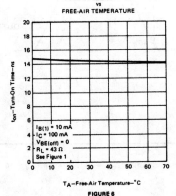

TURN-ON TIME
vs
FREE-AIR TEMPERATURE

FIGURE 6

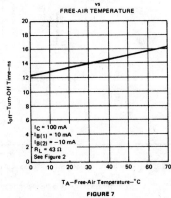

TURN-OFF TIME
vs
FREE-AIR TEMPERATURE

FIGURE 7

NOTE 2: These parameters must be measured using pulse techniques, t_W = 300 μs, duty cycle $\leqslant$ 2%.

TEXAS INSTRUMENTS
INCORPORATED
POST OFFICE BOX 5012 • DALLAS, TEXAS 75222

TYPICAL APPLICATION DATA

Use of the SN75303 in High-Speed Read-Only Memories

Significant advantages result from the use of a high-speed, read-only memory (ROM) in computers and calculators. This ROM is used for control, as a function generator, or for performing highly repetitive routines such as multiplying, dividing , or calculating square roots. The read-only memory has permanently stored data and usually operates with a very fast cycle time. It can perform repetitive operations much more efficiently and faster than the larger and slower read-write memory in the computer or calculator.

The SN75303 two-by-four transistor array is designed to perform the word-line drive or select function for medium current, high-speed, read-only memories organized in the word-oriented (2D) or linear-select configuration. Such memories use magnetic memory elements such as plated wires, planar thin-films, transformers (as in a braided-wire memory), or ferrite switch cores. They also may utilize passive elements such as resistors, capacitors, or diodes. The typical organization of a word-oriented ROM is shown in the figure below.

Information is read from the ROM by selecting the desired word line. This is accomplished by appropriate activiation of one base-select and one emitter-select line. The transistor in the SN75303 array at the intersection of the selected base and emitter lines will be activated, thus sinking current from the word-line load resistor, R_L, connected to its collector. Energy is coupled from the selected word line to the sense lines by the memory elements (ME) located at the intersections of the word line and the sense lines. The presence of an ME can represent a stored logic 1 bit of information while the absence of an ME represents a stored logic 0 bit. (The desired information is stored in such a memory during fabrication and is not electrically alterable.)

The stored word is read out at the sense-amplifier outputs. The selection of a sense amplifier will depend on the type of ME used in the memory and may take the form of a special amplifier, a comparator, or a logic gate.

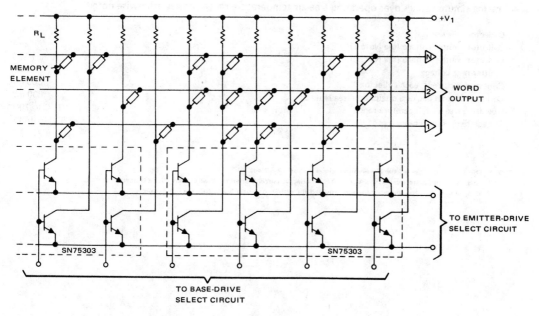

FIGURE 8

TEXAS INSTRUMENTS
INCORPORATED
POST OFFICE BOX 5012 • DALLAS, TEXAS 75222

- **For High-Current Switching . . . to 600 mA Rated Collector Current**

- **Low Storage Time . . . 13 ns Typical**

- **Cross-Coupled Bases and Emitters Arranged for Selection**

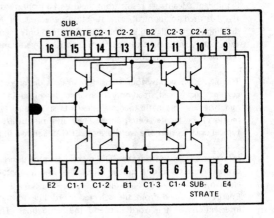

J OR N
DUAL-IN-LINE PACKAGE (TOP VIEW)

description

The SN75308 is an array of eight high-current (600 mA max) n-p-n transistors designed for use in linear select (2D) memory designs utilizing ferrite cores, plated wire, planar film, diodes, resistors, or other memory elements. One of eight transistors can be switched by selection of the appropriate base and emitter inputs. Drive of the base and emitter inputs can be provided by available circuits such as the SN7440, SN75450, and SN75451. The SN75308 transistors feature fast switching times.

absolute maximum ratings over operating free-air temperature range (unless otherwise noted)

Collector-base voltage . . . . 25 V
Collector-emitter voltage (see Note 1) . . . . 25 V
Collector-emitter voltage (see Note 2) . . . . 10 V
Emitter-base voltage . . . . 4.5 V
Continuous current, each collector . . . . 600 mA
Continuous total package dissipation (see Note 3) . . . . 800 mW
Operating free-air temperature range . . . . 0°C to 70°C
Storage temperature range . . . . −65°C to 150°C

NOTES: 1. This value applies when the base-emitter diode is short-circuited.
   2. This value applies between 100 μA and 10 mA collector current when the base-emitter diode is open-circuited.
   3. This value applies for any combination provided the ratings of single transistors are not exceeded.

TEXAS INSTRUMENTS
INCORPORATED
POST OFFICE BOX 5012 • DALLAS, TEXAS 75222

electrical characteristics for each transistor at 25°C free-air temperature †

	PARAMETER	TEST CONDITIONS			MIN	TYP	MAX	UNIT
$V_{(BR)CBO}$	Collector-base breakdown voltage	$I_C = 100 \mu A$,	$I_E = 0$		25			V
$V_{(BR)CEO}$	Collector-emitter breakdown voltage	$I_C = 10 mA$,	$I_B = 0$,	See Note 4	10			V
$V_{(BR)CES}$	Collector-emitter breakdown voltage	$I_C = 100 \mu A$,	$V_{BE} = 0$		25			V
$V_{(BR)EBO}$	Emitter-base breakdown voltage	$I_E = 100 \mu A$,	$I_C = 0$		5			V
$V_{(BR)CU}$	Collector-substrate breakdown voltage	$I_C = 100 \mu A$,	$I_B = 0$,	$I_E = 0$	25			V
h_{FE}	Static forward current transfer ratio	$V_{CB} = 1 V$,	$I_E = 30 mA$	See Note 4	15			
		$V_{CB} = 1 V$,	$I_E = 100 mA$		20			
		$V_{CB} = 1 V$,	$I_E = 500 mA$		20			
V_{BE}	Base-emitter voltage	$I_B = 3 mA$,	$I_C = 30 mA$	See Note 4		0.73	1	V
		$I_B = 10 mA$,	$I_C = 100 mA$			0.82	1.1	
		$I_B = 30 mA$,	$I_C = 300 mA$			1.0	1.2	
		$I_B = 50 mA$,	$I_C = 500 mA$			1.1	1.3	
$V_{CE(sat)}$	Collector-emitter saturation voltage	$I_B = 3 mA$,	$I_C = 30 mA$	See Note 4		0.15	0.3	V
		$I_B = 10 mA$,	$I_C = 100 mA$			0.2	0.4	
		$I_B = 30 mA$,	$I_C = 300 mA$			0.36	0.6	
		$I_B = 50 mA$,	$I_C = 500 mA$			0.55	0.8	
$|h_{fe}|$	Small-signal common-emitter forward current transfer ratio	$V_{CE} = 10 V$,	$I_C = 100 mA$,	$f = 100 MHz$		2		
C_{obo}	Common-base open-circuit output capacitance (1 transistor)	$V_{CB} = 10 V$, See Note 5	$I_E = 0$,	$f = 140 kHz$,		18		pF
C_{ibo}	Common-base open-circuit input capacitance (2 transistors in parallel)	$V_{EB} = 0.5 V$, See Note 6	$I_C = 0$,	$f = 140 kHz$,		65		pF

NOTES: 4. These parameters must be measured using pulse techniques. $t_w = 200 \mu s$, duty cycle ≤ 2%.
      5. For measuring C_{obo}, the emitter terminal of the transistor under test and all terminals of the other transistors are open.
      6. For measuring C_{ibo}, the base terminals are connected in parallel. The emitter terminals of the transistors not under test and all the collector terminals are open.

switching characteristics at 25°C free-air temperature†

	PARAMETER	TEST CONDITIONS‡			TYP	UNIT
t_d	Delay time	$I_C = 500 mA$,	$I_{B(1)} = 50 mA$,		16	
t_r	Rise time	$V_{BE(off)} = -0.9 V$,	$R_L = 28.7 \Omega$,		20	
t_{on}	Turn-on time	$C_L = 15 pF$,	See Figure 1		36	
t_s	Storage time	$I_C = 500 mA$,	$I_{B(1)} = 50 mA$,		13	ns
t_f	Fall time	$I_{B(2)} = -50 mA$,	$R_L = 28.7 \Omega$,		10	
t_{off}	Turn-off time	$C_L = 15 pF$,	See Figure 1		23	

†Test conditions and limits apply separately to each transistor unless otherwise noted. The terminals of the transistors not under test are open during the measurement of these characteristics.

‡Voltage and current values shown are nominal; exact values vary slightly with transistor parameters.

PARAMETER MEASUREMENT INFORMATION

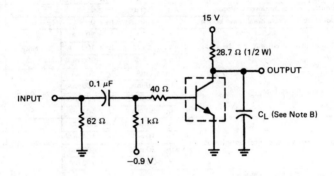

TEST CIRCUIT

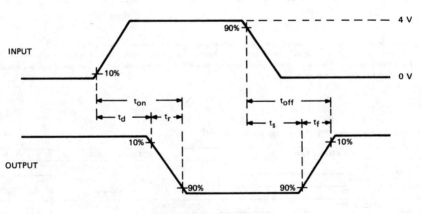

VOLTAGE WAVEFORMS

NOTES: A. The input waveform is supplied by a generator with the following characteristics: Z_{out} = 50 Ω, t_r ≤ 10 ns, t_f ≤ 10 ns, t_w ≈ 100 ns, duty cycle ≤ 2%.

       B. C_L includes probe and jig capacitance.

FIGURE 1—SWITCHING CHARACTERISTICS

10

TEXAS INSTRUMENTS
INCORPORATED
POST OFFICE BOX 5012 • DALLAS, TEXAS 75222

TYPICAL CHARACTERISTICS

STATIC FORWARD CURRENT TRANSFER RATIO
vs
EMITTER CURRENT

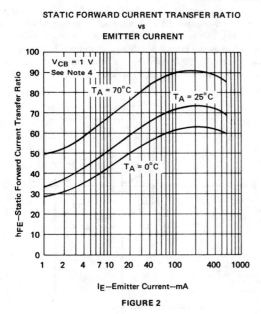

FIGURE 2

BASE-EMITTER VOLTAGE
vs
COLLECTOR CURRENT

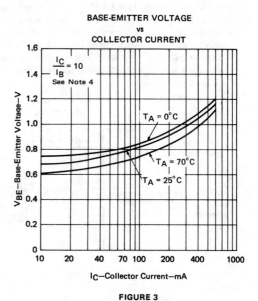

FIGURE 3

COLLECTOR-EMITTER SATURATION VOLTAGE
vs
COLLECTOR CURRENT

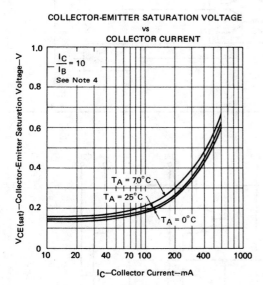

FIGURE 4

NORMALIZED COLLECTOR-EMITTER
BREAKDOWN VOLTAGE
vs
BASE-EMITTER RESISTANCE

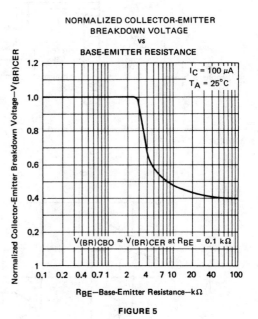

FIGURE 5

NOTE 4: These parameters must be measured using pulse techniques. t_W = 200 μs, duty cycle ≤ 2%.

10

TEXAS INSTRUMENTS
INCORPORATED
POST OFFICE BOX 5012 • DALLAS, TEXAS 75222

TYPE SN75308
2 X 4 TRANSISTOR ARRAY

TYPICAL APPLICATION DATA

The SN75308 two-by-four transistor array is designed to perform the word-line drive or select function for medium current, high-speed, read-only memories organized in the word-oriented (2D) or linear-select configuration. Such memories use magnetic memory elements such as plated wires, planar thin-films, transformers (as in a braided-wire memory), or ferrite switch cores. They also may utilize passive elements such as resistors, capacitors, or diodes. The typical organization of a word-oriented ROM is shown on the SN75303 data sheet; a base and emitter selection technique is shown below. A similar selection circuit can be used with the SN75303 although with it the SN75451's need not be paralleled.

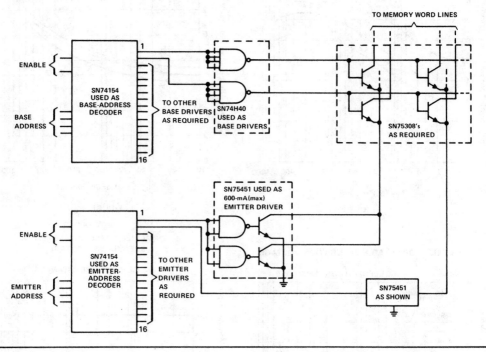

schematic

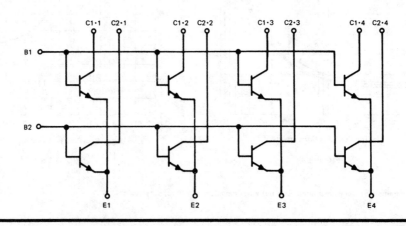

TEXAS INSTRUMENTS
INCORPORATED
POST OFFICE BOX 5012 • DALLAS, TEXAS 75222

SERIES 75 MEMORY DRIVER

PERFORMANCE

- fast switching times
- 400-mA output capability
- internal decoding and timing circuitry
- dual sink/source outputs
- output short-circuit protection

EASE OF DESIGN

- TTL or DTL compatibility
- eliminates transformer coupling
- reduces drive-line lengths
- increases reliability
- minimizes external components

description

The SN75324 is a monolithic memory driver with decode inputs designed for use with magnetic memories. The device contains two 400-milliampere (source/sink) switch pairs, with decoding capability from four address lines. Two address inputs (B and C) are used for mode selection, i.e., source or sink. The other two address inputs (A and D) are used for switch-pair selection, i.e., output switch-pair Y/Z or W/X respectively.

The sink circuit is composed of an inverting switch with a transistor-transistor-logic (TTL) input. The source circuit is an emitter-follower driven from a TTL input stage.

The SN75324 is characterized for operation from $0°C$ to $70°C$.

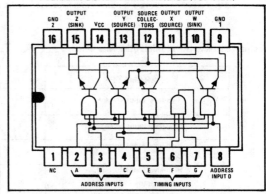

J CERAMIC DUAL-IN-LINE PACKAGE (TOP VIEW)

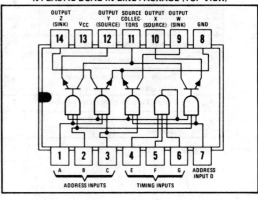

N PLASTIC DUAL-IN-LINE PACKAGE (TOP VIEW)

NC—No internal connection
GND 1 and GND 2 are to be used in parallel

FUNCTION TABLE

INPUTS							OUTPUTS			
ADDRESS				TIMING			SINK	SOURCES		SINK
A	B	C	D	E	F	G	W	X	Y	Z
L	L	H	H	H	H	H	ON	OFF	OFF	OFF
L	H	L	H	H	H	H	OFF	ON	OFF	OFF
H	H	L	L	H	H	H	OFF	OFF	ON	OFF
H	L	H	L	H	H	H	OFF	OFF	OFF	ON
X	X	X	X	L	X	X	OFF	OFF	OFF	OFF
X	X	X	X	X	L	X	OFF	OFF	OFF	OFF
X	X	X	X	X	X	L	OFF	OFF	OFF	OFF

H = high level, L = low level, X = irrelevant

NOTE: Not more than one output is to be on at one time:
When all timing inputs are high, two of the address
inputs must be low.

TEXAS INSTRUMENTS
INCORPORATED
POST OFFICE BOX 5012 • DALLAS, TEXAS 75222

TYPE SN75324
MEMORY DRIVER WITH DECODE INPUTS

absolute maximum ratings over operating case temperature range (unless otherwise noted)

Supply voltage V_{CC} (See Note 1) . . . . 17 V
Input voltage (See Note 2) . . . . 5.5 V
Operating case temperature range . . . . .0°C to 70°C
Continuous total power dissipation at (or below) 70°C case temperature . . . . 800 mW
Storage temperature range. . . . . -65°C to 150°C

NOTES: 1. Voltage values are with respect to network ground terminal.
        2. Input signals must be zero or positive with respect to network ground terminal.

electrical characteristics (unless otherwise noted, V_{CC} = 14 V, T_C = 0°C to 70°C)

	PARAMETER	TEST FIGURE	TEST CONDITIONS	MIN	TYP†	MAX	UNIT
V_{IH}	High-level input voltage	1		3.5			V
V_{IL}	Low-level input voltage	1				0.8	V
I_{IH}	High-level input current, address inputs	1	V_I = 5 V			200	μA
I_{IH}	High-level input current, timing inputs	1	V_I = 5 V			100	μA
I_{IL}	Low-level input current, address inputs	1	V_I = 0 V			−6	mA
I_{IL}	Low-level input current, timing inputs	1	V_I = 0 V			−12	mA
$V_{(sat)}$	Sink saturation voltage	2	I_{sink} ≃ 420 mA, R_L = 53 Ω		0.75	0.85	V
$V_{(sat)}$	Source saturation voltage	2	I_{source} ≃ −420 mA, R_L = 47.5 Ω		0.75	0.85	V
I_{off}	Output off-state current	1	V_I = 0 V		125	200	μA
I_{CC}	Supply current, all sources and sinks off	3	V_I = 0 V		12.5	15	mA
I_{CC}	Supply current, either sink selected	4			30	42	mA
I_{CC}	Supply current, either source selected	4			25	35	mA

† All typical values are at T_C = 25°C.

TEXAS INSTRUMENTS
INCORPORATED
POST OFFICE BOX 5012 • DALLAS, TEXAS 75222

switching characteristics, V_{CC} = 14 V, T_C = 25°C

	PARAMETER	TEST FIGURE	TEST CONDITIONS	MIN	TYP	MAX	UNIT
t_{PLH}	Propagation delay time, low-to-high-level source output	5	R_{L1} = 53 Ω, R_{L2} = 500 Ω, C_L = 20 pF			90	ns
t_{PHL}	Propagation delay time, high-to-low-level source output	5				50	ns
t_{PLH}	Propagation delay time, low-to-high-level sink output	6	R_L = 53 Ω, C_L = 20 pF			110	ns
t_{PHL}	Propagation delay time, high-to-low-level sink output	6				40	ns
t_s	Sink storage time	6				70	ns

schematic

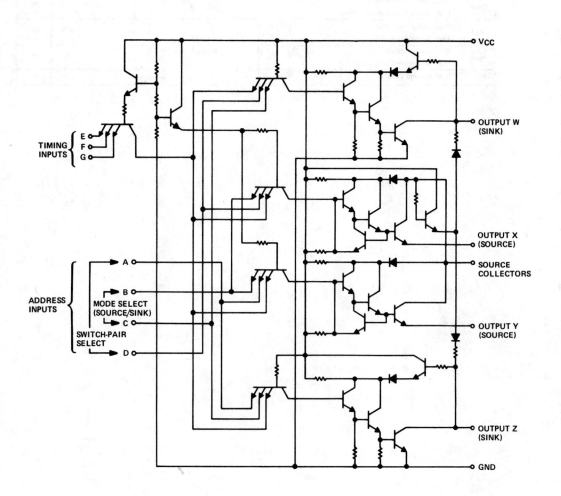

PARAMETER MEASUREMENT INFORMATION

d-c test circuits†

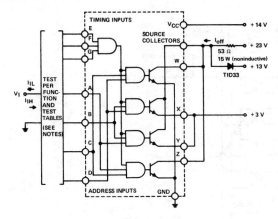

TEST TABLE FOR I_{IL}

APPLY 3.5 V	GROUND	TEST I_{IL}
B, C, E, F, and G	A and D	A
B, C, E, F, and G	A and D	D
A, D, E, F, and G	B and C	B
A, D, E, F, and G	B and C	C
A, B, C, D, F, and G	E	E
A, B, C, D, E, and G	F	F
A, B, C, D, E, and F	G	G

NOTES: 1. Check V_{IH} and V_{IL} per Function Table.
2. Measure I_{IL} per Test Table.
3. When measuring I_{IH}, all other inputs are at ground. Each input is tested separately.

FIGURE 1—V_{IL}, V_{IH}, I_{IL}, I_{IH}, and I_{off}

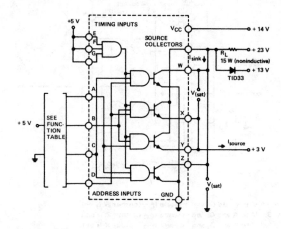

NOTE: This parameter must be using pulse techniques. t_w = 500 ns, duty cycle ≤ 1%.

FIGURE 2 — $V_{(sat)}$

†Arrows indicate actual direction of current flow. Current into a terminal is a positive value.

TEXAS INSTRUMENTS
INCORPORATED
POST OFFICE BOX 5012 • DALLAS, TEXAS 75222

TYPE SN75324
MEMORY DRIVER WITH DECODE INPUTS

PARAMETER MEASUREMENT INFORMATION

d-c test circuits † (continued)

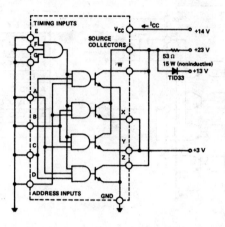

FIGURE 3 – I_{CC} (ALL OUTPUTS OFF)

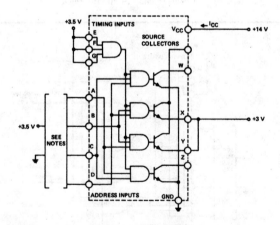

NOTES: 1. Ground A and B, apply 3.5 V to C and D, and measure I_{CC} (output W is on).
2. Ground B and D, apply 3.5 V to A and C, and measure I_{CC} (output Z is on).
3. Ground A and C, apply 3.5 V to B and D, and measure I_{CC} (output X is on).
4. Ground C and D, apply 3.5 V to A and B, and measure I_{CC} (output Y is on).

FIGURE 4 – I_{CC} (ONE OUTPUT ON)

†Arrows indicate actual direction of current flow. Current into a terminal is a positive value.

TEXAS INSTRUMENTS
INCORPORATED
POST OFFICE BOX 5012 • DALLAS, TEXAS 75222

PARAMETER MEASUREMENT INFORMATION

switching characteristics

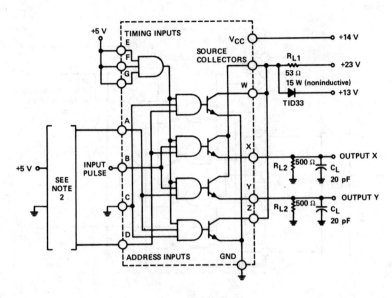

TEST CIRCUIT

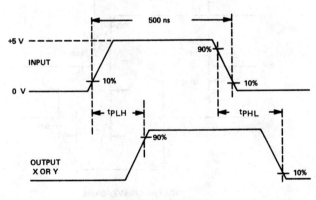

VOLTAGE WAVEFORMS

NOTES: 1. The input waveform is supplied by a generator with the following characteristics: $t_r = t_f = 10$ ns, duty cycle $\leqslant 1\%$, and $Z_{out} \approx 50\ \Omega$.
2. When measuring delay times at output X, apply +5 V to input D, and ground A. When measuring delay times at output Y, apply +5 V to input A, and ground D.
3. C_L includes probe and jig capacitance.
4. Unless otherwise noted all resistors are 0.5 W.

FIGURE 5 – SOURCE-OUTPUT SWITCHING TIMES

TEXAS INSTRUMENTS
INCORPORATED
POST OFFICE BOX 5012 • DALLAS, TEXAS 75222

TYPE SN75324
MEMORY DRIVER WITH DECODE INPUTS

PARAMETER MEASUREMENT INFORMATION

switching characteristics

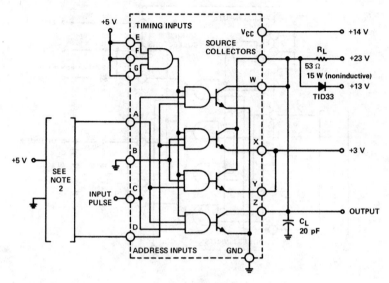

TEST CIRCUIT

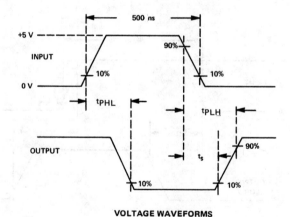

VOLTAGE WAVEFORMS

NOTES: 1. The input waveform is supplied by a generator with the following characteristics: $t_r = t_f = 10$ ns, duty cycle $\leqslant 1\%$, $Z_{out} \approx 50\ \Omega$.
2. When measuring delay times at output W, apply +5 V to input D, and ground A. When measuring delay times at output Z,
apply +5 V to input A, and ground D.
3. C_L includes probe and jig capacitance.

FIGURE 6 — SINK-OUTPUT SWITCHING TIMES

TEXAS INSTRUMENTS
INCORPORATED
POST OFFICE BOX 5012 • DALLAS, TEXAS 75222

SERIES 55/75 MEMORY DRIVER
featuring

PERFORMANCE

- 600-mA Output Capability
- Fast Switching Times
- Output Short-Circuit Protection
- Dual Sink and Dual Source Outputs
- Minimum Time Skew between Address and Output Current Rise
- 24-Volt Output Capability

EASE OF DESIGN

- Source Base Drive Externally Adjustable
- TTL or DTL Compatibility
- Input Clamping Diodes
- Transformer Coupling Eliminated
- Reliability Increased
- Drive-Line Lengths Reduced
- Use of External Components Minimized

description

The SN55325 and SN75325 are monolithic integrated circuit memory drivers with logic inputs and are designed for use with magnetic memories.

The devices contain two 600-milliampere source-switch pairs and two 600-milliampere sink-switch pairs. Source selection is determined by one of two logic inputs, and source turn-on is determined by the source strobe. Likewise, sink selection is determined by one of two logic inputs, and sink turn-on is determined by the sink strobe. This arrangement allows selection of one of the four switches and its subsequent turn-on with minimum time skew of the output current rise.

When R_{int} and node R are connected together, the amount of base drive available for the source-1 or source-2 output transistor is set internally by a 575-ohm resistor. This method provides adequate base drive for source currents up to 375 mA with a V_{CC2} voltage of 15 volts or 600 mA with a V_{CC2} voltage of 24 volts.

When source currents greater than 375 mA are required, it is recommended that a resistor of the appropriate value be connected between V_{CC2} and node R and R_{int} must remain open. By using this method the source base current may usually be regulated within ±5%. An advantage of this method of setting the base drive is that the power dissipated by this resistor is external to the package and allows the integrated circuit to operate at higher source currents for a given junction temperature.

**J, JB, OR N DUAL-IN-LINE
OR SB FLAT PACKAGE (TOP VIEW)**

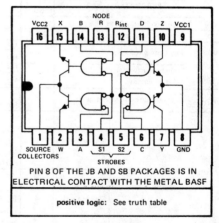

PIN 8 OF THE JB AND SB PACKAGES IS IN
ELECTRICAL CONTACT WITH THE METAL BASE

positive logic: See truth table

TRUTH TABLE

ADDRESS INPUTS		STROBE INPUTS		OUTPUTS			
SOURCE	SINK	SOURCE	SINK	SOURCE		SINK	
A B	C D	S1	S2	W	X	Y	Z
L H	X X	L	H	ON	OFF	OFF	OFF
H L	X X	L	H	OFF	ON	OFF	OFF
X X	L H	H	L	OFF	OFF	ON	OFF
X X	H L	H	L	OFF	OFF	OFF	ON
X X	X X	H	H	OFF	OFF	OFF	OFF
H H	H H	X	X	OFF	OFF	OFF	OFF

H = high level, L = low level, X = irrelevant
NOTE: Not more than one output is to be on at any one time.

Each sink-output collector has an internal pull-up resistor in parallel with a clamping diode connected to V_{CC2}. This arrangement provides protection from voltage surges associated with switching inductive loads.

The SN55325 is characterized for operation over the full military temperature range of −55°C to 125°C; the SN75325 is characterized for operation from 0°C to 70°C.

TYPES SN55325, SN75325
MEMORY DRIVERS

absolute maximum ratings over operating free-air temperature range (unless otherwise noted)

		SN55325	SN75325	UNIT
Supply voltage V$_{CC1}$ (see Note 1)		7	7	V
Supply voltage V$_{CC2}$ (see Note 1)		25	25	V
Input voltage (any address or strobe input)		5.5	5.5	V
Continuous total dissipation at (or below) 100°C case temperature (see Note 2)		1	1	W
Operating free-air temperature range		−55 to 125	0 to 70	°C
Storage temperature range		−65 to 150	−65 to 150	°C
Lead temperature 1/16 inch from case for 60 seconds	J, JB, or SB package	300	300	°C
Lead temperature 1/16 inch from case for 10 seconds	N package	260	260	°C

NOTES: 1. Voltage values are with respect to network ground terminal.
2. For operation above 100°C case temperature, refer to Dissipation Derating Curve, Figure 20. For dissipation ratings in free-air, see Figure 21.

electrical characteristics over rated operating free-air temperature range (unless otherwise noted)

PARAMETER		TEST FIGURE	TEST CONDITIONS		SN55325 MIN	SN55325 TYP†	SN55325 MAX	SN75325 MIN	SN75325 TYP†	SN75325 MAX	UNIT
V$_{IH}$	High-level input voltage	1 & 2			2			2			V
V$_{IL}$	Low-level input voltage	3 & 4					0.8			0.8	V
V$_I$	Input clamp voltage	5	V$_{CC1}$ = 4.5 V, I$_I$ = −10 mA,	V$_{CC2}$ = 24 V, T$_A$ = 25°C		−1.3	−1.7		−1.3	−1.7	V
I$_{(off)}$	Source-collectors terminal off-state current	1	V$_{CC1}$ = 4.5 V, V$_{CC2}$ = 24 V	Full range§			500			200	μA
				T$_A$ = 25°C		3	150		3	200	
V$_{OH}$	High-level sink output voltage	2	V$_{CC1}$ = 4.5 V, I$_O$ = 0	V$_{CC2}$ = 24 V,	19	23		19	23		V
V$_{(sat)}$	Saturation voltage‡	3	V$_{CC1}$ = 4.5 V, V$_{CC2}$ = 15 V, R$_L$ = 24 Ω, I(source) ≈ −600 mA, See Note 3	Full range§			0.9			0.9	V
	Source outputs			T$_A$ = 25°C		0.43	0.7		0.43	0.75	
		4	V$_{CC1}$ = 4.5 V, V$_{CC2}$ = 15 V, R$_L$ = 24 Ω, I(sink) ≈ 600 mA, See Note 3	Full range§			0.9			0.9	
	Sink outputs			T$_A$ = 25°C		0.43	0.7		0.43	0.75	
I$_I$	Input current at maximum input voltage	5	V$_{CC1}$ = 5.5 V, V$_I$ = 5.5 V	V$_{CC2}$ = 24 V,			1			1	mA
	address inputs										
	strobe inputs						2			2	
I$_{IH}$	High-level input current	5	V$_{CC1}$ = 5.5 V, V$_I$ = 2.4 V	V$_{CC2}$ = 24 V,	3	40		3	40		μA
	address inputs										
	strobe inputs				6	80		6	80		
I$_{IL}$	Low-level input current	5	V$_{CC1}$ = 5.5 V, V$_I$ = 0.4 V	V$_{CC2}$ = 24 V,	−1	−1.6		−1	−1.6		mA
	address inputs										
	strobe inputs				−2	−3.2		−2	−3.2		
I$_{CC(off)}$	Supply current, all sources and sinks off	6	V$_{CC1}$ = 5.5 V, T$_A$ = 25°C	V$_{CC2}$ = 24 V,	14	22		14	22		mA
	from V$_{CC1}$										
	from V$_{CC2}$				7.5	20		7.5	20		
I$_{CC1}$	Supply current from V$_{CC1}$, either sink on	7	V$_{CC1}$ = 5.5 V, I(sink) = 50 mA,	V$_{CC2}$ = 24 V, T$_A$ = 25°C	55	70		55	70		mA
I$_{CC2}$	Supply current from V$_{CC2}$, either source on	8	V$_{CC1}$ = 5.5 V, I(source) = −50 mA, See Note 3	V$_{CC2}$ = 24 V, T$_A$ = 25°C,	32	50		32	50		mA

† All typical values are at T$_A$ = 25°C.
‡ Not more than one output is to be on at any one time.
§ Full range for SN55325 is −55°C to 125°C and for SN75325 is 0°C to 70°C.
NOTE 3: These parameters must be measured using pulse techniques. t$_w$ = 200 μs, duty cycle ⩽ 2%.

TEXAS INSTRUMENTS
INCORPORATED
POST OFFICE BOX 5012 • DALLAS, TEXAS 75222

973

switching characteristics, V_{CC1} = 5 V, T_A = 25°C

PARAMETER¶	TO (OUTPUT)	TEST FIGURE	TEST CONDITIONS		MIN	TYP	MAX	UNIT
t_{PLH}	Source collectors	9	V_{CC2} = 15 V,	R_L = 24 Ω,		25	50	ns
t_{PHL}			C_L = 25 pF			25	50	
t_{TLH}	Source outputs	10	V_{CC2} = 20 V,	R_L = 1 kΩ,		55		ns
t_{THL}			C_L = 25 pF			7		
t_{PLH}	Sink outputs	9	V_{CC2} = 15 V,	R_L = 24 Ω,		20	45	ns
t_{PHL}			C_L = 25 pF			20	45	
t_{TLH}	Sink outputs	9	V_{CC2} = 15 V,	R_L = 24 Ω,		7	15	ns
t_{THL}			C_L = 25 pF			9	20	
t_s	Sink outputs	9	V_{CC2} = 15 V,	R_L = 24 Ω,		15	30	ns
			C_L = 25 pF					

¶t_{PLH} = propagation delay time, low-to-high-level output
t_{PHL} = propagation delay time, high-to-low-level output
t_{TLH} = transition time, low-to-high-level output
t_{THL} = transition time, high-to-low-level output
t_s = storage time

schematic

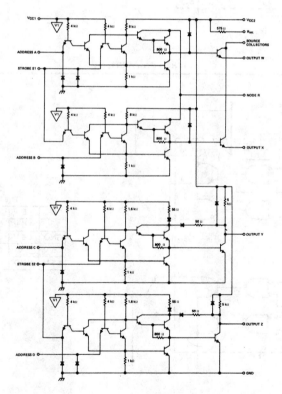

Component values shown are nominal.
$\nabla V1$ ... V_{CC1} bus

73

PARAMETER MEASUREMENT INFORMATION

d-c test circuits†

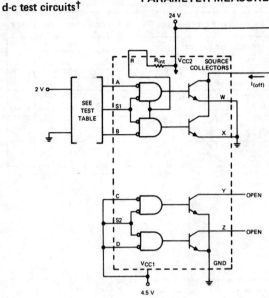

TEST TABLE		
A	**B**	**S1**
GND	GND	2 V
2 V	2 V	GND

FIGURE 1—V$_{IH}$ AND I$_{(off)}$

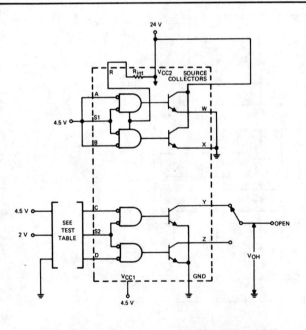

TEST TABLE				
C	**D**	**S2**	**Y**	**Z**
2 V	4.5 V	GND	V$_{OH}$	OPEN
GND	4.5 V	2 V	V$_{OH}$	OPEN
4.5 V	2 V	GND	OPEN	V$_{OH}$
4.5 V	GND	2 V	OPEN	V$_{OH}$

FIGURE 2—V$_{IH}$ AND V$_{OH}$

†Arrows indicate actual direction of current flow.

10

TEXAS INSTRUMENTS
INCORPORATED
POST OFFICE BOX 5012 • DALLAS, TEXAS 75222

PARAMETER MEASUREMENT INFORMATION

d-c test circuits (continued) †

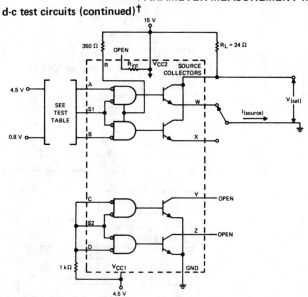

TEST TABLE

A	B	S1	W	X
0.8 V	4.5 V	0.8 V	GND	OPEN
4.5 V	0.8 V	0.8 V	OPEN	GND

NOTE A: These parameters must be measured using pulse techniques. t_w = 200 µs, duty cycle ⩽ 2%.

FIGURE 3—V_{IL} AND SOURCE $V_{(sat)}$

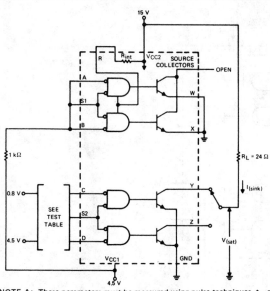

TEST TABLE

C	D	S2	Y	Z
0.8 V	4.5 V	0.8 V	R_L	OPEN
4.5 V	0.8 V	0.8 V	OPEN	R_L

NOTE A: These parameters must be measured using pulse techniques. t_w = 200 µs, duty cycle ⩽ 2%.

FIGURE 4—V_{IL} AND SINK $V_{(sat)}$

†Arrows indicate actual direction of current flow.

TEXAS INSTRUMENTS
INCORPORATED
POST OFFICE BOX 5012 • DALLAS, TEXAS 75222

PARAMETER MEASUREMENT INFORMATION

d-c test circuits (continued)[†]

TEST TABLES

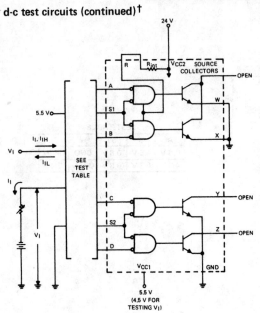

I_I, I_{IH}

APPLY V_I = 5.5 V, MEASURE I_I APPLY V_I = 2.4 V, MEASURE I_{IH}	GROUND	APPLY 5.5 V
A	S1	B, C, S2, D
S1	A, B	C, S2, D
B	S1	A, C, S2, D
C	S2	A, S1, B, D
S2	C, D	A, S1, B
D	S2	A, S1, B, C

V_I, I_{IL}

APPLY V_I = 0.4 V, MEASURE I_{IL} APPLY I_I = −10 mA MEASURE V_I	APPLY 5.5 V
A	S1, B, C, S2, D
S1	A, B, C, S2, D
B	A, S1, C, S2, D
C	A, S1, B, S2, D
S2	A, S1, B, C, D
D	A, S1, B, C, S2

FIGURE 5—V_I, I_I, I_{IH}, AND I_{IL}

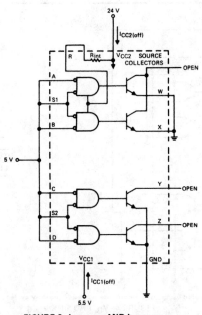

FIGURE 6—$I_{CC1(off)}$ AND $I_{CC2(off)}$

[†]Arrows indicate actual direction of current flow.

PARAMETER MEASUREMENT INFORMATION

d-c test circuits (continued)†

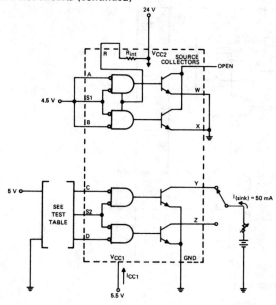

TEST TABLE

C	D	S2	Y	Z
GND	5 V	GND	I(sink)	OPEN
5 V	GND	GND	OPEN	I(sink)

FIGURE 7—I$_{CC1}$, EITHER SINK ON

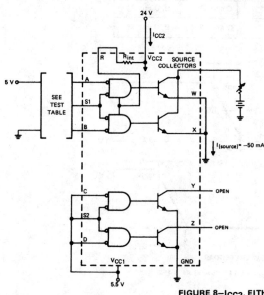

TEST TABLE

A	B	S1
GND	5 V	GND
5 V	GND	GND

FIGURE 8—I$_{CC2}$, EITHER SOURCE ON

†Arrows indicate actual direction of current flow.

PARAMETER MEASUREMENT INFORMATION

switching characteristics

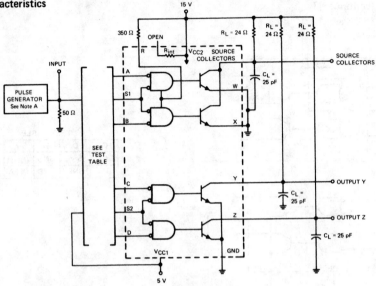

TEST CIRCUIT

TEST TABLE

PARAMETER	OUTPUT UNDER TEST	INPUT	CONNECT TO 5 V
t_{PLH} and t_{PHL}	Source collectors	A and S1	B, C, D and S2
		B and S1	A, C, D and S2
t_{PLH}, t_{PHL}, t_{TLH}, t_{THL}, and t_s	Sink output Y	C and S2	A, B, D and S1
	Sink output Z	D and S2	A, B, C and S1

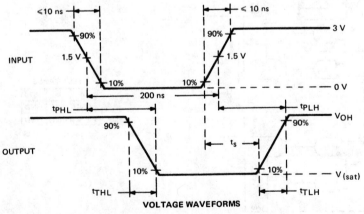

VOLTAGE WAVEFORMS

NOTES: A. The pulse generator has the following characteristics: $Z_{out} = 50\ \Omega$, duty cycle ≤ 1%.
B. C_L includes probe and jig capacitance.

FIGURE 9—SWITCHING TIMES

TEXAS INSTRUMENTS
INCORPORATED
POST OFFICE BOX 5012 • DALLAS, TEXAS 75222

PARAMETER MEASUREMENT INFORMATION

switching characteristics

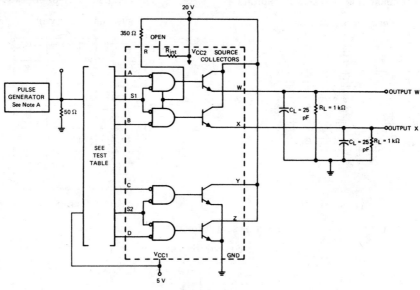

TEST CIRCUIT

TEST TABLE

PARAMETER	OUTPUT UNDER TEST	INPUT	CONNECT TO 5 V
t_{TLH} and t_{THL}	Source output W	A and S1	B, C, D, and S2
	Source output X	B and S1	A, C, D, and S2

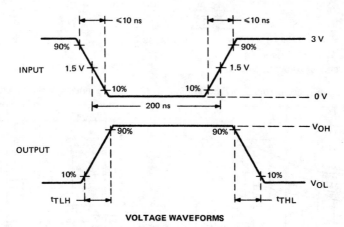

VOLTAGE WAVEFORMS

NOTES: A. The pulse generator has the following characteristics: Z_{out} = 50 Ω, duty cycle ≤ 1%.
 B. C_L includes probe and jig capacitance.

FIGURE 10—TRANSITION TIMES OF SOURCE OUTPUTS

10

TYPICAL CHARACTERISTICS

OFF-STATE CURRENT INTO SOURCE COLLECTORS
vs
FREE-AIR TEMPERATURE

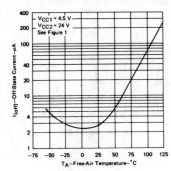

FIGURE 11

HIGH-LEVEL SINK OUTPUT VOLTAGE
vs
FREE-AIR TEMPERATURE

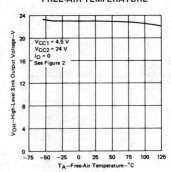

FIGURE 12

SOURCE OR SINK SATURATION VOLTAGE
vs
SOURCE CURRENT OR SINK CURRENT

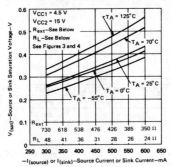

FIGURE 13

SOURCE OR SINK SATURATION VOLTAGE
vs
FREE-AIR TEMPERATURE

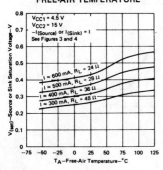

FIGURE 14

SUPPLY CURRENT, ALL SOURCES AND SINKS OFF
vs
FREE-AIR TEMPERATURE

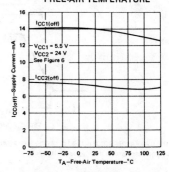

FIGURE 15

TEXAS INSTRUMENTS
INCORPORATED
POST OFFICE BOX 5012 • DALLAS, TEXAS 75222

TYPICAL APPLICATION DATA

balanced bipolar logic-line driver

The circuit shown in Figure 16 converts standard TTL logic to bipolar logic. Bipolar logic is primarily used in transmitting data or clock pulses over long lines. This line-driver may be operated from a single 5-volt supply; however, the output drive may be increased by raising the supply voltage to the source collectors. The circuit features a tri-state output which is off during the absence of data, thus not dissipating high power. It provides a balanced drive circuit giving maximum noise immunity when used with the proper line receiver. Large drive levels can be used to further increase noise immunity. The circuit is capable of driving twisted-pair lines of several miles in length or low-impedance coaxial lines.

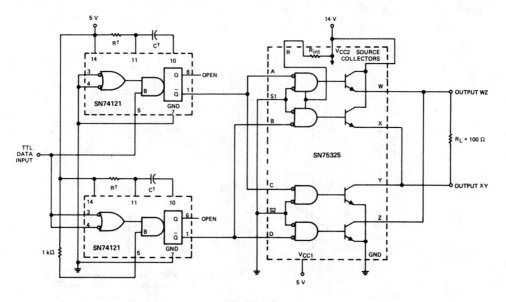

TEST CIRCUIT

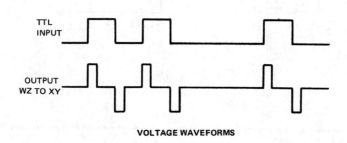

VOLTAGE WAVEFORMS

†R and C are adjusted to give the desired bipolar output pulse width.

FIGURE 16—BALANCED BIPOLAR LOGIC—LINE DRIVER

TYPICAL APPLICATION DATA

In memory-drive applications the SN75325 (or for full-temperature operation, the SN55325) can be connected in any of several ways. Typically, however, sources and sinks are arranged in pairs from which many drive-lines branch off as shown in Figure 17. Here each drive-line is served by a unique combination of two source/sink pairs so that a selection matrix is formed. To select drive-line 13, SN74154 No. 1 must be set to 3 (with mode select high), enabling source X of SN75325 No. 2 to drive lines 12 through 15, and SN74154 No. 2 must be set to 2, providing a sink at Y of SN75325 No. 4 for drive-line 13 only. Alternatively, to drive current in drive-line 13 in the opposite direction, only the mode-select voltage would be changed from high to low. The size of such a matrix is limited only by the number of drive-lines that a source/sink pair can serve. This number in turn depends on the capacitive and inductive load that each drive-line of the particular system imposes on the driver. A 256-drive-line selection matrix is shown in Figure 18. These 256 drive-lines are sufficient to serve $(256/2)^2 = 16,384$ individual cores.

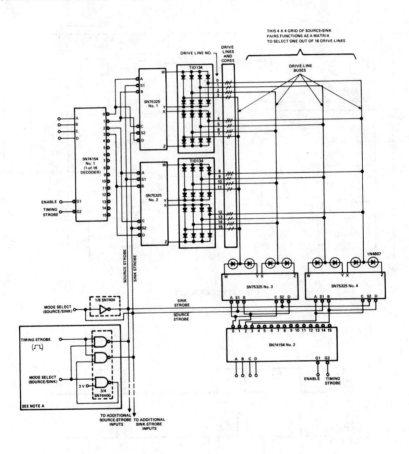

NOTE A: This optional mode-select and timing-strobe technique can be used in place of the SN7440 mode-select and SN74154 timing-strobe when minimum time skew is desired.

FIGURE 17—SN75325 USED AS A MEMORY DRIVER
TO SELECT ONE OF SIXTEEN DRIVE LINES

TEXAS INSTRUMENTS
INCORPORATED
POST OFFICE BOX 5012 • DALLAS, TEXAS 75222

TYPICAL APPLICATION DATA

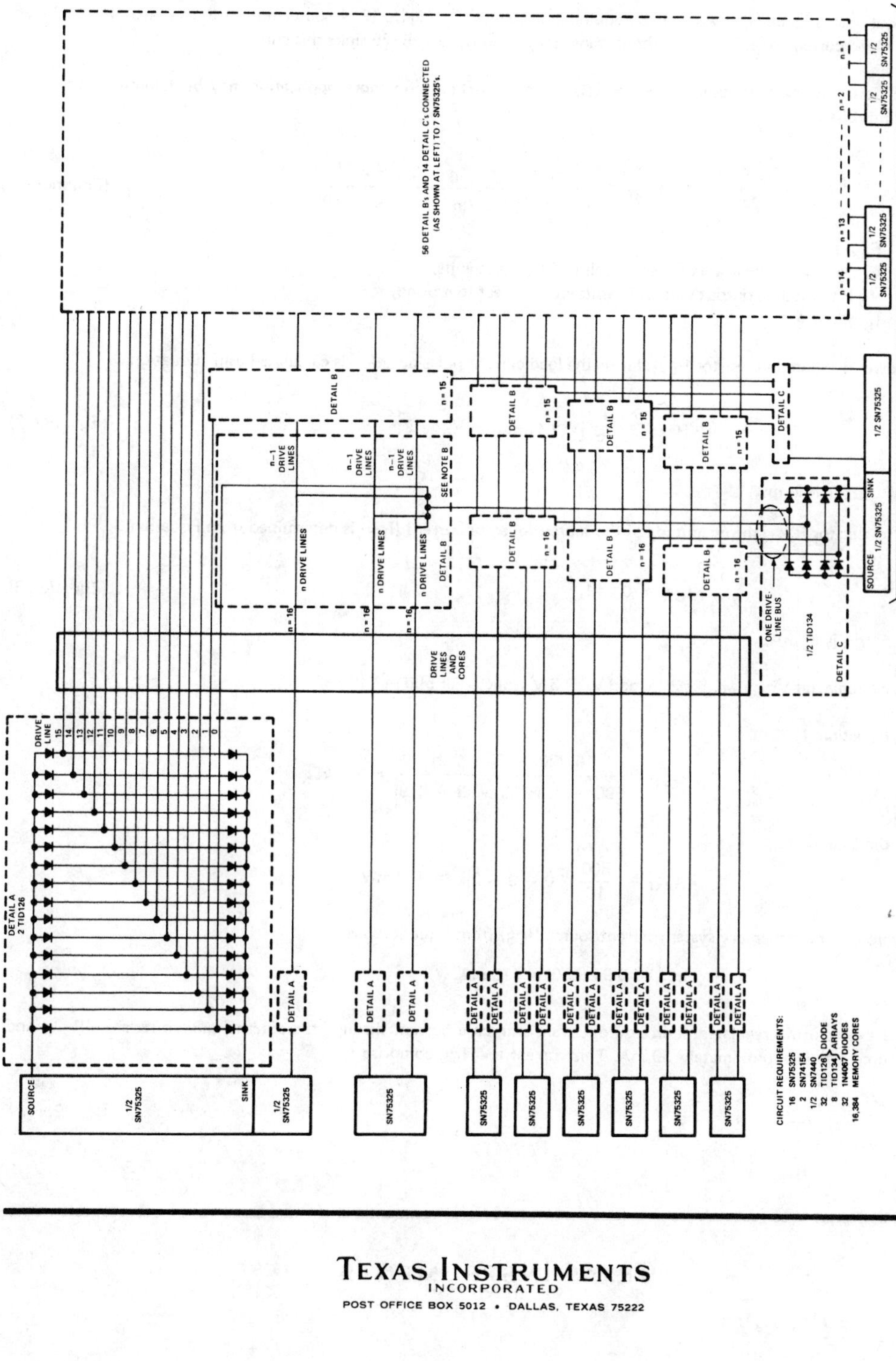

FIGURE 18—SN75325 SERVING 256 DRIVE LINES IN A MAGNETIC MEMORY

NOTES: A. Outputs from one SN74154 decoder are connected to each SN75325 as shown in Figure 17. Source strobe and sink strobe from an SN7440 are connected to each SN75325 as shown in Figure 17.

B. The division of the drive-line bus into four segments reduces the capacitive load on the SN75325 driver.

CIRCUIT REQUIREMENTS:

16	SN75325
2	SN74154
1/2	SN7440
32	TID126 DIODE
8	TID134 ARRAYS
32	1N4067 DIODES
16,384	MEMORY CORES

TEXAS INSTRUMENTS
INCORPORATED
POST OFFICE BOX 5012 • DALLAS, TEXAS 75222

TYPICAL APPLICATION DATA

external resistor calculation

A typical magnetic-memory word-drive requirement is shown in Figure 19. A source-output transistor of one SN75325 delivers load current (I_L). The sink-output transistor of another SN75325 sinks this current.

The value of the external pull-up resistor (R_{ext}) for a particular memory application may be determined using the following equation:

$$R_{ext} = \frac{16 \left[V_{CC2(min)} - V_S - 2.2 \right]}{I_L - 1.6 \left[V_{CC2(min)} - V_S - 2.9 \right]} \qquad \text{(Equation 1)}$$

where: R_{ext} is in kΩ,

$V_{CC2(min)}$ is the lowest expected value of V_{CC2} in volts,

V_S is the source output voltage in volts with respect to ground,

I_L is in mA.

The power dissipated in resistor R_{ext} during the load current pulse duration is calculated using Equation 2,

$$P_{Rext} \approx \frac{I_L}{16} \left[V_{CC2(min)} - V_S - 2 \right] \qquad \text{(Equation 2)}$$

where: P_{Rext} is in mW.

After solving for R_{ext}, the magnitude of the source collector current (I_{CS}) is determined from Equation 3,

$$I_{CS} \approx 0.94 \, I_L \qquad \text{(Equation 3)}$$

where: I_{CS} is in mA.

As an example, let $V_{CC2(min)} = 20$ V and $V_L = 3$ V while I_L of 500 mA flows.

Using Equation 1,

$$R_{ext} = \frac{16 \, (20 - 3 - 2.2)}{500 - 1.6 \, (20 - 3 - 2.9)} = 0.5 \text{ k}\Omega$$

and from Equation 2,

$$P_{Rext} \approx \frac{500}{16} \left[20 - 3 - 2 \right] \approx 470 \text{ mW}$$

The amount of the memory system current source (I_{CS}) from Equation 3 is:

$$I_{CS} \approx 0.94 \, (500) \approx 470 \text{ mA}$$

In this example the regulated source-output transistor base current through the external pull-up resistor (R_{ext}) and the source gate is approximately 30 mA. This current and I_{CS} comprise I_L.

TEXAS INSTRUMENTS
INCORPORATED
POST OFFICE BOX 5012 • DALLAS, TEXAS 75222

TYPICAL APPLICATION DATA

external resistor calculation (continued)

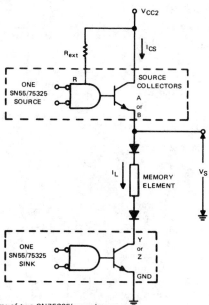

NOTES: A. For clarity, partial logic diagrams of two SN75325's are shown.
        B. Source and sink shown are in different packages.

FIGURE 19

THERMAL INFORMATION

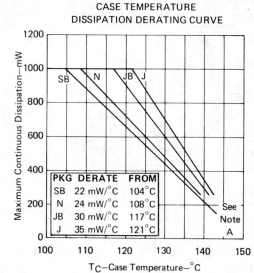

CASE TEMPERATURE
DISSIPATION DERATING CURVE

PKG	DERATE	FROM
SB	22 mW/°C	104°C
N	24 mW/°C	108°C
JB	30 mW/°C	117°C
J	35 mW/°C	121°C

T_C—Case Temperature—°C

NOTE A: Rated operating free-air temperature ranges must be observed regardless of heat-sinking.

FIGURE 20

FREE-AIR TEMPERATURE
DISSIPATION DERATING CURVE

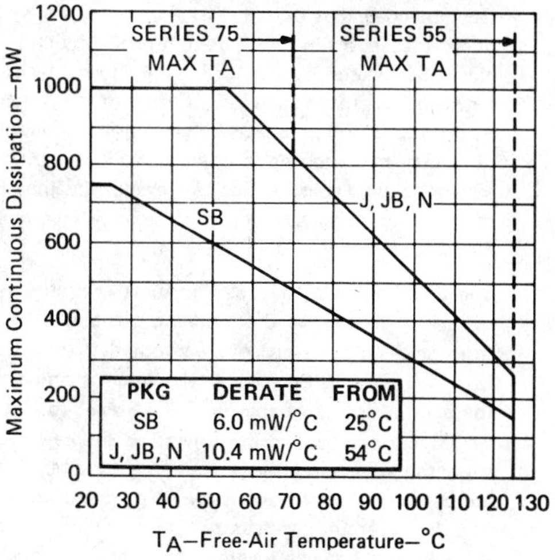

SERIES 75 MAX T_A SERIES 55 MAX T_A

PKG	DERATE	FROM
SB	6.0 mW/°C	25°C
J, JB, N	10.4 mW/°C	54°C

T_A—Free-Air Temperature—°C

FIGURE 21

TEXAS INSTRUMENTS
INCORPORATED
POST OFFICE BOX 5012 • DALLAS, TEXAS 75222

SERIES 55/75 MEMORY DRIVERS
featuring

SN55326, SN75326 PERFORMANCE

- Quad Positive-OR Sink Memory Drivers
- 600-mA Output Current Sink Capability
- 24-V Output Capability
- Clamp Voltage Variable to 24 V

SN55327, SN75327 PERFORMANCE

- Quad Memory Switches
- 600-mA Output Current Capability
- V_{CC2} Drive Voltage Variable to 24 V
- Output Capable of Swinging Between V_{CC2} and Ground

EASE OF DESIGN

- High-Repetition-Rate Driver Compatible with High-Speed Magnetic Memories
- Inputs Compatible with TTL Decoders
- Minimum Time Skew between Strobe and Output-Current Rise
- Pulse-Transformer Coupling Eliminated
- Drive-Line Lengths Reduced

description

The SN55326, SN55327, SN75326, and SN75327 are monolithic integrated circuit quadruple memory drivers. These devices accept standard TTL decoder input signals and provide high-current and high-voltage output levels suitable for driving magnetic memory elements. Output transistor selection is determined by using one of the four address inputs and the common timing strobe.

The SN55326 and SN75326 memory drivers can sink up to 600 milliamperes and operate from a single 5-volt supply. Each driver is similar to the sink drivers of the SN55325/SN75325. The four output transistors share a common base-drive resistor and it is recommended that only one of the four driver gates be selected at a time. Output-transistor base current may be increased by connecting an external resistor between R_{ext} (pin 4) and V_{CC}. Each output collector is protected from voltage surges during inductive switching by a clamp diode in parallel with its internal pull-up resistor. The two clamp pins may be returned to a power supply of from 4.5 volts to 24 volts.

The SN55327 and SN75327 memory switches can source or sink up to 600 milliamperes and operate from two supplies; one of five volts and the other from 4.5 volts to 24 volts. Each switch is similar to the source drivers of the SN55325/SN75325. They can function as either sink drivers or source drivers since the voltages at the output transistor terminals are capable of swinging between V_{CC2} and ground. The four output transistors share a common base-drive resistor and it is recommended that only one of the four outputs be selected at a time. An internal base-drive resistor is available on the chip and can be

SN55326, SN75326
J, JB, OR N DUAL-IN-LINE OR
SB FLAT PACKAGE (TOP VIEW)

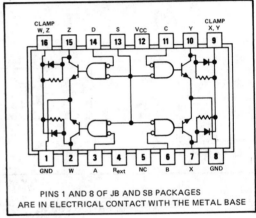

PINS 1 AND 8 OF JB AND SB PACKAGES
ARE IN ELECTRICAL CONTACT WITH THE METAL BASE

NC—No internal connection

SB55327, SN75327
J, JB, OR N DUAL-IN-LINE OR
SB FLAT PACKAGE (TOP VIEW)

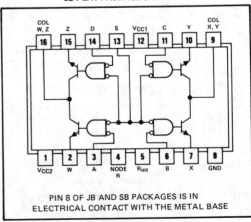

PIN 8 OF JB AND SB PACKAGES IS IN
ELECTRICAL CONTACT WITH THE METAL BASE

TEXAS INSTRUMENTS
INCORPORATED
POST OFFICE BOX 5012 • DALLAS, TEXAS 75222

description (continued)

used by connecting Node R (pin 4) to R_{int} (pin 5). This resistor provides adequate base current to the output transistors for output sink currents up to 375 milliamperes with V_{CC2} at 15 volts or 600 milliamperes with V_{CC2} at 24 volts. Base current can be regulated to within ±5 percent by substituting for this resistor an external resistor connected between Node R (pin 4) and V_{CC2} with R_{int} (pin 5) remaining open. This method is preferable in high-duty-cycle, high-power applications since the power dissipated in this resistor is outside the package. When a source current and V_{CC2} voltage other than the above values are required, it is recommended that the base drive be supplied through an external resistor of the appropriate value calculated using Equation 1 shown in the SN55325, SN75325 data sheet.

FUNCTION TABLE

INPUTS					OUTPUTS			
ADDRESS				STROBE	W	X	Y	Z
A	B	C	D	S				
L	H	H	H	L	ON	OFF	OFF	OFF
H	L	H	H	L	OFF	ON	OFF	OFF
H	H	L	H	L	OFF	OFF	ON	OFF
H	H	H	L	L	OFF	OFF	OFF	ON
H	H	H	H	X	OFF	OFF	OFF	OFF
X	X	X	X	H	OFF	OFF	OFF	OFF

H = high level, L = low level, X = irrelevant

NOTE: Not more than one output is to be on at any one time.

The SN55326 and SN55327 circuits are characterized for operation over the full military temperature range of −55°C to 125°C; the SN75326 and SN75327 are characterized for operation from 0°C to 70°C.

absolute maximum ratings over operating free-air temperature range (unless otherwise noted)

	SN55326	SN75326	SN55327	SN75327	UNIT
Supply voltage, V_{CC} or V_{CC1} (see Note 1)	7	7	7	7	V
Supply voltage, V_{CC2}			25	25	V
Input voltage, any address or strobe	5.5	5.5	5.5	5.5	V
Output collector voltage	25	25	25	25	V
Output clamp voltage	25	25			V
Output collector current	750	750	750	750	mA
Continuous total dissipation at (or below) 100°C case temperature (see Note 2)	1	1	1	1	W
Operating free-air temperature range	−55 to 125	0 to 70	−55 to 125	0 to 70	°C
Storage temperature range	−65 to 150	−65 to 150	−65 to 150	−65 to 150	°C
Lead temperature 1/16 inch from case for 60 seconds: J, JB, or SB package	300	300	300	300	°C
Lead temperature 1/16 inch from case for 10 seconds: N package	260	260	260	260	°C

recommended operating conditions

	SN55326			SN75326			SN55327			SN75327			UNIT
	MIN	NOM	MAX	MIN	NOM	MAX	MIN	NOM	MAX	MIN	NOM	MAX	
Supply voltage, V_{CC} or V_{CC1}	4.5	5	5.5	4.5	5	5.5	4.5	5	5.5	4.5	5	5.5	V
Supply voltage, V_{CC2}							4.5		24	4.5		24	V
Output collector voltage			24			24			24			24	V
Output-clamp voltage, $V_{(clamp)}$	4.5		24	4.5		24							V
Output collector current			600			600			600			600	mA
Operating free-air temperature, T_A	−55		125	0		70	−55		125	0		70	°C

NOTES: 1. Voltage values are with respect to network ground terminal(s).
2. For operation above 100°C case temperature, refer to Dissipation Derating Curve, Figure 1. For dissipation ratings in free-air, see Figure 2.

TEXAS INSTRUMENTS
INCORPORATED
POST OFFICE BOX 5012 • DALLAS, TEXAS 75222

SN55326, SN75326 electrical characteristics over recommended operating free-air temperature range (unless otherwise noted)

PARAMETER		TEST CONDITIONS[†]	SN55326 MIN	SN55326 TYP[‡]	SN55326 MAX	SN75326 MIN	SN75326 TYP[‡]	SN75326 MAX	UNIT
V_{IH}	High-level input voltage		2			2			V
V_{IL}	Low-level input voltage				0.8			0.8	V
V_I	Input clamp voltage	$V_{CC} = 4.5$ V, $I_I = -10$ mA, $T_A = 25°C$		−1	−1.7		−1	−1.7	V
V_{OH}	High-level output voltage	$V_{CC} = 4.5$ V, $I_O = 0$	19	23		19	23		V
$V_{(sat)}$	Saturation voltage	$V_{CC} = 4.5$ V, $I_{(sink)} = 600$ mA[§], See Note 3 — Full range			0.9			0.9	V
		$T_A = 25°C$		0.43	0.7		0.43	0.75	
$V_{F(clamp)}$	Output-clamp-diode forward voltage	$V_{(clamp)} = 0$, $I_{(clamp)} = -10$ mA, $T_A = 25°C$			1.5			1.5	V
$I_{(clamp)}$	Output-clamp current, one output on	$I_{(sink)} = 50$ mA, $T_A = 25°C$		5	7		5	7	mA
I_I	Input current at maximum input voltage — Address	$V_I = 5.5$ V			1			1	mA
	Strobe				4			4	
I_{IH}	High-level input current — Address	$V_I = 2.4$ V			40			40	μA
	Strobe				160			160	
I_{IL}	Low-level input current — Address	$V_I = 0.4$ V		−1	−1.6		−1	−1.6	mA
	Strobe			−4	−6.4		−4	−6.4	
$I_{CC(off)}$	Supply current, all outputs off	All inputs at 5 V, $T_A = 25°C$		18	25		18	25	mA
$I_{CC(on)}$	Supply current, one output on	$I_{(sink)} = 50$ mA, $T_A = 25°C$		58	75		58	75	mA

SN55326, SN75326 switching characteristics, $V_{CC} = 5$ V, $T_A = 25°C$

PARAMETER[¶]	TO (OUTPUT)	TEST CONDITIONS[§]	MIN	TYP	MAX	UNIT
t_{PLH}	W, X, Y, or Z	$V_S = V_{(clamp)} = 15$ V, $R_L = 24$ Ω, $C_L = 25$ pF, See Figure 5		30	50	ns
t_{PHL}				25	50	
t_{TLH}	W, X, Y, or Z			7	15	ns
t_{THL}				10	20	
t_s	W, X, Y, or Z			24	35	ns
V_{OH}	W, X, Y, or Z	$V_S = V_{(clamp)} = 24$ V, $R_L = 47$ Ω, $C_L = 25$ pF, $I_{(sink)} \approx 500$ mA, See Figure 5	$V_S - 25$			mV

[†]Unless otherwise noted, $V_{CC} = 5.5$ V, $V_{(clamp)} = 24$ V. See Figure 3.
[‡]All typical values are at $T_A = 25°C$.
[§]Under these conditions, not more than one output is to be on at any one time.
[¶]$t_{PLH} \equiv$ propagation delay time, low-to-high-level output
$t_{PHL} \equiv$ propagation delay time, high-to-low-level output
$t_{TLH} \equiv$ transition time, low-to-high-level output
$t_{THL} \equiv$ transition time, high-to-low-level output
$t_s \equiv$ Storage time
$V_{OH} \equiv$ High-level output voltage (after switching)
NOTE 3: These parameters must be measured using pulse techniques. $t_w = 200$ μs, duty cycle ⩽ 2%.

For typical characteristic curves, Figures 11 through 14 of the SN55325/SN75325 data sheet apply for these circuits.

TEXAS INSTRUMENTS
INCORPORATED
POST OFFICE BOX 5012 • DALLAS, TEXAS 75222

10
9

SN55327, SN75327 electrical characteristics over recommended operating free-air temperature range (unless otherwise noted)

PARAMETER		TEST CONDITIONS[†]		SN55327 MIN	SN55327 TYP[‡]	SN55327 MAX	SN75327 MIN	SN75327 TYP[‡]	SN75327 MAX	UNIT
V_{IH}	High-level input voltage			2			2			V
V_{IL}	Low-level input voltage					0.8			0.8	V
V_I	Input clamp voltage	$V_{CC} = 4.5$ V, $\quad I_I = -10$ mA $T_A = 25°C$			-1	-1.7		-1	-1.7	V
$I_{(off)}$	Collectors terminal off-state current	$V_{CC1} = 4.5$ V, $V_{(col)} = 24$ V	Full range			500			200	μA
			$T_A = 25°C$			150			200	
$V_{(sat)}$	Saturation voltage	$V_{CC1} = 4.5$ V, $V_O = 0$,	Full range			0.9			0.9	V
		$I_{(source)} = -600$ mA[§], See Notes 3 and 4	$T_A = 25°C$		0.43	0.7		0.43	0.75	
I_I	Input current at maximum input voltage	Address	$V_I = 5.5$ V			1			1	mA
		Strobe				4			4	
I_{IH}	High-level input current	Address	$V_I = 2.4$ V			40			40	μA
		Strobe				160			160	
I_{IL}	Low-level input current	Address	$V_I = 0.4$ V		-1	-1.6		-1	-1.6	mA
		Strobe			-4	-6.4		-4	-6.4	
$I_{CC(off)}$	Supply current, all outputs off	From V_{CC1}	All inputs at 5 V, $\quad T_A = 25°C$		7	10		7	10	mA
		From V_{CC2}			13	20		13	20	
$I_{CC(on)}$	Supply current, one output on	From V_{CC1}	$V_{(col)} = 6$ V, $\quad I_{(source)} = -50$ mA,		8	12		8	12	mA
		From V_{CC2}	$T_A = 25°C$, See Note 3		36	55		36	55	

SN55327, SN75327 switching characteristics, $V_{CC1} = 5$ V, $T_A = 25°C$

PARAMETER[¶]	TO (OUTPUT)	TEST CONDITIONS[§]		MIN	TYP	MAX	UNIT
t_{PLH}	Collectors	$V_S = V_{CC2} = 15$ V, $\quad R_L = 24\ \Omega$, $C_L = 25$ pF,			35	55	ns
t_{PHL}	W, Z or X, Y	See Figure 5 and Note 4			30	55	
t_{TLH}	W, X, Y, or Z	$V_{(col)} = V_{CC2} = 20$ V, $\quad R_L = 100\ \Omega$, $C_L = 25$ pF,			30		ns
t_{THL}		See Figure 6 and Note 4			10		
V_{OH}	Collectors W, Z or X, Y	$V_S = V_{CC2} = 24$ V, $\quad R_L = 47\ \Omega$, $C_L = 25$ pF, $I_{(sink)} \approx 500$ mA, $\quad$ See Figure 5 and Note 4		V_S-25			mV

[†]Unless otherwise noted, $V_{CC1} = 5.5$ V, $V_{CC2} = 24$ V. See Figure 3.
[‡]All typical values are at $T_A = 25°C$.
[§]Under these conditions, not more than one output is to be on at any one time.
[¶]$t_{PLH} \equiv$ propagation delay time, low-to-high-level output
$t_{PHL} \equiv$ propagation delay time, high-to-low-level output
$t_{TLH} \equiv$ transition time, low-to-high-level output
$t_{THL} \equiv$ transition time, high-to-low-level output
$V_{OH} \equiv$ High-level output voltage (after switching)
NOTES: 3. These parameters must be measured using pulse techniques. $t_w = 200\ \mu s$, duty cycle $\leqslant$ 2%.
4. A 350-Ω resistor is connected between node R (pin 4) and V_{CC2} (pin 1) with R_{int} (pin 5) open.

For typical characteristic curves, Figures 11 through 14 of the SN55325/SN75325 data sheet apply for these circuits.

73

TEXAS INSTRUMENTS
INCORPORATED
POST OFFICE BOX 5012 • DALLAS, TEXAS 75222

TYPES SN55326, SN55327, SN75326, SN75327
MEMORY DRIVERS

schematics

SN55326, SN75326

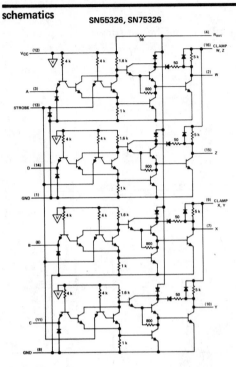

SN55327, SN75327

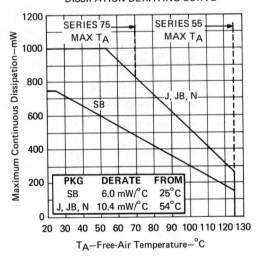

▽ ▽ ▽ ... V_CC, V_CC1, or V_CC2 bus, respectively.

Resistor values shown are nominal and in ohms.

THERMAL INFORMATION

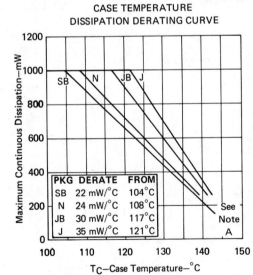

CASE TEMPERATURE
DISSIPATION DERATING CURVE

PKG	DERATE	FROM
SB	22 mW/°C	104°C
N	24 mW/°C	108°C
JB	30 mW/°C	117°C
J	35 mW/°C	121°C

See Note A

NOTE A: Rated operating free-air temperature ranges must be observed regardless of heat-sinking.

FIGURE 1

FREE-AIR TEMPERATURE
DISSIPATION DERATING CURVE

SERIES 75 MAX T_A   SERIES 55 MAX T_A

PKG	DERATE	FROM
SB	6.0 mW/°C	25°C
J, JB, N	10.4 mW/°C	54°C

FIGURE 2

TEXAS INSTRUMENTS
INCORPORATED
POST OFFICE BOX 5012 • DALLAS, TEXAS 75222

PARAMETER MEASUREMENT INFORMATION

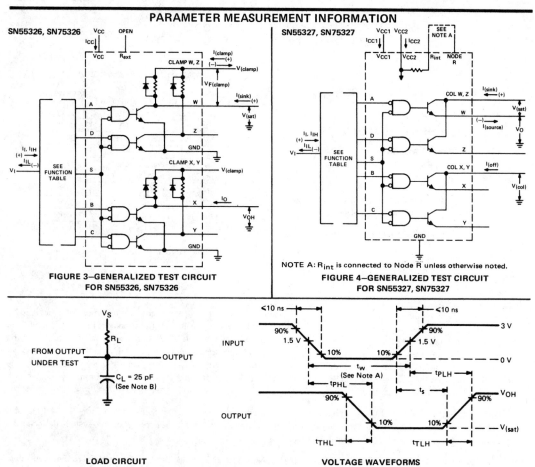

FIGURE 3—GENERALIZED TEST CIRCUIT FOR SN55326, SN75326

FIGURE 4—GENERALIZED TEST CIRCUIT FOR SN55327, SN75327

NOTE A: R_{int} is connected to Node R unless otherwise noted.

LOAD CIRCUIT

VOLTAGE WAVEFORMS

NOTES: A. Input pulses are supplied by generators having the following characteristics: $Z_{out} \approx 50\ \Omega$. For testing V_{OH} (after switching), $t_w = 40\ \mu s$, PRR = 12.5 kHz. For all other tests, $t_w = 200$ ns, duty cycle $\leqslant 1\%$.
B. C_L includes probe and jig capacitance.

FIGURE 5—SWITCHING TIMES

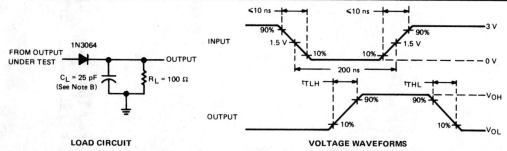

LOAD CIRCUIT

VOLTAGE WAVEFORMS

NOTES: A. Input pulses are supplied by generators having the following characteristics: $Z_{out} \approx 50\ \Omega$, duty cycle $\leqslant 1\%$.
B. C_L includes probe and jig capacitance.

FIGURE 6—SWITCHING TIMES

TEXAS INSTRUMENTS
INCORPORATED
POST OFFICE BOX 5012 • DALLAS, TEXAS 75222

PERIPHERAL DRIVERS FOR
HIGH-CURRENT SWITCHING AT HIGH SPEEDS

performance

- 300-mA Output Current Capability
- High-Voltage Outputs
- No Output Latch-Up at 20 V
- High-Speed Switching

ease-of-design

- Circuit Flexibility for Varied Applications and Choice of Logic Function
- TTL or DTL Compatible Diode-Clamped Inputs
- Standard Supply Voltages

SUMMARY OF SERIES 55450B/75450B

DEVICE	LOGIC OF COMPLETE CIRCUIT	PACKAGES
SN55450B	Positive-AND[†]	J, JB
SN55451B	Positive-AND	JP, L
SN55452B	Positive-NAND	JP, L
SN55453B	Positive-OR	JP, L
SN55454B	Positive-NOR	JP, L
SN75450B	Positive-AND[†]	J, N
SN75451B	Positive-AND	L, P
SN75452B	Positive-NAND	L, P
SN75453B	Positive-OR	L, P
SN75454B	Positive-NOR	L, P

[†]With output transistor base connected externally to output of gate.

description

Series 55450B/75450B dual peripheral drivers are a family of versatile devices designed for use in systems that employ TTL or DTL logic. The 55450B/75450B family is functionally interchangeable with and replaces the 75450 family and the 75450A family devices manufactured previously. The speed of the 55450B/75450B family is equal to that of the 75450 family and a test to ensure freedom from latch-up has been added. Diode-clamped inputs simplify circuit design. Typical applications include high-speed logic buffers, power drivers, relay drivers. lamp drivers, MOS drivers, line drivers, and memory drivers. Series 55450B drivers are characterized for operation over the full military temperature range of −55°C to 125°C; Series 75450B drivers are characterized for operation from 0°C to 70°C.

The SN55450B and SN75450B are unique general-purpose devices each featuring two standard Series 54/74 TTL gates and two uncommitted, high-current, high-voltage n-p-n transistors. These devices offer the system designer the flexibility of tailoring the circuit to the application.

The SN55451B/SN75451B, SN55452B/SN75452B, SN55453B/SN75453B, and SN55454B/SN75454B are dual peripheral AND, NAND, OR, and NOR drivers, respectively, (assuming positive logic) with the output of the logic gates internally connected to the bases of the n-p-n output transistors.

This data sheet replaces the Series 75450 data sheet, DL-S 7111444, dated March 1971

TENTATIVE DATA SHEET
10-42 This document provides tentative information on a new product. Texas Instruments reserves the right to change specifications for this product in any manner without notice.

TEXAS INSTRUMENTS
INCORPORATED
POST OFFICE BOX 5012 • DALLAS, TEXAS 75222

97

absolute maximum ratings over operating free-air temperature range (unless otherwise noted)

		SN55450B	SN55451B SN55452B SN55453B SN55454B	SN75450B	SN75451B SN75452B SN75453B SN75454B	UNIT
Supply voltage, V_{CC} (see Note 1)		7	7	7	7	V
Input voltage		5.5	5.5	5.5	5.5	V
Interemitter voltage (see Note 2)		5.5	5.5	5.5	5.5	V
V_{CC}-to-substrate voltage		35		35		V
Collector-to-substrate voltage		35		35		V
Collector-base voltage		35		35		V
Collector-emitter voltage (see Note 3)		30		30		V
Emitter-base voltage		5		5		V
Output voltage (see Note 4)			30		30	V
Collector current (see Note 5)		300		300		mA
Output current (see Note 5)			300		300	mA
Continuous total dissipation at (or below) 25°C free-air temperature (see Note 6)		800	800	800	800	mW
Operating free-air temperature range		−55 to 125	−55 to 125	0 to 70	0 to 70	°C
Storage temperature range		−65 to 150	−65 to 150	−65 to 150	−65 to 150	°C
Lead temperature 1/16 inch from case for 60 seconds	J, JB, JP, or L package	300	300	300	300	°C
Lead temperature 1/16 inch from case for 10 seconds	N or P package	260	260	260	260	°C

NOTES: 1. Voltage values are with respect to network ground terminal unless otherwise specified.
2. This is the voltage between two emitters of a multiple-emitter transistor.
3. This value applies when the base-emitter resistance (R_{BE}) is equal to or less than 500 Ω.
4. This is the maximum voltage which should be applied to any output when it is in the off state.
5. Both halves of these dual circuits may conduct rated current simultaneously; however, power dissipation averaged over a short time interval must fall within the continuous dissipation rating.
6. For operation above 25°C free-air temperature, refer to Dissipation Derating Curve, Figure 20. This rating for the L package requires a heat sink that provides a thermal resistance from case to free-air, $R_{\theta CA}$, of not more than 95°C/W.

recommended operating conditions (see Note 7)

	SERIES 55450B			SERIES 75450B			UNIT
	MIN	NOM	MAX	MIN	NOM	MAX	
Supply voltage, V_{CC}	4.5	5	5.5	4.75	5	5.25	V
Operating free-air temperature, T_A	−55		125	0		70	°C

NOTE 7: For the SN55450B and SN75450B only, the substrate (pin 8) must always be at the most-negative device voltage for proper operation.

schematic

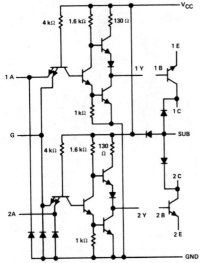

Resistor values shown are nominal.

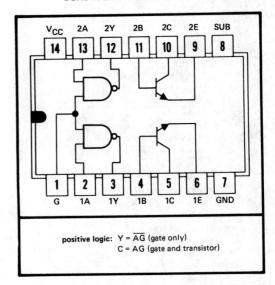

J OR JB
DUAL-IN-LINE PACKAGE (TOP VIEW)

positive logic: Y = $\overline{AG}$ (gate only)
C = AG (gate and transistor)

electrical characteristics over recommended operating free-air temperature range (unless otherwise noted)

TTL gates

PARAMETER		TEST FIGURE	TEST CONDITIONS		MIN	TYP†	MAX	UNIT
V_{IH}	High-level input voltage	1			2			V
V_{IL}	Low-level input voltage	2					0.8	V
V_I	Input clamp voltage	3	$V_{CC} = 4.5$ V,	$= -12$ mA			−1.5	V
V_{OH}	High-level output voltage	2	$V_{CC} = 4.5$ V, $V_{IL} = 0.8$ V, $I_{OH} = -400 \mu$A		2.4	3.3		V
V_{OL}	Low-level output voltage	1	$V_{CC} = 4.5$ V, $V_{IH} = 2$ V, $I_{OL} = 16$ mA			0.22	0.5	V
I_I	Input current at maximum input voltage	input A	4	$V_{CC} = 5.5$ V, $V_I = 5.5$ V			1	mA
		input G					2	
I_{IH}	High-level input current	input A	4	$V_{CC} = 5.5$ V, $V_I = 2.4$ V			40	μA
		input G					80	
I_{IL}	Low-level input current	input A	3	$V_{CC} = 5.5$ V, $V_I = 0.4$ V			−1.6	mA
		input G					−3.2	
I_{OS}	Short-circuit output current‡		5	$V_{CC} = 5.5$ V,		−18		−55	mA
I_{CCH}	Supply current, outputs high		6	$V_{CC} = 5.5$ V, $V_I = 0$			2	4	mA
I_{CCL}	Supply current, outputs low			$V_{CC} = 5.5$ V, $V_I = 5$ V			6	11	mA

†All typical values at $V_{CC} = 5$ V, $T_A = 25°$C.
‡Not more than one output should be shorted at a time.

TEXAS INSTRUMENTS
INCORPORATED
POST OFFICE BOX 5012 • DALLAS, TEXAS 75222

electrical characteristics over recommended operating free-air temperature range (unless otherwise noted)

output transistors

PARAMETER		TEST CONDITIONS		MIN	TYP†	MAX	UNIT
$V_{(BR)CBO}$	Collector-Base Breakdown Voltage	I_C = 100 μA,	I_E = 0	35			V
$V_{(BR)CER}$	Collector-Emitter Breakdown Voltage	I_C = 100 μA,	R_{BE} = 500 Ω	30			V
$V_{(BR)EBO}$	Emitter-Base Breakdown Voltage	I_E = 100 μA,	I_C = 0	5			V
h_{FE}	Static Forward Current Transfer Ratio	V_{CE} = 3 V, T_A = 25°C	I_C = 100 mA,	See Note 8	25		
		V_{CE} = 3 V, T_A = 25°C	I_C = 300 mA,		30		
		V_{CE} = 3 V, T_A = −55°C	I_C = 100 mA,		10		
		V_{CE} = 3 V, T_A = −55°C	I_C = 300 mA,		15		
V_{BE}	Base-Emitter Voltage	I_B = 10 mA, I_C = 100 mA	See Note 8		0.85	1.2	V
		I_B = 30 mA, I_C = 300 mA			1.05	1.4	
$V_{CE(sat)}$	Collector-Emitter Saturation Voltage	I_B = 10 mA, I_C = 100 mA	See Note 8		0.25	0.5	V
		I_B = 30 mA, I_C = 300 mA			0.5	0.8	

†All typical values are at V_{CC} = 5 V, T_A = 25°C.
NOTE 8: These parameters must be measured using pulse techniques. t_w = 300 μs, duty cycle $\leqslant$ 2%.

switching characteristics, V_{CC} = 5 V, T_A = 25°C

TTL gates

	PARAMETER	TEST FIGURE	TEST CONDITIONS		MIN	TYP	MAX	UNIT
t_{PLH}	Propagation delay time, low-to-high-level output	12	C_L = 15 pF,	R_L = 400 Ω		12	22	ns
t_{PHL}	Propagation delay time, high-to-low-level output					8	15	ns

output transistors

	PARAMETER	TEST FIGURE	TEST CONDITIONS‡		MIN	TYP	MAX	UNIT
t_d	Delay time	13	I_C = 200 mA, $I_{B(1)}$ = 20 mA, $I_{B(2)}$ = −40 mA, $V_{BE(off)}$ = −1 V, C_L = 15 pF, R_L = 50 Ω			8	15	ns
t_r	Rise time					12	20	ns
t_s	Storage time					7	15	ns
t_f	Fall time					6	15	ns

‡Voltage and current values shown are nominal; exact values vary slightly with transistor parameters.

gates and transistors combined

	PARAMETER	TEST FIGURE	TEST CONDITIONS		MIN	TYP	MAX	UNIT
t_{PLH}	Propagation delay time, low-to-high-level output	14	$I_C \approx$ 200 mA, C_L = 15 pF, R_L = 50 Ω			20	30	ns
t_{PHL}	Propagation delay time, high-to-low-level output					20	30	ns
t_{TLH}	Transition time, low-to-high-level output					7	12	ns
t_{THL}	Transition time, high-to-low-level output					9	15	ns
V_{OH}	High-level output voltage after switching	15	V_S = 20 V, $I_C \approx$ 300 mA, R_{BE} = 500 Ω		V_S−6.5			mV

973

TEXAS INSTRUMENTS
INCORPORATED
POST OFFICE BOX 5012 • DALLAS, TEXAS 75222

TYPE SN75450B
DUAL PERIPHERAL POSITIVE-AND DRIVER

schematic

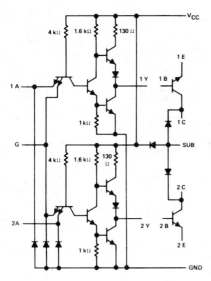

Resistor values shown are nominal.

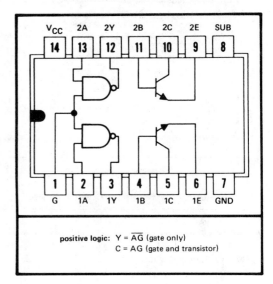

J OR N
DUAL-IN-LINE PACKAGE (TOP VIEW)

V_{CC}	2A	2Y	2B	2C	2E	SUB
14	13	12	11	10	9	8

1	2	3	4	5	6	7
G	1A	1Y	1B	1C	1E	GND

positive logic: Y = $\overline{AG}$ (gate only)
C = AG (gate and transistor)

electrical characteristics over recommended operating free-air temperature range (unless otherwise noted)

TTL gates

PARAMETER			TEST FIGURE	TEST CONDITIONS		MIN	TYP†	MAX	UNIT
V_{IH}	High-level input voltage		1			2			V
V_{IL}	Low-level input voltage		2					0.8	V
V_I	Input clamp voltage		3	V_{CC} = 4.75 V,	I_I = −12 mA			−1.5	V
V_{OH}	High-level output voltage		2	V_{CC} = 4.75 V, I_{OH} = −400 μA	V_{IL} = 0.8 V,	2.4	3.3		V
V_{OL}	Low-level output voltage		1	V_{CC} = 4.75 V, I_{OL} = 16 mA	V_{IH} = 2 V,		0.22	0.4	V
I_I	Input current at maximum input voltage	input A	4	V_{CC} = 5.25 V,	V_I = 5.5 V			1	mA
		input G						2	
I_{IH}	High-level input current	input A	4	V_{CC} = 5.25 V,	V_I = 2.4 V			40	μA
		input G						80	
I_{IL}	Low-level input current	input A	3	V_{CC} = 5.25 V,	V_I = 0.4 V			−1.6	mA
		input G						−3.2	
I_{OS}	Short-circuit output current‡		5	V_{CC} = 5.25 V		−18		−55	mA
I_{CCH}	Supply current, outputs high		6	V_{CC} = 5.25 V,	V_I = 0		2	4	mA
I_{CCL}	Supply current, outputs low			V_{CC} = 5.25 V,	V_I = 5 V		6	11	mA

†All typical values at V_{CC} = 5 V, T_A = 25°C.

‡Not more than one output should be shorted at a time.

973

electrical characteristics over recommended operating free-air temperature range (unless otherwise noted)

output transistors

PARAMETER		TEST CONDITIONS			MIN	TYP†	MAX	UNIT
$V_{(BR)CBO}$	Collector-Base Breakdown Voltage	$I_C = 100\ \mu A$,	$I_E = 0$		35			V
$V_{(BR)CER}$	Collector-Emitter Breakdown Voltage	$I_C = 100\ \mu A$,	$R_{BE} = 500\ \Omega$		30			V
$V_{(BR)EBO}$	Emitter-Base Breakdown Voltage	$I_E = 100\ \mu A$,	$I_C = 0$		5			V
h_{FE}	Static Forward Current Transfer Ratio	$V_{CE} = 3$ V, $T_A = 25°C$	$I_C = 100$ mA,	See Note 8	25			
		$V_{CE} = 3$ V, $T_A = 25°C$	$I_C = 300$ mA,		30			
		$V_{CE} = 3$ V, $T_A = 0°C$	$I_C = 100$ mA,		20			
		$V_{CE} = 3$ V, $T_A = 0°C$	$I_C = 300$ mA,		25			
V_{BE}	Base-Emitter Voltage	$I_B = 10$ mA,	$I_C = 100$ mA	See Note 8		0.85	1	V
		$I_B = 30$ mA,	$I_C = 300$ mA			1.05	1.2	
$V_{CE(sat)}$	Collector-Emitter Saturation Voltage	$I_B = 10$ mA,	$I_C = 100$ mA	See Note 8		0.25	0.4	V
		$I_B = 30$ mA,	$I_C = 300$ mA			0.5	0.7	

†All typical values are at $V_{CC} = 5$ V, $T_A = 25°C$.
NOTE 8: These parameters must be measured using pulse techniques. $t_w = 300\ \mu s$, duty cycle $\leqslant 2\%$.

switching characteristics, $V_{CC} = 5$ V, $T_A = 25°C$

TTL gates

PARAMETER		TEST FIGURE	TEST CONDITIONS		MIN	TYP	MAX	UNIT
t_{PLH}	Propagation delay time, low-to-high-level output	12	$C_L = 15$ pF,	$R_L = 400\ \Omega$		12	22	ns
t_{PHL}	Propagation delay time, high-to-low-level output					8	15	ns

output transistors

PARAMETER		TEST FIGURE	TEST CONDITIONS‡		MIN	TYP	MAX	UNIT
t_d	Delay time	13	$I_C = 200$ mA, $I_{B(1)} = 20$ mA, $I_{B(2)} = -40$ mA, $V_{BE(off)} = -1$ V, $C_L = 15$ pF, $R_L = 50\ \Omega$			8	15	ns
t_r	Rise time					12	20	ns
t_s	Storage time					7	15	ns
t_f	Fall time					6	15	ns

‡Voltage and current values shown are nominal; exact values vary slightly with transistor parameters.

gates and transistors combined

PARAMETER		TEST FIGURE	TEST CONDITIONS	MIN	TYP	MAX	UNIT
t_{PLH}	Propagation delay time, low-to-high-level output	14	$I_C \approx 200$ mA, $C_L = 15$ pF, $R_L = 50\ \Omega$		20	30	ns
t_{PHL}	Propagation delay time, high-to-low-level output				20	30	ns
t_{TLH}	Transition time, low-to-high-level output				7	12	ns
t_{THL}	Transition time, high-to-low-level output				9	15	ns
V_{OH}	High-level output voltage after switching	15	$V_S = 20$ V, $I_C \approx 300$ mA, $R_{BE} = 500\ \Omega$	$V_S - 6.5$			mV

73

TYPE SN55451B
DUAL PERIPHERAL POSITIVE-AND DRIVER

logic

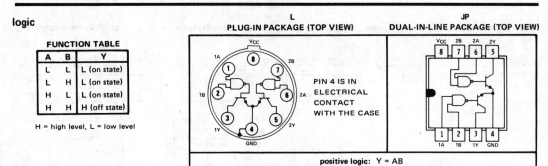

FUNCTION TABLE

A	B	Y
L	L	L (on state)
L	H	L (on state)
H	L	L (on state)
H	H	H (off state)

H = high level, L = low level

L PLUG-IN PACKAGE (TOP VIEW)

PIN 4 IS IN ELECTRICAL CONTACT WITH THE CASE

JP DUAL-IN-LINE PACKAGE (TOP VIEW)

positive logic: Y = AB

schematic (each driver)

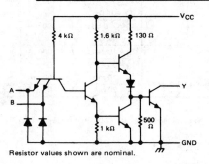

Resistor values shown are nominal.

electrical characteristics over recommended operating free-air temperature range (unless otherwise noted)

PARAMETER		TEST FIGURE	TEST CONDITIONS		MIN	TYP†	MAX	UNIT
V_{IH}	High-level input voltage	7			2			V
V_{IL}	Low-level input voltage	7					0.8	V
V_I	Input clamp voltage	8	$V_{CC} = 4.5$ V,	$I_I = -12$ mA			-1.5	V
I_{OH}	High-level output current	7	$V_{CC} = 4.5$ V, $V_{OH} = 30$ V	$V_{IH} = 2$ V,			300	µA
V_{OL}	Low-level output voltage	7	$V_{CC} = 4.5$ V, $I_{OL} = 100$ mA	$V_{IL} = 0.8$ V,		0.25	0.5	V
			$V_{CC} = 4.5$ V, $I_{OL} = 300$ mA	$V_{IL} = 0.8$ V,		0.5	0.8	
I_I	Input current at maximum input voltage	9	$V_{CC} = 5.5$ V,	$V_I = 5.5$ V			1	mA
I_{IH}	High-level input current	9	$V_{CC} = 5.5$ V,	$V_I = 2.4$ V			40	µA
I_{IL}	Low-level input current	8	$V_{CC} = 5.5$ V,	$V_I = 0.4$ V		-1	-1.6	mA
I_{CCH}	Supply current, outputs high	10	$V_{CC} = 5.5$ V,	$V_I = 5$ V		7	11	mA
I_{CCL}	Supply current, outputs low		$V_{CC} = 5.5$ V,	$V_I = 0$		52	65	mA

† All typical values are at $V_{CC} = 5$ V, $T_A = 25°$C.

switching characteristics, $V_{CC} = 5$ V, $T_A = 25°$C

PARAMETER		TEST FIGURE	TEST CONDITIONS	MIN	TYP	MAX	UNIT
t_{PLH}	Propagation delay time, low-to-high-level output	14	$I_O \approx 200$ mA, $C_L = 15$ pF, $R_L = 50$ Ω		18	25	ns
t_{PHL}	Propagation delay time, high-to-low-level output				18	25	ns
t_{TLH}	Transition time, low-to-high-level output				5	8	ns
t_{THL}	Transition time, high-to-low-level output				7	12	ns
V_{OH}	High-level output voltage after switching	15	$V_S = 20$ V, $I_O \approx 300$ mA	V_S-6.5			mV

TEXAS INSTRUMENTS
INCORPORATED
POST OFFICE BOX 5012 • DALLAS, TEXAS 75222

logic

FUNCTION TABLE

A	B	Y
L	L	L (on state)
L	H	L (on state)
H	L	L (on state)
H	H	H (off state)

H = high level, L = low level

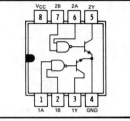

L
PLUG-IN PACKAGE (TOP VIEW)

PIN 4 IS IN ELECTRICAL CONTACT WITH THE CASE

P
DUAL-IN-LINE PACKAGE (TOP VIEW)

positive logic: Y = AB

schematic (each driver)

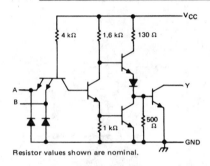

Resistor values shown are nominal.

electrical characteristics over recommended operating free-air temperature range (unless otherwise noted)

PARAMETER		TEST FIGURE	TEST CONDITIONS		MIN	TYP†	MAX	UNIT
V_{IH}	High-level input voltage	7			2			V
V_{IL}	Low-level input voltage	7					0.8	V
V_I	Input clamp voltage	8	V_{CC} = 4.75 V,	I_I = −12 mA			−1.5	V
I_{OH}	High-level output current	7	V_{CC} = 4.75 V, V_{OH} = 30 V	V_{IH} = 2 V,			100	μA
V_{OL}	Low-level output voltage	7	V_{CC} = 4.75 V, I_{OL} = 100 mA	V_{IL} = 0.8 V,		0.25	0.4	V
			V_{CC} = 4.75 V, I_{OL} = 300 mA	V_{IL} = 0.8 V,		0.5	0.7	
I_I	Input current at maximum input voltage	9	V_{CC} = 5.25 V,	V_I = 5.5 V			1	mA
I_{IH}	High-level input current	9	V_{CC} = 5.25 V,	V_I = 2.4 V			40	μA
I_{IL}	Low-level input current	8	V_{CC} = 5.25 V,	V_I = 0.4 V		−1	−1.6	mA
I_{CCH}	Supply current, outputs high	10	V_{CC} = 5.25 V,	V_I = 5 V		7	11	mA
I_{CCL}	Supply current, outputs low		V_{CC} = 5.25 V,	V_I = 0		52	65	mA

†All typical values are at V_{CC} = 5 V, T_A = 25°C.

switching characteristics, V_{CC} = 5 V, T_A = 25°C

PARAMETER		TEST FIGURE	TEST CONDITIONS	MIN	TYP	MAX	UNIT
t_{PLH}	Propagation delay time, low-to-high-level output	14	I_O ≈ 200 mA, C_L = 15 pF, R_L = 50 Ω		18	25	ns
t_{PHL}	Propgation delay time, high-to-low-level output				18	25	ns
t_{TLH}	Transition time, low-to-high-level output				5	8	ns
t_{THL}	Transition time, high-to-low-level output				7	12	ns
V_{OH}	High-level output voltage after switching	15	V_S = 20 V, I_O ≈ 300 mA	V_S−6.5			mV

TEXAS INSTRUMENTS
INCORPORATED
POST OFFICE BOX 5012 • DALLAS, TEXAS 75222

TYPE SN55452B
DUAL PERIPHERAL POSITIVE-NAND DRIVER

logic

FUNCTION TABLE

A	B	Y
L	L	H (off state)
L	H	H (off state)
H	L	H (off state)
H	H	L (on state)

H = high level, L = low level

L PLUG-IN PACKAGE (TOP VIEW)

PIN 4 IS IN ELECTRICAL CONTACT WITH THE CASE

JP DUAL-IN-LINE PACKAGE (TOP VIEW)

positive logic: Y = $\overline{AB}$

schematic (each driver)

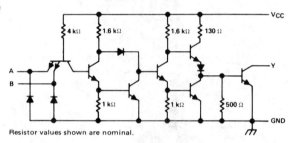

Resistor values shown are nominal.

electrical characteristics over recommended operating free-air temperature range (unless otherwise noted)

	PARAMETER	TEST FIGURE	TEST CONDITIONS		MIN	TYP†	MAX	UNIT
V_{IH}	High-level input voltage	7			2			V
V_{IL}	Low-level input voltage	7					0.8	V
V_I	Input clamp voltage	8	V_{CC} = 4.5 V,	I_I = −12 mA			−1.5	V
I_{OH}	High-level output current	7	V_{CC} = 4.5 V, V_{OH} = 30 V	V_{IL} = 0.8 V,			300	µA
V_{OL}	Low-level output voltage	7	V_{CC} = 4.5 V, I_{OL} = 100 mA	V_{IH} = 2 V,		0.25	0.5	V
			V_{CC} = 4.5 V, I_{OL} = 300 mA	V_{IH} = 2 V,		0.5	0.8	
I_I	Input current at maximum input voltage	9	V_{CC} = 5.5 V,	V_I = 5.5 V			1	mA
I_{IH}	High-level input current	9	V_{CC} = 5.5 V,	V_I = 2.4 V			40	µA
I_{IL}	Low-level input current	8	V_{CC} = 5.5 V,	V_I = 0.4 V	−1		−1.6	mA
I_{CCH}	Supply current, outputs high	10	V_{CC} = 5.5 V,	V_I = 0 V		11	14	mA
I_{CCL}	Supply current, outputs low		V_{CC} = 5.5 V,	V_I = 5 V		56	71	mA

† All typical values are at V_{CC} = 5 V, T_A = 25°C.

switching characteristics, V_{CC} = 5 V, T_A = 25°C

	PARAMETER	TEST FIGURE	TEST CONDITIONS	MIN	TYP	MAX	UNIT
t_{PLH}	Propagation delay time, low-to-high-level output	14	I_O ≈ 200 mA, C_L = 15 pF, R_L = 50 Ω		26	35	ns
t_{PHL}	Propagation delay time, high-to-low-level output				24	35	ns
t_{TLH}	Transition time, low-to-high-level output				5	8	ns
t_{THL}	Transition time, high-to-low-level output				7	12	ns
V_{OH}	High-level output voltage after switching	15	V_S = 20 V, I_O ≈ 300 mA	V_S−6.5			mV

TEXAS INSTRUMENTS
INCORPORATED
POST OFFICE BOX 5012 • DALLAS, TEXAS 75222

logic

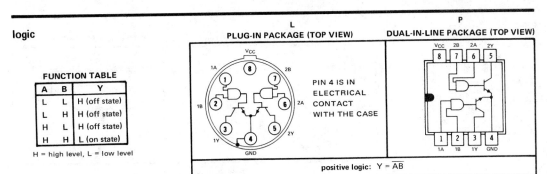

FUNCTION TABLE

A	B	Y
L	L	H (off state)
L	H	H (off state)
H	L	H (off state)
H	H	L (on state)

H = high level, L = low level

L
PLUG-IN PACKAGE (TOP VIEW)

PIN 4 IS IN ELECTRICAL CONTACT WITH THE CASE

P
DUAL-IN-LINE PACKAGE (TOP VIEW)

positive logic: $Y = \overline{AB}$

schematic (each driver)

Resistor values shown are nominal.

electrical characteristics over recommended operating free-air temperature range (unless otherwise noted)

	PARAMETER	TEST FIGURE	TEST CONDITIONS	MIN	TYP†	MAX	UNIT
V_{IH}	High-level input voltage	7		2			V
V_{IL}	Low-level input voltage	7				0.8	V
V_I	Input clamp voltage	8	$V_{CC} = 4.75$ V, $I_I = -12$ mA			-1.5	V
I_{OH}	High-level output current	7	$V_{CC} = 4.75$ V, $V_{IL} = 0.8$ V, $V_{OH} = 30$ V			100	μA
V_{OL}	Low-level output voltage	7	$V_{CC} = 4.75$ V, $V_{IH} = 2$ V, $I_{OL} = 100$ mA		0.25	0.4	V
			$V_{CC} = 4.75$ V, $V_{IH} = 2$ V, $I_{OL} = 300$ mA		0.5	0.7	
I_I	Input current at maximum input voltage	9	$V_{CC} = 5.25$ V, $V_I = 5.5$ V			1	mA
I_{IH}	High-level input current	9	$V_{CC} = 5.25$ V, $V_I = 2.4$ V			40	μA
I_{IL}	Low-level input current	8	$V_{CC} = 5.25$ V, $V_I = 0.4$ V		-1	-1.6	mA
I_{CCH}	Supply current, outputs high	10	$V_{CC} = 5.25$ V, $V_I = 0$ V		11	14	mA
I_{CCL}	Supply current, outputs low		$V_{CC} = 5.25$ V, $V_I = 5$ V		56	71	mA

† All typical values are at $V_{CC} = 5$ V, $T_A = 25°$C.

switching characteristics, $V_{CC} = 5$ V, $T_A = 25°$C

	PARAMETER	TEST FIGURE	TEST CONDITIONS	MIN	TYP	MAX	UNIT
t_{PLH}	Propagation delay time, low-to-high-level output	14	$I_O \approx 200$ mA, $C_L = 15$ pF, $R_L = 50$ Ω		26	35	ns
t_{PHL}	Propagation delay time, high-to-low-level output				24	35	ns
t_{TLH}	Transition time, low-to-high-level output				5	8	ns
t_{THL}	Transition time, high-to-low-level output				7	12	ns
V_{OH}	High-level output voltage after switching	15	$V_S = 20$ V, $I_O \approx 300$ mA	$V_S-6.5$			mV

TYPE SN55453B
DUAL PERIPHERAL POSITIVE-OR DRIVER

logic

FUNCTION TABLE

A	B	Y
L	L	L (on state)
L	H	H (off state)
H	L	H (off state)
H	H	H (off state)

H = high level, L = low level

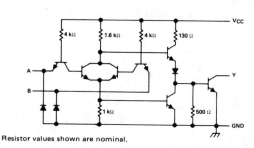

L PLUG-IN PACKAGE (TOP VIEW)

PIN 4 IS IN ELECTRICAL CONTACT WITH THE CASE

JP DUAL-IN-LINE PACKAGE (TOP VIEW)

positive logic: Y = A + B

schematic (each driver)

Resistor values shown are nominal.

electrical characteristics over recommended operating free-air temperature range (unless otherwise noted)

	PARAMETER	TEST FIGURE	TEST CONDITIONS		MIN	TYP†	MAX	UNIT
V_{IH}	High-level input voltage	7			2			V
V_{IL}	Low-level input voltage	7					0.8	V
V_I	Input clamp voltage	8	V_{CC} = 4.5 V,	I_I = −12 mA			−1.5	V
I_{OH}	High-level output current	7	V_{CC} = 4.5 V, V_{OH} = 30 V	V_{IH} = 2 V,			300	µA
V_{OL}	Low-level output voltage	7	V_{CC} = 4.5 V, I_{OL} = 100 mA	V_{IL} = 0.8 V,		0.25	0.5	V
			V_{CC} = 4.5 V, I_{OL} = 300 mA	V_{IL} = 0.8 V,		0.5	0.8	
I_I	Input current at maximum input voltage	9	V_{CC} = 5.5 V,	V_I = 5.5 V			1	mA
I_{IH}	High-level input current	9	V_{CC} = 5.5 V,	V_I = 2.4 V			40	µA
I_{IL}	Low-level input current	8	V_{CC} = 5.5 V,	V_I = 0.4 V		−1	−1.6	mA
I_{CCH}	Supply current, outputs high	11	V_{CC} = 5.5 V,	V_I = 5 V		8	11	mA
I_{CCL}	Supply current, outputs low		V_{CC} = 5.5 V,	V_I = 0		54	68	mA

†All typical values are at V_{CC} = 5 V, T_A = 25°C.

switching characteristics, V_{CC} = 5 V, T_A = 25°C

	PARAMETER	TEST FIGURE	TEST CONDITIONS		MIN	TYP	MAX	UNIT
t_{PLH}	Propagation delay time, low-to-high-level output	14	I_O ≈ 200 mA, R_L = 50 Ω	C_L = 15 pF,		18	25	ns
t_{PHL}	Propagation delay time, high-to-low-level output					16	25	ns
t_{TLH}	Transition time, low-to-high-level output					5	8	ns
t_{THL}	Transition time, high-to-low-level output					7	12	ns
V_{OH}	High-level output voltage after switching	15	V_S = 20 V,	I_O ≈ 300 mA	V_S−6.5			mV

TEXAS INSTRUMENTS
INCORPORATED
POST OFFICE BOX 5012 • DALLAS, TEXAS 75222

logic

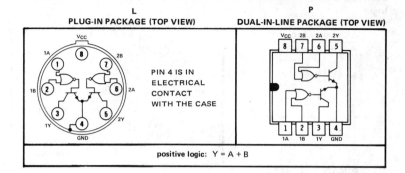

FUNCTION TABLE

A	B	Y
L	L	L (on state)
L	H	H (off state)
H	L	H (off state)
H	H	H (off state)

H = high level, L = low level

PIN 4 IS IN
ELECTRICAL
CONTACT
WITH THE CASE

positive logic: Y = A + B

schematic (each driver)

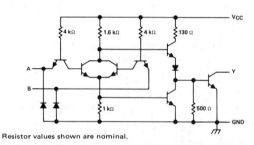

Resistor values shown are nominal.

electrical characteristics over recommended operating free-air temperature range (unless otherwise noted)

PARAMETER		TEST FIGURE	TEST CONDITIONS		MIN	TYP†	MAX	UNIT
V_{IH}	High-level input voltage	7			2			V
V_{IL}	Low-level input voltage	7					0.8	V
V_I	Input clamp voltage	8	$V_{CC} = 4.75$ V,	$I_I = -12$ mA			-1.5	V
I_{OH}	High-level output current	7	$V_{CC} = 4.75$ V, $V_{OH} = 30$ V	$V_{IH} = 2$ V,			100	μA
V_{OL}	Low-level output voltage	7	$V_{CC} = 4.75$ V, $I_{OL} = 100$ mA	$V_{IL} = 0.8$ V,		0.25	0.4	V
			$V_{CC} = 4.75$ V, $I_{OL} = 300$ mA	$V_{IL} = 0.8$ V,		0.5	0.7	
I_I	Input current at maximum input voltage	9	$V_{CC} = 5.25$ V,	$V_I = 5.5$ V			1	mA
I_{IH}	High-level input current	9	$V_{CC} = 5.25$ V,	$V_I = 2.4$ V			40	μA
I_{IL}	Low-level input current	8	$V_{CC} = 5.25$ V,	$V_I = 0.4$ V		-1	-1.6	mA
I_{CCH}	Supply current, outputs high	11	$V_{CC} = 5.25$ V,	$V_I = 5$ V		8	11	mA
I_{CCL}	Supply current, outputs low		$V_{CC} = 5.25$ V,	$V_I = 0$		54	68	mA

†All typical values are at $V_{CC} = 5$ V, $T_A = 25°$C.

switching characteristics, $V_{CC} = 5$ V, $T_A = 25°$C

PARAMETER		TEST FIGURE	TEST CONDITIONS		MIN	TYP	MAX	UNIT
t_{PLH}	Propagation delay time, low-to-high-level output	14	$I_O \approx 200$ mA, $R_L = 50$ Ω	$C_L = 15$ pF,			18	25	ns
t_{PHL}	Propagation delay time, high-to-low-level output					16	25	ns
t_{TLH}	Transition time, low-to-high-level output					5	8	ns
t_{THL}	Transition time, high-to-low-level output					7	12	ns
V_{OH}	High-level output voltage after switching	15	$V_S = 20$ V,	$I_O \approx 300$ mA	V_S-6.5			mV

10

73

TEXAS INSTRUMENTS
INCORPORATED
POST OFFICE BOX 5012 • DALLAS, TEXAS 75222

TYPE SN55454B
DUAL PERIPHERAL POSITIVE-NOR DRIVER

logic

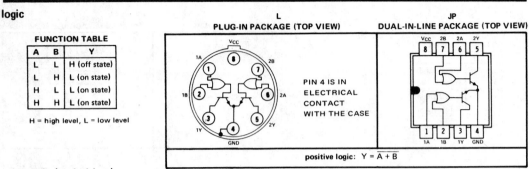

FUNCTION TABLE

A	B	Y
L	L	H (off state)
L	H	L (on state)
H	L	L (on state)
H	H	L (on state)

H = high level, L = low level

L
PLUG-IN PACKAGE (TOP VIEW)

PIN 4 IS IN
ELECTRICAL
CONTACT
WITH THE CASE

JP
DUAL-IN-LINE PACKAGE (TOP VIEW)

positive logic: $Y = \overline{A + B}$

schematic (each driver)

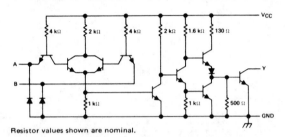

Resistor values shown are nominal.

electrical characteristics over recommended operating free-air temperature range (unless otherwise noted)

PARAMETER		TEST FIGURE	TEST CONDITIONS		MIN	TYP†	MAX	UNIT
V_{IH}	High-level input voltage	7			2			V
V_{IL}	Low-level input voltage	7					0.8	V
V_I	Input clamp voltage	8	$V_{CC} = 4.5$ V,	$I_I = -12$ mA			−1.5	V
I_{OH}	High-level output current	7	$V_{CC} = 4.5$ V, $V_{OH} = 30$ V	$V_{IL} = 0.8$ V,			300	μA
V_{OL}	Low-level output voltage	7	$V_{CC} = 4.5$ V, $I_{OL} = 100$ mA	$V_{IH} = 2$ V,		0.25	0.5	V
			$V_{CC} = 4.5$ V, $I_{OL} = 300$ mA	$V_{IH} = 2$ V,		0.5	0.8	
I_I	Input current at maximum input voltage	9	$V_{CC} = 5.5$ V,	$V_I = 5.5$ V			1	mA
I_{IH}	High-level input current	9	$V_{CC} = 5.5$ V,	$V_I = 2.4$ V			40	μA
I_{IL}	Low-level input current	8	$V_{CC} = 5.5$ V,	$V_I = 0.4$ V		−1	−1.6	mA
I_{CCH}	Supply current, outputs high	11	$V_{CC} = 5.5$ V,	$V_I = 0$ V		13	17	mA
I_{CCL}	Supply current, outputs low		$V_{CC} = 5.5$ V,	$V_I = 5$ V		61	79	mA

†All typical values are at $V_{CC} = 5$ V, $T_A = 25°$C.

switching characteristics, $V_{CC} = 5$ V, $T_A = 25°$C

PARAMETER		TEST FIGURE	TEST CONDITIONS	MIN	TYP	MAX	UNIT
t_{PLH}	Propagation delay time, low-to-high-level output	14	$I_O \approx 200$ mA, $C_L = 15$ pF, $R_L = 50$ Ω		27	35	ns
t_{PHL}	Propagation delay time, high-to-low-level output				24	35	ns
t_{TLH}	Transition time, low-to-high-level output				5	8	ns
t_{THL}	Transition time, high-to-low-level output				7	12	ns
V_{OH}	High-level output voltage after switching	15	$V_S = 20$ V, $I_O \approx 300$ mA	V_S−6.5			mV

TEXAS INSTRUMENTS
INCORPORATED
POST OFFICE BOX 5012 • DALLAS, TEXAS 75222

973

logic

FUNCTION TABLE

A	B	Y
L	L	H (off state)
L	H	L (on state)
H	L	L (on state)
H	H	L (on state)

H = high level, L = low level

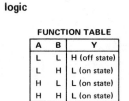

L
PLUG-IN PACKAGE (TOP VIEW)

PIN 4 IS IN ELECTRICAL CONTACT WITH THE CASE

P
DUAL-IN-LINE PACKAGE (TOP VIEW)

positive logic: $Y = \overline{A + B}$

schematic (each driver)

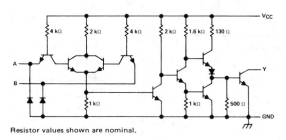

Resistor values shown are nominal.

electrical characteristics over recommended operating free-air temperature range (unless otherwise noted)

PARAMETER		TEST FIGURE	TEST CONDITIONS	MIN	TYP†	MAX	UNIT
V_{IH}	High-level input voltage	7		2			V
V_{IL}	Low-level input voltage	7				0.8	V
V_I	Input clamp voltage	8	$V_{CC} = 4.75$ V, $I_I = -12$ mA			-1.5	V
I_{OH}	High-level output current	7	$V_{CC} = 4.75$ V, $V_{IL} = 0.8$ V, $V_{OH} = 30$ V			100	µA
V_{OL}	Low-level output voltage	7	$V_{CC} = 4.75$ V, $V_{IH} = 2$ V, $I_{OL} = 100$ mA		0.25	0.4	V
			$V_{CC} = 4.75$ V, $V_{IH} = 2$ V, $I_{OL} = 300$ mA		0.5	0.7	
I_I	Input current at maximum input voltage	9	$V_{CC} = 5.25$ V, $V_I = 5.5$ V			1	mA
I_{IH}	High-level input current	9	$V_{CC} = 5.25$ V, $V_I = 2.4$ V			40	µA
I_{IL}	Low-level input current	8	$V_{CC} = 5.25$ V, $V_I = 0.4$ V		-1	-1.6	mA
I_{CCH}	Supply current, outputs high	11	$V_{CC} = 5.25$ V, $V_I = 0$ V		13	17	mA
I_{CCL}	Supply current, outputs low		$V_{CC} = 5.25$ V, $V_I = 5$ V		61	79	mA

† All typical values are at $V_{CC} = 5$ V, $T_A = 25°$C.

switching characteristics, $V_{CC} = 5$ V, $T_A = 25°$C

PARAMETER		TEST FIGURE	TEST CONDITIONS	MIN	TYP	MAX	UNIT
t_{PLH}	Propagation delay time, low-to-high-level output	14	$I_O \approx 200$ mA, $C_L = 15$ pF, $R_L = 50$ Ω		27	35	ns
t_{PHL}	Propagation delay time, high-to-low-level output				24	35	ns
t_{TLH}	Transition time, low-to-high-level output				5	8	ns
t_{THL}	Transition time, high-to-low-level output				7	12	ns
V_{OH}	High-level output voltage after switching	15	$V_S = 20$ V, $I_O \approx 300$ mA	$V_S - 6.5$			mV

TEXAS INSTRUMENTS
INCORPORATED
POST OFFICE BOX 5012 • DALLAS, TEXAS 75222

PARAMETER MEASUREMENT INFORMATION

d-c test circuits †

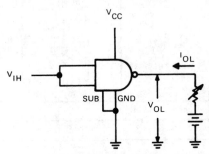

Both inputs are tested simultaneously.

FIGURE 1–V_{IH}, V_{OL}

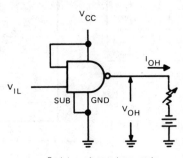

Each input is tested separately.

FIGURE 2–V_{IL}, V_{OH}

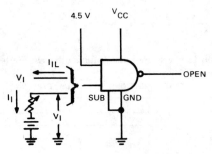

Each input is tested separately.

FIGURE 3–V_I, I_{IL}

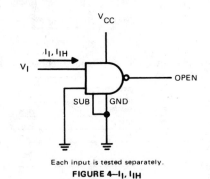

Each input is tested separately.

FIGURE 4–I_I, I_{IH}

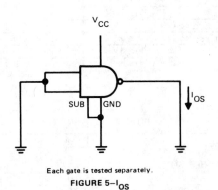

Each gate is tested separately.

FIGURE 5–I_{OS}

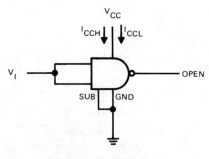

Both gates are tested simultaneously.

FIGURE 6–I_{CCH}, I_{CCL}

†Arrows indicate actual direction of current flow. Current into a terminal is a positive value.

TEXAS INSTRUMENTS
INCORPORATED
POST OFFICE BOX 5012 • DALLAS, TEXAS 75222

d-c test circuits† (continued)

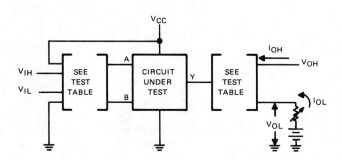

TEST TABLE

CIRCUIT	INPUT UNDER TEST	OTHER INPUT	OUTPUT	
			APPLY	MEASURE
'451B	V_{IH}	V_{IH}	V_{OH}	I_{OH}
	V_{IL}	V_{CC}	I_{OL}	V_{OL}
'452B	V_{IH}	V_{IH}	I_{OL}	V_{OL}
	V_{IL}	V_{CC}	V_{OH}	I_{OH}
'453B	V_{IH}	GND	V_{OH}	I_{OH}
	V_{IL}	V_{IL}	I_{OL}	V_{OL}
'454B	V_{IH}	GND	I_{OL}	V_{OL}
	V_{IL}	V_{IL}	V_{OH}	I_{OH}

NOTE: Each input is tested separately.

FIGURE 7—V_{IH}, V_{IL}, I_{OH}, V_{OL}

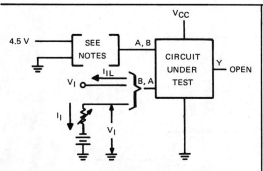

NOTES: A. Each input is tested separately.
      B. When testing SN55453B, SN75453B, SN55454B, and
         SN75454B, input not under test is grounded. For all
         other circuits, it is at 4.5 V.

FIGURE 8—V_I, I_{IL}

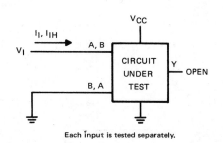

Each input is tested separately.

FIGURE 9—I_I, I_{IH}

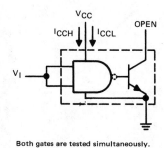

Both gates are tested simultaneously.

FIGURE 10—I_{CCH}, I_{CCL} FOR AND, NAND CIRCUITS

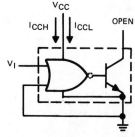

Both gates are tested simultaneously.

FIGURE 11—I_{CCH}, I_{CCL} FOR OR, NOR CIRCUITS

†Arrows indicate actual direction of current flow. Current into a terminal is a positive value.

TEXAS INSTRUMENTS
INCORPORATED
POST OFFICE BOX 5012 • DALLAS, TEXAS 75222

PARAMETER MEASUREMENT INFORMATION

switching characteristics

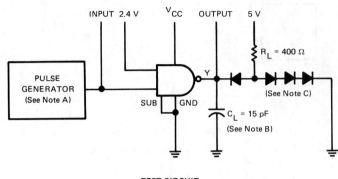

TEST CIRCUIT

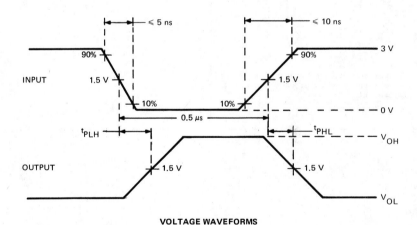

VOLTAGE WAVEFORMS

NOTES: A. The pulse generator has the following characteristics: PRR = 1 MHz, $Z_{out} \approx 50 \ \Omega$.
      B. C_L include probe and jig capacitance.
      C. All diodes are 1N3064.

FIGURE 12—PROPAGATION DELAY TIMES, EACH GATE (SN55450B and SN75450B ONLY)

TEXAS INSTRUMENTS
INCORPORATED
POST OFFICE BOX 5012 • DALLAS, TEXAS 75222

PARAMETER MEASUREMENT INFORMATION

switching characteristics (continued)

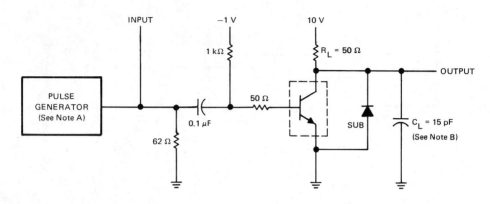

TEST CIRCUIT

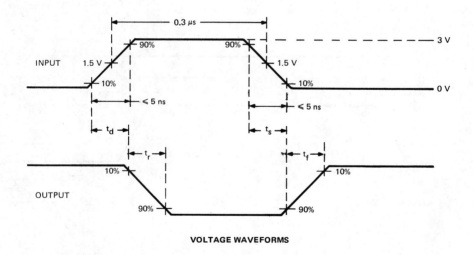

VOLTAGE WAVEFORMS

NOTES: A. The pulse generator has the following characteristics: duty cycle $\leqslant$ 1%, $Z_{out} \approx$ 50 Ω.
   B. C_L includes probe and jig capacitance.

FIGURE 13—SWITCHING TIMES, EACH TRANSISTOR (SN55450B AND SN75450B ONLY)

SERIES 55450B/75450B
DUAL PERIPHERAL DRIVERS

PARAMETER MEASUREMENT INFORMATION

switching characteristics (continued)

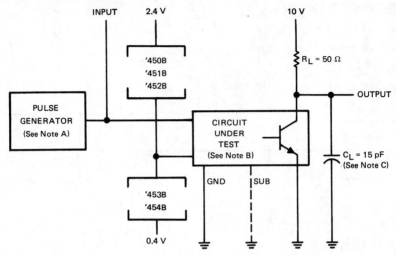

TEST CIRCUIT

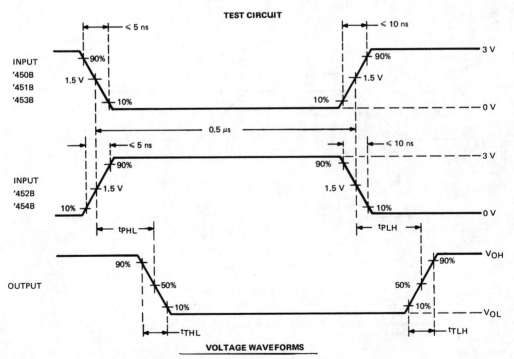

VOLTAGE WAVEFORMS

NOTES: A. The pulse generator has the following characteristics: PRR = 1 MHz, $Z_{out} \approx 50\ \Omega$
B. When testing SN55450B or SN75450B, connect output Y to transistor base and ground the substrate terminal.
C. C_L includes probe and jig capacitance.

FIGURE 14–SWITCHING TIMES OF COMPLETE DRIVERS

TEXAS INSTRUMENTS
INCORPORATED
POST OFFICE BOX 5012 • DALLAS, TEXAS 75222

PARAMETER MEASUREMENT INFORMATION

switching characteristics (continued)

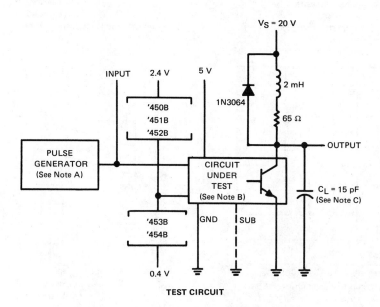

TEST CIRCUIT

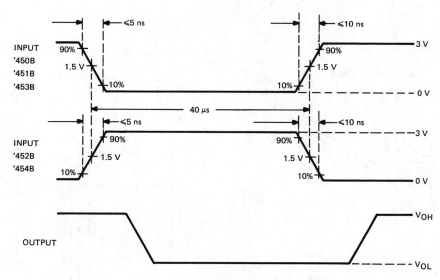

VOLTAGE WAVEFORMS

NOTES: A. The pulse generator has the following characteristics: PRR = 12.5 kHz, Z_{out} = 50 Ω.
        B. When testing SN55450B or SN75450B, connect output Y to transistor base with a 500-Ω resistor from there to ground, and ground the substrate terminal.
        C. C_L includes probe and jig capacitance.

FIGURE 15—LATCH-UP TEST OF COMPLETE DRIVERS

73

TEXAS INSTRUMENTS
INCORPORATED
POST OFFICE BOX 5012 • DALLAS, TEXAS 75222

TYPICAL CHARACTERISTICS

SN55450B, SN75450B
TTL GATE
HIGH-LEVEL OUTPUT VOLTAGE
vs
HIGH-LEVEL OUTPUT CURRENT

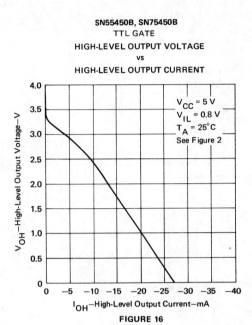

FIGURE 16

SN55450B, SN75450B
TRANSISTOR
STATIC FORWARD CURRENT TRANSFER RATIO
vs
COLLECTOR CURRENT

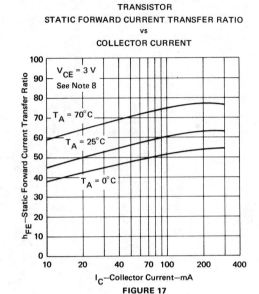

FIGURE 17

SN55450B, SN75450B
TRANSISTOR
BASE-EMITTER VOLTAGE
vs
COLLECTOR CURRENT

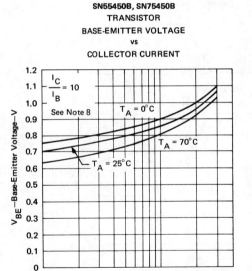

FIGURE 18

TRANSISTOR
COLLECTOR-EMITTER SATURATION VOLTAGE
vs
COLLECTOR CURRENT

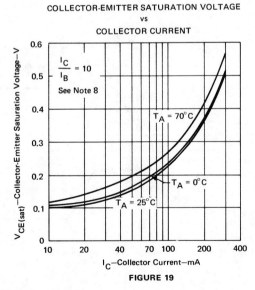

FIGURE 19

NOTE 8: These parameters must be measured using pulse techniques. t_W = 300 μs, duty cycle ⩽ 2%.

9

TEXAS INSTRUMENTS
INCORPORATED
POST OFFICE BOX 5012 • DALLAS, TEXAS 75222

THERMAL INFORMATION

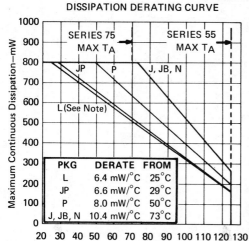

DISSIPATION DERATING CURVE

PKG	DERATE	FROM
L	6.4 mW/°C	25°C
JP	6.6 mW/°C	29°C
P	8.0 mW/°C	50°C
J, JB, N	10.4 mW/°C	73°C

NOTE 9: This rating for the L package requires a heat sink that provides a thermal resistance from case to free-air, $R_{\theta CA}$, of not more than 95°C/W.

FIGURE 20

TYPICAL APPLICATION DATA

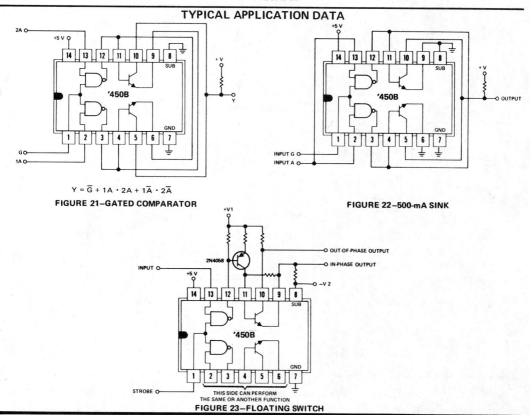

$$Y = \overline{G} + 1A \cdot 2A + 1\overline{A} \cdot 2\overline{A}$$

FIGURE 21—GATED COMPARATOR

FIGURE 22—500-mA SINK

FIGURE 23—FLOATING SWITCH

TEXAS INSTRUMENTS
INCORPORATED
POST OFFICE BOX 5012 • DALLAS, TEXAS 75222

SERIES 55450B/75450B
DUAL PERIPHERAL DRIVERS

TYPICAL APPLICATION DATA

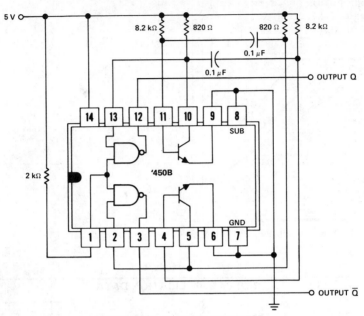

FIGURE 24 – SQUARE-WAVE GENERATOR

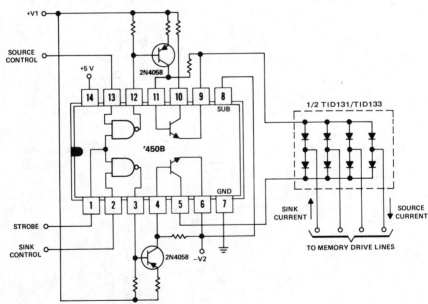

Source and sink controls are activated by high-level input voltages ($V_{IH} \geq 2V$).

FIGURE 25 – CORE MEMORY DRIVER

TEXAS INSTRUMENTS
INCORPORATED
POST OFFICE BOX 5012 • DALLAS, TEXAS 75222

TYPICAL APPLICATION DATA

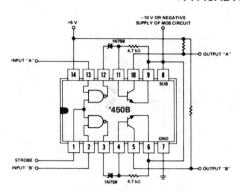

FIGURE 26—DUAL TTL-TO-MOS DRIVER

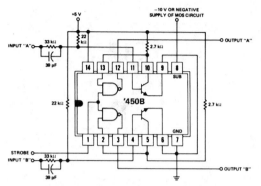

FIGURE 27—DUAL MOS-TO-TTL DRIVER

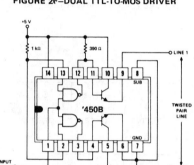

Termination is made at the receiving end as follows:
   Line 1 is terminated to ground through $Z_O/2$;
   Line 2 is terminated to +5 volts through $Z_O/2$;
where Z_O is the line impedence.

FIGURE 28—BALANCED LINE DRIVER

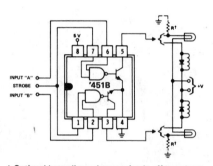

† Optional keep-alive resistors maintain off-state lamp
  current at ≈ 10% to reduce surge current.

FIGURE 29—DUAL LAMP OR RELAY DRIVER

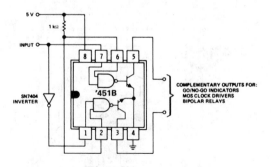

FIGURE 30—COMPLEMENTARY DRIVER

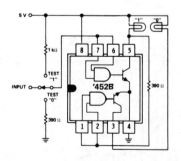

FIGURE 31—TTL OR DTL POSITIVE LOGIC-LEVEL DETECTOR

TYPICAL APPLICATION DATA (Continued)

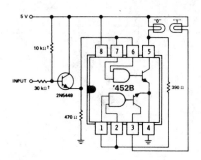

† The two input resistors must be adjusted for the level of MOS input.

FIGURE 32—MOS NEGATIVE-LOGIC-LEVEL DETECTOR

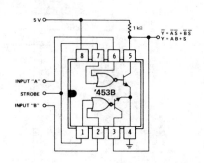

FIGURE 33—LOGIC SIGNAL COMPARATOR

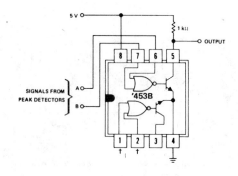

† If inputs are unused, they should be connected to +5 V through a 1 kΩ resistor.

Low output occurs only when inputs are low simultaneously.

FIGURE 34—IN-PHASE DETECTOR

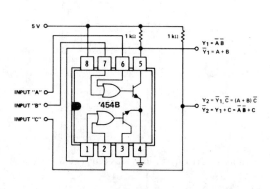

FIGURE 35—MULTIFUNCTION LOGIC-SIGNAL COMPARATOR

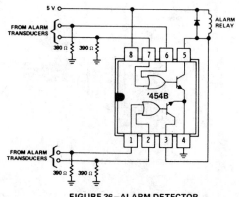

FIGURE 36—ALARM DETECTOR

PRINTED IN U.S.A.

TEXAS INSTRUMENTS
INCORPORATED
POST OFFICE BOX 5012 • DALLAS, TEXAS 75222

TI cannot assume any responsibility for any circuits shown
or represent that they are free from patent infringement.

TEXAS INSTRUMENTS RESERVES THE RIGHT TO MAKE CHANGES AT ANY TIM
IN ORDER TO IMPROVE DESIGN AND TO SUPPLY THE BEST PRODUCT POSSIBLE

10

PERIPHERAL DRIVERS FOR
HIGH-VOLTAGE, HIGH-CURRENT DRIVER APPLICATIONS

performance

- 300-mA Output Current Capability
- High-Voltage Outputs
- No Output Latch-Up at 30 V
- Medium-Speed Switching

ease-of-design

- Circuit Flexibility for Varied Applications and Choice of Logic Function
- TTL or DTL Compatible Diode-Clamped Inputs
- Standard Supply Voltages

SUMMARY OF SERIES 55460/75460

DEVICE	LOGIC OF COMPLETE CIRCUIT	PACKAGES
SN55460	AND[†]	J, JB
SN55461	AND	JP, L
SN55462	NAND	JP, L
SN55463	OR	JP, L
SN55464	NOR	JP, L
SN75460	AND[†]	J, N
SN75461	AND	L, P
SN75462	NAND	L, P
SN75463	OR	L, P
SN75464	NOR	L, P

[†]With output transistor base connected externally to output of gate

description

Series 55460/75460 dual peripheral drivers are functionally interchangeable with Series 55450B/75450B peripheral drivers, but are designed for use in systems that require higher breakdown voltages than Series 55450B/75450B can provide at the expense of slightly slower switching speeds. Typical applications include logic buffers, power drivers, relay drivers, lamp drivers, MOS drivers, line drivers, and memory drivers. Series 55460 drivers are characterized for operation over the full military temperature range of −55°C to 125°C; Series 75460 drivers are characterized for operation from 0°C to 70°C.

The SN55460 and SN75460 are unique general-purpose devices each featuring two standard Series 54/74 TTL gates and two uncommitted, high-current, high-voltage, n-p-n transistors. These devices offer the system designer the flexibility of tailoring the circuit to the application.

The SN55461/SN75461, SN55462/SN75462, SN55463/SN75463, and SN55464/SN75464 are dual peripheral AND, NAND, OR, and NOR drivers, respectively, (assuming positive logic) with the output of the logic gates internally connected to the bases of the n-p-n output transistors.

10

TEXAS INSTRUMENTS
INCORPORATED
POST OFFICE BOX 5012 • DALLAS, TEXAS 75222

absolute maximum ratings over operating free-air temperature range (unless otherwise noted)

		SN55460	SN55461 SN55462 SN55463 SN55464	SN75460	SN75461 SN75462 SN75463 SN75464	UNIT
Supply voltage, V_{CC} (see Note 1)		7	7	7	7	V
Input voltage		5.5	5.5	5.5	5.5	V
Interemitter voltage (see Note 2)		5.5	5.5	5.5	5.5	V
V_{CC}-to-substrate voltage		40		40		V
Collector-to-substrate voltage		40		40		V
Collector-base voltage		40		40		V
Collector-emitter voltage (see Note 3)		40		40		V
Collector-emitter voltage (see Note 4)		25		25		V
Emitter-base voltage		5		5		V
Output voltage (see Note 5)			35		35	V
Collector current (see Note 6)		300		300		mA
Output current (see Note 6)			300		300	mA
Continuous total dissipation at (or below) 25°C free-air temperature (see Note 7)		800	800	800	800	mW
Operating free-air temperature range		−55 to 125	−55 to 125	0 to 70	0 to 70	°C
Storage temperature range		−65 to 150	−65 to 150	−65 to 150	−65 to 150	°C
Lead temperature 1/16 inch from case for 60 seconds	J, JB, JP, or L package	300	300	300	300	°C
Lead temperature 1/16 inch from case for 10 seconds	N or P package	260	260	260	260	°C

NOTES: 1. Voltage values are with respect to network ground terminal unless otherwise specified.
2. This is the voltage between two emitters of a multiple-emitter transistor.
3. This value applies when the base-emitter resistance (R_{BE}) is equal to or less than 500 Ω.
4. This value applies between 0 and 10 mA collector current when the base-emitter diode is open-circuited.
5. This is the maximum voltage which should be applied to any output when it is in the off state.
6. Both halves of these dual circuits may conduct rated current simultaneously; however, power dissipation averaged over a short time interval must fall within the continuous dissipation rating.
7. For operation above 25°C free-air temperature, refer to Dissipation Derating Curve, Figure 16. This rating for the L package requires a heat sink that provides a thermal resistance from case to free-air, $R_{\theta CA}$, of not more than 95 °C/W.

recommended operating conditions (see Note 8)

	SERIES 55460			SERIES 75460			UNIT
	MIN	NOM	MAX	MIN	NOM	MAX	
Supply voltage, V_{CC}	4.5	5	5.5	4.75	5	5.25	V
Operating free-air temperature, T_A	−55		125	0		70	°C

NOTE 8: For the SN55450B and SN75450B only, the substrate (pin 8) must always be at the most-negative device voltage for proper operation.

TEXAS INSTRUMENTS
INCORPORATED
POST OFFICE BOX 5012 • DALLAS, TEXAS 75222

schematic

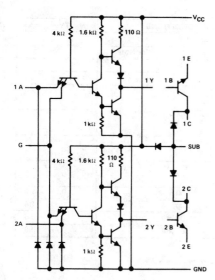

Resistor values shown are nominal.

J OR JB
DUAL-IN-LINE PACKAGE (TOP VIEW)

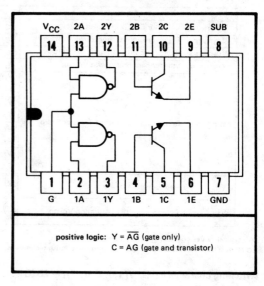

positive logic: Y = $\overline{AG}$ (gate only)
C = AG (gate and transistor)

electrical characteristics over recommended operating free-air temperature range (unless otherwise noted)

TTL gates

PARAMETER		TEST FIGURE	TEST CONDITIONS	MIN	TYP[†]	MAX	UNIT
V_{IH}	High-level input voltage	1		2			V
V_{IL}	Low-level input voltage	2				0.8	V
V_I	Input clamp voltage	3	V_{CC} = 4.5 V, I_I = −12 mA		−1.2	−1.5	V
V_{OH}	High-level output voltage	2	V_{CC} = 4.5 V, V_{IL} = 0.8 V, I_{OH} = −400 μA	2.4	3.3		V
V_{OL}	Low-level output voltage	1	V_{CC} = 4.5 V, V_{IH} = 2 V, I_{OL} = 16 mA		0.25	0.5	V
I_I	Input current at maximum input voltage input A	4	V_{CC} = 5.5 V, V_I = 5.5 V			1	mA
	input G					2	
I_{IH}	High-level input current input A	4	V_{CC} = 5.5 V, V_I = 2.4 V			40	μA
	input G					80	
I_{IL}	Low-level input current input A	3	V_{CC} = 5.5 V, V_I = 0.4 V			−1.6	mA
	input G					−3.2	
I_{OS}	Short-circuit output current‡	5	V_{CC} = 5.5 V,	−18	−35	−55	mA
I_{CCH}	Supply current, outputs high	6	V_{CC} = 5.5 V, V_I = 0		2.8	4	mA
I_{CCL}	Supply current, outputs low		V_{CC} = 5.5 V, V_I = 5 V		7	11	mA

[†]All typical values at V_{CC} = 5 V, T_A = 25°C.

‡Not more than one output should be shorted at a time.

10

electrical characteristics over recommended operating free-air temperature range (unless otherwise noted)

output transistors

PARAMETER		TEST CONDITIONS		MIN	TYP†	MAX	UNIT
$V_{(BR)CBO}$ Collector-Base Breakdown Voltage		$I_C = 100\ \mu A$, $I_E = 0$		40			V
$V_{(BR)CEO}$ Collector-Emitter Breakdown Voltage		$I_C = 10\ mA$, $I_B = 0$,	See Note 9	25			V
$V_{(BR)CER}$ Collector-Emitter Breakdown Voltage		$I_C = 100\ \mu A$, $R_{BE} = 500\ \Omega$		40			V
$V_{(BR)EBO}$ Emitter-Base Breakdown Voltage		$I_E = 100\ \mu A$, $I_C = 0$		5			V
h_{FE}	Static Forward Current Transfer Ratio	$V_{CE} = 3\ V$, $I_C = 100\ mA$, $T_A = 25°C$	See Note 9	25			
		$V_{CE} = 3\ V$, $I_C = 300\ mA$, $T_A = 25°C$		30			
		$V_{CE} = 3\ V$, $I_C = 100\ mA$, $T_A = -55°C$		10			
		$V_{CE} = 3\ V$, $I_C = 300\ mA$, $T_A = -55°C$		15			
V_{BE}	Base-Emitter Voltage	$I_B = 10\ mA$, $I_C = 100\ mA$	See Note 9		0.85	1.2	V
		$I_B = 30\ mA$, $I_C = 300\ mA$			1	1.4	
$V_{CE(sat)}$	Collector-Emitter Saturation Voltage	$I_B = 10\ mA$, $I_C = 100\ mA$	See Note 9		0.25	0.5	V
		$I_B = 30\ mA$, $I_C = 300\ mA$			0.45	0.8	

†All typical values are at $V_{CC} = 5\ V$, $T_A = 25°C$.

NOTE 9: These parameters must be measured using pulse techniques. $t_w = 300\ \mu s$, duty cycle $\leqslant 2\%$.

switching characteristics, $V_{CC} = 5\ V$, $T_A = 25°C$

TTL gates

PARAMETER		TEST FIGURE	TEST CONDITIONS	MIN	TYP	MAX	UNIT
t_{PLH}	Propagation delay time, low-to-high-level output	12	$C_L = 15\ pF$, $R_L = 400\ \Omega$		22		ns
t_{PHL}	Propagation delay time, high-to-low-level output				8		ns

output transistors

PARAMETER		TEST FIGURE	TEST CONDITIONS‡	MIN	TYP	MAX	UNIT
t_d	Delay time	13	$I_C = 200\ mA$, $I_{B(1)} = 20\ mA$, $I_{B(2)} = -40\ mA$, $V_{BE(off)} = -1\ V$, $C_L = 15\ pF$, $R_L = 50\ \Omega$		10		ns
t_r	Rise time				16		ns
t_s	Storage time				23		ns
t_f	Fall time				14		ns

‡Voltage and current values shown are nominal; exact values vary slightly with transistor parameters.

gates and transistors combined

PARAMETER		TEST FIGURE	TEST CONDITIONS	MIN	TYP	MAX	UNIT
t_{PLH}	Propagation delay time, low-to-high-level output	14	$I_C \approx 200\ mA$, $C_L = 15\ pF$, $R_L = 50\ \Omega$		45	65	ns
t_{PHL}	Propagation delay time, high-to-low-level output				35	50	ns
t_{TLH}	Transition time, low-to-high-level output				10	20	ns
t_{THL}	Transition time, high-to-low-level output				10	20	ns
V_{OH}	High-level output voltage after switching	15	$V_S = 30\ V$, $I_C \approx 300\ mA$, $R_{BE} = 500\ \Omega$	V_S-10			mV

10

TEXAS INSTRUMENTS
INCORPORATED

POST OFFICE BOX 5012 • DALLAS, TEXAS 75222

schematic

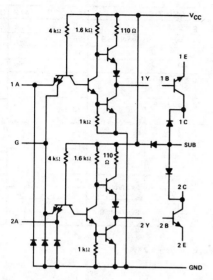

Resistor values shown are nominal.

**J OR N
DUAL-IN-LINE PACKAGE (TOP VIEW)**

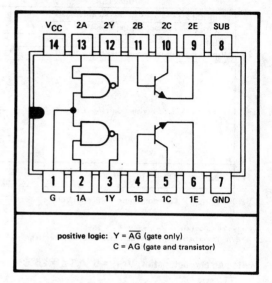

positive logic: $Y = \overline{AG}$ (gate only)
$C = AG$ (gate and transistor)

electrical characteristics over recommended operating free-air temperature range (unless otherwise noted)

TTL gates

PARAMETER		TEST FIGURE	TEST CONDITIONS		MIN	TYP†	MAX	UNIT
V_{IH}	High-level input voltage	1			2			V
V_{IL}	Low-level input voltage	2					0.8	V
V_I	Input clamp voltage	3	$V_{CC} = 4.75$ V,	$I_I = -12$ mA		-1.2	-1.5	V
V_{OH}	High-level output voltage	2	$V_{CC} = 4.75$ V,	$V_{IL} = 0.8$ V, $I_{OH} = -400\ \mu A$	2.4	3.3		V
V_{OL}	Low-level output voltage	1	$V_{CC} = 4.75$ V,	$V_{IH} = 2$ V, $I_{OL} = 16$ mA		0.25	0.4	V
I_I	Input current at maximum input voltage	input A	4	$V_{CC} = 5.25$ V, $V_I = 5.5$ V			1	mA
		input G					2	
I_{IH}	High-level input current	input A	4	$V_{CC} = 5.25$ V, $V_I = 2.4$ V			40	μA
		input G					80	
I_{IL}	Low-level input current	input A	3	$V_{CC} = 5.25$ V, $V_I = 0.4$ V			-1.6	mA
		input G					-3.2	
I_{OS}	Short-circuit output current‡		5	$V_{CC} = 5.25$ V		-18	-35	-55	mA
I_{CCH}	Supply current, outputs high		6	$V_{CC} = 5.25$ V, $V_I = 0$			2.8	4	mA
I_{CCL}	Supply current, outputs low			$V_{CC} = 5.25$ V, $V_I = 5$ V			7	11	mA

†All typical values at $V_{CC} = 5$ V, $T_A = 25°C$.

‡Not more than one output should be shorted at a time.

DUAL PERIPHERAL POSITIVE-AND DRIVER

electrical characteristics over recommended operating free-air temperature range (unless otherwise noted)

output transistors

PARAMETER		TEST CONDITIONS		MIN	TYP†	MAX	UNIT
$V_{(BR)CBO}$	Collector-Base Breakdown Voltage	$I_C = 100 \mu A$, $I_E = 0$		40			V
$V_{(BR)CEO}$	Collector-Emitter Breakdown Voltage	$I_C = 10$ mA, $I_B = 0$,	See Note 9	25			V
$V_{(BR)CER}$	Collector-Emitter Breakdown Voltage	$I_C = 100 \mu A$, $R_{BE} = 500 \Omega$		40			V
$V_{(BR)EBO}$	Emitter-Base Breakdown Voltage	$I_E = 100 \mu A$, $I_C = 0$		5			V
h_{FE}	Static Forward Current Transfer Ratio	$V_{CE} = 3$ V, $I_C = 100$ mA, $T_A = 25°C$	See Note 9	25			
		$V_{CE} = 3$ V, $I_C = 300$ mA, $T_A = 25°C$		30			
		$V_{CE} = 3$ V, $I_C = 100$ mA, $T_A = 0°C$		20			
		$V_{CE} = 3$ V, $I_C = 300$ mA, $T_A = 0°C$		25			
V_{BE}	Base-Emitter Voltage	$I_B = 10$ mA, $I_C = 100$ mA	See Note 9		0.85	1	V
		$I_B = 30$ mA, $I_C = 300$ mA			1	1.2	
$V_{CE(sat)}$	Collector-Emitter Saturation Voltage	$I_B = 10$ mA, $I_C = 100$ mA	See Note 9		0.25	0.4	V
		$I_B = 30$ mA, $I_C = 300$ mA			0.45	0.7	

†All typical values are at $V_{CC} = 5$ V, $T_A = 25°C$.
NOTE 9: These parameters must be measured using pulse techniques. $t_w = 300 \mu s$, duty cycle ≤ 2%.

switching characteristics, $V_{CC} = 5$ V, $T_A = 25°C$

TTL gates

PARAMETER		TEST FIGURE	TEST CONDITIONS		MIN	TYP	MAX	UNIT
t_{PLH}	Propagation delay time, low-to-high-level output	12	$C_L = 15$ pF,	$R_L = 400 \Omega$		22		ns
t_{PHL}	Propagation delay time, high-to-low-level output					8		ns

output transistors

PARAMETER		TEST FIGURE	TEST CONDITIONS‡		MIN	TYP	MAX	UNIT
t_d	Delay time	13	$I_C = 200$ mA, $I_{B(1)} = 20$ mA, $I_{B(2)} = -40$ mA, $V_{BE(off)} = -1$ V, $C_L = 15$ pF, $R_L = 50 \Omega$			10		ns
t_r	Rise time					16		ns
t_s	Storage time					23		ns
t_f	Fall time					14		ns

‡Voltage and current values shown are nominal; exact values vary slightly with transistor parameters.

gates and transistors combined

PARAMETER		TEST FIGURE	TEST CONDITIONS		MIN	TYP	MAX	UNIT
t_{PLH}	Propagation delay time, low-to-high-level output	14	$I_C \approx 200$ mA, $C_L = 15$ pF, $R_L = 50 \Omega$			45	65	ns
t_{PHL}	Propagation delay time, high-to-low-level output					35	50	ns
t_{TLH}	Transition time, low-to-high-level output					10	20	ns
t_{THL}	Transition time, high-to-low-level output					10	20	ns
V_{OH}	High-level output voltage after switching	15	$V_S = 30$ V, $I_C \approx 300$ mA, $R_{BE} = 500 \Omega$		V_S-10			mV

TEXAS INSTRUMENTS
INCORPORATED
POST OFFICE BOX 5012 • DALLAS, TEXAS 75222

logic

FUNCTION TABLE

A	B	Y
L	L	L (on state)
L	H	L (on state)
H	L	L (on state)
H	H	H (off state)

H = high level, L = low level

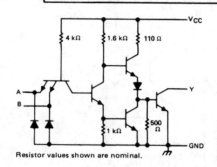

L
PLUG-IN PACKAGE (TOP VIEW)

PIN 4 IS IN ELECTRICAL CONTACT WITH THE CASE

JP
DUAL-IN-LINE PACKAGE (TOP VIEW)

positive logic: Y = AB

schematic (each driver)

Resistor values shown are nominal.

electrical characteristics over recommended operating free-air temperature range (unless otherwise noted)

	PARAMETER	TEST FIGURE	TEST CONDITIONS		MIN	TYP†	MAX	UNIT
V_{IH}	High-level input voltage	7			2			V
V_{IL}	Low-level input voltage	7					0.8	V
V_I	Input clamp voltage	8	V_{CC} = 4.5 V,	I_I = −12 mA		−1.2	−1.5	V
I_{OH}	High-level output current	7	V_{CC} = 4.5 V, V_{OH} = 35 V	V_{IH} = 2 V,			300	μA
V_{OL}	Low-level output voltage	7	V_{CC} = 4.5 V, I_{OL} = 100 mA	V_{IL} = 0.8 V,		0.15	0.5	V
			V_{CC} = 4.5 V, I_{OL} = 300 mA	V_{IL} = 0.8 V,		0.36	0.8	
I_I	Input current at maximum input voltage	9	V_{CC} = 5.5 V,	V_I = 5.5 V			1	mA
I_{IH}	High-level input current	9	V_{CC} = 5.5 V,	V_I = 2.4 V			40	μA
I_{IL}	Low-level input current	8	V_{CC} = 5.5 V,	V_I = 0.4 V		−1	−1.6	mA
I_{CCH}	Supply current, outputs high	10	V_{CC} = 5.5 V,	V_I = 5 V		8	11	mA
I_{CCL}	Supply current, outputs low		V_{CC} = 5.5 V,	V_I = 0		61	76	mA

† All typical values are at V_{CC} = 5 V, T_A = 25°C.

switching characteristics, V_{CC} = 5 V, T_A = 25°C

	PARAMETER	TEST FIGURE	TEST CONDITIONS	MIN	TYP	MAX	UNIT
t_{PLH}	Propagation delay time, low-to-high-level output	14	$I_O \approx$ 200 mA, C_L = 15 pF, R_L = 50 Ω		45	55	ns
t_{PHL}	Propgation delay time, high-to-low-level output				30	40	ns
t_{TLH}	Transition time, low-to-high-level output				8	20	ns
t_{THL}	Transition time, high-to-low-level output				10	20	ns
V_{OH}	High-level output voltage after switching	15	V_S = 30 V, $I_O \approx$ 300 mA	V_S−10			mV

10

TEXAS INSTRUMENTS
INCORPORATED
POST OFFICE BOX 5012 • DALLAS, TEXAS 75222

TYPE SN75461
DUAL PERIPHERAL POSITIVE-AND DRIVER

logic

FUNCTION TABLE		
A	**B**	**Y**
L	L	L (on state)
L	H	L (on state)
H	L	L (on state)
H	H	H (off state)

H = high level, L = low level

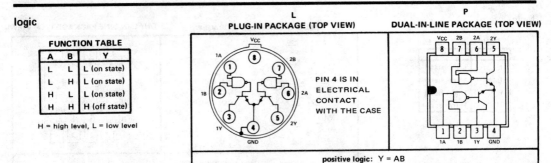

L
PLUG-IN PACKAGE (TOP VIEW)

PIN 4 IS IN ELECTRICAL CONTACT WITH THE CASE

P
DUAL-IN-LINE PACKAGE (TOP VIEW)

positive logic: Y = AB

schematic (each driver)

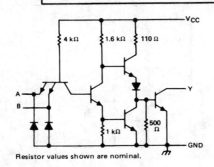

Resistor values shown are nominal.

electrical characteristics over recommended operating free-air temperature range (unless otherwise noted)

PARAMETER		TEST FIGURE	TEST CONDITIONS		MIN	TYP†	MAX	UNIT
V_{IH}	High-level input voltage	7			2			V
V_{IL}	Low-level input voltage	7					0.8	V
V_I	Input clamp voltage	8	$V_{CC} = 4.75$ V,	$I_I = -12$ mA		-1.2	-1.5	V
I_{OH}	High-level output current	7	$V_{CC} = 4.75$ V, $V_{OH} = 35$ V	$V_{IH} = 2$ V,			100	μA
V_{OL}	Low-level output voltage	7	$V_{CC} = 4.75$ V, $I_{OL} = 100$ mA	$V_{IL} = 0.8$ V,		0.15	0.4	V
			$V_{CC} = 4.75$ V, $I_{OL} = 300$ mA	$V_{IL} = 0.8$ V,		0.36	0.7	
I_I	Input current at maximum input voltage	9	$V_{CC} = 5.25$ V,	$V_I = 5.5$ V			1	mA
I_{IH}	High-level input current	9	$V_{CC} = 5.25$ V,	$V_I = 2.4$ V			40	μA
I_{IL}	Low-level input current	8	$V_{CC} = 5.25$ V,	$V_I = 0.4$ V		-1	-1.6	mA
I_{CCH}	Supply current, outputs high	10	$V_{CC} = 5.25$ V,	$V_I = 5$ V		8	11	mA
I_{CCL}	Supply current, outputs low		$V_{CC} = 5.25$ V,	$V_I = 0$		61	76	mA

† All typical values are at $V_{CC} = 5$ V, $T_A = 25°$C.

switching characteristics, $V_{CC} = 5$ V, $T_A = 25°$C

PARAMETER		TEST FIGURE	TEST CONDITIONS	MIN	TYP	MAX	UNIT
t_{PLH}	Propagation delay time, low-to-high-level output	14	$I_O \approx 200$ mA, $C_L = 15$ pF, $R_L = 50$ Ω		45	55	ns
t_{PHL}	Propgation delay time, high-to-low-level output				30	40	ns
t_{TLH}	Transition time, low-to-high-level output				8	20	ns
t_{THL}	Transition time, high-to-low-level output				10	20	ns
V_{OH}	High-level output voltage after switching	15	$V_S = 30$ V, $I_O \approx 300$ mA	V_S-10			mV

10

TEXAS INSTRUMENTS
INCORPORATED
POST OFFICE BOX 5012 • DALLAS, TEXAS 75222

logic

FUNCTION TABLE

A	B	Y
L	L	H (off state)
L	H	H (off state)
H	L	H (off state)
H	H	L (on state)

H = high level, L = low level

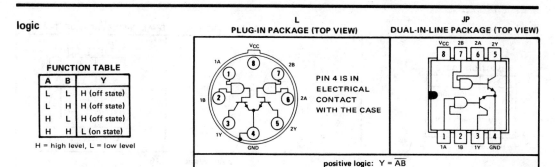

L
PLUG-IN PACKAGE (TOP VIEW)

PIN 4 IS IN ELECTRICAL CONTACT WITH THE CASE

JP
DUAL-IN-LINE PACKAGE (TOP VIEW)

positive logic: $Y = \overline{AB}$

schematic (each driver)

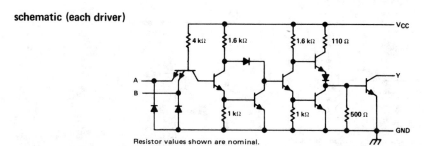

Resistor values shown are nominal.

electrical characteristics over recommended operating free-air temperature range (unless otherwise noted)

	PARAMETER	TEST FIGURE	TEST CONDITIONS		MIN	TYP†	MAX	UNIT
V_{IH}	High-level input voltage	7			2			V
V_{IL}	Low-level input voltage	7					0.8	V
V_I	Input clamp voltage	8	$V_{CC} = 4.5$ V,	$I_I = -12$ mA		−1.2	−1.5	V
I_{OH}	High-level output current	7	$V_{CC} = 4.5$ V, $V_{OH} = 35$ V,	$V_{IL} = 0.8$ V,			300	μA
V_{OL}	Low-level output voltage	7	$V_{CC} = 4.5$ V, $I_{OL} = 100$ mA	$V_{IH} = 2$ V,		0.16	0.5	V
			$V_{CC} = 4.5$ V, $I_{OL} = 300$ mA	$V_{IH} = 2$ V,		0.35	0.8	
I_I	Input current at maximum input voltage	9	$V_{CC} = 5.5$ V,	$V_I = 5.5$ V			1	mA
I_{IH}	High-level input current	9	$V_{CC} = 5.5$ V,	$V_I = 2.4$ V			40	μA
I_{IL}	Low-level input current	8	$V_{CC} = 5.5$ V,	$V_I = 0.4$ V		−1.1	−1.6	mA
I_{CCH}	Supply current, outputs high	10	$V_{CC} = 5.5$ V,	$V_I = 0$ V		13	17	mA
I_{CCL}	Supply current, outputs low		$V_{CC} = 5.5$ V,	$V_I = 5$ V		65	76	mA

† All typical values are at $V_{CC} = 5$ V, $T_A = 25°$C.

switching characteristics, $V_{CC} = 5$ V, $T_A = 25°$C

	PARAMETER	TEST FIGURE	TEST CONDITIONS	MIN	TYP	MAX	UNIT
t_{PLH}	Propagation delay time, low-to-high-level output	14	$I_O \approx 200$ mA, $C_L = 15$ pF, $R_L = 50$ Ω		50	65	ns
t_{PHL}	Propagation delay time, high-to-low-level output				40	50	ns
t_{TLH}	Transition time, low-to-high-level output				12	25	ns
t_{THL}	Transition time, high-to-low-level output				15	20	ns
V_{OH}	High-level output voltage after switching	15	$V_S = 30$ V, $I_O \approx 300$ mA	V_S-10			mV

TYPE SN75462
DUAL PERIPHERAL POSITIVE-NAND DRIVER

logic

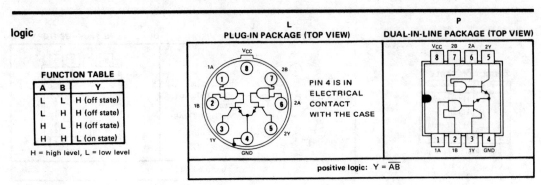

FUNCTION TABLE

A	B	Y
L	L	H (off state)
L	H	H (off state)
H	L	H (off state)
H	H	L (on state)

H = high level, L = low level

L
PLUG-IN PACKAGE (TOP VIEW)

PIN 4 IS IN ELECTRICAL CONTACT WITH THE CASE

P
DUAL-IN-LINE PACKAGE (TOP VIEW)

positive logic: $Y = \overline{AB}$

schematic (each driver)

Resistor values shown are nominal.

electrical characteristics over recommended operating free-air temperature range (unless otherwise noted)

PARAMETER		TEST FIGURE	TEST CONDITIONS		MIN	TYP†	MAX	UNIT
V_{IH}	High-level input voltage	7			2			V
V_{IL}	Low-level input voltage	7					0.8	V
V_I	Input clamp voltage	8	$V_{CC} = 4.75$ V,	$I_I = -12$ mA		-1.2	-1.5	V
I_{OH}	High-level output current	7	$V_{CC} = 4.75$ V, $V_{OH} = 35$ V	$V_{IL} = 0.8$ V,			100	μA
V_{OL}	Low-level output voltage	7	$V_{CC} = 4.75$ V, $I_{OL} = 100$ mA	$V_{IH} = 2$ V,		0.16	0.4	V
			$V_{CC} = 4.75$ V, $I_{OL} = 300$ mA	$V_{IH} = 2$ V,		0.35	0.7	
I_I	Input current at maximum input voltage	9	$V_{CC} = 5.25$ V,	$V_I = 5.5$ V			1	mA
I_{IH}	High-level input current	9	$V_{CC} = 5.25$ V,	$V_I = 2.4$ V			40	μA
I_{IL}	Low-level input current	8	$V_{CC} = 5.25$ V,	$V_I = 0.4$ V		-1.1	-1.6	mA
I_{CCH}	Supply current, outputs high	10	$V_{CC} = 5.25$ V,	$V_I = 0$ V		13	17	mA
I_{CCL}	Supply current, outputs low		$V_{CC} = 5.25$ V,	$V_I = 5$ V		65	76	mA

† All typical values are at $V_{CC} = 5$ V, $T_A = 25°C$.

switching characteristics, $V_{CC} = 5$ V, $T_A = 25°C$

PARAMETER		TEST FIGURE	TEST CONDITIONS	MIN	TYP	MAX	UNIT
t_{PLH}	Propagation delay time, low-to-high-level output	14	$I_O \approx 200$ mA, $C_L = 15$ pF, $R_L = 50$ Ω		50	65	ns
t_{PHL}	Propagation delay time, high-to-low-level output				40	50	ns
t_{TLH}	Transition time, low-to-high-level output				12	25	ns
t_{THL}	Transition time, high-to-low-level output				15	20	ns
V_{OH}	High-level output voltage after switching	15	$V_S = 30$ V, $I_O \approx 300$ mA	V_S-10			mV

TEXAS INSTRUMENTS
INCORPORATED
POST OFFICE BOX 5012 • DALLAS, TEXAS 75222

97

logic

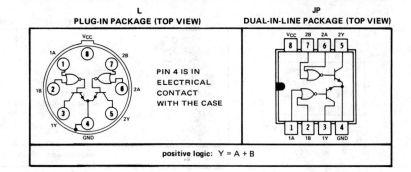

FUNCTION TABLE

A	B	Y
L	L	L (on state)
L	H	H (off state)
H	L	H (off state)
H	H	H (off state)

H = high level, L = low level

L
PLUG-IN PACKAGE (TOP VIEW)

PIN 4 IS IN ELECTRICAL CONTACT WITH THE CASE

JP
DUAL-IN-LINE PACKAGE (TOP VIEW)

positive logic: Y = A + B

schematic (each driver)

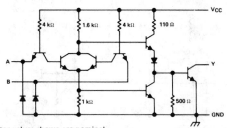

Resistor values shown are nominal.

electrical characteristics over recommended operating free-air temperature range (unless otherwise noted)

PARAMETER		TEST FIGURE	TEST CONDITIONS		MIN	TYP†	MAX	UNIT
V_{IH}	High-level input voltage	7			2			V
V_{IL}	Low-level input voltage	7					0.8	V
V_I	Input clamp voltage	8	V_{CC} = 4.5 V,	I_I = −12 mA		−1.2	−1.5	V
I_{OH}	High-level output current	7	V_{CC} = 4.5 V, V_{OH} = 35 V	V_{IH} = 2 V,			300	µA
V_{OL}	Low-level output voltage	7	V_{CC} = 4.5 V, I_{OL} = 100 mA	V_{IL} = 0.8 V,		0.18	0.5	V
			V_{CC} = 4.5 V, I_{OL} = 300 mA	V_{IL} = 0.8 V,		0.39	0.8	
I_I	Input current at maximum input voltage	9	V_{CC} = 5.5 V,	V_I = 5.5 V			1	mA
I_{IH}	High-level input current	9	V_{CC} = 5.5 V,	V_I = 2.4 V			40	µA
I_{IL}	Low-level input current	8	V_{CC} = 5.5 V,	V_I = 0.4 V		−1	−1.6	mA
I_{CCH}	Supply current, outputs high	11	V_{CC} = 5.5 V,	V_I = 5 V		8	11	mA
I_{CCL}	Supply current, outputs low		V_{CC} = 5.5 V,	V_I = 0		63	76	mA

†All typical values are at V_{CC} = 5 V, T_A = 25°C.

switching characteristics, V_{CC} = 5 V, T_A = 25°C

PARAMETER		TEST FIGURE	TEST CONDITIONS		MIN	TYP	MAX	UNIT
t_{PLH}	Propagation delay time, low-to-high-level output	14	$I_O \approx$ 200 mA, R_L = 50 Ω	C_L = 15 pF,		45	55	ns
t_{PHL}	Propagation delay time, high-to-low-level output					30	40	ns
t_{TLH}	Transition time, low-to-high-level output					8	25	ns
t_{THL}	Transition time, high-to-low-level output					10	25	ns
V_{OH}	High-level output voltage after switching	15	V_S = 30 V,	$I_O \approx$ 300 mA	V_S−10			mV

TEXAS INSTRUMENTS
INCORPORATED
POST OFFICE BOX 5012 • DALLAS, TEXAS 75222

TYPE SN75463
DUAL PERIPHERAL POSITIVE-OR DRIVER

logic

FUNCTION TABLE

A	B	Y
L	L	L (on state)
L	H	H (off state)
H	L	H (off state)
H	H	H (off state)

H = high level, L = low level

L
PLUG-IN PACKAGE (TOP VIEW)

PIN 4 IS IN
ELECTRICAL
CONTACT
WITH THE CASE

P
DUAL-IN-LINE PACKAGE (TOP VIEW)

positive logic: Y = A + B

schematic (each driver)

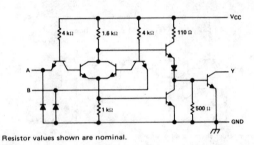

Resistor values shown are nominal.

electrical characteristics over recommended operating free-air temperature range (unless otherwise noted)

PARAMETER		TEST FIGURE	TEST CONDITIONS		MIN	TYP†	MAX	UNIT
V_{IH}	High-level input voltage	7			2			V
V_{IL}	Low-level input voltage	7					0.8	V
V_I	Input clamp voltage	8	V_{CC} = 4.75 V,	I_I = −12 mA		−1.2	−1.5	V
I_{OH}	High-level output current	7	V_{CC} = 4.75 V, V_{OH} = 35 V	V_{IH} = 2 V,			100	µA
V_{OL}	Low-level output voltage	7	V_{CC} = 4.75 V, I_{OL} = 100 mA	V_{IL} = 0.8 V,		0.18	0.4	V
			V_{CC} = 4.75 V, I_{OL} = 300 mA	V_{IL} = 0.8 V,		0.39	0.7	
I_I	Input current at maximum input voltage	9	V_{CC} = 5.25 V,	V_I = 5.5 V			1	mA
I_{IH}	High-level input current	9	V_{CC} = 5.25 V,	V_I = 2.4 V			40	µA
I_{IL}	Low-level input current	8	V_{CC} = 5.25 V,	V_I = 0.4 V		−1	−1.6	mA
I_{CCH}	Supply current, outputs high	11	V_{CC} = 5.25 V,	V_I = 5 V		8	11	mA
I_{CCL}	Supply current, outputs low		V_{CC} = 5.25 V,	V_I = 0		63	76	mA

†All typical values are at V_{CC} = 5 V, T_A = 25°C.

switching characteristics, V_{CC} = 5 V, T_A = 25°C

PARAMETER		TEST FIGURE	TEST CONDITIONS		MIN	TYP	MAX	UNIT
t_{PLH}	Propagation delay time, low-to-high-level output	14	I_O ≈ 200 mA, R_L = 50 Ω	C_L = 15 pF,		45	55	ns
t_{PHL}	Propagation delay time, high-to-low-level output					30	40	ns
t_{TLH}	Transition time, low-to-high-level output					8	25	ns
t_{THL}	Transition time, high-to-low-level output					10	25	ns
V_{OH}	High-level output voltage after switching	15	V_S = 30 V,	I_O ≈ 300 mA	V_S−10			mV

TEXAS INSTRUMENTS
INCORPORATED
POST OFFICE BOX 5012 • DALLAS, TEXAS 75222

logic

FUNCTION TABLE

A	B	Y
L	L	H (off state)
L	H	L (on state)
H	L	L (on state)
H	H	L (on state)

H = high level, L = low level

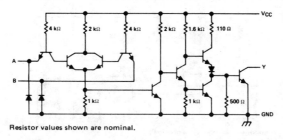

L
PLUG-IN PACKAGE (TOP VIEW)

PIN 4 IS IN ELECTRICAL CONTACT WITH THE CASE

JP
DUAL-IN-LINE PACKAGE (TOP VIEW)

positive logic: $Y = \overline{A + B}$

schematic (each driver)

Resistor values shown are nominal.

electrical characteristics over recommended operating free-air temperature range (unless otherwise noted)

PARAMETER		TEST FIGURE	TEST CONDITIONS		MIN	TYP†	MAX	UNIT
V_{IH}	High-level input voltage	7			2			V
V_{IL}	Low-level input voltage	7					0.8	V
V_I	Input clamp voltage	8	$V_{CC} = 4.5$ V,	$I_I = -12$ mA		−1.2	−1.5	V
I_{OH}	High-level output current	7	$V_{CC} = 4.5$ V, $V_{OH} = 35$ V	$V_{IL} = 0.8$ V,			300	µA
V_{OL}	Low-level output voltage	7	$V_{CC} = 4.5$ V, $I_{OL} = 100$ mA	$V_{IH} = 2$ V,		0.17	0.5	V
			$V_{CC} = 4.5$ V, $I_{OL} = 300$ mA	$V_{IH} = 2$ V,		0.38	0.8	
I_I	Input current at maximum input voltage	9	$V_{CC} = 5.5$ V,	$V_I = 5.5$ V			1	mA
I_{IH}	High-level input current	9	$V_{CC} = 5.5$ V,	$V_I = 2.4$ V			40	µA
I_{IL}	Low-level input current	8	$V_{CC} = 5.5$ V,	$V_I = 0.4$ V		−1	−1.6	mA
I_{CCH}	Supply current, outputs high	11	$V_{CC} = 5.5$ V,	$V_I = 0$ V		14	19	mA
I_{CCL}	Supply current, outputs low		$V_{CC} = 5.5$ V,	$V_I = 5$ V		72	85	mA

†All typical values are at $V_{CC} = 5$ V, $T_A = 25°$C.

switching characteristics, $V_{CC} = 5$ V, $T_A = 25°$C

PARAMETER		TEST FIGURE	TEST CONDITIONS		MIN	TYP	MAX	UNIT
t_{PLH}	Propagation delay time, low-to-high-level output	14	$I_O \approx 200$ mA, $C_L = 15$ pF, $R_L = 50$ Ω			50	65	ns
t_{PHL}	Propagation delay time, high-to-low-level output					40	50	ns
t_{TLH}	Transition time, low-to-high-level output					12	20	ns
t_{THL}	Transition time, high-to-low-level output					15	20	ns
V_{OH}	High-level output voltage after switching	15	$V_S = 30$ V,	$I_O \approx 300$ mA	V_S-10			mV

TYPE SN75464
DUAL PERIPHERAL POSITIVE-NOR DRIVER

logic

FUNCTION TABLE

A	B	Y
L	L	H (off state)
L	H	L (on state)
H	L	L (on state)
H	H	L (on state)

H = high level, L = low level

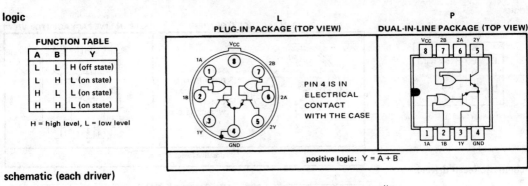

L
PLUG-IN PACKAGE (TOP VIEW)

PIN 4 IS IN ELECTRICAL CONTACT WITH THE CASE

P
DUAL-IN-LINE PACKAGE (TOP VIEW)

positive logic: $Y = \overline{A + B}$

schematic (each driver)

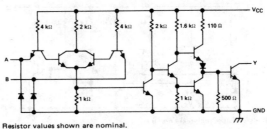

Resistor values shown are nominal.

electrical characteristics over recommended operating free-air temperature range (unless otherwise noted)

PARAMETER		TEST FIGURE	TEST CONDITIONS		MIN	TYP†	MAX	UNIT
V_{IH}	High-level input voltage	7			2			V
V_{IL}	Low-level input voltage	7					0.8	V
V_I	Input clamp voltage	8	V_{CC} = 4.75 V,	I_I = −12 mA		−1.2	−1.5	V
I_{OH}	High-level output current	7	V_{CC} = 4.75 V, V_{OH} = 35 V	V_{IL} = 0.8 V,			100	µA
V_{OL}	Low-level output voltage	7	V_{CC} = 4.75 V, I_{OL} = 100 mA	V_{IH} = 2 V,		0.17	0.4	V
			V_{CC} = 4.75 V, I_{OL} = 300 mA	V_{IH} = 2 V,		0.38	0.7	
I_I	Input current at maximum input voltage	9	V_{CC} = 5.25 V,	V_I = 5.5 V			1	mA
I_{IH}	High-level input current	9	V_{CC} = 5.25 V,	V_I = 2.4 V			40	µA
I_{IL}	Low-level input current	8	V_{CC} = 5.25 V,	V_I = 0.4 V		−1	−1.6	mA
I_{CCH}	Supply current, outputs high	11	V_{CC} = 5.25 V,	V_I = 0 V		14	19	mA
I_{CCL}	Supply current, outputs low		V_{CC} = 5.25 V,	V_I = 5 V		72	85	mA

†All typical values are at V_{CC} = 5 V, T_A = 25°C.

switching characteristics, V_{CC} = 5 V, T_A = 25°C

PARAMETER		TEST FIGURE	TEST CONDITIONS		MIN	TYP	MAX	UNIT
t_{PLH}	Propagation delay time, low-to-high-level output	14	$I_O \approx$ 200 mA, R_L = 50 Ω	C_L = 15 pF,		50	65	ns
t_{PHL}	Propagation delay time, high-to-low-level output					40	50	ns
t_{TLH}	Transition time, low-to-high-level output					12	20	ns
t_{THL}	Transition time, high-to-low-level output					15	20	ns
V_{OH}	High-level output voltage after switching	15	V_S = 30 V	$I_O \approx$ 300 mA	V_S−10			mV

TEXAS INSTRUMENTS
INCORPORATED
POST OFFICE BOX 5012 • DALLAS, TEXAS 75222

PARAMETER MEASUREMENT INFORMATION

d-c test circuits †

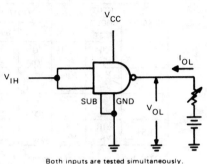

Both inputs are tested simultaneously.

FIGURE 1–V_{IH}, V_{OL}

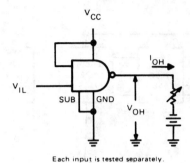

Each input is tested separately.

FIGURE 2–V_{IL}, V_{OH}

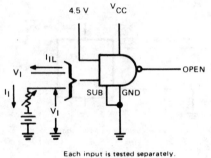

Each input is tested separately.

FIGURE 3–V_I, I_{IL}

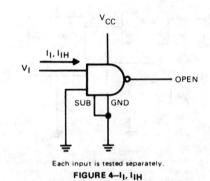

Each input is tested separately.

FIGURE 4–I_I, I_{IH}

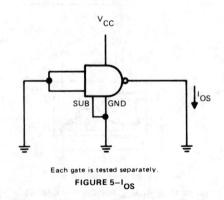

Each gate is tested separately.

FIGURE 5–I_{OS}

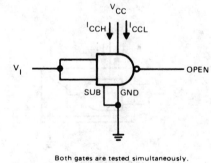

Both gates are tested simultaneously.

FIGURE 6–I_{CCH}, I_{CCL}

†Arrows indicate actual direction of current flow. Current into a terminal is a positive value.

TEXAS INSTRUMENTS
INCORPORATED
POST OFFICE BOX 5012 • DALLAS, TEXAS 75222

d-c test circuits† (continued)

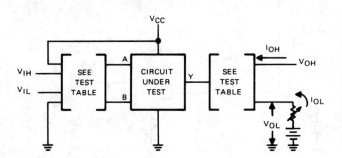

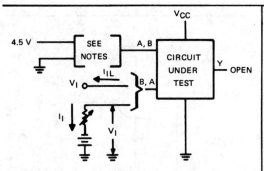

CIRCUIT	INPUT UNDER TEST	OTHER INPUT	OUTPUT	
			APPLY	MEASURE
'461	V_{IH}	V_{IH}	V_{OH}	I_{OH}
	V_{IL}	V_{CC}	I_{OL}	V_{OL}
'462	V_{IH}	V_{IH}	I_{OL}	V_{OL}
	V_{IL}	V_{CC}	V_{OH}	I_{OH}
'463	V_{IH}	GND	V_{OH}	I_{OH}
	V_{IL}	V_{IL}	I_{OL}	V_{OL}
'464	V_{IH}	GND	I_{OL}	V_{OL}
	V_{IL}	V_{IL}	V_{OH}	I_{OH}

TEST TABLE

NOTE: Each input is tested separately.

FIGURE 7—V_{IH}, V_{IL}, I_{OH}, V_{OL}

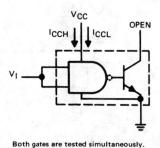

NOTES: A. Each input is tested separately.
B. When testing SN55463, SN75463, SN75464, and SN75464, input not under test is grounded. For all other circuits, it is at 4.5 V.

FIGURE 8—V_I, I_{IL}

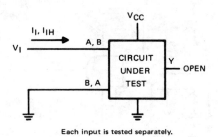

Each input is tested separately.

FIGURE 9—I_I, I_{IH}

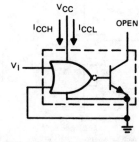

Both gates are tested simultaneously.

FIGURE 10—I_{CCH}, I_{CCL} FOR AND, NAND CIRCUITS

Both gates are tested simultaneously.

FIGURE 11—I_{CCH}, I_{CCL} FOR OR, NOR CIRCUITS

†Arrows indicate actual direction of current flow. Current into a terminal is a positive value.

TEXAS INSTRUMENTS
INCORPORATED
POST OFFICE BOX 5012 • DALLAS, TEXAS 75222

10

PARAMETER MEASUREMENT INFORMATION

switching characteristics

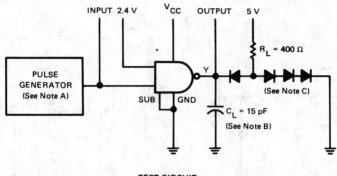

TEST CIRCUIT

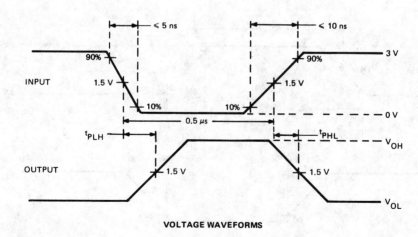

VOLTAGE WAVEFORMS

NOTES: A. The pulse generator has the following characteristics: PRR = 1 MHz, $Z_{out} \approx 50\ \Omega$.
     B. C_L include probe and jig capacitance.
     C. All diodes are 1N3064.

FIGURE 12—PROPAGATION DELAY TIMES, EACH GATE (SN55460 AND SN75460 ONLY)

TEXAS INSTRUMENTS
INCORPORATED
POST OFFICE BOX 5012 • DALLAS, TEXAS 75222

PARAMETER MEASUREMENT INFORMATION

switching characteristics (continued)

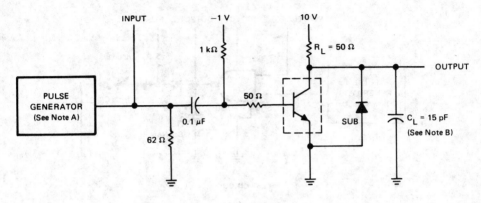

TEST CIRCUIT

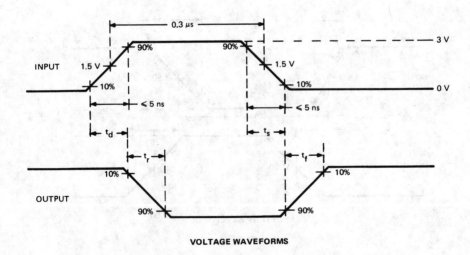

VOLTAGE WAVEFORMS

NOTES: A. The pulse generator has the following characteristics: duty cycle ≤ 1%, $Z_{out} \approx 50\ \Omega$.
B. C_L includes probe and jig capacitance.

FIGURE 13—SWITCHING TIMES, EACH TRANSISTOR (SN55460 AND SN75460 ONLY)

TEXAS INSTRUMENTS
INCORPORATED
POST OFFICE BOX 5012 • DALLAS, TEXAS 75222

PARAMETER MEASUREMENT INFORMATION

switching characteristics (continued)

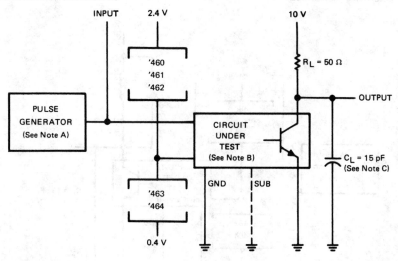

TEST CIRCUIT

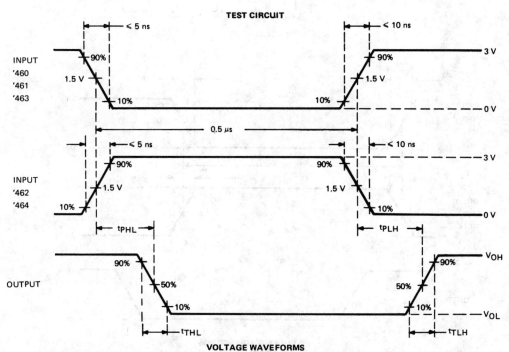

VOLTAGE WAVEFORMS

NOTES: A. The pulse generator has the following characteristics: PRR = 1 MHz, $Z_{out} \approx 50\ \Omega$.
      B. When testing SN55460 or SN75460, connect output Y to transistor base and ground the substrate terminal.
      C. C_L includes probe and jig capacitance.

FIGURE 14—SWITCHING TIMES OF COMPLETE DRIVERS

TEXAS INSTRUMENTS
INCORPORATED
POST OFFICE BOX 5012 • DALLAS, TEXAS 75222

PARAMETER MEASUREMENT INFORMATION

switching characteristics (continued)

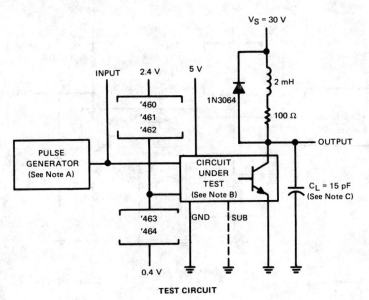

TEST CIRCUIT

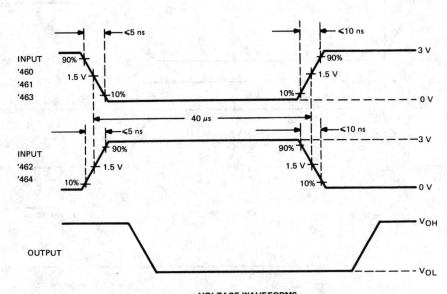

VOLTAGE WAVEFORMS

NOTES: A. The pulse generator has the following characteristics: PRR = 12.5 kHz, Z_{out} = 50 Ω.
   B. When testing SN55460 or SN75460, connect output Y to transistor base with a 500-Ω resistor from there to ground, and ground the substrate terminal.
   C. C_L includes probe and jig capacitance.

FIGURE 15—LATCH-UP TEST OF COMPLETE DRIVERS

TEXAS INSTRUMENTS
INCORPORATED
POST OFFICE BOX 5012 • DALLAS, TEXAS 75222

THERMAL INFORMATION

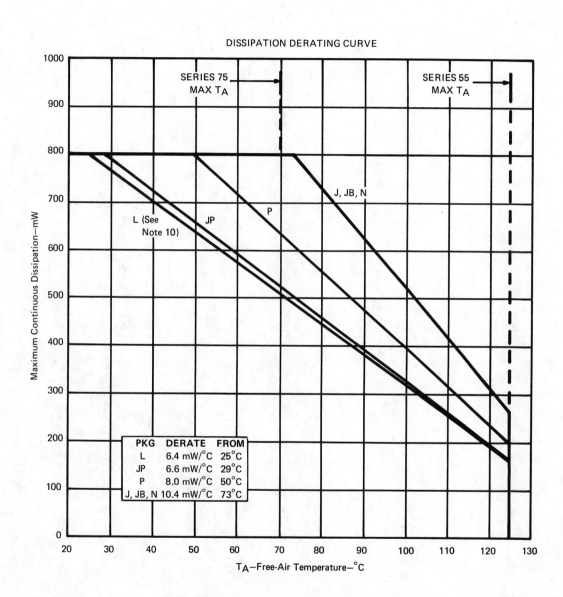

DISSIPATION DERATING CURVE

PKG	DERATE	FROM
L	6.4 mW/°C	25°C
JP	6.6 mW/°C	29°C
P	8.0 mW/°C	50°C
J, JB, N	10.4 mW/°C	73°C

NOTE 10: This rating for the L package requires a heat sink that provides a thermal resistance from case to free-air, $R_{\theta CA}$, of not more than 95°C/W.

FIGURE 16

TEXAS INSTRUMENTS
INCORPORATED
POST OFFICE BOX 5012 • DALLAS, TEXAS 75222

Sense Amplifiers

TEMPERATURE RANGE		FEATURES	PACKAGE TYPES		APPLICATIONS[†]
−55°C to 125°C	0°C to 70°C		SERIES 55	SERIES 75	
SN5520 SN5521	SN7520 SN7521	• Provides Memory Data Register • Complementary Outputs	J, JA	J, N	Large Memories
SN5522 SN5523	SN7522 SN7523	• Open-Collector Output	J, JA	J, N	Large Memories
SN5524 SN5525	SN7524 SN7525	• Dual Channels • Independent Strobes	J, JA	J, N	General Purpose

	SN7526
	SN7527
		• Internally Compensated
		  Reference Amplifier
		• Complete Memory Data Register
		• Effective Strobe Width of
		  Less than 10 ns
				J, N	High Performance

SN5528 SN5529	SN7528 SN7529	• Dual Channels • Test Points for Strobe Timing Adjustment	J, JA	J, N	General Purpose
SN55232 SN55233	SN75232 SN75233	• Internally Compensated Reference Amplifier • Dual Channels • Open-Collector Output	J, JA	J, N	General Purpose
SN55234 SN55235	SN75234 SN75235	• Internally Compensated Reference Amplifier • Dual Channels	J, JA	J, N	General Purpose

SN55236
SN55237
	SN75236
	SN75237
		• Tight Threshold Specifications
		• Dual Channels
		• Built-In Data Register and
		  Data Buffer
		• Reference Amplifier
		  Compensation Unnecessary
			SB	SB	High Performance,
					Military

SN55238
SN55239
	SN75238
	SN75239
		• Internally Compensated
		  Reference Amplifier
		• Test Points for Strobe Timing
		  Adjustments
			J, JA	J, N	General Purpose

SN55244	SN75244	• Quad Channel with Decode • A-C Coupled with D-C Restore • 1-mV Typ Threshold	J, JA, N	J, JA, N	Plated-Wire or Thin-Film Memories

[†]See Bulletin No. CA-101, Operation and Use of Series 7520N Sense Amplifiers.

11

TEXAS INSTRUMENTS
INCORPORATED
POST OFFICE BOX 5012 • DALLAS, TEXAS 75222

FULL MILITARY TEMPERATURE RANGE
HIGH-SPEED SENSE AMPLIFIERS FOR CONVERSION OF
COINCIDENT-CURRENT MEMORY READOUT TO SATURATED DIGITAL-LOGIC LEVELS

performance features

- high speed and fast recovery time
- time and amplitude signal discrimination
- adjustable input threshold voltage levels
- narrow region of threshold voltage uncertainty
- multiple differential-input preamplifiers
- high d-c noise margin—typically one volt
- good fan-out capability

ease-of-design features

- choice of output circuit function
- TTL or DTL drive capability
- standard logic supply voltages
- plug-in configuration ideal for flow-soldering techniques
- pins on 100-mil grid spacings for industrial-type circuit boards

description

Series 5520 monolithic sense amplifiers are designed for use with high-speed memory systems. These sense amplifiers detect bipolar differential-input signals from the memory and provide the interface circuitry between the memory and the logic section. Low-level pulses originating in the memory are transformed into logic levels compatible with standard transistor-transistor-logic (TTL) and diode-transistor-logic (DTL) circuits.

These sense amplifiers feature multiple differential-input preamplifiers and versatile gating and output circuits, permitting a significant reduction in the circuitry required to accomplish the sensing function. A unique circuit design provides inherent stability of the input threshold level over a wide range of power-supply voltage levels and temperature ranges. Independent strobing of each of the dual sense-input channels ensures maximum versatility and permits detection to occur when the signal-to-noise ratio is at a maximum. The gate and strobe inputs and the outputs are compatible with standard TTL and DTL digital logic circuits.

The SN5520 and SN5521 circuits may be used to perform the functions of a flip-flop or register which responds to the sense and strobe input conditions.

The SN5522 and SN5523 circuits feature a high-fan-out, single-ended, open-collector output stage. In addition, they may be used to expand the inputs to an SN5520 or SN5521 circuit, or to perform the wired-AND function.

The SN5524 and SN5525 circuits provide for independent, dual-channel sensing with separate outputs. SN55234 and SN55235 are similar but have inverted outputs and internal compensation. SN55232 and SN55233 are identical to the SN55234 and SN55235, respectively, except that their output gates each feature an open-collector output.

The SN5528 and SN5529 circuits are identical to the SN5524 and SN5525, respectively, except that the output of each preamplifier is available as a test point. SN55238 and SN55239 are similar to SN5528 and SN5529, respectively, but have inverted outputs and internal compensation.

Series 5520 sense amplifiers are available in the J ceramic dual-in-line package and are characterized for operation over the full military temperature range of −55°C to 125°C. Terminal assignments and functions are identical to the corresponding Series 7520 circuits.

11

TEXAS INSTRUMENTS
INCORPORATED

POST OFFICE BOX 5012 • DALLAS, TEXAS 75222

absolute maximum ratings over operating free-air temperature range (unless otherwise noted)

Supply voltages (see Note 1)
V_{CC+} . . . . 7 V
V_{CC-} . . . . −7 V
Differential input voltage, V_{ID} or V_{ref} . . . . ±5 V
Voltage from any input to ground (see Note 2) . . . . 5.5 V
Off-state voltage applied to open-collector outputs . . . . 5.5 V
Operating free-air temperature range . . . . −55°C to 125°C
Storage temperature range . . . . −65°C to 150°C

recommended operating conditions

	MIN	NOM	MAX	UNIT
V_{CC+} (see Note 1)	4.75	5	5.25	V
V_{CC-} (see Note 1)	−4.75	−5	−5.25	V
V_{ref}	15		40	mV

NOTES: 1. These voltage values are with respect to network ground terminal.
2. Strobe and gate input voltages must be zero or positive with respect to network ground terminal.

electrical characteristics (unless otherwise noted V_{CC+} = 5 V, V_{CC-} = −5 V, T_A = −55°C to 125°C)

All electrical characteristics and test conditions are identical to those of the corresponding Series 7520 types with the exception of the items shown below. Limits which apply to Series 7520 circuits over the temperature range 0°C to 70°C apply to Series 5520 circuits over the range −55°C to 125°C.

PARAMETER		TEST CONDITIONS	SN5520 SN5522 SN5524 SN5528 SN55232 SN55234 SN55238			SN5521 SN5523 SN5525 SN5529 SN55233 SN55235 SN55239			UNIT
			MIN	TYP‡	MAX	MIN	TYP‡	MAX	
V_T	Differential input threshold voltage†	V_{ref} = 15 mV	T_A = −55°C to 0°C and 70°C to 125°C						mV
			10	15	20	8	15	22	
			T_A = 0°C to 70°C						
			11	15	19	8	15	22	
		V_{ref} = 40 mV	T_A = −55°C to 0°C and 70°C to 125°C						
			35	40	45	33	40	47	
			T_A = 0°C to 70°C						
			36	40	44	33	40	47	
I_{IB}	Differential input bias current	V_{CC+} = 5.25 V, V_{CC-} = −5.25 V, V_{ID} = 0	T_A = −55°C to 0°C		100			100	µA
			T_A = 0°C to 125°C	30	75		30	75	

†The differential input threshold voltage (V_T) is defined as the d-c differential input voltage (V_{ID}) required to force the output of the sense amplifier to the logic-gate threshold voltage level.
‡All typical values are at V_{CC+} = 5 V, V_{CC-} = −5 V, T_A = 25°C.

switching characteristics and typical recovery and cycle times, V_{CC+} = 5 V, V_{CC-} = −5 V, T_A = 25°C

These characteristics are identical to those of the corresponding Series 7520 types.

TEXAS INSTRUMENTS
INCORPORATED
POST OFFICE BOX 5012 • DALLAS, TEXAS 75222

HIGH-SPEED SENSE AMPLIFIERS FOR CONVERSION OF
COINCIDENT-CURRENT MEMORY READOUT TO SATURATED DIGITAL-LOGIC LEVELS

performance features

- high speed and fast recovery time
- time and amplitude signal discrimination
- adjustable input threshold voltage levels
- narrow region of threshold voltage uncertainty
- multiple differential-input preamplifiers
- high d-c noise margin—typically one volt
- good fan-out capability

ease-of-design features

- choice of output circuit function
- TTL or DTL drive capability
- standard logic supply voltages
- plug-in configuration ideal for flow-soldering techniques
- pins on 100-mil grid spacings for industrial-type circuit boards

description

Series 7520 monolithic sense amplifiers are designed for use with high-speed memory systems. These sense amplifiers detect bipolar differential-input signals from the memory and provide the interface circuitry between the memory and the logic section. Low-level pulses originating in the memory are transformed into logic levels compatible with standard transistor-transistor-logic (TTL) and diode-transistor-logic (DTL) circuits.

These sense amplifiers feature multiple differential-input preamplifiers and versatile gating and output circuits, permitting a significant reduction in the circuitry required to accomplish the sensing function. A unique circuit design provides inherent stability of the input threshold level over a wide range of power-supply voltage levels and temperature ranges. Independent strobing of each of the dual sense-input channels ensures maximum versatility and permits detection to occur when the signal-to-noise ratio is at a maximum. The gate and strobe inputs and the outputs are compatible with standard TTL and DTL digital logic circuits.

The SN7520 and SN7521 circuits may be used to perform the functions of a flip-flop or register which responds to the sense and strobe input conditions.

The SN7522 and SN7523 circuits feature a high-fan-out, single-ended, open-collector output stage. In addition, they may be used to expand the inputs to an SN7520 or SN7521 circuit, or to perform the wired-AND function.

The SN7524 and SN7525 circuits provide for independent, dual-channel sensing with separate outputs. SN75234 and SN75235 are similar but have inverted outputs and internal compensation. SN75232 and SN75233 are identical to the SN75234 and SN75235, except that their output gates each feature an open-collector output.

The SN7526 and SN7527 circuits have a D-type flip-flop output with external clear and preset inputs.

The SN7528 and SN7529 circuits are identical to the SN7524 and SN7525 except that the output of each preamplifier is available as a test point. SN75238 and SN75239 are similar to SN7528 and SN7529 but have inverted outputs and internal compensation.

11

SERIES 7520
SENSE AMPLIFIERS

design characteristics

Series 7520 sense amplifiers are completely d-c coupled. Previous designs have resulted in circuits in which the threshold level could not be closely controlled because they were highly sensitive to changes in the d-c levels throughout the amplifier. This was due primarily to the required tolerances on the absolute value of resistors and the resistor temperature coefficients. The "matched-amplifier" design of Series 7520 circuits depends on resistor ratios rather than absolute values. In this design, excellent stability of the threshold level can be maintained despite component variations and changes in bias levels. The capability of multiple-input amplifiers increases the versatility of the design.

The basic circuit is used to implement several sense-amplifier designs. Additional logic circuitry is added to the strobe-gate output to provide versatile sensing functions. The outputs of two or more input amplifiers can be combined to implement multiple-input amplifiers, a function not previously available in integrated form. The d-c coupled design eliminates many of the problems associated with overload recovery time and threshold shift (with high input repetition rates) usually encountered in sense amplifier designs that use reactive coupling components.

circuit operation

The basic Series 7520 sense amplifier strobe and threshold circuit is shown in Figure A. The design uses a "matched-amplifier" concept which takes advantage of the inherent excellent component matching and thermal tracking characteristics of monolithic integrated circuits. A reference amplifier is used to generate the collector reference voltage which is distributed to the input amplifiers. Application of an external reference voltage, V_{ref}, establishes the input-amplifier threshold voltage level, V_T. The design is such that there is 1:1 correspondence between the applied reference voltage, V_{ref}, and the nominal threshold voltage level, V_T. The reference and input amplifiers use identical circuit configurations; therefore, changes in bias levels introduced into the input amplifier through changes in temperature or power-supply voltage levels are compensated by similar changes in the reference amplifier.

The collector reference voltage, supplied by the reference amplifier, can be used to control the threshold-voltage level of more than one input amplifier, thereby establishing equal threshold levels to all of the input sense channels simultaneously.

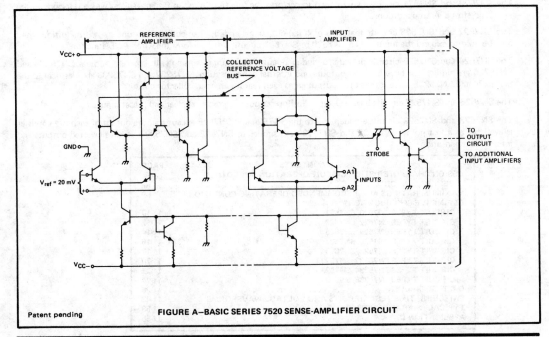

Patent pending

FIGURE A—BASIC SERIES 7520 SENSE-AMPLIFIER CIRCUIT

11

TEXAS INSTRUMENTS
INCORPORATED
POST OFFICE BOX 5012 • DALLAS, TEXAS 75222

circuit operation (continued)

The second stage of the input amplifier is a TTL gate. This gate provides the threshold action for the input sense channel and provides a convenient point in the circuit to accomplish the strobe function. The differential-input sense signal switches the output of the TTL gate only when the strobe input voltage is higher than the logic input threshold voltage. The strobe input, therefore, provides the sense amplifier with the capability of time discrimination, allowing the input signal to be detected when the signal-to-noise ratio is at a maximum.

The logic inputs (i.e., gate and strobe) of Series 7520 sense amplifiers are designed to be compatible with Series 74 TTL digital integrated circuits. The multiple-emitter transistors are utilized to provide inherent switching-time advantages over other saturated-logic schemes. The same noise margin and logic threshold voltage as guaranteed for Series 74 are assured for each of the gate and strobe inputs. This is accomplished by testing each logic input under standard Series 74 test conditions, i.e., 2 volts for high-level input condition and 0.8 volt for low-level input conditions. Since the guaranteed minimum high-level output voltage is 2.4 volts and the guaranteed maximum low-level output voltage is 0.4 volt, a minimum noise margin of 0.4 volt is assured at each input.

SN7520 and SN7521 circuit

This circuit is a dual-channel sense amplifier with the preamplifiers connected to a common output stage and a complementary output stage. The output circuit is composed of two cascaded NAND gates, each with external gate inputs. External connection of the Z output and the G_Y input results in a flip-flop

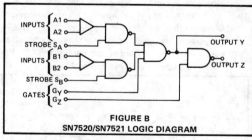

FIGURE B
SN7520/SN7521 LOGIC DIAGRAM

logic: $Y = \overline{G}_Y + A \cdot S_A + B \cdot S_B$

$Z = \overline{G}_Z + \overline{Y}$

$Z = \overline{G}_Z + G_Y\,(\overline{A} + \overline{S}_A)\,(\overline{B} + \overline{S}_B)$

or register that is set by signals at the differential-input terminals. Reset of the register is performed at the G_Z input. Capacitive coupling from output Z to G_Y results in output pulse stretching. With either connection, complementary output levels are available. The gate and strobe inputs and the outputs are compatible with standard TTL logic. The input function of SN7520/SN7521 can be expanded by connecting the Y output of SN7522/SN7523 to the G_Y input of the circuit being expanded.

SN7522 and SN7523 circuit

This circuit is a dual-channel sense amplifier with the preamplifiers connected to a common output stage. The output circuit features an open-collector output which permits two or more of these outputs to be connected in the wire-AND configuration. Each package includes a load resistor that may be used as the output pull-up resistor. High sink-current capability is a feature of this design, and a separate ground terminal is used for the output circuitry. These devices can also be used as input expanders for the SN7520/SN7521 circuit.

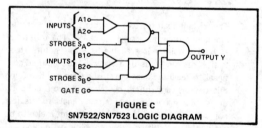

FIGURE C
SN7522/SN7523 LOGIC DIAGRAM

logic: $Y = G\,(\overline{A} + \overline{S}_A)\,(\overline{B} + \overline{S}_B)$

SN7524 and SN7525 circuit

This circuit features two completely independent sense amplifiers in a single package. Each amplifier features high fan-out capability.

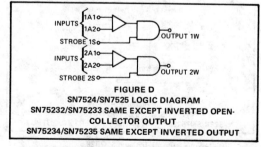

FIGURE D
SN7524/SN7525 LOGIC DIAGRAM
SN75232/SN75233 SAME EXCEPT INVERTED OPEN-COLLECTOR OUTPUT
SN75234/SN75235 SAME EXCEPT INVERTED OUTPUT

logic: $W = AS$ for SN7524 and SN7525

$W = \overline{AS}$ for SN75232, SN75233, SN75234, and SN75235

SN7526 and SN7527 circuit

This circuit is a dual-channel sense amplifier with the preamplifiers connected to a D-type flip-flop with external clear and preset inputs. A delay between the strobe input terminals and the clock input of the flip-flop ensures that data is set up at the D input of the flip-flop prior to clocking.

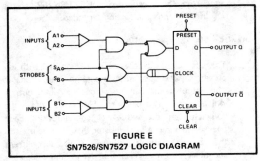

FIGURE E
SN7526/SN7527 LOGIC DIAGRAM

logic: See function table on page 11-16.

SN7528 and SN7529 circuit

This circuit features two separate single-preamplifier sense amplifiers in a single package. The output of each preamplifier is available as a test point. These test points can be used to observe the amplified core signal to facilitate accurate strobe timing. When using this device, care should be taken to avoid coupling the strobe signal or other stray signals to the test point. Excessive loading of the test point is also to be avoided. The result of either coupling or loading will be a change in the threshold voltage of the device. The output circuit of each channel features a simple TTL gate configuration with a high fan-out capability.

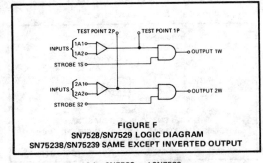

FIGURE F
SN7528/SN7529 LOGIC DIAGRAM
SN75238/SN75239 SAME EXCEPT INVERTED OUTPUT

logic: W = AS for SN7528 and SN7529
W = $\overline{AS}$ for SN75238 and SN75239

SN75232, SN75233, SN75234, SN75235, SN75238, and SN75239 circuits

The SN75234, SN75235, SN75238, and SN75239 dual sense amplifier circuits are the same as SN7524, SN7525, SN7528, and SN7529, respectively, except that an additional stage has been added to the output gate to provide an inverted output and internal compensation has been added. Compared to using a separate gate for inversion, not only is package count reduced, but less propagation delay is added. The need for an external roll-off capacitor has been eliminated. SN75232 and SN75233 are identical to the SN75234 and SN75235, respecitvely, except that their output gates each have an open-collector output. This permits two or more outputs to be connected in wire-AND configuration.

reference voltage considerations

These sense amplifiers feature a variable-threshold voltage level with simultaneous adjustment of both sense channels or both sense amplifiers by a single reference voltage. The operating threshold voltage level of the input amplifiers is established by and is approximately equal to the applied reference input voltage, V_{ref}. These sense amplifiers are recommended for use in systems requiring threshold voltage levels of ±15 to ±40 mV.

A simple method of generating the reference voltage is the use of a resistor voltage divider from either the positive (V_{CC+}) or negative (V_{CC-}) voltage supplies. See Figure G. This type of voltage divider may be used to supply an individual reference amplifier or to supply a number of paralleled reference amplifiers. The bias current required at the reference amplifier input is low (nominally 30 μA); therefore, voltage dividers of this type may normally be operated with very low current requirements. In noisy environments, the use of a filter capacitor across the inputs is recommended. By locating the capacitor as close to the device terminals as possible, noise and stray signals will be presented common-mode to the reference amplifier and thus be rejected.

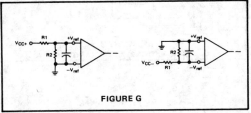

FIGURE G

11

TEXAS INSTRUMENTS
INCORPORATED
POST OFFICE BOX 5012 • DALLAS, TEXAS 75222

input line layout considerations

Input sensitivity and device speed require adequate precautions in the routing of signal input and reference lines to prevent noise pickup. Bypassing of supply and reference inputs at the device with low-inductance disc ceramic capacitors, and use of a good ground plane to separate strobe and output lines from sense and reference input lines, is recommended.

sense-input termination resistor considerations

Termination resistors are intentionally omitted from the sense-input terminals so the designer may select resistor values which will be compatible with the particular application. Matched termination resistors, (R_T, Figure H), normally in the range of 25 Ω to 200 Ω each, are required not only to terminate the sense line in a desired impedance but also to provide a d-c path for the sense-input bias currents. Careful matching of the resistor pairs should be observed or effective common-mode rejection will be reduced.

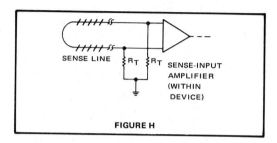

FIGURE H

output drive capability

The output circuits of these sense amplifiers feature the ability to sink or supply load current. This capability permits direct use with both TTL- and DTL-type loads. The open-collector output of the SN7522/SN7523 circuit may be connected to similar outputs to perform the wire-AND function. Load currents (out of the output terminal) are specified as negative values. Arrows on the d-c test circuit indicate the actual direction of current flow.

logic input current requirements

Logic input current requirements are specified at worst-case power-supply conditions over the operating free-air temperature range of 0°C to 70°C. The logic input currents are identical to those of, and compatible with, Series 74 TTL digital integrated circuits. Each logic input of the multiple-emitter input transistors requires no more than a 1.6-mA flow out of the input at a low logic level. Each input emitter requires current into the input when it is at a high-logic level. This current is 40 μA maximum. Currents into the input terminals are specified as positive values. Arrows on the d-c test circuits indicate the actual direction of current flow.

absolute maximum ratings over operating free-air temperature range (unless otherwise noted)

Supply voltages (see Note 1)

V_{CC+}	7 V
V_{CC-}	−7 V
Differential input voltage, V_{ID} or V_{ref}	±5 V
Voltage from any input to ground (see Note 2)	5.5 V
Off-state voltage applied to open-collector outputs	5.5 V
Operating free-air temperature range	0°C to 70°C
Storage temperature range	−55°C to 150°C

recommended operating conditions

	MIN	NOM	MAX	UNIT
V_{CC+} (see Note 1)	4.75	5	5.25	V
V_{CC-} (see Note 1)	−4.75	−5	−5.25	V
V_{ref}	15		40	mV

NOTES: 1. These voltage values are with respect to network ground terminal.
2. Strobe and gate input voltages must be zero or positive with respect to network ground terminal.

11

TEXAS INSTRUMENTS
INCORPORATED
POST OFFICE BOX 5012 • DALLAS, TEXAS 75222

TYPES SN7520, SN7521
DUAL-CHANNEL SENSE AMPLIFIERS WITH COMPLEMENTARY OUTPUTS

FUNCTION TABLE

INPUTS						OUTPUTS	
A	B	G_Y	G_Z	S_A	S_B	Y	Z
X	X	L	X	X	X	H	$\overline{G}_Z$
H	X	X	X	H	X	H	$\overline{G}_Z$
X	H	X	X	X	H	H	$\overline{G}_Z$
L	L	H	X	X	X	L	H
L	X	H	X	X	X	L	H
X	L	H	X	L	X	L	H
X	X	H	X	L	L	L	H
X	X	X	L	X	X	X	H

definition of logic levels

INPUT	H	L	X
A or B†	$V_{ID} \geqslant V_T$ max	$V_{ID} \leqslant V_T$ min	Irrelevant
Any G or S	$V_I \geqslant V_{IH}$ min	$V_I \leqslant V_{IL}$ max	Irrelevant

†A and B are differential voltages (V_{ID}) between A1 and A2 or B1 and B2, respectively. For these circuits, V_{ID} is considered positive regardless of which terminal of each pair is positive with respect to the other.

J OR N
DUAL-IN-LINE PACKAGE (TOP VIEW)

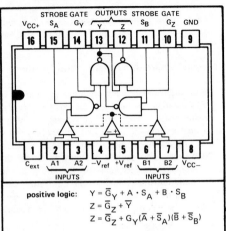

positive logic:
$$Y = \overline{G}_Y + A \cdot S_A + B \cdot S_B$$
$$Z = \overline{G}_Z + \overline{Y}$$
$$Z = \overline{G}_Z + G_Y(\overline{A} + \overline{S}_A)(\overline{B} + \overline{S}_B)$$

electrical characteristics (unless otherwise noted $V_{CC+} = 5$ V, $V_{CC-} = -5$ V, $T_A = 0°$C to $70°$C)

PARAMETER		TEST FIGURE	TEST CONDITIONS		MIN	TYP‡	MAX	UNIT
V_T	Differential input threshold voltage (see Note 3)	1	$V_{ref} = 15$ mV	SN7520	11	15	19	mV
				SN7521	8	15	22	
			$V_{ref} = 40$ mV	SN7520	36	40	44	
				SN7521	33	40	47	
V_{ICF}	Common-mode input firing voltage (see Note 4)	none	$V_{ref} = 40$ mV, $V_{I(S)} = V_{IH}$ *Common-mode input pulse:* $t_r \leqslant 15$ ns, $t_f \leqslant 15$ ns, $t_w = 50$ ns			±2.5		V
I_{IB}	Differential-input bias current	2	$V_{CC+} = 5.25$ V, $V_{CC-} = -5.25$ V, $V_{ID} = 0$			30	75	µA
I_{IO}	Differential-input offset current	2	$V_{CC+} = 5.25$ V, $V_{CC-} = -5.25$ V, $V_{ID} = 0$			0.5		µA
V_{IH}	High-level input voltage (strobe and gate inputs)	3			2			V
V_{IL}	Low-level input voltage (strobe and gate inputs)	3					0.8	V
V_{OH}	High-level output voltage	3	$V_{CC+} = 4.75$ V, $V_{CC-} = -4.75$ V, $I_{OH} = -400$ µA		2.4	4		V
V_{OL}	Low-level output voltage	3	$V_{CC+} = 4.75$ V, $V_{CC-} = -4.75$ V, $I_{OL} = 16$ mA			0.25	0.4	V
I_{IH}	High-level input current (strobe and gate inputs)	4	$V_{CC+} = 5.25$ V, $V_{CC-} = -5.25$ V, $V_{IH} = 2.4$ V				40	µA
I_{IL}	Low-level input current (strobe and gate inputs)	4	$V_{CC+} = 5.25$ V, $V_{CC-} = -5.25$ V, $V_{IL} = 0.4$ V			−1	−1.6	mA
$I_{OS(Y)}$	Short-circuit output current into Y	5	$V_{CC+} = 5.25$ V, $V_{CC-} = -5.25$ V		−3		−5	mA
$I_{OS(Z)}$	Short-circuit output current into Z	5	$V_{CC+} = 5.25$ V, $V_{CC-} = -5.25$ V		−2.1		−3.5	mA
I_{CC+}	Supply current from V_{CC+}	6	$V_{CC+} = 5.25$ V, $V_{CC-} = -5.25$ V, $T_A = 25°$C			28	40	mA
I_{CC-}	Supply current from V_{CC-}	6	$V_{CC+} = 5.25$ V, $V_{CC-} = -5.25$ V, $T_A = 25°$C			−14	−20	mA

‡All typical values are at $V_{CC+} = 5$ V, $V_{CC-} = -5$ V, $T_A = 25°$C.
NOTES: 3. The differential-input threshold voltage (V_T) is defined as the d-c differential-input voltage (V_{ID}) required to force the output of the sense amplifier to the logic gate threshold voltage level.
4. Common-mode input firing voltage is the minimum common-mode voltage that will exceed the dynamic range of the input at the specified conditions and cause the logic output to switch. The specified common-mode input signal is applied with a strobe-enable pulse present.

TEXAS INSTRUMENTS
INCORPORATED
POST OFFICE BOX 5012 • DALLAS, TEXAS 75222

switching characteristics, V_{CC+} = 5 V, V_{CC-} = −5 V, $C_{ext} \geqslant$ 100 pF, T_A = 25°C

PROPAGATION DELAY TIMES			TEST	TEST CONDITIONS	MIN	TYP	MAX	UNIT
SYMBOL	FROM INPUT	TO OUTPUT	FIGURE					
$t_{PLH(DY)}$	A1-A2 OR B1-B2	Y	32	C_L = 15 pF, R_L = 288 Ω		25	40	ns
$t_{PHL(DY)}$						20		
$t_{PLH(DZ)}$	A1-A2 OR B1-B2	Z	32	C_L = 15 pF, R_L = 288 Ω		30		ns
$t_{PHL(DZ)}$						35	55	
$t_{PLH(SY)}$	STROBE A OR B	Y	32	C_L = 15 pF, R_L = 288 Ω		15	30	ns
$t_{PHL(SY)}$						20		
$t_{PLH(SZ)}$	STROBE A OR B	Z	32	C_L = 15 pF, R_L = 288 Ω		30		ns
$t_{PHL(SZ)}$						35	55	
$t_{PLH(GY, Y)}$	GATE G_Y	Y	33	C_L = 15 pF, R_L = 288 Ω		15	25	ns
$t_{PHL(GY, Y)}$						10		
$t_{PLH(GY, Z)}$	GATE G_Y	Z	33	C_L = 15 pF, R_L = 288 Ω		15		ns
$t_{PHL(GY, Z)}$						20	30	
$t_{PLH(GZ, Z)}$	GATE G_Z	Z	34	C_L = 15 pF, R_L = 288 Ω		15		ns
$t_{PHL(GZ, Z)}$						10	20	

typical recovery and cycle times, V_{CC+} = 5 V, V_{CC-} = −5 V, $C_{ext} \geqslant$ 100 pF, T_A = 25°C

	PARAMETER	TEST CONDITIONS	MIN	TYP	MAX	UNIT
t_{orD}	Differential-input overload recovery time (see Note 5)	*Differential Input Pulse:* V_{ID} = 2 V, t_r = t_f = 20 ns		20		ns
t_{orC}	Common-mode-input overload recovery time (see Note 6)	*Common-Mode Input Pulse:* V_{IC} = ±2 V, t_r = t_f = 20 ns		20		ns
$t_{cyc(min)}$	Minimum cycle time			200		ns

NOTES: 5. Differential-input overload recovery time is the time necessary for the device to recover from the specified differential-input overload signal prior to the strobe-enable signal.

6. Common-mode-input overload recovery time is the time necessary for the device to recover from the specified common-mode-input overload signal prior to the strobe-enable signal.

schematic

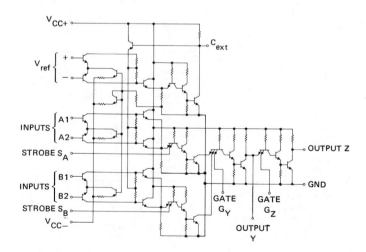

TYPES SN7522, SN7523
DUAL-CHANNEL SENSE AMPLIFIERS

FUNCTION TABLE

INPUTS					OUTPUT
A	B	G	S_A	S_B	Y
L	L	H	X	X	H
L	X	H	X	L	H
X	L	H	L	X	H
X	X	H	L	L	H
X	X	L	X	X	L
H	X	X	H	X	L
X	H	X	X	H	L

definition of logic levels

INPUT	H	L	X
A or B†	$V_{ID} \geqslant V_T$ max	$V_{ID} \leqslant V_T$ min	Irrelevant
Any G or S	$V_I \geqslant V_{IH}$ min	$V_I \leqslant V_{IL}$ max	Irrelevant

†A and B are differential voltages (V_{ID}) between A1 and A2 or B1 and B2, respectively. For these circuits, V_{ID} is considered positive regardless of which terminal of each pair is positive with respect to the other.

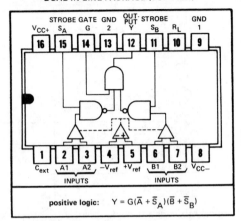

J OR N
DUAL-IN-LINE PACKAGE (TOP VIEW)

positive logic: $Y = G(\overline{A} + \overline{S}_A)(\overline{B} + \overline{S}_B)$

electrical characteristics (unless otherwise noted V_{CC+} = 5 V, V_{CC-} = −5 V, T_A = 0°C to 70°C)

PARAMETER		TEST FIGURE	TEST CONDITIONS		MIN	TYP‡	MAX	UNIT
V_T	Differential input threshold voltage (see Note 3)	7	V_{ref} = 15 mV	SN7522	11	15	19	mV
				SN7523	8	15	22	
			V_{ref} = 40 mV	SN7522	36	40	44	
				SN7523	33	40	47	
V_{ICF}	Common-mode input firing voltage (see Note 4)	none	V_{ref} = 40 mV, $V_{I(S)}$ = V_{IH} *Common-mode input pulse:* $t_r \leqslant$ 15 ns, $t_f \leqslant$ 15 ns, t_w = 50 ns			±2.5		V
I_{IB}	Differential-input bias current	2	V_{CC+} = 5.25 V, V_{CC-} = −5.25 V, V_{ID} = 0			30	75	μA
I_{IO}	Differential-input offset current	2	V_{CC+} = 5.25 V, V_{CC-} = −5.25 V, V_{ID} = 0			0.5		μA
V_{IH}	High-level input voltage (strobe and gate inputs)	8			2			V
V_{IL}	Low-level input voltage (strobe and gate inputs)	8					0.8	V
V_{OH}	High-level output voltage	8	V_{CC+} = 4.75 V, V_{CC-} = −4.75 V, I_{OH} = −400 μA		2.4	4		V
V_{OL}	Low-level output voltage	8	V_{CC+} = 4.75 V, V_{CC-} = −4.75 V, I_{OL} = 16 mA			0.25	0.4	V
I_{IH}	High-level input current (strobe and gate inputs)	9	V_{CC+} = 5.25 V, V_{CC-} = −5.25 V, V_{IH} = 2.4 V				40	μA
			V_{CC+} = 5.25 V, V_{CC-} = −5.25 V, V_{IH} = 5.25 V				1	mA
I_{IL}	Low-level input current (strobe and gate inputs)	9	V_{CC+} = 5.25 V, V_{CC-} = −5.25 V, V_{IL} = 0.4 V			−1	−1.6	mA
I_{OH}	High-level output current	10	V_{CC+} = 4.75 V, V_{CC-} = −4.75 V, V_O = 5.25 V				250	μA
I_{OS}	Short-circuit output current	11	V_{CC+} = 5.25 V, V_{CC-} = −5.25 V		−2.1		−3.5	mA
I_{CC+}	Supply current from V_{CC+}	6	V_{CC+} = 5.25 V, V_{CC-} = −5.25 V, T_A = 25°C			27	40	mA
I_{CC-}	Supply current from V_{CC-}	6	V_{CC+} = 5.25 V, V_{CC-} = −5.25 V, T_A = 25°C			−15	−20	mA

‡All typical values are at V_{CC+} = 5 V, V_{CC-} = −5 V, T_A = 25°C.

NOTES: 3. The differential-input threshold voltage (V_T) is defined as the d-c differential-input voltage (V_{ID}) required to force the output of the sense amplifier to the logic gate threshold voltage level.

4. Common-mode input firing voltage is the minimum common-mode voltage that will exceed the dynamic range of the input at the specified conditions and cause the logic output to switch. The specified common-mode input signal is applied with a strobe-enable pulse present.

TEXAS INSTRUMENTS
INCORPORATED
POST OFFICE BOX 5012 • DALLAS, TEXAS 75222

switching characteristics, V_{CC+} = 5 V, V_{CC-} = −5 V, $C_{ext} \geqslant$ 100 pF, T_A = 25°C

SYMBOL	PROPAGATION DELAY TIMES		TEST FIGURE	TEST CONDITIONS	MIN	TYP	MAX	UNIT
	FROM INPUT	TO OUTPUT						
$t_{PLH(D)}$	A1-A2 OR B1-B2	Y	35	C_L = 15 pF, R_L = 288 Ω		20		ns
$t_{PHL(D)}$						30	45	
$t_{PLH(S)}$	STROBE A OR B	Y	35	C_L = 15 pF, R_L = 288 Ω		20		ns
$t_{PHL(S)}$						20	40	
$t_{PLH(G)}$	GATE	Y	36	C_L = 15 pF, R_L = 288 Ω		10		ns
$t_{PHL(G)}$						15	25	

typical recovery and cycle times, V_{CC+} = 5 V, V_{CC-} = −5 V, $C_{ext} \geqslant$ 100 pF, T_A = 25°C

	PARAMETER	TEST CONDITIONS	MIN	TYP	MAX	UNIT
t_{orD}	Differential-input overload recovery time (see Note 5)	*Differential Input Pulse:* V_{ID} = 2 V, $t_r = t_f$ = 20 ns		20		ns
t_{orC}	Common-mode-input overload recovery time (see Note 6)	*Common-Mode Input Pulse:* V_{IC} = ±2 V, $t_r = t_f$ = 20 ns		20		ns
$t_{cyc(min)}$	Minimum cycle time			200		ns

NOTES: 5. Differential-input overload recovery time is the time necessary for the device to recover from the specified differential input-overload signal prior to the strobe-enable signal.

6. Common-mode-input overload recovery time is the time necessary for the device to recover from the specified common-mode-input overload signal prior to the strobe-enable signal.

schematic

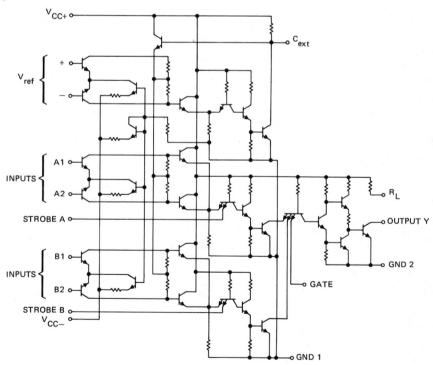

TEXAS INSTRUMENTS
INCORPORATED
POST OFFICE BOX 5012 • DALLAS, TEXAS 75222

TYPES SN7524, SN7525
DUAL SENSE AMPLIFIERS

FUNCTION TABLE

INPUTS		OUTPUT
A	S	W
H	H	H
L	X	L
X	L	L

definition of logic levels

INPUT	H	L	X
A†	$V_{ID} \geqslant V_{T\,max}$	$V_{ID} \leqslant V_{T\,min}$	Irrelevant
S	$V_I \geqslant V_{IH\,min}$	$V_I \leqslant V_{IL\,max}$	Irrelevant

†A is a differential voltage (V_{ID}) between A1 and A2. For these circuits, V_{ID} is considered positive regardless of which terminal is positive with respect to the other.

J OR N
DUAL-IN-LINE PACKAGE (TOP VIEW)

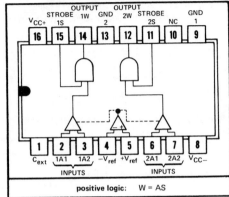

positive logic: W = AS

NC—No internal connection

electrical characteristics (unless otherwise noted V_{CC+} = 5 V, V_{CC-} = −5 V, T_A = 0°C to 70°C)

PARAMETER		TEST FIGURE	TEST CONDITIONS		MIN	TYP‡	MAX	UNIT
V_T	Differential-input threshold voltage (see Note 3)	12	V_{ref} = 15 mV	SN7524	11	15	19	mV
				SN7525	8	15	22	
			V_{ref} = 40 mV	SN7524	36	40	44	
				SN7525	33	40	47	
V_{ICF}	Common-mode input firing voltage (see Note 4)	none	V_{ref} = 40 mV, $V_{I(S)}$ = V_{IH} *Common-Mode Input Pulse:* $t_r \leqslant$ 15 ns, $t_f \leqslant$ 15 ns, t_w = 50 ns			±2.5		V
I_{IB}	Differential-input bias current	2	V_{CC+} = 5.25 V, V_{CC-} = −5.25 V, V_{ID} = 0			30	75	µA
I_{IO}	Differential-input offset current	2	V_{CC+} = 5.25 V, V_{CC-} = −5.25 V, V_{ID} = 0			0.5		µA
V_{IH}	High-level input voltage (strobe inputs)	13			2			V
V_{IL}	Low-level input voltage (strobe inputs)	13					0.8	V
V_{OH}	High-level output voltage	13	V_{CC+} = 4.75 V, V_{CC-} = −4.75 V, I_{OH} = −400 µA		2.4	4		V
V_{OL}	Low-level output voltage	13	V_{CC+} = 4.75 V, V_{CC-} = −4.75 V, I_{OL} = 16 mA			0.25	0.4	V
I_{IH}	High-level input current (strobe inputs)	14	V_{CC+} = 5.25 V, V_{CC-} = −5.25 V, V_{IH} = 2.4 V				40	µA
			V_{CC+} = 5.25 V, V_{CC-} = −5.25 V, V_{IH} = 5.25 V				1	mA
I_{IL}	Low-level input current (strobe inputs)	14	V_{CC+} = 5.25 V, V_{CC-} = −5.25 V, V_{IL} = 0.4 V			−1	−1.6	mA
I_{OS}	Short-circuit output current	15	V_{CC+} = 5.25 V, V_{CC-} = −5.25 V		−2.1		−3.5	mA
I_{CC+}	Supply current from V_{CC+}	6	V_{CC+} = 5.25 V, V_{CC-} = −5.25 V, T_A = 25°C			25	40	mA
I_{CC-}	Supply current from V_{CC-}	6	V_{CC+} = 5.25 V, V_{CC-} = −5.25 V, T_A = 25°C			−15	−20	mA

‡All typical values are at V_{CC+} = 5 V, V_{CC-} = −5 V, T_A = 25°C.

NOTES: 3. The differential-input threshold voltage (V_T) is defined as the d-c differential-input voltage (V_{ID}) required to force the output of the sense amplifier to the logic gate threshold voltage level.

4. Common-mode input firing voltage is the minimum common-mode voltage that will exceed the dynamic range of the input at the specified conditions and cause the logic output to switch. The specified common-mode input signal is applied with a strobe-enable pulse present.

TEXAS INSTRUMENTS
INCORPORATED
POST OFFICE BOX 5012 • DALLAS, TEXAS 75222

switching characteristics, V_{CC+} = 5 V, V_{CC-} = −5 V, $C_{ext} \geqslant$ 100 pF, T_A = 25°C

PROPAGATION DELAY TIMES			TEST FIGURE	TEST CONDITIONS	MIN	TYP	MAX	UNIT
SYMBOL	FROM INPUT	TO OUTPUT						
$t_{PLH(D)}$	A1–A2	W	37	C_L = 15 pF, R_L = 288 Ω		25	40	ns
$t_{PHL(D)}$						20		
$t_{PLH(S)}$	STROBE	W	37	C_L = 15 pF, R_L = 288 Ω		15	30	ns
$t_{PHL(S)}$						20		

typical recovery and cycle times, V_{CC+} = 5 V, V_{CC-} = −5 V, $C_{ext} \geqslant$ 100 pF, T_A = 25°C

	PARAMETER	TEST CONDITIONS	MIN	TYP	MAX	UNIT
t_{orD}	Differential-input overload recovery time (see Note 5)	*Differential Input Pulse:* V_{ID} = 2 V, t_r = t_f = 20 ns		20		ns
t_{orC}	Common-mode-input overload recovery time (see Note 6)	*Common-Mode Input Pulse:* V_{IC} = ±2 V, t_r = t_f = 20 ns		20		ns
$t_{cyc(min)}$	Minimum cycle time			200		ns

NOTES: 5. Differential-input overload recovery time is the time necessary for the device to recover from the specified differential-input-overload signal prior to the strobe-enable signal.
6. Common-mode-input overload recovery time is the time necessary for the device to recover from the specified common-mode-input overload signal prior to the strobe-enable signal.

schematic

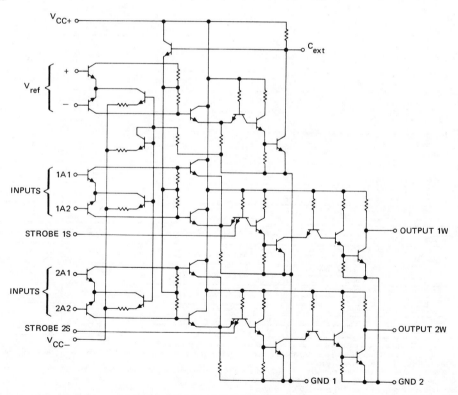

FUNCTION TABLE

INPUTS AT TIME OF STROBE TRANSITION				OUTPUTS	
A	B	S_A	S_B	Q	$\overline{Q}$
H	X	↑	L	H	L
H	X	↑	↑	H	L
X	H	L	↑	H	L
X	H	↑	↑	H	L
L	L	↑	↑	L	H
L	X	↑	L	L	H
X	L	L	↑	L	H
X	X	H	↑	No Change	
X	X	↑	H	No Change	

NOTES: A. H = high level (steady state), L = low level (steady state),
↑ = transition from low level to high level, X = irrelevant.
B. Information at the inputs is transferred to the outputs on the positive-going edge of the strobe pulse.

definition of logic levels

INPUT	H	L
A or B†	$V_{ID} \geqslant V_{T\ max}$	$V_{ID} \leqslant V_{T\ min}$
S_A or S_B	$V_I \geqslant V_{IH\ min}$	$V_I \leqslant V_{IL\ max}$

†A and B are differential voltages (V_{ID}) between A1 and A2 or B1 and B2, respectively. For these circuits, V_{ID} is considered positive regardless of which terminal of each pair is positive with respect to the other.

J OR N
DUAL-IN-LINE PACKAGE (TOP VIEW)

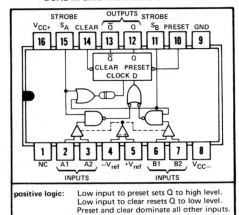

NC—No internal connection

positive logic: Low input to preset sets Q to high level.
Low input to clear resets Q to low level.
Preset and clear dominate all other inputs.

recommended operating conditions¶

	MIN	MAX	UNIT
Width of clear or preset pulse, t_w	30		ns
Width of strobe pulse, t_w	30		ns
Input setup time, t_{setup}◇	20		ns
Input hold time, t_{hold}□	5		ns

electrical characteristics (unless otherwise noted V_{CC+} = 5 V, V_{CC-} = −5 V, T_A = 0°C to 70°C)

PARAMETER			TEST FIGURE	TEST CONDITIONS		MIN	TYP‡	MAX	UNIT
V_T	Differential input threshold voltage (see Note 3)		16	V_{ref} = 15 mV	SN7526	11	15	19	mV
					SN7527	8	15	22	
				V_{ref} = 40 mV	SN7526	36	40	44	
					SN7527	33	40	47	
V_{ICF}	Common-mode input firing voltage (see Note 4)		none	V_{ref} = 40 mV, $V_{I(S)}$ = V_{IH} Common-Mode Input Pulse: $t_r \leqslant$ 15 ns, $t_f \leqslant$ 15 ns, t_w = 50 ns			±2.5		V
I_{IB}	Differential input bias current		2	V_{CC+} = 5.25 V, V_{CC-} = −5.25 V, V_{ID} = 0			30	75	μA
I_{IO}	Differential-input offset current		2	V_{CC+} = 5.25 V, V_{CC-} = −5.25 V, V_{ID} = 0			0.5		μA
V_{IH}	High-level input voltage at strobe, preset, and clear inputs		17			2			V
V_{IL}	Low-level input voltage at strobe, preset and clear inputs		17					0.8	V
V_{OH}	High-level output voltage		17	V_{CC+} = 4.75 V, V_{CC-} = −4.75 V, I_{OH} = −400 μA		2.4	3.6		V
V_{OL}	Low-level output voltage		17	V_{CC+} = 4.75 V, V_{CC-} = −4.75 V, I_{OL} = 16 mA			0.26	0.4	V
I_{IH}	High-level input current	clear and strobe inputs	19	V_{CC+} = 5.25 V, V_{CC-} = −5.25 V, V_{IH} = 2.4 V				80	μA
		preset input						120	
		clear and strobe inputs	19	V_{CC+} = 5.25 V, V_{CC-} = −5.25 V, V_{IH} = 5.25 V				2	mA
		preset input						3	
I_{IL}	Low-level input current	clear and strobe inputs	19	V_{CC+} = 5.25 V, V_{CC-} = −5.25 V, V_{IL} = 0.4 V			−2	−3.2	mA
		preset input					−3	−4.8	
I_{OS}	Short-circuit output current§		18	V_{CC+} = 5.25 V, V_{CC-} = −5.25 V		−18		−57	mA
I_{CC+}	Supply current from V_{CC+}		6	V_{CC+} = 5.25 V, V_{CC-} = −5.25 V, T_A = 25°C			27	40	mA
I_{CC-}	Supply current from V_{CC-}		6	V_{CC+} = 5.25 V, V_{CC-} = −5.25 V, T_A = 25°C			−10	−20	mA

¶These are in addition to the recommended operating conditions previously given for Series 7520. See waveforms in Figure 38.
◇Setup time is the interval immediately preceding the positive-going edge of the strobe pulse during which interval the data to be recognized must be maintained at the input to ensure its recognition.
□Hold time is the interval immediately following the positive-going edge of the strobe pulse during which interval the data to be recognized must be maintained at the input to ensure its continued recognition.
‡All typical values are at V_{CC+} = 5 V, V_{CC-} = −5 V, T_A = 25°C.
§Not more than one output should be shorted at a time, and duration of the short-circuit test should not exceed one second.

11

87

TEXAS INSTRUMENTS
INCORPORATED
POST OFFICE BOX 5012 • DALLAS, TEXAS 75222

switching characteristics, V_{CC+} = 5 V, V_{CC-} = −5 V, T_A = 25°C

	PROPAGATION DELAY TIMES			TEST	TEST CONDITIONS	MIN	TYP	MAX	UNIT
SYMBOL	FROM INPUT	TO OUTPUT		FIGURE					
$t_{PLH(SQ)}$	STROBE S_A or S_B	Q		38	C_L = 15 pF, R_L = 288 Ω		25	45	ns
$t_{PHL(SQ)}$							30	45	
$t_{PLH(S\overline{Q})}$	STROBE S_A or S_B	$\overline{Q}$		38	C_L = 15 pF, R_L = 288 Ω		25	45	ns
$t_{PHL(S\overline{Q})}$							30	45	
$t_{PLH(CQ)}$	CLEAR	$\overline{Q}$		38	C_L = 15 pF, R_L = 288 Ω		15	25	ns
$t_{PHL(CQ)}$		Q					20	40	
$t_{PLH(PQ)}$	PRESET	Q		38	C_L = 15 pF, R_L = 288 Ω		15	25	ns
$t_{PHL(P\overline{Q})}$		$\overline{Q}$					20	40	

typical recovery and cycle times, V_{CC+} = 5 V, V_{CC-} = −5 V, T_A = 25°C

	PARAMETER	TEST CONDITIONS	MIN	TYP	MAX	UNIT
t_{orD}	Differential-input overload recovery time (see Note 5)	*Differential Input Pulse:* V_{ID} = 2 V, t_r = t_f = 20 ns		20		ns
t_{orC}	Common-mode-input overload recovery time (see Note 6)	*Common-Mode Input Pulse:* V_{IC} = ±2 V, t_r = t_f = 20 ns		20		ns
$t_{cyc(min)}$	Minimum cycle time			200		ns

NOTES: 3. The differential-input threshold voltage (V_T) is defined as the d-c differential-input voltage (V_{ID}) required to force the output of the sense amplifier to the logic gate threshold voltage level.
      4. Common-mode input firing voltage is the minimum common-mode voltage that will exceed the dynamic range of the input at the specified conditions and cause the logic output to switch. The specified common-mode input signal is applied with a strobe-enable pulse present.
      5. Differential-input overload recovery time is the time necessary for the device to recover from the specified differential-input-overload signal prior to the strobe-enable signal.
      6. Common-mode-input overload recovery time is the time necessary for the device to recover from the specified common-mode-input overload signal prior to the strobe-enable signal.

schematic

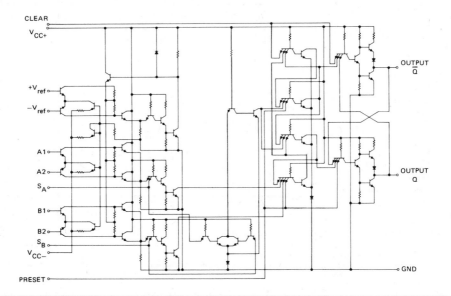

TEXAS INSTRUMENTS
INCORPORATED
POST OFFICE BOX 5012 • DALLAS, TEXAS 75222

TYPES SN7528, SN7529
DUAL SENSE AMPLIFIERS WITH PREAMPLIFIER TEST POINTS

FUNCTION TABLE

INPUTS		OUTPUT
A	S	W
H	H	H
L	X	L
X	L	L

definition of logic levels

INPUT	H	L	X
A†	$V_{ID} \geqslant V_{T\,max}$	$V_{ID} \leqslant V_{T\,min}$	Irrelevant
S	$V_I \geqslant V_{IH\,min}$	$V_I \leqslant V_{IL\,max}$	Irrelevant

†A is a differential voltage (V_{ID}) between A1 and A2. For these circuits, V_{ID} is considered positive regardless of which terminal is positive with respect to the other.

J OR N
DUAL-IN-LINE PACKAGE (TOP VIEW)

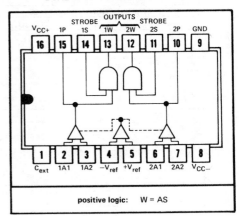

positive logic: W = AS

electrical characteristics (unless otherwise noted V_{CC+} = 5 V, V_{CC-} = −5 V, T_A = 0°C to 70°C)

PARAMETER		TEST FIGURE	TEST CONDITIONS		MIN	TYP‡	MAX	UNIT
V_T	Differential-input threshold voltage (see Note 3)	20	V_{ref} = 15 mV	SN7528	11	15	19	mV
				SN7529	8	15	22	
			V_{ref} = 40 mV	SN7528	36	40	44	
				SN7529	33	40	47	
V_{ICF}	Common-mode input firing voltage (see Note 4)	none	V_{ref} = 40 mV, $V_{I(S)} = V_{IH}$ *Common-Mode Input Pulse:* $t_r \leqslant$ 15 ns, $t_f \leqslant$ 15 ns, t_w = 50 ns			±2.5		V
I_{IB}	Differential-input bias current	2	V_{CC+} = 5.25 V, V_{CC-} = −5.25 V, V_{ID} = 0			30	75	µA
I_{IO}	Differential-input offset current	2	V_{CC+} = 5.25 V, V_{CC-} = −5.25 V, V_{ID} = 0			0.5		µA
V_{IH}	High-level input voltage (strobe inputs)	21			2			V
V_{IL}	Low-level input voltage (strobe inputs)	21					0.8	V
V_{OH}	High-level output voltage	21	V_{CC+} = 4.75 V, V_{CC-} = −4.75 V, I_{OH} = −400 µA		2.4	4		V
V_{OL}	Low-level output voltage	21	V_{CC+} = 4.75 V, V_{CC-} = −4.75 V, I_{OL} = 16 mA			0.25	0.4	V
I_{IH}	High-level input current (strobe inputs)	22	V_{CC+} = 5.25 V, V_{CC-} = −5.25 V, V_{IH} = 2.4 V				40	µA
			V_{CC+} = 5.25 V, V_{CC-} = −5.25 V, V_{IH} = 5.25 V				1	mA
I_{IL}	Low-level input current (strobe inputs)	22	V_{CC+} = 5.25 V, V_{CC-} = −5.25 V, V_{IL} = 0.4 V			−1	−1.6	mA
I_{OS}	Short-circuit output current	23	V_{CC+} = 5.25 V, V_{CC-} = −5.25 V		−2.1		−3.5	mA
I_{CC+}	Supply current from V_{CC+}	6	V_{CC+} = 5.25 V, V_{CC-} = −5.25 V, T_A = 25°C			25	40	mA
I_{CC-}	Supply current from V_{CC-}	6	V_{CC+} = 5.25 V, V_{CC-} = −5.25 V, T_A = 25°C			−15	−20	mA

‡All typical values are at V_{CC+} = 5 V, V_{CC-} = −5 V, T_A = 25°C.

NOTES: 3. The differential-input threshold voltage (V_T) is defined as the d-c differential-input voltage (V_{ID}) required to force the output of the sense amplifier to the logic gate threshold voltage level.
   4. Common-mode input firing voltage is the minimum common-mode voltage that will exceed the dynamic range of the input at the specified conditions and cause the logic output to switch. The specified common-mode input signal is applied with a strobe-enable pulse present.

TEXAS INSTRUMENTS
INCORPORATED
POST OFFICE BOX 5012 • DALLAS, TEXAS 75222

switching characteristics, V_{CC+} = 5 V, V_{CC-} = −5 V, T_A = 25°C

PROPAGATION DELAY TIMES			TEST	TEST CONDITIONS		MIN	TYP	MAX	UNIT
SYMBOL	FROM INPUT	TO OUTPUT	FIGURE						
$t_{PLH(D)}$	A1−A2	W	39	C_L = 15 pF,	R_L = 288 Ω		25	40	ns
$t_{PHL(D)}$							20		ns
$t_{PLH(S)}$	STROBE	W	39	C_L = 15 pF,	R_L = 288 Ω		15	30	ns
$t_{PHL(S)}$							20		ns

typical recovery and cycle times, V_{CC+} = 5 V, V_{CC-} = −5 V, T_A = 25°C

PARAMETER		TEST CONDITIONS	MIN	TYP	MAX	UNIT
t_{orD}	Differential-input overload recovery time (see Note 5)	*Differential Input Pulse:* V_{ID} = 2 V, t_f = 20 ns		20		ns
t_{orC}	Common-mode-input overload recovery time (see Note 6)	*Common-Mode Input Pulse:* V_{IC} = ±2 V, t_r = t_f = 20 ns		20		ns
$t_{cyc(min)}$	Minimum cycle time			200		ns

NOTES: 5. Differential-input overload recovery time is the time necessary for the device to recover from the specified differential-input overload signal prior to the strobe-enable signal.
6. Common-mode-input overload recovery time is the time necessary for the device to recover from the specified common-mode-input overload signal prior to the strobe-enable signal.

schematic

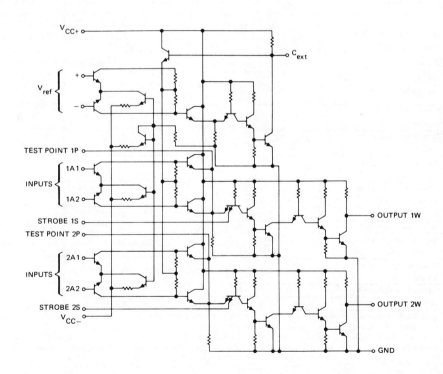

TEXAS INSTRUMENTS
INCORPORATED
POST OFFICE BOX 5012 • DALLAS, TEXAS 75222

TYPES SN75232, SN75233
DUAL SENSE AMPLIFIERS

FUNCTION TABLE

INPUTS		OUTPUT
A	S	W
H	H	L
L	X	H
X	L	H

definition of logic levels

INPUT	H	L	X
A†	$V_{ID} \geqslant V_{T\ max}$	$V_{ID} \leqslant V_{T\ min}$	Irrelevant
S	$V_I \geqslant V_{IH\ min}$	$V_I \leqslant V_{IL\ max}$	Irrelevant

†A is a differential voltage (V_{ID}) between A1 and A2. For these circuits, V_{ID} is considered positive regardless of which terminal is positive with respect to the other.

J OR N
DUAL-IN-LINE PACKAGE (TOP VIEW)

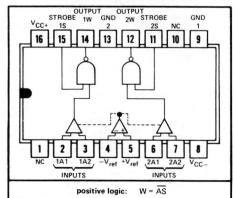

positive logic: $W = \overline{AS}$

NC—No internal connection

electrical characteristics (unless otherwise noted V_{CC+} = 5 V, V_{CC-} = −5 V, T_A = 0°C to 70°C)

PARAMETER		TEST FIGURE	TEST CONDITIONS		MIN	TYP‡	MAX	UNIT
V_T	Differential-input threshold voltage (see Note 3)	24	V_{ref} = 15 mV	SN75232	11	15	19	mV
				SN75233	8	15	22	
			V_{ref} = 40 mV	SN75232	36	40	44	
				SN75233	33	40	47	
V_{ICF}	Common-mode input firing voltage (see Note 4)	none	V_{ref} = 40 mV, $V_{I(S)} = V_{IH}$ *Common-Mode Input Pulse:* $t_r \leqslant$ 15 ns, $t_f \leqslant$ 15 ns, t_w = 50 ns			±2.5		V
I_{IB}	Differential-input bias current	2	V_{CC+} = 5.25 V, V_{CC-} = −5.25 V, V_{ID} = 0			30	75	µA
I_{IO}	Differential-input offset current	2	V_{CC+} = 5.25 V, V_{CC-} = −5.25 V, V_{ID} = 0			0.5		µA
V_{IH}	High-level input voltage (strobe inputs)	25			2			V
V_{IL}	Low-level input voltage (strobe inputs)	25					0.8	V
I_{OH}	High-level output current	25	V_{CC+} = 4.75 V, V_{CC-} = −4.75 V, V_{OH} = 5.25 V				250	µA
V_{OL}	Low-level output voltage	25	V_{CC+} = 4.75 V, V_{CC-} = −4.75 V, I_{OL} = 16 mA			0.25	0.4	V
I_{IH}	High-level input current (strobe inputs)	26	V_{CC+} = 5.25 V, V_{CC-} = −5.25 V, V_{IH} = 2.4 V				40	µA
			V_{CC+} = 5.25 V, V_{CC-} = −5.25 V, V_{IH} = 5.25 V				1	mA
I_{IL}	Low-level input current (strobe inputs)	26	V_{CC+} = 5.25 V, V_{CC-} = −5.25 V, V_{IL} = 0.4 V			−1	−1.6	mA
I_{CC+}	Supply current from V_{CC+}	6	V_{CC+} = 5.25 V, V_{CC-} = −5.25 V, T_A = 25°C			25	40	mA
I_{CC-}	Supply current from V_{CC-}	6	V_{CC+} = 5.25 V, V_{CC-} = −5.25 V, T_A = 25°C			−15	−20	mA

NOTES: 3. The differential-input threshold voltage (V_T) is defined as the d-c differential-input voltage (V_{ID}) required to force the output of the sense amplifier to the logic gate threshold voltage level.
      4. Common-mode input firing voltage is the minimum common-mode voltage that will exceed the dynamic range of the input at the specified conditions and cause the logic output to switch. The specified common-mode input signal is applied with a strobe-enable pulse present.

‡All typical values are at V_{CC+} = 5 V, V_{CC-} = −5 V, T_A = 25°C.

TEXAS INSTRUMENTS
INCORPORATED
POST OFFICE BOX 5012 • DALLAS, TEXAS 75222

switching characteristics, V_{CC+} = 5 V, V_{CC-} = −5 V, T_A = 25°C

PROPAGATION DELAY TIMES			TEST FIGURE	TEST CONDITIONS	MIN	TYP	MAX	UNIT
SYMBOL	FROM INPUT	TO OUTPUT						
$t_{PLH(D)}$	A1−A2	W	40	C_L = 15 pF, R_L = 288 Ω		25		ns
$t_{PHL(D)}$						25	40	
$t_{PLH(S)}$	STROBE	W	40	C_L = 15 pF, R_L = 288 Ω		25		ns
$t_{PHL(S)}$						15	30	

typical recovery and cycle times, V_{CC+} = 5 V, V_{CC-} = −5 V, T_A = 25°C

	PARAMETER	TEST CONDITIONS	MIN	TYP	MAX	UNIT
t_{orD}	Differential-input overload recovery time (see Note 5)	*Differential Input Pulse:* V_{ID} = 2 V, t_r = t_f = 20 ns		20		ns
t_{orC}	Common-mode-input overload recovery time (see Note 6)	*Common-Mode Input Pulse:* V_{IC} = ±2 V, t_r = t_f = 20 ns		20		ns
$t_{cyc(min)}$	Minimum cycle time			200		ns

NOTES: 5. Differential-input overload recovery time is the time necessary for the device to recover from the specified differential-input-overload signal prior to the strobe-enable signal.
6. Common-mode-input overload recovery time is the time necessary for the device to recover from the specified common-mode-input overload signal prior to the strobe-enable signal.

schematic

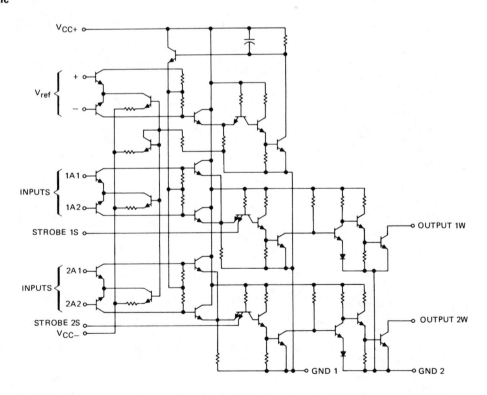

TEXAS INSTRUMENTS
INCORPORATED
POST OFFICE BOX 5012 • DALLAS, TEXAS 75222

TYPES SN75234, SN75235
DUAL SENSE AMPLIFIERS

FUNCTION TABLE

INPUTS		OUTPUT
A	S	W
H	H	L
L	X	H
X	L	H

definition of logic levels

INPUT	H	L	X
A†	$V_{ID} \geqslant V_{T\,max}$	$V_{ID} \leqslant V_{T\,min}$	Irrelevant
S	$V_I \geqslant V_{IH\,min}$	$V_I \leqslant V_{IL\,max}$	Irrelevant

†A is a differential voltage (V_{ID}) between A1 and A2. For these circuits, V_{ID} is considered positive regardless of which terminal is positive with respect to the other.

**J OR N
DUAL-IN-LINE PACKAGE (TOP VIEW)**

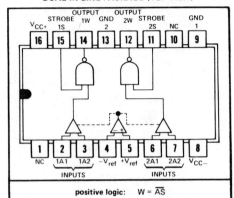

positive logic: $W = \overline{AS}$

NC—No internal connection

electrical characteristics (unless otherwise noted V_{CC+} = 5 V, V_{CC-} = –5 V, T_A = 0°C to 70°C)

PARAMETER		TEST FIGURE	TEST CONDITIONS		MIN	TYP‡	MAX	UNIT
V_T	Differential-input threshold voltage (see Note 3)	24	V_{ref} = 15 mV	SN75234	11	15	19	mV
				SN75235	8	15	22	
			V_{ref} = 40 mV	SN75234	36	40	44	
				SN75235	33	40	47	
V_{ICF}	Common-mode input firing voltage (see Note 4)	none	V_{ref} = 40 mV, $V_{I(S)} = V_{IH}$ *Common-Mode Input Pulse:* $t_r \leqslant$ 15 ns, $t_f \leqslant$ 15 ns, t_w = 50 ns			±2.5		V
I_{IB}	Differential-input bias current	2	V_{CC+} = 5.25 V, V_{CC-} = –5.25 V, V_{ID} = 0			30	75	μA
I_{IO}	Differential-input offset current	2	V_{CC+} = 5.25 V, V_{CC-} = –5.25 V, V_{ID} = 0			0.5		μA
V_{IH}	High-level input voltage (strobe inputs)	25			2			V
V_{IL}	Low-level input voltage (strobe inputs)	25					0.8	V
V_{OH}	High-level output voltage	25	V_{CC+} = 4.75 V, V_{CC-} = –4.75 V, I_{OH} = –400 μA		2.4	4		V
V_{OL}	Low-level output voltage	25	V_{CC+} = 4.75 V, V_{CC-} = –4.75 V, I_{OL} = 16 mA			0.25	0.4	V
I_{IH}	High-level input current (strobe inputs)	26	V_{CC+} = 5.25 V, V_{CC-} = –5.25 V, V_{IH} = 2.4 V				40	μA
			V_{CC+} = 5.25 V, V_{CC-} = –5.25 V, V_{IH} = 5.25 V				1	mA
I_{IL}	Low-level input current (strobe inputs)	26	V_{CC+} = 5.25 V, V_{CC-} = –5.25 V, V_{IL} = 0.4 V			–1	–1.6	mA
I_{OS}	Short-circuit output current	27	V_{CC+} = 5.25 V, V_{CC-} = –5.25 V		–2.1		–3.5	mA
I_{CC+}	Supply current from V_{CC+}	6	V_{CC+} = 5.25 V, V_{CC-} = –5.25 V, T_A = 25°C			25	40	mA
I_{CC-}	Supply current from V_{CC-}	6	V_{CC+} = 5.25 V, V_{CC-} = –5.25 V, T_A = 25°C			–15	–20	mA

‡All typical values are at V_{CC+} = 5 V, V_{CC-} = –5 V, T_A = 25°C.

NOTES: 3. The differential-input threshold voltage (V_T) is defined as the d-c differential-input voltage (V_{ID}) required to force the output of the sense amplifier to the logic gate threshold voltage level.
4. Common-mode input firing voltage is the minimum common-mode voltage that will exceed the dynamic range of the input at the specified conditions and cause the logic output to switch. The specified common-mode input signal is applied with a strobe-enable pulse present.

TEXAS INSTRUMENTS
INCORPORATED
POST OFFICE BOX 5012 • DALLAS, TEXAS 75222

switching characteristics, V_{CC+} = 5 V, V_{CC-} = −5 V, T_A = 25°C

PROPAGATION DELAY TIMES			TEST FIGURE	TEST CONDITIONS	MIN	TYP	MAX	UNIT
SYMBOL	FROM INPUT	TO OUTPUT						
$t_{PLH(D)}$	A1−A2	W	40	C_L = 15 pF, R_L = 288 Ω		25		ns
$t_{PHL(D)}$						25	40	
$t_{PLH(S)}$	STROBE	W	40	C_L = 15 pF, R_L = 288 Ω		25		ns
$t_{PHL(S)}$						15	30	

typical recovery and cycle times, V_{CC+} = 5 V, V_{CC-} = −5 V, T_A = 25°C

PARAMETER		TEST CONDITIONS	MIN	TYP	MAX	UNIT
t_{orD}	Differential-input overload recovery time (see Note 5)	*Differential Input Pulse:* V_{ID} = 2 V, t_r = t_f = 20 ns		20		ns
t_{orC}	Common-mode-input overload recovery time (see Note 6)	*Common-Mode Input Pulse:* V_{IC} = ±2 V, t_r = t_f = 20 ns		20		ns
$t_{cyc(min)}$	Minimum cycle time			200		ns

NOTES: 5. Differential-input overload recovery time is the time necessary for the device to recover from the specified differential-input-overload signal prior to the strobe-enable signal.
      6. Common-mode-input overload recovery time is the time necessary for the device to recover from the specified common-mode-input overload signal prior to the strobe-enable signal.

schematic

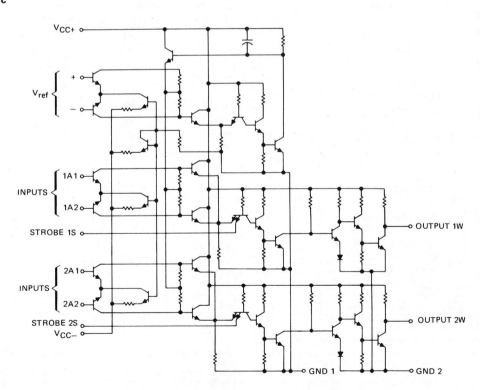

TEXAS INSTRUMENTS
INCORPORATED
POST OFFICE BOX 5012 • DALLAS, TEXAS 75222

FUNCTION TABLE

INPUTS		OUTPUT
A	S	W
H	H	L
L	X	H
X	L	H

definition of logic levels

INPUT	H	L	X
A†	$V_{ID} \geqslant V_{T\ max}$	$V_{ID} \leqslant V_{T\ min}$	Irrelevant
S	$V_I \geqslant V_{IH\ min}$	$V_I \leqslant V_{IL\ max}$	Irrelevant

†A is a differential voltage (V_{ID}) between A1 and A2. For these circuits, V_{ID} is considered positive regardless of which terminal is positive with respect to the other.

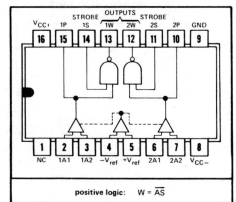

J OR N
DUAL-IN-LINE PACKAGE (TOP VIEW)

positive logic: $W = \overline{AS}$

NC—No internal connection

electrical characteristics (unless otherwise noted V_{CC+} = 5 V, V_{CC-} = –5 V, T_A = 0°C to 70°C)

PARAMETER		TEST FIGURE	TEST CONDITIONS		MIN	TYP‡	MAX	UNIT
V_T	Differential-input threshold voltage (see Note 3)	28	V_{ref} = 15 mV	SN75238	11	15	19	mV
				SN75239	8	15	22	
			V_{ref} = 40 mV	SN75238	36	40	44	
				SN75239	33	40	47	
V_{ICF}	Common-mode input firing voltage (see Note 4)	none	V_{ref} = 40 mV, $V_{I(S)} = V_{IH}$ *Common-Mode Input Pulse:* $t_r \leqslant$ 15 ns, $t_f \leqslant$ 15 ns, t_w = 50 ns			±2.5		V
I_{IB}	Differential-input bias current	2	V_{CC+} = 5.25 V, V_{CC-} = –5.25 V, V_{ID} = 0				30	µA
I_{IO}	Differential-input offset current	2	V_{CC+} = 5.25 V, V_{CC-} = –5.25 V, V_{ID} = 0				0.5	µA
V_{IH}	High-level input voltage (strobe inputs)	29			2			V
V_{IL}	Low-level input voltage (strobe inputs)	29					0.8	V
V_{OH}	High-level output voltage	29	V_{CC+} = 4.75 V, V_{CC-} = –4.75 V, I_{OH} = –400 µA		2.4	4		V
V_{OL}	Low-level output voltage	29	V_{CC+} = 4.75 V, V_{CC-} = –4.75 V, I_{OL} = 16 mA			0.25	0.4	V
I_{IH}	High-level input current (strobe inputs)	30	V_{CC+} = 5.25 V, V_{CC-} = –5.25 V, V_{IH} = 2.4 V				40	µA
			V_{CC+} = 5.25 V, V_{CC-} = –5.25 V, V_{IH} = 5.25 V				1	mA
I_{IL}	Low-level input current (strobe inputs)	30	V_{CC+} = 5.25 V, V_{CC-} = –5.25 V, V_{IL} = 0.4 V			–1	–1.6	mA
I_{OS}	Short-circuit output current	31	V_{CC+} = 5.25 V, V_{CC-} = –5.25 V		–2.1		–3.5	mA
I_{CC+}	Supply current from V_{CC+}	6	V_{CC+} = 5.25 V, V_{CC-} = –5.25 V, T_A = 25°C			25	40	mA
I_{CC-}	Supply current from V_{CC-}	6	V_{CC+} = 5.25 V, V_{CC-} = –5.25 V, T_A = 25°C			–15	–20	mA

‡All typical values are at V_{CC+} = 5 V, V_{CC-} = –5 V, T_A = 25°C.

NOTES: 3. The differential-input threshold voltage (V_T) is defined as the d-c differential-input voltage (V_{ID}) required to force the output of the sense amplifier to the logic gate threshold voltage level.
4. Common-mode input firing voltage is the minimum common-mode voltage that will exceed the dynamic range of the input at the specified conditions and cause the logic output to switch. The specified common-mode input signal is applied with a strobe-enable pulse present.

1

873

TEXAS INSTRUMENTS
INCORPORATED
POST OFFICE BOX 5012 • DALLAS, TEXAS 75222

switching characteristics, V_{CC+} = 5 V, V_{CC-} = −5 V, T_A = 25°C

PROPAGATION DELAY TIMES			TEST FIGURE	TEST CONDITIONS		MIN	TYP	MAX	UNIT
SYMBOL	FROM INPUT	TO OUTPUT							
$t_{PLH(D)}$	A1−A2	W	41	C_L = 15 pF,	R_L = 288 Ω		25		ns
$t_{PHL(D)}$							25	40	ns
$t_{PLH(S)}$	STROBE	W	41	C_L = 15 pF,	R_L = 288 Ω		25		ns
$t_{PHL(S)}$							15	30	ns

typical recovery and cycle times, V_{CC+} = 5 V, V_{CC-} = −5 V, T_A = 25°C

PARAMETER		TEST CONDITIONS		MIN	TYP	MAX	UNIT
t_{orD}	Differential-input overload recovery time (see Note 5)	*Differential Input Pulse:* V_{ID} = 2 V, t_f = 20 ns			20		ns
t_{orC}	Common-mode-input overload recovery time (see Note 6)	*Common-Mode Input Pulse:* V_{IC} = ±2 V, t_r = t_f = 20 ns			20		ns
$t_{cyc(min)}$	Minimum cycle time				200		ns

NOTES: 5. Differential-input overload recovery time is the time necessary for the device to recover from the specified differential-input overload signal prior to the strobe-enable signal.

6. Common-mode-input overload recovery time is the time necessary for the device to recover from the specified common-mode-input overload signal prior to the strobe-enable signal.

schematic

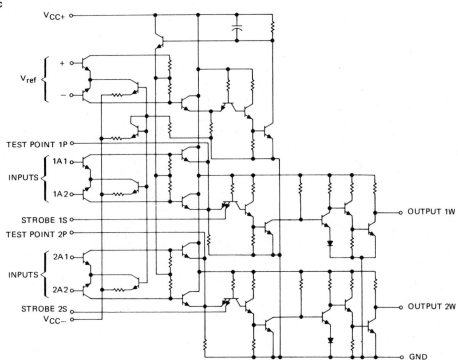

TEXAS INSTRUMENTS
INCORPORATED
POST OFFICE BOX 5012 • DALLAS, TEXAS 75222

PARAMETER MEASUREMENT INFORMATION

d-c test circuits†

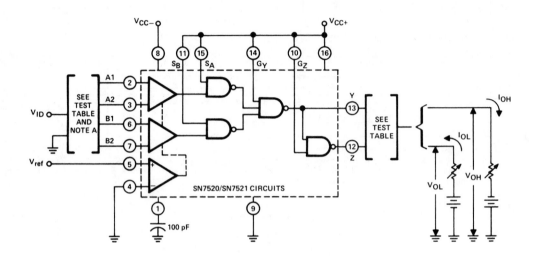

TEST TABLE

CIRCUIT TYPE	INPUTS	V_{ref}	V_{ID}	OUTPUT Y			OUTPUT Z		
				V_O	I_{OH}	I_{OL}	V_O	I_{OH}	I_{OL}
SN7520	A1-A2 or B1-B2	15 mV	≤11 mV	≤0.4 V		16 mA	≥2.4 V	−400 µA	
	A1-A2 or B1-B2	15 mV	≥19 mV	≥2.4 V	−400 µA		≤0.4 V		16 mA
	A1-A2 or B1-B2	40 mV	≤36 mV	≤0.4 V		16 mA	≥2.4 V	−400 µA	
	A1-A2 or B1-B2	40 mV	≥44 mV	≥2.4 V	−400 µA		≤0.4 V		16 mA
SN7521	A1-A2 or B1-B2	15 mV	≤ 8 mV	≤0.4 V		16 mA	≥2.4 V	−400 µA	
	A1-A2 or B1-B2	15 mV	≥22 mV	≥2.4 V	−400 µA		≤0.4 V		16 mA
	A1-A2 or B1-B2	40 mV	≤33 mV	≤0.4 V		16 mA	≥2.4 V	−400 µA	
	A1-A2 or B1-B2	40 mV	≥47 mV	≥2.4 V	−400 µA		≤0.4 V		16 mA

NOTE A: Each pair of differential inputs is tested separately with the other pair grounded.

FIGURE 1—V_T

†Arrows indicate actual direction of current flow. Current into a terminal is a positive value.

TEXAS INSTRUMENTS
INCORPORATED
POST OFFICE BOX 5012 • DALLAS, TEXAS 75222

PARAMETER MEASUREMENT INFORMATION

d-c test circuits[†] (continued)

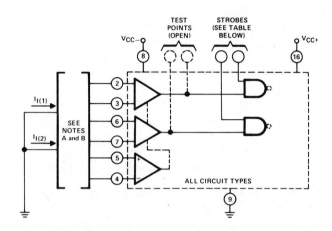

NOTES: A. Each preamplifier is tested separately. Inputs not under test are grounded.
  B. $I_{IB} = I_{I(1)}$ or $I_{I(2)}$ (limit applies to each); $I_{IO} = I_{I(1)} - I_{I(2)}$; $I_{I(1)}$ and $I_{I(2)}$ are the currents into the two inputs of the pair under test.

PIN CONNECTIONS (OTHER THAN THOSE SHOWN ABOVE)

CIRCUIT TYPES	100 pF to GND	APPLY V_CC+	APPLY GND	LEAVE OPEN	OTHER
SN7520, SN7521	C_ext ①	G_Y, G_Z ⑭ ⑩	S_A, S_B ⑮ ⑪	Y, Z ⑬ ⑫	
SN7522, SN7523	C_ext ①	G ⑭	S_A, S_B, GND 2 ⑮ ⑪ ⑬		R_L, Y ⑩ ⑫
SN7524, SN7525	C_ext ①		1S, 2S, GND 2 ⑮ ⑪ ⑬	1W, 2W ⑭ ⑫	
SN7526, SN7527		PRESET, CLEAR ⑩ ⑭	S_A, S_B ⑮ ⑪	Q, $\bar{Q}$ ⑫ ⑬	
SN7528, SN7529	C_ext ①		1S, 2S ⑭ ⑪	1P, 2P, 1W, 2W ⑮ ⑩ ⑬ ⑫	
SN75232, SN75233, SN75234, SN75235			1S, 2S, GND 2 ⑮ ⑪ ⑬	1W, 2W ⑭ ⑫	
SN75238, SN75239			1S, 2S ⑭ ⑪	1P, 2P, 1W, 2W ⑮ ⑩ ⑬ ⑫	

FIGURE 2—I_{IB}, I_{IO}

[†] Arrows indicate actual direction of current flow. Current into a terminal is a positive value.

TEXAS INSTRUMENTS
INCORPORATED
POST OFFICE BOX 5012 • DALLAS, TEXAS 75222

SERIES 7520
SENSE AMPLIFIERS

PARAMETER MEASUREMENT INFORMATION

d-c test circuits† (continued)

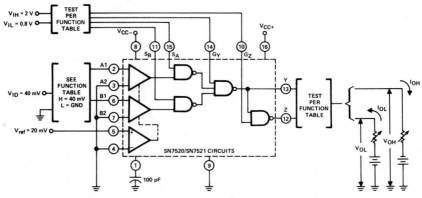

FIGURE 3—V_{IH}, V_{IL}, V_{OH}, V_{OL}

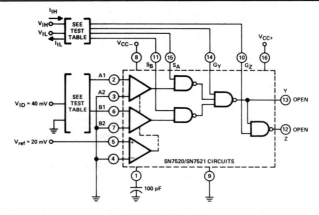

TEST TABLE

TEST	INPUT A1	INPUT B1	STROBE S_A	STROBE S_B	GATE G_Y	GATE G_Z
I_{IH} at STROBE S_A	GND	GND	V_{IH}	V_{IL}	V_{IL}	V_{IL}
I_{IH} at STROBE S_B	GND	GND	V_{IL}	V_{IH}	V_{IL}	V_{IL}
I_{IH} at GATE G_Y	V_{ID}	V_{ID}	V_{IH}	V_{IH}	V_{IH}	V_{IL}
I_{IH} at GATE G_Z	GND	GND	V_{IL}	V_{IL}	V_{IH}	V_{IH}
I_{IL} at STROBE S_A	V_{ID}	GND	V_{IL}	V_{IL}	V_{IL}	V_{IL}
I_{IL} at STROBE S_B	GND	V_{ID}	V_{IL}	V_{IL}	V_{IL}	V_{IL}
I_{IL} at GATE G_Y	GND	GND	V_{IL}	V_{IL}	V_{IL}	V_{IL}
I_{IL} at GATE G_Z	GND	GND	V_{IL}	V_{IL}	V_{IL}	V_{IL}

FIGURE 4—I_{IH}, I_{IL}

†Arrows indicate actual direction of current flow. Current into a terminal is a positive value.

11-28

TEXAS INSTRUMENTS
INCORPORATED
POST OFFICE BOX 5012 • DALLAS, TEXAS 75222

87

PARAMETER MEASUREMENT INFORMATION

d-c test circuits† (continued)

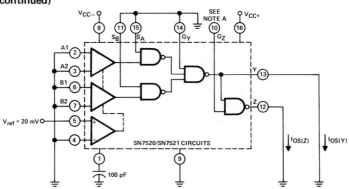

FIGURE 5—I_{OS}

NOTE A: When testing $I_{OS(Y)}$, Pin 10 is open; when testing $I_{OS(Z)}$, Pin 10 is grounded.

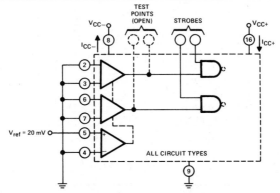

PIN CONNECTIONS (OTHER THAN THOSE SHOWN ABOVE)

CIRCUIT TYPES	100 pF to GND	APPLY GND	LEAVE OPEN
SN7520, SN7521	C_{ext} (1)	G_Y, G_Z, S_A, S_B (14)(10)(15)(11)	Y, Z (13)(12)
SN7522, SN7523	C_{ext} (1)	G, S_A, S_B, GND 2 (14)(15)(11) (13)	R_L, Y (10)(12)
SN7524, SN7525	C_{ext} (1)	1S, 2S, GND 2 (15)(11) (13)	1W, 2W (14)(12)
SN7526, SN7527		S_A, S_B (15)(11)	PRESET, CLEAR, Q, Q̄ (10) (14) (12)(13)
SN7528, SN7529	C_{ext} (1)	1S, 2S (14)(11)	1P, 2P, 1W, 2W (15)(10)(13)(12)
SN75234, SN75235		1S, 2S, GND 2 (15)(11) (13)	1W, 2W (14)(12)
SN75238, SN75239		1S, 2S (14)(11)	1P, 2P, 1W, 2W (15)(10)(13)(12)

FIGURE 6—I_{CC+}, I_{CC-}

† Arrows indicate actual direction of current flow. Current into a terminal is a positive value.

TEXAS INSTRUMENTS
INCORPORATED
POST OFFICE BOX 5012 • DALLAS, TEXAS 75222

PARAMETER MEASUREMENT INFORMATION

d-c test circuits[†] (continued)

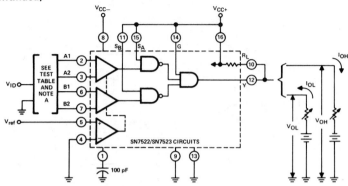

TEST TABLE

CIRCUIT TYPE	INPUTS	V_{ref}	V_{ID}	OUTPUT		
				V_O	I_{OH}	I_{OL}
SN7522	A1-A2 or B1-B2	15 mV	≤11 mV	≥2.4 V	−400 µA	
	A1-A2 or B1-B2	15 mV	≥19 mV	≤0.4 V		16 mA
	A1-A2 or B1-B2	40 mV	≤36 mV	≥2.4 V	−400 µA	
	A1-A2 or B1-B2	40 mV	≥44 mV	≤0.4 V		16 mA
SN7523	A1-A2 or B1-B2	15 mV	≤ 8 mV	≥2.4 V	−400 µA	
	A1-A2 or B1-B2	15 mV	≥22 mV	≤0.4 V		16 mA
	A1-A2 or B1-B2	40 mV	≤33 mV	≥2.4 V	−400 µA	
	A1-A2 or B1-B2	40 mV	≥47 mV	≤0.4 V		16 mA

NOTE A: Each pair of differential inputs is tested separately with the other pair grounded.

FIGURE 7—V_T

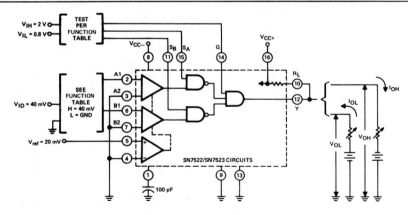

FIGURE 8—$V_{IH}, V_{IL}, V_{OH}, V_{OL}$

[†]Arrows indicate actual direction of current flow. Current into a terminal is a positive value.

TEXAS INSTRUMENTS
INCORPORATED
POST OFFICE BOX 5012 • DALLAS, TEXAS 75222

PARAMETER MEASUREMENT INFORMATION

d-c test circuits† (continued)

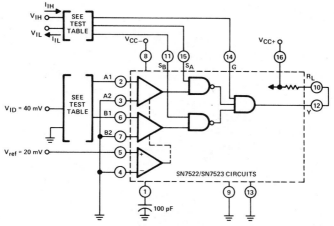

TEST TABLE

TEST	INPUT A1	INPUT B1	STROBE S_A	STROBE S_B	GATE G
I_{IH} at STROBE S_A	GND	GND	V_{IH}	V_{IL}	V_{IH}
I_{IH} at STROBE S_B	GND	GND	V_{IL}	V_{IH}	V_{IH}
I_{IH} at GATE	V_{ID}	V_{ID}	V_{IH}	V_{IH}	V_{IH}
I_{IL} at STROBE S_A	V_{ID}	GND	V_{IL}	V_{IL}	V_{IH}
I_{IL} at STROBE S_B	GND	V_{ID}	V_{IL}	V_{IL}	V_{IH}
I_{IL} at GATE	GND	GND	V_{IL}	V_{IL}	V_{IL}

FIGURE 9—I_{IH}, I_{IL}

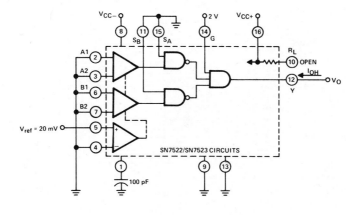

FIGURE 10—I_{OH}

†Arrows indicate actual direction of current flow. Current into a terminal is a positive value.

TEXAS INSTRUMENTS
INCORPORATED
POST OFFICE BOX 5012 • DALLAS, TEXAS 75222

PARAMETER MEASUREMENT INFORMATION

d-c test circuits[†] (continued)

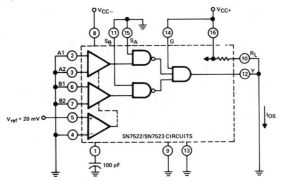

FIGURE 11—I$_{OS}$

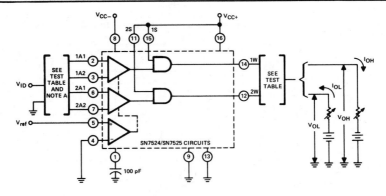

TEST TABLE

CIRCUIT TYPE	INPUTS	V$_{ref}$	V$_{ID}$	OUTPUT		
				V$_O$	I$_{OH}$	I$_{OL}$
SN7524	A1-A2	15 mV	≤11 mV	≤0.4 V		16 mA
	A1-A2	15 mV	≥19 mV	≥2.4 V	−400 µA	
	A1-A2	40 mV	≤36 mV	≤0.4 V		16 mA
	A1-A2	40 mV	≥44 mV	≥2.4 V	−400 µA	
SN7525	A1-A2	15 mV	≤ 8 mV	≤0.4 V		16 mA
	A1-A2	15 mV	≥22 mV	≥2.4 V	−400 µA	
	A1-A2	40 mV	≤33 mV	≤0.4 V		16 mA
	A1-A2	40 mV	≥47 mV	≥2.4 V	−400 µA	

NOTE A: Each pair of differential inputs is tested separately with its corresponding output.

FIGURE 12—V$_T$

[†]Arrows indicate actual direction of current flow. Current into a terminal is a positive value.

TEXAS INSTRUMENTS
INCORPORATED
POST OFFICE BOX 5012 • DALLAS, TEXAS 75222

PARAMETER MEASUREMENT INFORMATION

d-c test circuits† (continued)

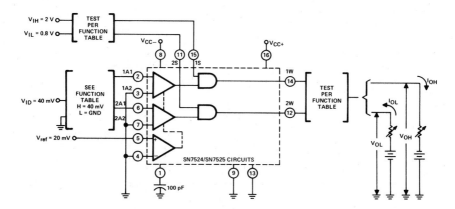

FIGURE 13—V_{IH}, V_{IL}, V_{OH}, V_{OL}

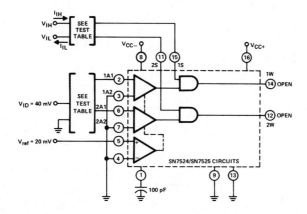

TEST TABLE

TEST	INPUT 1A1	INPUT 2A1	STROBE 1S	STROBE 2S
I_{IH} at STROBE 1S	GND	GND	V_{IH}	V_{IL}
I_{IH} at STROBE 2S	GND	GND	V_{IL}	V_{IH}
I_{IL} at STROBE 1S	V_{ID}	GND	V_{IL}	V_{IL}
I_{IL} at STROBE 2S	GND	V_{ID}	V_{IL}	V_{IL}

FIGURE 14—I_{IH}, I_{IL}

†Arrows indicate actual direction of current flow. Current into a terminal is a positive value.

TEXAS INSTRUMENTS
INCORPORATED
POST OFFICE BOX 5012 • DALLAS, TEXAS 75222

PARAMETER MEASUREMENT INFORMATION

d-c test circuits† (continued)

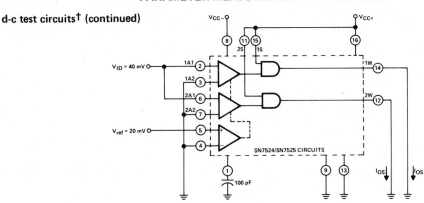

FIGURE 15—I_{OS}

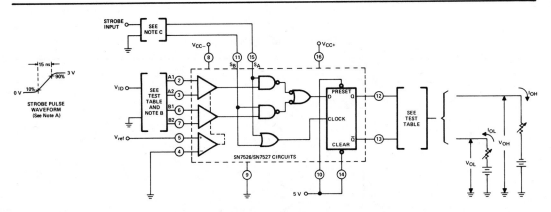

TEST TABLE

CIRCUIT TYPE	INPUTS	V_{ref}	V_{ID}	OUTPUT Q			OUTPUT $\overline{Q}$		
				V_O	I_{OH}	I_{OL}	V_O	I_{OH}	I_{OL}
SN7526	A1-A2 or B1-B2	15 mV	≤11 mV	≤0.4 V		16 mA	≥2.4 V		16 mA
	A1-A2 or B1-B2	15 mV	≥19 mV	≥2.4 V	−400 µA		≤0.4 V	−400 µA	
	A1-A2 or B1-B2	40 mV	≤36 mV	≤0.4 V		16 mA	≥2.4 V		16 mA
	A1-A2 or B1-B2	40 mV	≥44 mV	≥2.4 V	−400 µA		≤0.4 V	−400 µA	
SN7527	A1-A2 or B1-B2	15 mV	≤ 8 mV	≤0.4 V		16 mA	≥2.4 V		16 mA
	A1-A2 or B1-B2	15 mV	≥22 mV	≥2.4 V	−400 µA		≤0.4 V	−400 µA	
	A1-A2 or B1-B2	40 mV	≤33 mV	≤0.4 V		16 mA	≥2.4 V		16 mA
	A1-A2 or B1-B2	40 mV	≥47 mV	≥2.4 V	−400 µA		≤0.4 V	−400 µA	

NOTES: A. The strobe input pulse is supplied by a generator with the following characteristics: Z_O = 50 Ω, t_r = t_f = 15 ± 5 ns, t_w = 500 ns, PRR = 1 MHz.

      B. Each pair of differential inputs is tested separately with the other pair grounded.

      C. Strobe input pulse is applied to Strobe A when inputs A1-A2 are being tested and to Strobe B when inputs B1-B2 are being tested. In each case, the other strobe input is grounded.

FIGURE 16—V_T

†Arrows indicate actual direction of current flow. Current into a terminal is a positive value.

TEXAS INSTRUMENTS
INCORPORATED
POST OFFICE BOX 5012 • DALLAS, TEXAS 75222

PARAMETER MEASUREMENT INFORMATION

d-c test circuits[†] (continued)

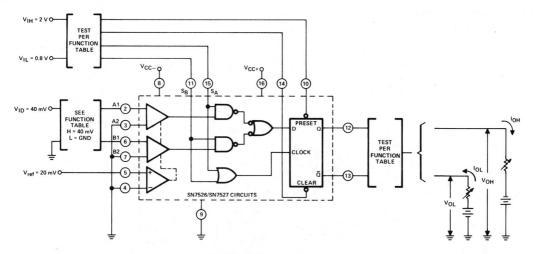

FIGURE 17—V_{IH}, V_{IL}, V_{OH}, V_{OL}

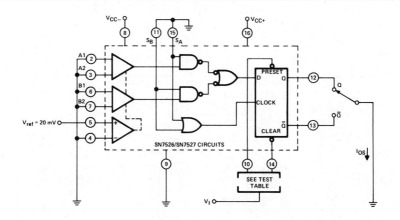

TEST TABLE

PARAMETER	PRESET	CLEAR
I_{OS} at OUTPUT Q	V_{IL}	V_{IH}
I_{OS} at OUTPUT $\bar{Q}$	V_{IH}	V_{IL}

FIGURE 18—I_{OS}

[†] Arrows indicate actual direction of current flow. Current into a terminal is a positive value.

11

TEXAS INSTRUMENTS
INCORPORATED
POST OFFICE BOX 5012 • DALLAS, TEXAS 75222

PARAMETER MEASUREMENT INFORMATION

d-c test circuits† (continued)

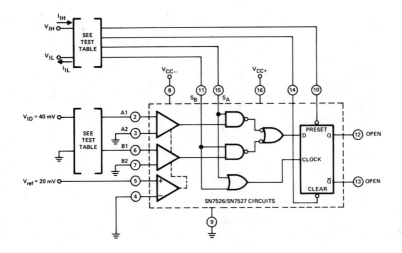

TEST TABLE

PARAMETER	INPUT A1	INPUT B1	STROBE S_A	STROBE S_B	PRESET	CLEAR
I_{IH} at STROBE S_A	GND	GND	V_{IH}	V_{IL}	OPEN	OPEN
I_{IH} at STROBE S_B	GND	GND	V_{IL}	V_{IH}	OPEN	OPEN
I_{IH} at PRESET	GND	V_{ID}	V_{IL}	NOTE B	V_{IH}	V_{IH}
I_{IH} at CLEAR	GND	GND	V_{IL}	NOTE B	V_{IH}	V_{IH}
I_{IL} at STROBE S_A	V_{ID}	GND	V_{IL}	V_{IH}	OPEN	OPEN
I_{IL} at STROBE S_B	GND	V_{ID}	V_{IH}	V_{IL}	OPEN	OPEN
I_{IL} at PRESET	GND	GND	V_{IL}	V_{IL}	V_{IL}	V_{IL}
I_{IL} at PRESET	V_{ID}	GND	V_{IH}	V_{IL}	V_{IL}	V_{IL}
I_{IL} at CLEAR	V_{ID}	GND	V_{IL}	V_{IL}	V_{IL}	V_{IL}

NOTES: A. Each input is tested separately.
B. Momentary ground, then V_{IH}.

FIGURE 19—I_{IH}, I_{IL}

†Arrows indicate actual direction of current flow. Current into a terminal is a positive value.

TEXAS INSTRUMENTS
INCORPORATED
POST OFFICE BOX 5012 • DALLAS, TEXAS 75222

PARAMETER MEASUREMENT INFORMATION

d-c test circuits† (continued)

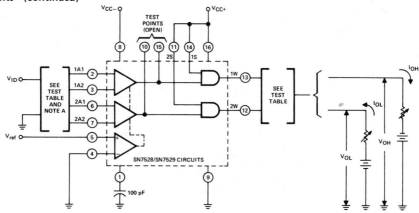

TEST TABLE

CIRCUIT TYPE	INPUTS	V_{ref}	V_{ID}	OUTPUT		
				V_O	I_{OH}	I_{OL}
SN7528	A1-A2	15 mV	≤11 mV	≤0.4 V		16 mA
	A1-A2	15 mV	≥19 mV	≥2.4 V	−400 µA	
	A1-A2	40 mV	≤36 mV	≤0.4 V		16 mA
	A1-A2	40 mV	≥44 mV	≥2.4 V	−400 µA	
SN7529	A1-A2	15 mV	≤ 8 mV	≤0.4 V		16 mA
	A1-A2	15 mV	≥22 mV	≥2.4 V	−400 µA	
	A1-A2	40 mV	≤33 mV	≤0.4 V		16 mA
	A1-A2	40 mV	≥47 mV	≥2.4 V	−400 µA	

NOTE A: Each pair of inputs is tested separately with its corresponding output.

FIGURE 20−V_T

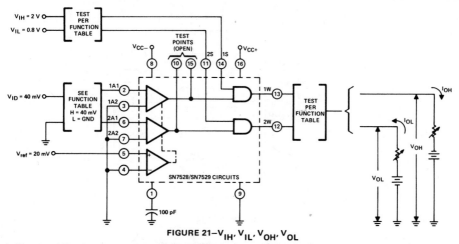

FIGURE 21−V_{IH}, V_{IL}, V_{OH}, V_{OL}

†Arrows indicate actual direction of current flow. Current into a terminal is a positive value.

11

PARAMETER MEASUREMENT INFORMATION

d-c test circuits† (continued)

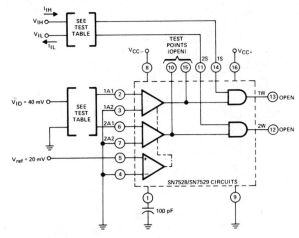

TEST TABLE

TEST	INPUT 1A1	INPUT 2A1	STROBE 1S	STROBE 2S
I_{IH} at STROBE 1S	GND	GND	V_{IH}	V_{IL}
I_{IH} at STROBE 2S	GND	GND	V_{IL}	V_{IH}
I_{IL} at STROBE 1S	V_{ID}	GND	V_{IL}	V_{IL}
I_{IL} at STROBE 2S	GND	V_{ID}	V_{IL}	V_{IL}

FIGURE 22—I_{IH}, I_{IL}

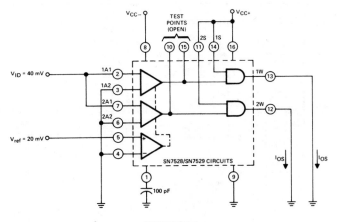

FIGURE 23—I_{OS}

†Arrows indicate actual direction of current flow. Current into a terminal is a positive value.

TEXAS INSTRUMENTS
INCORPORATED
POST OFFICE BOX 5012 • DALLAS, TEXAS 75222

PARAMETER MEASUREMENT INFORMATION

dc test circuits†

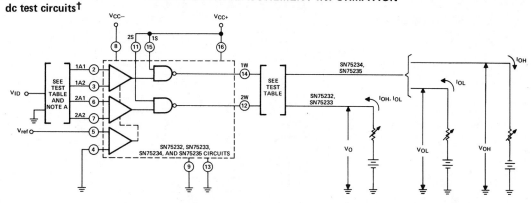

CIRCUIT TYPE	INPUTS	V_ref	V_ID	OUTPUTS					
				SN75232, SN75233			SN75234, SN75235		
				V_O	I_{OH}	I_{OL}	V_O	I_{OH}	I_{OL}
SN75232, SN75234	A1-A2	15 mV	≤11 mV	5.25 V	≤250 μA		≥2.4 V	−400 μA	
	A1-A2	15 mV	≥19 mV	≤ 0.4 V		16 mA	≤0.4 V		16 mA
	A1-A2	40 mV	≤36 mV	5.25 V	≤250 μA		≥2.4 V	−400 μA	
	A1-A2	40 mV	≥44 mV	≤ 0.4 V		16 mA	≤0.4 V		16 mA
SN75233, SN75235	A1-A2	15 mV	≤8 mV	5.25 V	≤250 μA		≥2.4 V	−400 μA	
	A1-A2	15 mV	≥22 mV	≤ 0.4 V		16 mA	≤0.4 V		16 mA
	A1-A2	40 mV	≤33 mV	5.25 V	≤250 μA		≥2.4 V	−400 μA	
	A1-A2	40 mV	≥47 mV	≤ 0.4 V		16 mA	≤0.4 V		16 mA

NOTE A: Each pair of differential inputs is tested separately with its corresponding output.

FIGURE 24—V_T

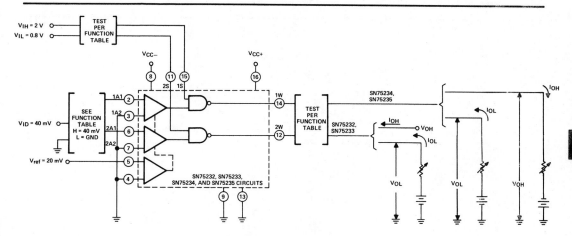

FIGURE 25—V_{IH}, V_{IL}, I_{OH}, V_{OL}

†Arrows indicate actual direction of current flow. Current into a terminal is a positive value.

PARAMETER MEASUREMENT INFORMATION

d-c test circuits† (continued)

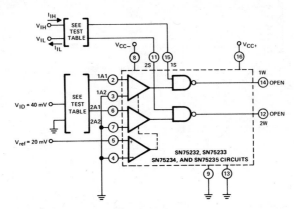

TEST TABLE

TEST	INPUT 1A1	INPUT 2A1	STROBE 1S	STROBE 2S
I_{IH} at STROBE 1S	GND	GND	V_{IH}	V_{IL}
I_{IH} at STROBE 2S	GND	GND	V_{IL}	V_{IH}
I_{IL} at STROBE 1S	V_{ID}	GND	V_{IL}	V_{IL}
I_{IL} at STROBE 2S	GND	V_{ID}	V_{IL}	V_{IL}

FIGURE 26—I_{IH}, I_{IL}

†Arrows indicate actual direction of current flow. Current into a terminal is a positive value.

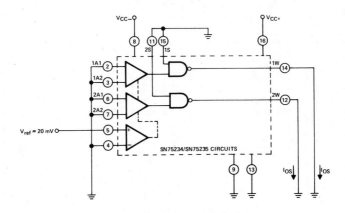

FIGURE 27—I_{OS}

TEXAS INSTRUMENTS
INCORPORATED
POST OFFICE BOX 5012 • DALLAS, TEXAS 75222

PARAMETER MEASUREMENT INFORMATION

d-c test circuits† (continued)

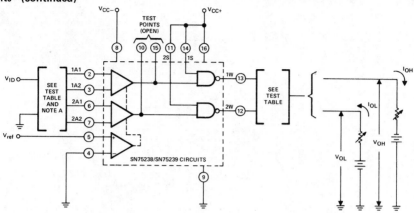

TEST TABLE

CIRCUIT TYPE	INPUTS	V_{ref}	V_{ID}	OUTPUT		
				V_O	I_{OH}	I_{OL}
SN75238	A1-A2	15 mV	≤11 mV	≥2.4 V	−400 µA	
	A1-A2	15 mV	≥19 mV	≤0.4 V		16 mA
	A1-A2	40 mV	≤36 mV	≥2.4 V	−400 µA	
	A1-A2	40 mV	≥44 mV	≤0.4 V		16 mA
SN75239	A1-A2	15 mV	≤ 8 mV	≥2.4 V	−400 µA	
	A1-A2	15 mV	≥22 mV	≤0.4 V		16 mA
	A1-A2	40 mV	≤33 mV	≥2.4 V	−400 µA	
	A1-A2	40 mV	≥47 mV	≤0.4 V		16 mA

NOTE A: Each pair of inputs is tested separately with its corresponding output.

FIGURE 28—V_T

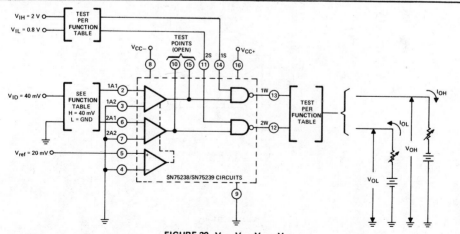

FIGURE 29—V_{IH}, V_{IL}, V_{OH}, V_{OL}

†Arrows indicate actual direction of current flow. Current into a terminal is a positive value.

TEXAS INSTRUMENTS
INCORPORATED
POST OFFICE BOX 5012 • DALLAS, TEXAS 75222

PARAMETER MEASUREMENT INFORMATION

d-c test circuits† (continued)

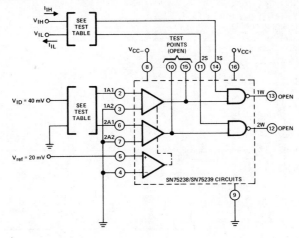

TEST TABLE

TEST	INPUT 1A1	INPUT 2A1	STROBE 1S	STROBE 2S
I_{IH} at STROBE 1S	GND	GND	V_{IH}	V_{IL}
I_{IH} at STROBE 2S	GND	GND	V_{IL}	V_{IH}
I_{IL} at STROBE 1S	V_{ID}	GND	V_{IL}	V_{IL}
I_{IL} at STROBE 2S	GND	V_{ID}	V_{IL}	V_{IL}

FIGURE 30—I_{IH}, I_{IL}

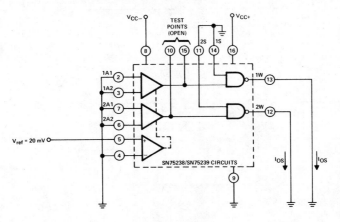

FIGURE 31—I_{OS}

†Arrows indicate actual direction of current flow. Current into a terminal is a positive value.

TEXAS INSTRUMENTS
INCORPORATED
POST OFFICE BOX 5012 • DALLAS, TEXAS 75222

PARAMETER MEASUREMENT INFORMATION

switching characteristics

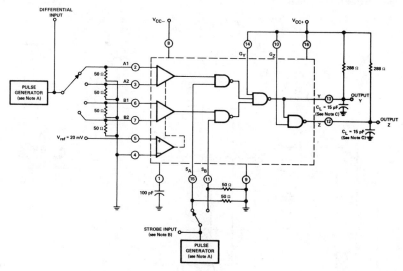

TEST CIRCUIT

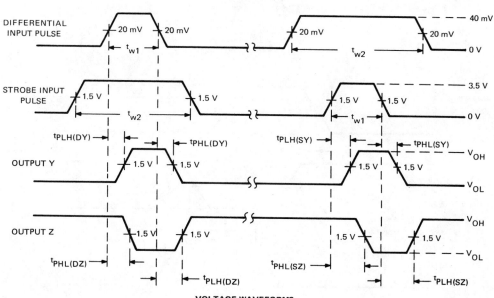

VOLTAGE WAVEFORMS

NOTES: A. The pulse generators have the following characteristics: $Z_O = 50 \, \Omega$, $t_r = 15 \pm 5$ ns, $t_f = 15 \pm 5$ ns, $t_{w1} = 100$ ns, $t_{w2} = 300$ ns, and PRR = 1 MHz.

B. The strobe input pulse is applied to Strobe S_A when inputs A1-A2 are being tested and to Strobe S_B when inputs B1-B2 are being tested.

C. C_L includes probe and jig capacitance.

FIGURE 32—SN7520/SN7521 PROPAGATION DELAY TIMES FROM DIFFERENTIAL AND STROBE INPUTS

PARAMETER MEASUREMENT INFORMATION

switching characteristics (continued)

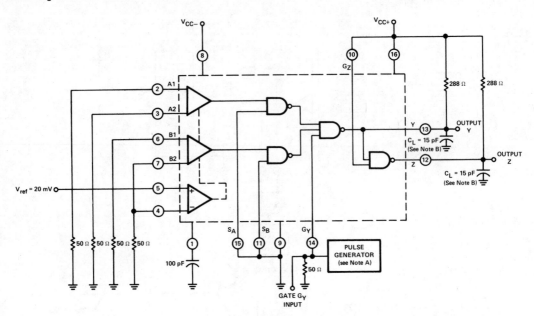

TEST CIRCUIT

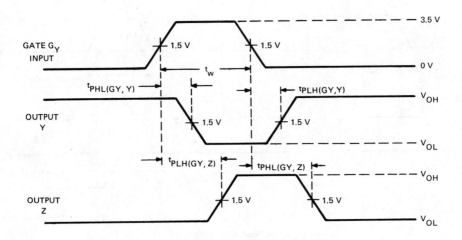

VOLTAGE WAVEFORMS

NOTES: A. The pulse generator has the following characteristics: $Z_O = 50 \ \Omega$, $t_r = 15 \pm 5$ ns, $t_f = 15 \pm 5$ ns, $t_w = 100$ ns, and PRR = 1 MHz.
        B. C_L includes probe and jig capacitance.

FIGURE 33—SN7520/SN7521 PROPAGATION DELAY TIMES FROM GATE G_Y

TEXAS INSTRUMENTS
INCORPORATED
POST OFFICE BOX 5012 • DALLAS, TEXAS 75222

PARAMETER MEASUREMENT INFORMATION

switching characteristics (continued)

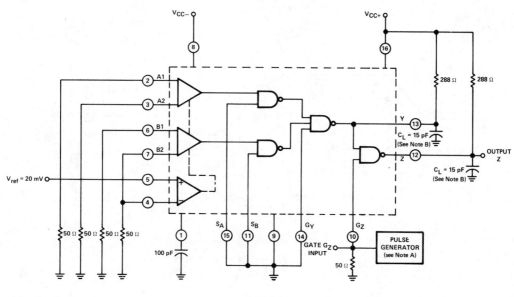

TEST CIRCUIT

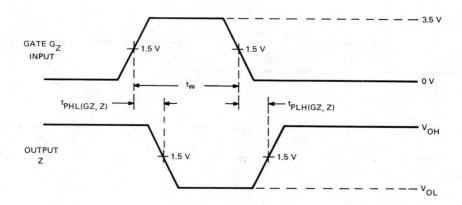

VOLTAGE WAVEFORMS

NOTES: A. The pulse generator has the following characteristics: $Z_O = 50\ \Omega$, $t_r = 15 \pm 5$ ns, $t_f = 15 \pm 5$ ns, $t_w = 100$ ns, and PRR = 1 MHz.
B. C_L includes probe and jig capacitance.

FIGURE 34—SN7520/SN7521 PROPAGATION DELAY TIMES FROM GATE G_Z

TEXAS INSTRUMENTS
INCORPORATED
POST OFFICE BOX 5012 • DALLAS, TEXAS 75222

PARAMETER MEASUREMENT INFORMATION

switching characteristics (continued)

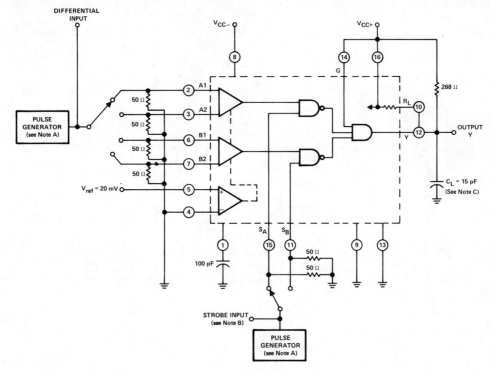

TEST CIRCUIT

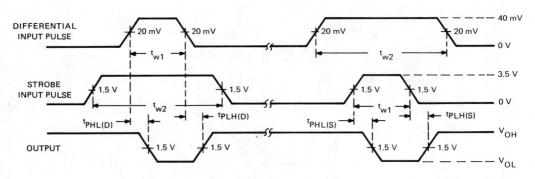

VOLTAGE WAVEFORMS

NOTES: A. The pulse generators have the following characteristics: $Z_{out} \approx 50 \, \Omega$, $t_r = t_f = 15 \pm 5$ ns, $t_{w1} = 100$ ns, $t_{w2} = 300$ ns, PRR = 1 MHz.
B. The strobe input pulse is applied to Strobe S_A when testing inputs A1-A2 and to Strobe S_B when testing inputs B1-B2.
C. C_L includes probe and jig capacitance.

FIGURE 35—SN7522/SN7523 PROPAGATION DELAY TIMES FROM DIFFERENTIAL AND STROBE INPUTS

TEXAS INSTRUMENTS
INCORPORATED
POST OFFICE BOX 5012 • DALLAS, TEXAS 75222

PARAMETER MEASUREMENT INFORMATION

switching characteristics (continued)

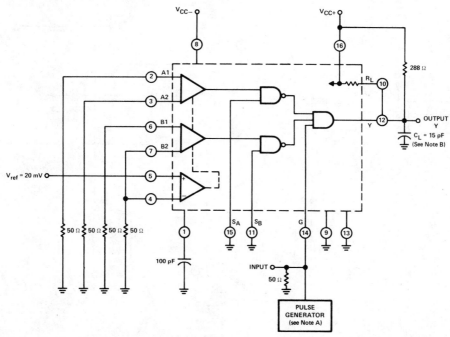

TEST CIRCUIT

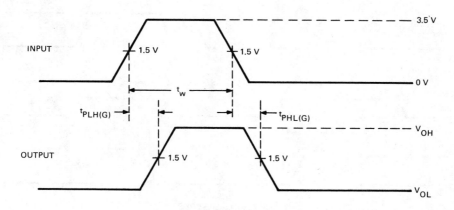

VOLTAGE WAVEFORMS

NOTES: A. The pulse generator has the following characteristics: $Z_O = 50\ \Omega$, $t_r = 15 \pm 5$ ns, $t_f = 15 \pm 5$ ns, $t_w = 100$ ns, and PRR = 1 MHz.
B. C_L includes probe and jig capacitance.

FIGURE 36—SN7522/SN7523 PROPAGATION DELAY TIMES FROM GATE INPUT

TEXAS INSTRUMENTS
INCORPORATED
POST OFFICE BOX 5012 • DALLAS, TEXAS 75222

PARAMETER MEASUREMENT INFORMATION

switching characteristics (continued)

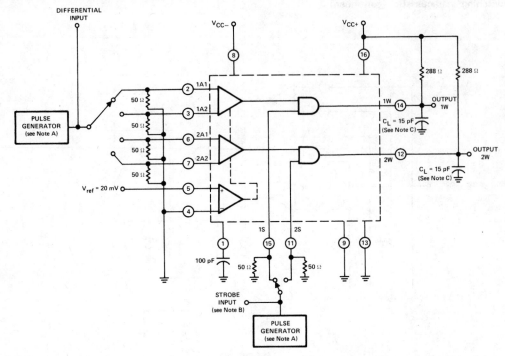

TEST CIRCUIT

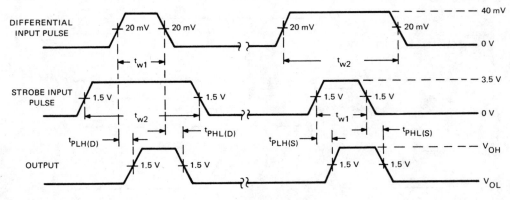

VOLTAGE WAVEFORMS

NOTES: A. The pulse generators have the following characteristics: $Z_O = 50\ \Omega$, $t_r = 15 \pm 5$ ns, $t_f = 15 \pm 5$ ns, $t_{w1} = 100$ ns, $t_{w2} = 300$ ns, and PRR = 1 MHz.
 B. The strobe input pulse is applied to Strobe 1S when inputs 1A1-1A2 are being tested and to Strobe 2S when inputs 2A1-2A2 are being tested.
 C. C_L includes probe and jig capacitance.

FIGURE 37—SN7524/SN7525 PROPAGATION DELAY TIMES

TEXAS INSTRUMENTS
INCORPORATED
POST OFFICE BOX 5012 • DALLAS, TEXAS 75222

PARAMETER MEASUREMENT INFORMATION

switching characteristics (continued)

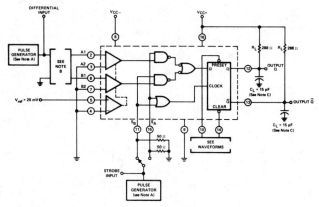

TEST CIRCUIT

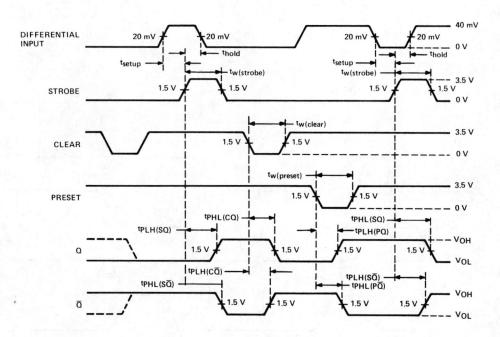

VOLTAGE WAVEFORMS

NOTES: A. The pulse generators have the following characteristics: $Z_O = 50 \ \Omega$, $t_r = 15 \pm 5$ ns, $t_f = 15 \pm 5$ ns, $t_w = 50$ ns, and PRR = 1 MHz.
B. Each preamplifier is tested separately. Apply 40-mV pulse to input A1 when testing Strobe S_A and to B1 when testing Strobe S_B.
C. C_L includes probe and jig capacitance.

FIGURE 38—SN7526/SN7527 PROPAGATION DELAY TIMES

TEXAS INSTRUMENTS
INCORPORATED
POST OFFICE BOX 5012 • DALLAS, TEXAS 75222

PARAMETER MEASUREMENT INFORMATION

switching characteristics (continued)

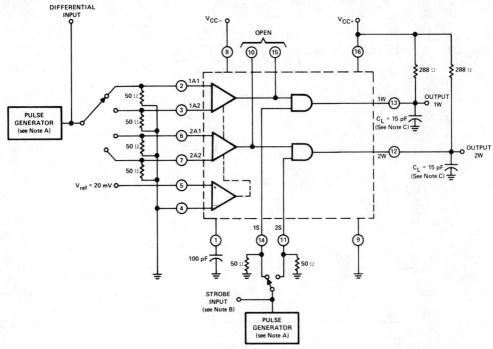

TEST CIRCUIT

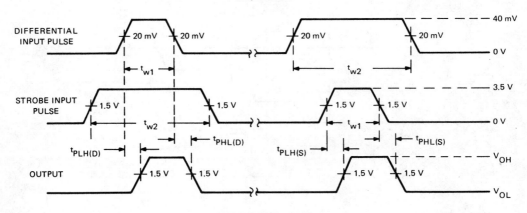

VOLTAGE WAVEFORMS

NOTES: A. The pulse generators have the following characteristics: $Z_O = 50\ \Omega$, $t_r = 15 \pm 5$ ns, $t_f = 15 \pm 5$ ns, $t_{w1} = 100$ ns, $t_{w2} = 300$ ns, and PRR = 1 MHz.
      B. The strobe input pulse is applied to Strobe 1S when inputs 1A1-1A2 are being tested and to Strobe 2S when inputs 2A1-2S2 are being tested.
      C. C_L includes probe and jig capacitance.

FIGURE 39–SN7528/SN7529 PROPAGATION DELAY TIMES

TEXAS INSTRUMENTS
INCORPORATED
POST OFFICE BOX 5012 • DALLAS, TEXAS 75222

PARAMETER MEASUREMENT INFORMATION

switching characteristics (continued)

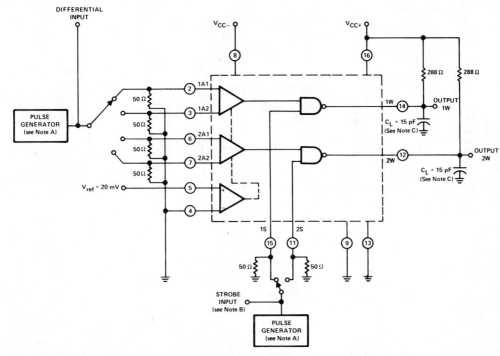

TEST CIRCUIT

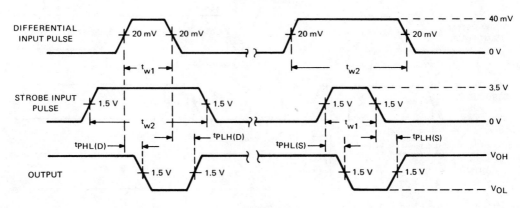

VOLTAGE WAVEFORMS

NOTES: A. The pulse generators have the following characteristics: $Z_{out} = 50\ \Omega$, $t_r = 15 \pm 5$ ns, $t_f = 15 \pm 5$ ns, $t_{w1} = 100$ ns, $t_{w2} = 300$ ns, and PRR = 1 MHz.
B. The strobe input pulse is applied to Strobe 1S when inputs 1A1-1A2 are being tested and to Strobe 2S when inputs 2A1-2A2 are being tested.
C. C_L includes probe and jig capacitance.

FIGURE 40—SN75232, SN75233, SN75234, and SN75235 PROPAGATION DELAY TIMES

TEXAS INSTRUMENTS
INCORPORATED
POST OFFICE BOX 5012 • DALLAS, TEXAS 75222

SERIES 7520
SENSE AMPLIFIERS

PARAMETER MEASUREMENT INFORMATION

switching characteristics (continued)

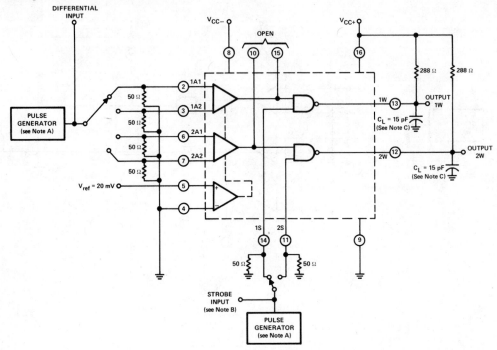

TEST CIRCUIT

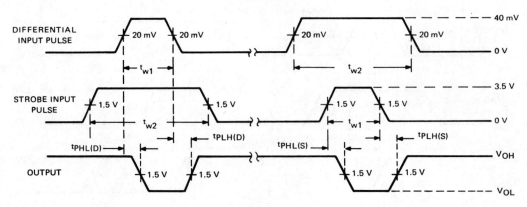

VOLTAGE WAVEFORMS

NOTES: A. The pulse generators have the following characteristics: $Z_O = 50\ \Omega$, $t_r = 15 \pm 5$ ns, $t_f = 15 \pm 5$ ns, $t_{w1} = 100$ ns, $t_{w2} = 300$ ns, and PRR = 1 MHz.

B. The strobe input pulse is applied to Strobe 1S when inputs 1A1-1A2 are being tested and to Strobe 2S when inputs 2A1-2S2 are being tested.

C. C_L includes probe and jig capacitance.

FIGURE 41—SN75238/SN75239 PROPAGATION DELAY TIMES

873

TEXAS INSTRUMENTS
INCORPORATED
POST OFFICE BOX 5012 • DALLAS, TEXAS 75222

TYPICAL CHARACTERISTICS

THRESHOLD VOLTAGE
vs
REFERENCE VOLTAGE

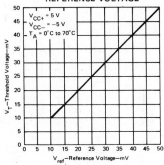

FIGURE 42

THRESHOLD VOLTAGE
vs
SUPPLY VOLTAGE

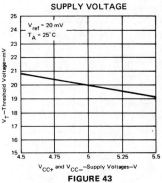

FIGURE 43

NORMALIZED THRESHOLD VOLTAGE
vs
PULSE REPETITION RATE

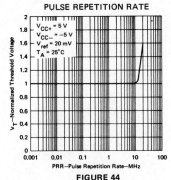

FIGURE 44

COMMON-MODE FIRING VOLTAGE
vs
FREE-AIR TEMPERATURE

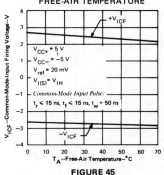

FIGURE 45

DIFFERENTIAL-INPUT BIAS CURRENT
vs
FREE-AIR TEMPERATURE

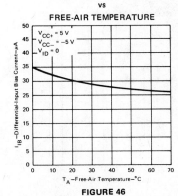

FIGURE 46

DIFFERENTIAL-INPUT OFFSET CURRENT
vs
FREE-AIR TEMPERATURE

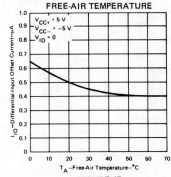

FIGURE 47

TEXAS INSTRUMENTS
INCORPORATED
POST OFFICE BOX 5012 • DALLAS, TEXAS 75222

SERIES 7520
SENSE AMPLIFIERS

TYPICAL CHARACTERISTICS

HIGH-LEVEL INPUT CURRENT
vs
INPUT VOLTAGE

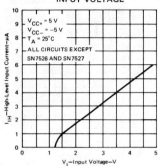

FIGURE 48

LOW-LEVEL INPUT CURRENT
vs
INPUT VOLTAGE

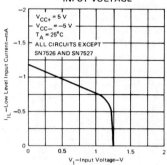

FIGURE 49

OUTPUT VOLTAGE
vs
DIFFERENTIAL-INPUT VOLTAGE

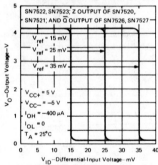

FIGURE 50

OUTPUT VOLTAGE
vs
DIFFERENTIAL-INPUT VOLTAGE

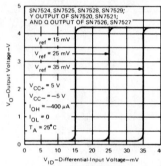

FIGURE 51

HIGH-LEVEL OUTPUT VOLTAGE
vs
HIGH-LEVEL OUTPUT CURRENT

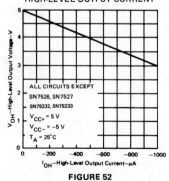

FIGURE 52

LOW-LEVEL OUTPUT VOLTAGE
vs
LOW-LEVEL OUTPUT CURRENT

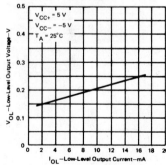

FIGURE 53

TEXAS INSTRUMENTS
INCORPORATED
POST OFFICE BOX 5012 • DALLAS, TEXAS 75222

APPLICATION DATA

combined fan-out and wire-AND capabilities

The open-collector TTL gate, when supplied with a proper load resistor (R_L), may be paralleled with other similar TTL gates to perform the wire-AND function, and simultaneously, will drive from one to nine Series 54/74 loads. When no other open-collector gates are paralleled, this gate may be used to drive ten Series 54/74 loads. For any of these conditions an appropriate load resistor value must be determined for the desired circuit configuration. A maximum resistor value must be determined which will ensure that sufficient load current (to TTL loads) and off current (through paralleled outputs) will be available while the output is high. A minimum resistor value must be determined which will ensure that current through this resistor and sink current from the TTL loads will not cause the output voltage to rise above the low level even if one of the paralleled outputs is sinking all the current.

In both conditions (low and high level) the value of R_L is determined by:

$$R_L = \frac{V_{RL}}{I_{RL}}$$

where V_{RL} is the voltage drop in volts, and I_{RL} is the current in amperes.

high-level (off-state) circuit calculations (see figure I)

The allowable voltage drop across the load resistor (V_{RL}) is the difference between V_{CC} applied and the V_{OH} level required at the load:

$$V_{RL} = V_{CC} - V_{OH\,min}$$

The total current through the load resistor (I_{RL}) is the sum of the load currents (I_{IH}) and off-state reverse currents (I_{OH}) through each of the wire-AND-connected outputs:

$$I_{RL} = \eta \cdot I_{OH} + N \cdot I_{IH} \text{ to TTL loads}$$

Therefore, calculations for the maximum value of R_L would be:

$$R_{L(max)} = \frac{V_{CC} - V_{OH\,min}}{\eta \cdot I_{OH} + N \cdot I_{IH}}$$

where η = number of gates wire-AND-connected, and N = number of TTL loads.

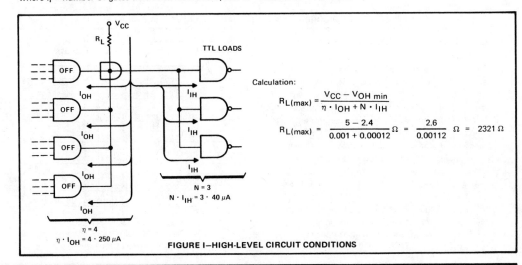

Calculation:

$$R_{L(max)} = \frac{V_{CC} - V_{OH\,min}}{\eta \cdot I_{OH} + N \cdot I_{IH}}$$

$$R_{L(max)} = \frac{5 - 2.4}{0.001 + 0.00012}\,\Omega = \frac{2.6}{0.00112}\,\Omega = 2321\,\Omega$$

N = 3

$N \cdot I_{IH} = 3 \cdot 40\,\mu A$

$\eta = 4$

$\eta \cdot I_{OH} = 4 \cdot 250\,\mu A$

FIGURE I—HIGH-LEVEL CIRCUIT CONDITIONS

TEXAS INSTRUMENTS
INCORPORATED
POST OFFICE BOX 5012 • DALLAS, TEXAS 75222

APPLICATION DATA

low-level (on-state) circuit calculations (see figure J)

The current through the resistor must be limited to the maximum sink-current of one output transistor. Note that if several output transistors are wire-AND connected, the current through R_L may be shared by those paralleled transistors. However, unless it can be absolutely guaranteed that more than one transistor will be on during low-level periods, the current must be limited to 16 mA, the maximum current which will ensure a low-level maximum of 0.4 volt.

Also, fan-out must be considered. Part of the 16 mA will be supplied from the inputs which are being driven. This reduces the amount of current which can be allowed through R_L.

Therefore, the equation used to determine the minimum value of R_L would be:

$$R_{L(min)} = \frac{V_{CC} - V_{OL}\,max}{I_{OL}\,capability - N \cdot I_{IL}}$$

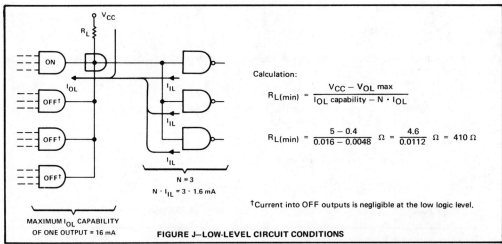

Calculation:

$$R_{L(min)} = \frac{V_{CC} - V_{OL}\,max}{I_{OL}\,capability - N \cdot I_{OL}}$$

$$R_{L(min)} = \frac{5 - 0.4}{0.016 - 0.0048}\ \Omega = \frac{4.6}{0.0112}\ \Omega = 410\ \Omega$$

†Current into OFF outputs is negligible at the low logic level.

FIGURE J—LOW-LEVEL CIRCUIT CONDITIONS

driving series 54/74 loads and combining outputs

Table 1 provides minimum and maximum resistor values, calculated from equations shown above, for driving one to ten Series 54/74 loads and wire-AND connecting two to seven parallel outputs. Each value shown for one wire-AND output is determined by the fan-out plus the cutoff current of a single output transistor. Extension beyond seven wire-AND connections is permitted with fan-outs of seven or less if a valid minimum and maximum R_L is possible. When fanning-out to ten Series 54/74 loads, the calculation for the minimum value of R_L indicates that an infinite resistance should be used ($V_{RL} \div 0 = \infty$); however, the use of a 4-kΩ resistor in this case will satisfy the high-level condition and limit the low level to less than 0.43 volt.

TABLE 1

FAN-OUT TO TTL LOADS	WIRE-AND OUTPUTS							
	1	2	3	4	5	6	7	1 to 7
1	8965	4814	3291	2500	2015	1688	1452	319
2	7878	4482	3132	2407	1954	1645	1420	359
3	7027	4193	2988	2321	1897	1604	1390	410
4	6341	3939	2857	2241	1843	1566	1361	479
5	5777	3714	2736	2166	1793	1529	1333	575
6	5306	3513	2626	2096	1744	1494	1306	718
7	4905	3333	2524	2031	1699	1460	1280	958
8	4561	3170	2429	1969	1656	X	X	1437
9	4262	3023	X	X	X	X	X	2875
10	4000	X	X	X	X	X	X	4000§
	MAXIMUM							**MIN**
	LOAD RESISTOR VALUE IN OHMS							

‡—All values shown in the table are based on:
   High-level conditions: V_{CC} = 5 V, $V_{OH\,min}$ = 2.4 V
   Low-level conditions: V_{CC} = 5 V, $V_{OL\,max}$ = 0.4 V
X—Not recommended or not possible.
§—The theoretical value is ∞. See explanation in text.

TEXAS INSTRUMENTS
INCORPORATED
POST OFFICE BOX 5012 • DALLAS, TEXAS 75222

1

TYPICAL APPLICATIONS

small memory systems

This application demonstrates an improved method of sensing data from relatively small memory systems. Two individual core planes, usually consisting of 4096 cores each, can be interfaced by each of the dual-channel SN7524 or SN7525 sense amplifiers, see Figure K. Standard TTL or DTL integrated circuits, driven directly from the compatible sense-amplifier outputs, may be selected to serve as the memory data register (MDR).

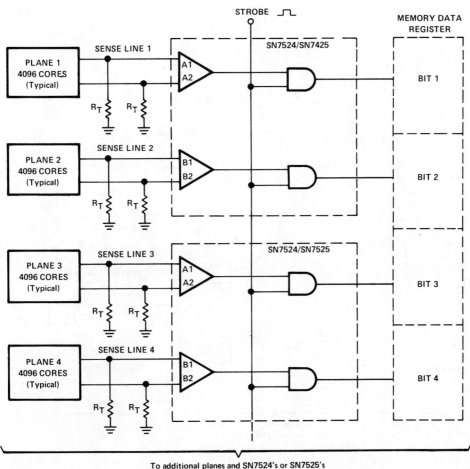

To additional planes and SN7524's or SN7525's
as necessary for complete memory word

FIGURE K—SENSING SMALL MEMORY SYSTEMS

SERIES 7520
SENSE AMPLIFIERS

TYPICAL APPLICATIONS (continued)

large memory systems

This application demonstrates an improved method of sensing data from large memory systems. The signal-to-noise ratio can be increased by sectioning the large core planes as illustrated in Figure L. Two segments, usually consisting of 4096 cores each, can be interfaced by each of the dual-input channels of the SN7420/SN7421 or SN7422/SN7423 sense amplifiers. The cascaded output gates of the SN7520/SN7521 circuits may be connected to serve as the memory data register (MDR). A number of SN7522/SN7523 sense amplifiers may be wire-AND connected to expand the input function of the MDR to interface all the segments of the plane. Complementary outputs, clear, and preset functions are provided for the MDR. Rules for combined fan-out and wire-AND capabilities must be observed.

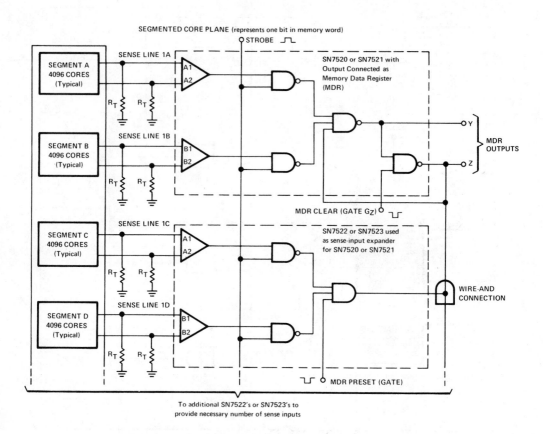

FIGURE L—SENSING LARGE MEMORY SYSTEMS

TEXAS INSTRUMENTS
INCORPORATED
POST OFFICE BOX 5012 • DALLAS, TEXAS 75222

HIGH-SPEED SENSE AMPLIFIERS WITH BUILT-IN DATA REGISTER AND BUFFER FOR APPLICATION IN COINCIDENT-CURRENT CORE MEMORIES

- ± 2-mV Threshold Sensitivity with Threshold Voltage Independent of Temperature and Supply-Voltage Variations

- Adjustable Differential-Input Threshold Voltage

- Reference Amplifier Inherently Stable with No External Frequency Compensation Required

- Built-In Data Register with Provisions for External Data Inputs

- Built-In Data Buffer Drives 450-pF Load in 15 ns

- Low Power Consumption

- Internal Reference Voltage Attenuator Makes Reference Amplifier Less Sensitive to Noise

- Two Independent Channels with TTL Compatible Logic Inputs and Outputs

SB FLAT PACKAGE (TOP VIEW)

PIN 5 IS IN ELECTRICAL CONTACT WITH METAL BASE

NC—No internal connection

description

The SN55236 and SN75236 are dual devices with each sense-amplifier channel having a data register and an output buffer. These circuits are designed for use in high-speed core-memory systems. They detect bipolar differential-input signals from the memory and provide complete interface between the memory and logic section. These sense amplifiers are completely coupled, and utilize a "matched amplifier" technique similar to Series 7520. Unlike the Series 7520, however, the reference amplifier circuit is inherently stable and requires no external or internal frequency compensation.

To enable sensing, the channel-select, strobe, and reset inputs should be high and the data-load input should be low. With sensing enabled, the detector output will be low only while a differential-input pulse is above the threshold level. Taking channel-select low will disable the sensing inputs of the respective channel; taking the strobe low disables both differential input channels. When the sense inputs are disabled, the respective detector output terminal is high.

The detector outputs are intended to drive the internal data registers. For normal operation, the output of detector channel 2 (pin 14) is connected to the input of register 2 (pin 9). For dual-channel operation, pin 14 is connected to the input of register 1 (pin 17); this ANDs the two sense channels and provides an extra data register for other system applications.

When the register input is at its normally high level, the data input can be used to load the register by taking the data-load terminal high. In this case, the register output will be complementary to the data input and the reset terminal will have no effect. With the register input high but with the data-load terminal low, taking the reset input low will cause the register output to go or remain low. Subsequent changes of the reset input will have no further effect. When the buffer input is high, the buffer output is the complement of the register output. When the buffer input is low, the buffer output is disabled high.

The differential-input threshold voltage of both channels is determined by applying an external voltage to the V_{ref} terminal. The ratio of the external reference voltage to the internal threshold reference voltage

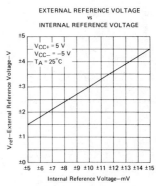

EXTERNAL REFERENCE VOLTAGE
vs
INTERNAL REFERENCE VOLTAGE

$V_{CC+} = 5$ V
$V_{CC-} = -5$ V
$T_A = 25°C$

V_{ref}—External Reference Voltage—V

Internal Reference Voltage—mV

FIGURE A

description (continued)

(which is approximately equal to the differential-input threshold voltage) is nominally 300 to 1. An internal reference of 7 mV may be established by applying ±2.1 V to the V_{ref} terminal. Thus, by adjusting the external reference voltage, the differential-input threshold voltage may be varied in accordance with the needs of the particular application as shown in Figure A on the previous page.

Logic-input current requirements are specified at worst-case power-supply conditions over the operating free-air temperature ranges. These requirements are identical to and compatible with Series 54/74 TTL digital integrated circuits.

The data-register outputs feature the ability to sink or supply load current and are rated for 10 Series 74 loads. The open-collector outputs of the buffer may be connected to similar outputs to perform the wire-AND function. These outputs are specially designed to drive high-capacitance loads.

FUNCTION TABLE

INPUTS								OUTPUTS	
A	C	S	W/RI†	L	D	R	G	Y	Z
H	H	H	L	X	X	X	H	H	L
H	H	H	L	X	X	X	L	H	H
↓	H	H	↑	L	X	H	H	H	L
↓	H	H	↑	L	X	H	L	H	H
H	↓	H	↑	L	X	H	H	H	L
H	↓	H	↑	L	X	H	L	H	H
H	H	↓	↑	L	X	H	H	H	L
H	H	↓	↑	L	X	H	H	H	H
L	X	X	H	H	H	X	X	L	H
L	X	X	H	H	L	X	H	H	L
L	X	X	H	H	L	X	L	H	H
L	X	X	H	L	X	L	X	L	H
L	X	X	H	L	X	↑	X	L	H
X	L	X	H	H	H	X	X	L	X
X	L	X	H	H	L	X	H	H	L
X	L	X	H	H	L	X	L	H	H
X	L	X	H	L	X	L	X	L	H
X	L	X	H	L	X	↑	X	L	H
X	X	L	H	H	H	X	X	L	X
X	X	L	H	H	L	X	H	H	L
X	X	L	H	H	L	X	L	H	H
X	X	L	H	L	X	L	X	L	H
X	X	L	H	L	X	↑	X	L	H

The normal sequence of operation is shown in the timing diagram, Figure 20.

FUNCTION TABLE FOR DUAL-CHANNEL DETECTOR OPERATION
(2W connected to 1W/1R1)

INPUTS					OUTPUT
1A	1C	2A	2C	S	1W·2W
H	H	X	X	H	L
X	X	H	H	H	L
↓	H	L	X	H	↑
↓	H	X	L	H	↑
L	X	↓	H	H	↑
X	L	↓	H	H	↑
Any Other Combination					H

H = high level (steady state), L = low level (steady state)
X = irrelevant (any input, including transitions)
↓ = transition from high level to low level, ↑ = transition from low level to high level
†The W/RI column shows the output from the detector resulting from the inputs A, C, and S. In positive logic, $W = \overline{ACS}$. For dual operation with 2W connected to 2RI, this column represents an intermediate node and can be ignored.

For independent operation of register 2, this column is an input and the A, C, and S columns should be ignored.

For dual-channel operation with 2W connected to 1W/1RI, this column is the result of $W = \overline{S(1A \cdot 1C + 2A \cdot 2C)}$ as shown in the table above.

definition of logic levels

INPUT	H	L
A‡	$V_{ID} \geq V_{T\,max}$	$V_{ID} \leq V_{T\,min}$
LOGIC	$V_I \geq V_{IH\,min}$	$V_I \leq V_{IL\,max}$

‡A is a differential voltage (V_{ID}) between A1 and A2. For these circuits, V_{ID} is consider positive regardless of which terminal is positive with respect to the other.

functional block diagram

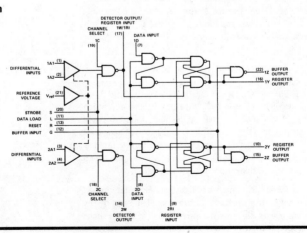

TEXAS INSTRUMENTS
INCORPORATED
POST OFFICE BOX 5012 • DALLAS, TEXAS 75222

schematics of inputs and outputs

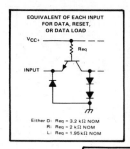

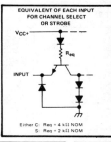

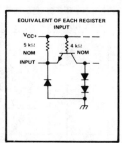

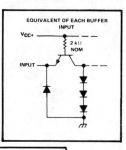

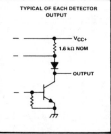

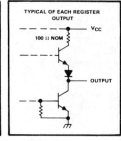

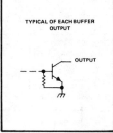

absolute maximum ratings over operating free-air temperature range (unless otherwise noted)

Supply voltages (see Note 1)

V_{CC+} . . . . 7 V

V_{CC-} . . . . −7 V

Reference voltage, V_{ref} . . . . ±5 V

Differential input voltage, V_{ID} . . . . ±5 V

Voltage from any input to ground (see Note 2) . . . . 5.25 V

Continuous total dissipation at (or below) 70°C free-air temperature (see Note 3) . . . . 450 mW

Operating free-air temperature range: SN55236, SN55237 . . . . −55°C to 125°C

SN75236, SN75237 . . . . 0°C to 70°C

Storage Temperature range . . . . −65°C to 150°C

Lead temperature 1/16 inch from case for 60 seconds . . . . 300°C

NOTES: 1. Voltage values, except differential input voltage, are with respect to the network ground terminal.
2. For operation of SN55236 and SN55237 above 70°C free-air temperature, refer to Dissipation Derating Curve, Figure 18.

recommended operating conditions

		MIN	NOM	MAX	UNIT
Supply voltage, V_{CC+}		4.75	5	5.25	V
Supply voltage, V_{CC-}		−4.75	−5	−5.25	V
Reference voltage, V_{ref}		±1.5	±2.1	±4.5	V
High-level output voltage, V_{OH}	Detector and buffer			V_{CC}	V
High-level output current, I_{OH}	Register			−400	µA
Low-level output current, I_{OL}	Register			16	mA
	Buffer			25	
	Detector			3.2	
Width of reset pulse, $t_{w(R)}$ (see Figure 7)		115			ns

11

TYPES SN55236, SN55237, SN75236, SN75237
DUAL SENSE AMPLIFIERS/DATA REGISTERS

electrical characteristics over recommended operating free-air temperature range, V_{ref} = ±2.1 V (unless otherwise noted)

PARAMETER		TEST FIGURE	TEST CONDITIONS			MIN	TYP†	MAX	UNIT
V_T	Differential-input threshold voltage (see Note 3)	1	V_{CC+} = 5 V, T_A = 25°C	V_{CC-} = −5 V,	SN55236	5	7	9	mV
					SN55237	3	7	11	
					SN75236	4	7	10	
					SN75237	1	7	13	
			V_{CC+} = 5 V ± 5%, V_{CC-} = −5 V ± 5%		SN55236	4.5	7	9.5	
					SN55237	2	7	12	
			V_{CC+} = 5 V,	V_{CC-} = −5 V	SN75236	4	7	10	
					SN75237	1	7	13	
V_{ICF}	Common-mode input firing voltage		f = 0.1 MHz to 20 MHz				±1.5		V
I_{IB}	Differential-input bias current	2	V_{CC+} = 5 V,	V_{CC-} = −5 V,	V_{ID} = 0			20	µA
I_{IO}	Differential-input offset current	2	V_{CC+} = 5 V,	V_{CC-} = −5 V,	V_{ID} = 0			0.5	µA
V_{IH}	High-level input voltage (strobe and logic inputs)	3 & 4				2			V
V_{IL}	Low-level input voltage (strobe and logic inputs)	3 & 4						0.8	V
V_{OH}	High-level output voltage	Register	3	V_{CC+} = 4.75 V, V_{IL} = 0.8 V,	V_{CC-} = −4.75 V, V_{IH} = 2 V, I_{OH} = −400 µA		2.4			V
		Detector	4	V_{CC+} = 4.75 V, V_{IL} = 0.8 V	V_{CC-} = −4.75 V, V_{IH} = 2 V,					
I_{OH}	High-level output current	Buffer	3	V_{CC+} = 4.75 V, V_{IL} = 0.8 V,	V_{CC-} = −4.75 V, V_{IH} = 2 V, V_{OH} = 4.75 V				250	µA
V_{OL}	Low-level output voltage	Register	3	V_{CC} = 4.75 V, V_{IL} = 0.8 V,	V_{CC-} = −4.75 V, V_{IH} = 2 V, I_{OL} = 16 mA				0.4	V
		Buffer	3	V_{CC} = 4.75 V, V_{IL} = 0.8 V,	V_{CC-} = −4.75 V, V_{IH} = 2 V, I_{OL} = 25 mA				0.5	V
		Detector	4	V_{CC} = 4.75 V, V_{IL} = 0.8 V	V_{CC-} = −4.75 V, V_{IH} = 2 V,				0.4	V
I_I	Input current at maximum input voltage (logic inputs)	5	V_{CC+} = 5.25 V,	V_{CC-} = −5.25 V, V_{IH} = 5.25 V				1	mA
I_{IH}	High-level input current	Data in or channel select	5	V_{CC+} = 5.25 V, V_{CC-} = −5.25 V, V_{IH} = 2.4 V				40	µA
		Register input 2RI						−750	
		Strobe, reset, or buffer input						80	
		Data load						160	
I_{IL}	Low-level input current	Strobe, reset, or buffer input	5	V_{CC+} = 5.25 V, V_{CC-} = −5.25 V, V_{IL} = 0.4 V				−3.2	mA
		Register input 2RI						−3	
		Channel select						−1.6	
		Data load						−6.4	
		Data in						−2	
I_{OS}	Short-circuit output current‡	Register	6	V_{CC+} = 5.25 V,	V_{CC-} = −5.25 V, V_O = 0	−20		−60	mA
I_{ref}	Reference-input current		2	V_{CC+} = 5.25 V, T_A = 25°C	V_{CC-} = −5.25 V, V_{ref} = −2.1 V,			0.5	mA
I_{CC+}	Supply current from V_{CC+}		2	V_{CC+} = 5.25 V,	V_{CC-} = −5.25 V, T_A = 25°C			55	mA
I_{CC-}	Supply current from V_{CC-}		2	V_{CC+} = 5.25 V,	V_{CC-} = −5.25 V, T_A = 25°C			18	mA

†All typical values are at T_A = 25°C. ‡Not more than one output should be shorted at a time.
NOTE 3: The differential input threshold voltage (V_T) is defined as the d-c differential-input voltage (V_{ID}) required to force the detector output to the logic-threshold voltage level.

TEXAS INSTRUMENTS
INCORPORATED
POST OFFICE BOX 5012 • DALLAS, TEXAS 75222

switching characteristics, V_{CC+} = 5 V, V_{CC-} = −5 V, V_{ref} = −2.1 V, T_A = 25°C

PARAMETER§	INPUT	OUTPUT	TEST FIGURE	TEST CONDITIONS	MIN	TYP	MAX	UNIT
t_{PLH}	1A1-1A2 or 2A1-2A2	Y	7	$R_{L(Y)}$ = 820 Ω, $C_{L(Y)}$ = 50 pF, $R_{L(Z)}$ = 520 Ω, $C_{L(Z)}$ = 450 pF		28	50	ns
	Strobe	Y	8			18	35	
	Data input	Y	9			17	40	
t_{PHL}	Data load	Y	8			15	35	ns
	Reset	Y	9			12	30	
t_{PLH}	Reset	Z	9			100	200	ns
t_{PHL}	Buffer input	Z	9			22	55	ns
	1A1-1A2 or 2A1-2A2	Z	7			42	90	
t_{TLH}		Y	9	$R_{L(Y)}$ = 820 Ω, $C_{L(Y)}$ = 50 pF, $R_{L(Z)}$ = 520 Ω, $C_{L(Z)}$ = 450 pF		13	35	ns
t_{THL}		Y				7	20	
t_{TLH}		Z				150	185	ns
t_{THL}		Z				20	50	

§$t_{PLH} \equiv$ propagation delay time, low-to-high-level output
$t_{PHL} \equiv$ propagation delay time, high-to-low-level output
$t_{TLH} \equiv$ transition time, low-to-high-level output
$t_{THL} \equiv$ transition time, high-to-low-level output

PARAMETER MEASUREMENT INFORMATION

d-c test circuits†

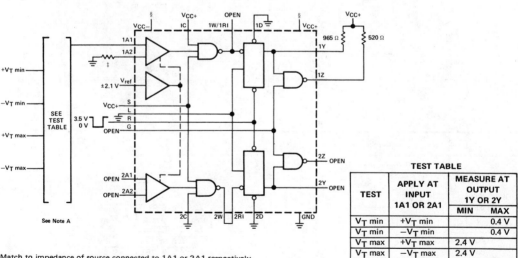

TEST TABLE

TEST	APPLY AT INPUT 1A1 OR 2A1	MEASURE AT OUTPUT 1Y OR 2Y	
		MIN	MAX
V_T min	+V_T min		0.4 V
V_T min	−V_T min		0.4 V
V_T max	+V_T max	2.4 V	
V_T max	−V_T max	2.4 V	

‡Match to impedance of source connected to 1A1 or 2A1 respectively.
§V_{CC+} and V_{CC-} are as specified in the electrical characteristics table.

NOTE A: Connections are shown for testing channel 1. To test channel 2, reverse connections of 1C and 2C along with inputs and outputs.

FIGURE 1—V_T

†Arrows indicate actual direction of current flow. Current into a terminal is a positive value.

73

TYPES SN55236, SN55237, SN75236, SN75237
DUAL SENSE AMPLIFIERS/DATA REGISTERS

PARAMETER MEASUREMENT INFORMATION

d-c test circuits† (continued)

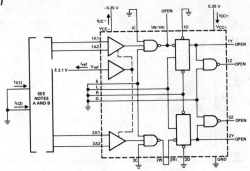

NOTES: A. Each channel is tested separately. Inputs not under test are grounded.
B. $I_{IB} = I_{I(1)}$ or $I_{I(2)}$, (typical value applies to each). $I_{IO} = I_{I(1)} - I_{I(2)}$. $I_{I(1)}$ and $I_{I(2)}$ are the differential-input currents of the channel under test.

FIGURE 2—I_{IB}, I_{IO}, I_{CC+}, I_{CC-}, I_{ref}

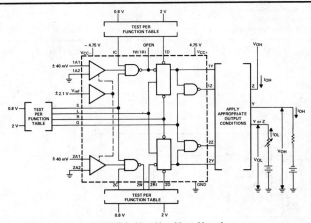

FIGURE 3—V_{IH}, V_{IL}, V_{OH}, V_{OL}, I_{OH}

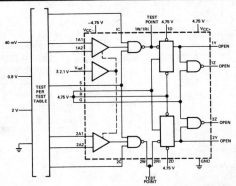

FIGURE 4—V_{IH}, V_{IL}, V_{OH}, V_{OL}

TEST TABLE

TEST	DIFF INPUT	S	CS1	CS2
V_{OH} AT 1W/1RI	0 V	2 V	2 V	0.8 V
V_{OH} AT 1W/1RI	40 mV	0.8 V	2 V	0.8 V
V_{OH} AT 1W/1RI	40 mV	2 V	0.8 V	0.8 V
V_{OL} AT 1W/1RI	40 mV	2 V	2 V	0.8 V
V_{OH} AT 2W/2RI	0 V	2 V	0.8 V	2 V
V_{OH} AT 2W/2RI	40 mV	0.8 V	0.8 V	2 V
V_{OH} AT 2W/2RI	40 mV	2 V	0.8 V	0.8 V
V_{OL} AT 2W/2RI	40 mV	2 V	0.8 V	2 V

†Arrows indicate actual direction of current flow. Current into a terminal is a positive value.

TEXAS INSTRUMENTS
INCORPORATED
POST OFFICE BOX 5012 • DALLAS, TEXAS 75222

PARAMETER MEASUREMENT INFORMATION

d-c test circuits† (continued)

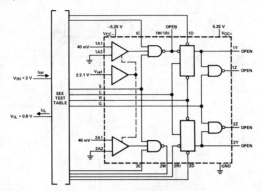

TEST TABLE

TEST	S	1C	2C	1D	2D	L	R	G	2RI
I_{IH} AT S	2 V	0.8 V	0.8 V	X	X	X	X	X	2W
I_{IH} AT 1C	0.8 V	2 V	X	X	X	X	X	X	2W
I_{IH} AT 2C	0.8 V	X	2 V	X	X	X	X	X	2W
I_{IH} AT 1D	X	X	X	2 V	X	0.8 V	X	X	2W
I_{IH} AT 2D	X	X	X	X	2 V	0.8 V	X	X	2W
I_{IH} AT L	X	X	X	0.8 V	0.8 V	2 V	X	X	2W
I_{IH} AT R	X	X	X	2 V	2 V	2 V	2 V	X	2W
I_{IH} AT G	0.8 V	X	X	X	X	0.8 V	0.8 V	2 V	2W
I_{IL} AT S	0.8 V	2 V	2 V	X	X	X	X	X	2W
I_{IL} AT 1C	2 V	0.8 V	0.8 V	X	X	X	X	X	2W
I_{IL} AT 2C	2 V	0.8 V	0.8 V	X	X	X	X	X	2W
I_{IL} AT 1D	X	X	X	0.8 V	0.8 V	2 V	X	X	2W
I_{IL} AT 2D	X	X	X	0.8 V	0.8 V	2 V	X	X	2W
I_{IL} AT L	X	X	X	2 V	2 V	0.8 V	X	X	2W
I_{IL} AT R	2 V	2 V	2 V	X	X	0.8 V	0.8 V	X	2W
I_{IL} AT G	X	X	X	0.8 V	0.8 V	2 V	X	0.8 V	2W
I_{IH} AT 2RI	X	X	X	X	0.8 V	2 V	X	X	2 V
I_{IL} AT 2RI	X	X	X	X	0.8 V	0.8 V	0.8 V	X	0.8 V

X = irrelevant

FIGURE 5—I_{IH}, I_{IL}

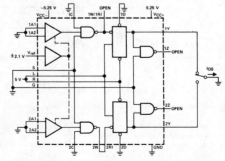

NOTE A: Not more than one output should be shorted at a time.

FIGURE 6—I_{OS}

†Arrows indicate actual direction of current flow. Current into a terminal is a positive value.

TYPES SN55236, SN55237, SN75236, SN75237
DUAL SENSE AMPLIFIERS/DATA REGISTERS

PARAMETER MEASUREMENT INFORMATION

switching characteristics

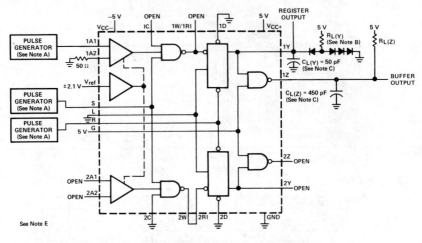

TEST CIRCUIT

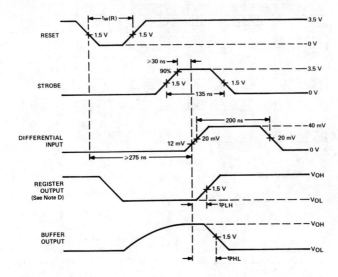

VOLTAGE WAVEFORMS

NOTES: A. The pulse generators have the following characteristics: $Z_O = 50\ \Omega$, $t_r = 15$ ns, $t_f = 15$ ns, $t_{w(R)} \geq 115$ ns, PRR = 500 kHz.
     B. All diodes are 1N3064.
     C. $C_{L(Y)}$ and $C_{L(Z)}$ include probe and jig capacitance.
     D. Initially high output condition can be established by repetitive cycling.
     E. Connections are shown for testing channel 1. To test channel 2, reverse connections of 1C and 2C along with inputs and outputs.

**FIGURE 7–PROPAGATION DELAY TIMES, DIFFERENTIAL INPUT TO
REGISTER OUTPUT AND BUFFER OUTPUT**

1

TEXAS INSTRUMENTS
INCORPORATED
POST OFFICE BOX 5012 • DALLAS, TEXAS 75222

PARAMETER MEASUREMENT INFORMATION

switching characteristics (continued)

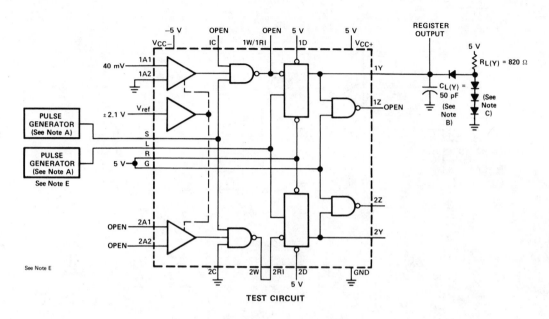

TEST CIRCUIT

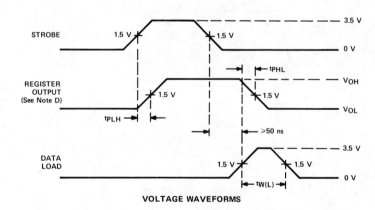

VOLTAGE WAVEFORMS

NOTES: A. The pulse generators have the following characteristics: Z_O = 50 Ω, t_r = 15 ns, t_f = 15 ns, $t_{w(L)}$ ⩾ 35 ns, PRR = 500 kHz.
      B. $C_{L(Y)}$ includes probe and jig capacitance.
      C. All diodes are 1N3064.
      D. Initially low output condition can be established by repetitive cycling.
      E. Connections are shown for testing channel 1. To test channel 2, reverse connections of 1C and 2C along with inputs and outputs.

FIGURE 8—PROPAGATION DELAY TIMES, STROBE AND DATA LOAD TO REGISTER OUTPUT

PARAMETER MEASUREMENT INFORMATION

switching characteristics

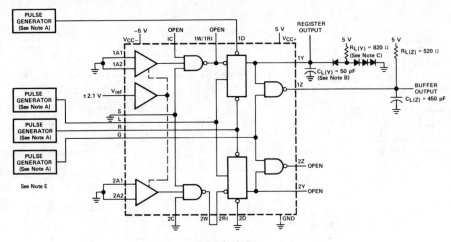

TEST CIRCUIT

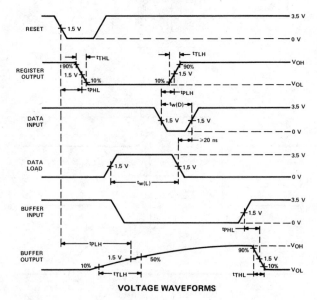

VOLTAGE WAVEFORMS

NOTES: A. The pulse generators have the following characteristics: $Z_O = 50\ \Omega$, $t_r = 15$ ns, $t_f = 15$ ns, $t_{w1} \geqslant 40$ ns, $t_{w2} \geqslant 100$ ns, PRR = 500 kHz.
B. $C_{L(Y)}$ and $C_{L(Z)}$ include probe and jig capacitance.
C. All diodes are 1N3064.
D. Initially high output condition can be established by repetitive cycling.
E. Connections are shown for testing channel 1. To test channel 2, reverse connections of 1C and 2C along with inputs and outputs.

**FIGURE 9—PROPAGATION DELAY TIMES FROM DATA INPUT AND RESET TO REGISTER OUTPUT,
TRANSITION TIMES OF REGISTER OUTPUT AND BUFFER OUTPUT**

TEXAS INSTRUMENTS
INCORPORATED
POST OFFICE BOX 5012 • DALLAS, TEXAS 75222

TYPICAL CHARACTERISTICS†

LOW-TO-HIGH-LEVEL-OUTPUT PROPAGATION DELAY TIME
FROM DIFFERENTIAL INPUT TO REGISTER OUTPUT
vs
FREE-AIR TEMPERATURE

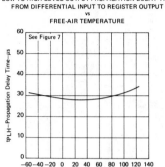

FIGURE 10

LOW-TO-HIGH-LEVEL-OUTPUT PROPAGATION DELAY TIME
FROM STROBE INPUT TO REGISTER OUTPUT
vs
FREE-AIR TEMPERATURE

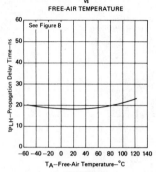

FIGURE 11

LOW-TO-HIGH-LEVEL-OUTPUT PROPAGATION DELAY TIME
FROM DATA INPUT TO REGISTER OUTPUT
vs
FREE-AIR TEMPERATURE

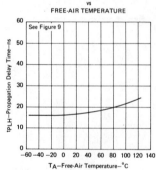

FIGURE 12

HIGH-TO-LOW-LEVEL-OUTPUT PROPAGATION DELAY TIME
FROM DATA LOAD TO REGISTER OUTPUT
vs
FREE-AIR TEMPERATURE

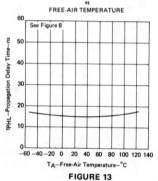

FIGURE 13

HIGH-TO-LOW-LEVEL-OUTPUT PROPAGATION DELAY TIME
FROM RESET TO REGISTER OUTPUT
vs
FREE-AIR TEMPERATURE

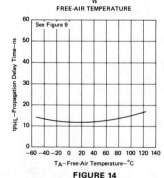

FIGURE 14

HIGH-TO-LOW-LEVEL-OUTPUT PROPAGATION DELAY TIME
FROM DIFFERENTIAL INPUT TO BUFFER OUTPUT
vs
FREE-AIR TEMPERATURE

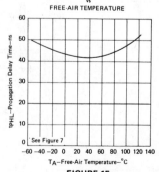

FIGURE 15

†Data for temperatures below 0°C and above 70°C are applicable for Series 55 devices only.

11

TEXAS INSTRUMENTS
INCORPORATED
POST OFFICE BOX 5012 • DALLAS, TEXAS 75222

TYPICAL CHARACTERISTICS†

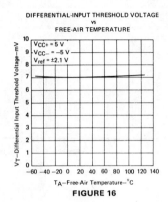

DIFFERENTIAL-INPUT THRESHOLD VOLTAGE
vs
FREE-AIR TEMPERATURE

FIGURE 16

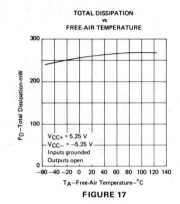

TOTAL DISSIPATION
vs
FREE-AIR TEMPERATURE

FIGURE 17

†Data for temperatures below $0°C$ and above $70°C$ are applicable for Series 55 devices only.

THERMAL INFORMATION

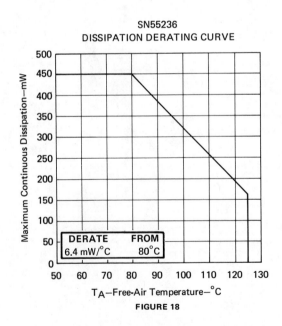

SN55236
DISSIPATION DERATING CURVE

DERATE 6.4 mW/$°C$ FROM 80$°C$

FIGURE 18

TEXAS INSTRUMENTS
INCORPORATED
POST OFFICE BOX 5012 • DALLAS, TEXAS 75222

11

TYPICAL APPLICATION DATA

input line layout considerations

Input sensitivity and device speed require adequate precautions in the routing of signal input and reference lines to prevent noise pickup. Bypassing of supply and reference inputs at the device with low-inductance disc ceramic capacitors, and use of a good ground plane to separate strobe and output lines from sense and reference input lines, are recommended procedures.

sense-input termination resistor considerations

Termination resistors are intentionally omitted from the sense-input terminals so the designer may select resistor values which will be compatible with the particular application. Matched termination resistors, (R_T, Figure 19), normally in the range of 25 Ω to 200 Ω each, are required not only to terminate the sense line in a desired impedance but also to provide a d-c path for the sense-input bias currents. Careful matching of the resistor pairs should be observed or effective common-mode rejection will be reduced.

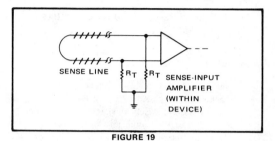

FIGURE 19

timing diagram

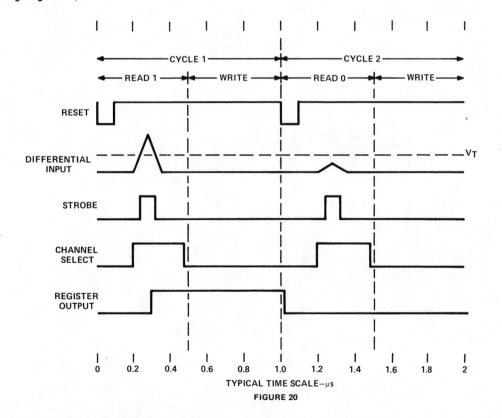

FIGURE 20

973

TEXAS INSTRUMENTS
INCORPORATED

POST OFFICE BOX 5012 • DALLAS, TEXAS 75222

IDEAL FOR PLATED-WIRE, THIN-FILM, AND OTHER HIGH-SPEED LOW-LEVEL SENSING APPLICATIONS

- **Input Threshold Level . . . 0.7 mV Typical**
- **t_{PHL} from Selected Channel . . . 18 ns Typical**
- **Decoded Input Channel Selection**
- **TTL Compatible Logic Inputs and Output**
- **Wired-AND Output Capability**
- **D-C Level-Restore Gate for Capacitors**
- **Output Strobe Capability**

description

The SN55244 and SN75244 each comprise four input channels with decoded selection, two stages of gain employing capacitive coupling, and a TTL-compatible output gate. A-c coupling reduces access time by eliminating the problems usually associated with d-c offset voltages on the input lines. The output is normally high and pulses low only when the relationships shown in the function table take place.

The SN55244 is characterized for operation over the full military temperature of $-55°C$ to $125°C$; and the SN75244 is characterized for operation from $0°C$ to $70°C$.

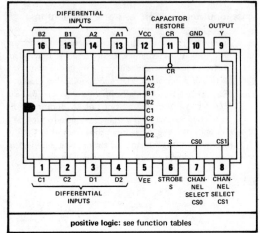

J,JA, OR N
DUAL-IN-LINE PACKAGE (TOP VIEW)

positive logic: see function tables

CHANNEL SELECTION TABLE

CS1	CS0	CHANNEL SELECTED
H	H	A
H	L	B
L	H	C
L	L	D

FUNCTION TABLE

INPUTS			OUTPUT Y
STROBE	CAPACITOR RESTORE	SELECTED CHANNEL	
L	X	X	H
X	H	X	H
X	X	L	H
H	L	↑	⊔
↑	L	H	⊔

H = high level (steady state, $V_I \geqslant V_{IH}$ min or $V_{ID} > V_T$
L = low level (steady state), $V_I \leqslant V_{IL}$ max or $V_{ID} < V_T$
X = irrelevant (any input, including transitions)
↑ = transition from low level to high level
⊔ = low-level output pulse

1

TEXAS INSTRUMENTS
INCORPORATED
POST OFFICE BOX 5012 • DALLAS, TEXAS 75222

functional block diagram

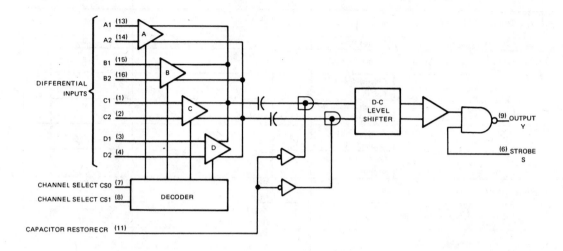

absolute maximum ratings over operating free-air temperature range (unless otherwise noted)

Supply voltages (see Note 1)

V_{CC} . . . . 7 V

V_{EE} . . . . −8 V

Differential input voltage (see Note 2) . . . . −6 V to 5 V

Common-mode input voltage . . . . −6 V to 5 V

Capacitor restore, channel select, or strobe input voltage . . . . 5.5 V

Continuous total dissipation at (or below) 25°C free-air temperature (see Note 3) . . . . 1 W

Operating free-air temperature range: SN55244 . . . . −55°C to 125°C

SN75244 . . . . 0°C to 70°C

Storage temperature range . . . . −65°C to 150°C

Lead temperature 1/16 inch from case for 60 seconds: J or JA package . . . . 300°C

Lead temperature 1/16 inch from case for 10 seconds: N package . . . . 260°C

NOTES: 1. All voltage values, except differential voltages, are with respect to the network ground terminal.
2. Differential input voltages are at A1 with respect to A2, and similarly B1 to B2, C1 to C2, and D1 to D2.
3. For operation above 25°C free-air temperature, refer to Dissipation Derating Curve, Figure 10.

recommended operating conditions

	SN55244			SN75244			UNIT
	MIN	NOM	MAX	MIN	NOM	MAX	
Supply voltage, V_{CC}	4.75	5	5.25	4.75	5	5.25	V
Supply voltage, V_{EE}	−5.7	−6	−6.3	−5.7	−6	−6.3	V
Common-mode input current, I_{IC}			+200			+200	μA
			−10			−10	
Differential input current, I_{ID}			200			200	μA
Operating free-air temperature, T_A	−55		125	0		70	°C

TEXAS INSTRUMENTS
INCORPORATED
POST OFFICE BOX 5012 • DALLAS, TEXAS 75222

electrical characteristics at 25°C free-air temperature (unless otherwise noted)

PARAMETER		TEST FIGURE	TEST CONDITIONS†	MIN	TYP	MAX	UNIT
V_T Differential input threshold voltage‡		1, 4	$V_{CC} = 5$ V, $V_{EE} = -6$ V, T_A = MIN to MAX		0.7		mV
I_{IB} Differential input bias current of selected channel		2	$V_{CC} = 5.25$ V, $V_{EE} = -6.3$ V		20		μA
I_{IO} Differential input offset current of selected channel		2	$V_{CC} = 5.25$, $V_{EE} = -6.3$ V		0.5		μA
V_{IH} High-level input voltage	Channel Select CS0 or CS1	3	$V_{CC} = 5$ V, $V_{EE} = -6$ V	2.1			V
	Capacitor Restore or Strobe	1, 4		2			
V_{IL} Low-level input voltage	Channel Select CS0 or CS1	3	$V_{CC} = 5$ V, $V_{EE} = -6$ V			0.7	V
	Capacitor Restore or Strobe	1, 4				0.8	
V_{ICR} Common-mode input voltage range			$V_{CC} = 5$ V, $V_{EE} = -6$ V, $I_{IC} = -10$ μA to +200 μA		-6 to 4.7		V
V_{IDR} Differential input voltage range			$V_{CC} = 5$ V, $V_{EE} = -6$ V, $I_{ID} = 200$ μA		0 to 3.7		V
V_{OH} High-level output voltage			$V_{CC} = 4.75$ V, $V_{EE} = -5.7$ V, $V_{IL(S)} = 0.8$ V, $I_{OH} = -400$ μA	2.4	3.6		V
V_{OL} Low-level output voltage		1, 4	$V_{CC} = 4.75$ V, $V_{EE} = -5.7$ V, $I_{OL} = 10$ mA		0.4	0.5	V
I_{IH} High-level input current	Channel select CS0 or CS1		$V_{CC} = 5.25$ V, $V_{EE} = -6.3$ V, $V_I = 3.5$ V		1.8	3	mA
	Capacitor restore					10	μA
	Strobe				40	200	μA
I_{IL} Low-level input current	Channel select CS0 or CS1		$V_{CC} = 5.25$ V, $V_{EE} = -6.3$ V, $V_I = 0$		-0.6	-1	mA
	Capacitor restore				-2.5	-3.5	μA
I_{CC} Supply current from V_{CC}			$V_{CC} = 5.25$ V, $V_{EE} = -6.3$ V, See Note 4	15	22	30	mA
I_{EE} Supply current from V_{EE}				-15	-20	-30	

†For conditions shown as MIN or MAX, use the appropriate value specified under recommended operating conditions.
‡This is the lowest value of differential voltage signal that will cause the output to drop to a level that sets the latch shown in Figure 1, the latch being in free air at 25°C.
NOTE 4: Supply currents are measured with the output open; CS0, CS1, and CR at 3.5 V; and A1, A2, and S at 0 V.

TEXAS INSTRUMENTS
INCORPORATED
POST OFFICE BOX 5012 • DALLAS, TEXAS 75222

switching characteristics, V_{CC} = 5 V, V_{EE} = −6 V, T_A = 25°C

PARAMETER[†]	FROM (INPUT)	TEST FIGURE	TEST CONDITIONS	MIN	TYP	MAX	UNIT
t_{PLH}	Differential input	1, 5, 8			40		ns
t_{PHL}	channel A, B, C, or D				18	25	ns
t_{PLH}	Strobe	1, 6	C_L = 15 pF		30		ns
t_{PHL}					18	25	ns
t_{PLH}	Channel select	1, 7			40		ns
t_{PHL}	CS0 or CS1				25		ns

[†]t_{PLH} ≡ propagation delay time, low-to-high-level output.
t_{PHL} ≡ propagation delay time, high-to-low-level output.

operating characteristics, V_{CC} = 5 V, V_{EE} = −6 V, T_A = 25°C

PARAMETER		TEST FIGURE	TEST CONDITIONS	MIN	TYP	MAX	UNIT
t_{su}min Minimum setup time	Channel select CS0 or CS1	5			15		ns
	Capacitor restore				10		
	strobe				10		
$t_h$min	Minimum hold time for capacitor restore high	8			130		ns
t_{orC}	Common-mode-input overload recovery time	9	V_{IC} = ±2 V		50		ns
t_{orD}	Differential-input overload recovery time	9	V_{ID} = ±1 V		65		ns

PARAMETER MEASUREMENT INFORMATION

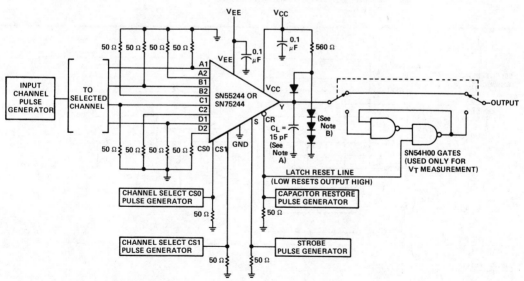

NOTES: A. C_L includes probe and jig capacitance.
B. All diodes are 1N916 or 1N3064.
C. Each channel is tested separately. Inputs not under test are left open.
D. The pulse generators shown above have the following characteristics: Z_O = 50 Ω, t_r = 10 ns, t_f = 10 ns.

FIGURE 1—V_T, V_{IH}, V_{IL}, V_{OL}, t_{PLH}, t_{PHL}

PARAMETER MEASUREMENT INFORMATION

d-c test circuits

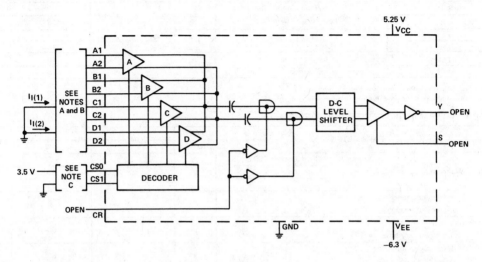

NOTES: A. Each channel is tested separately. Channel inputs not under test are open.
B. $I_{IB} = I_{I(1)}$ or $I_{I(2)}$ (typical value applies to each). $I_{IO} = I_{I(1)} - I_{I(2)}$. $I_{I(1)}$ and $I_{I(2)}$ are the currents into the differential inputs of the channel under test.
C. Each channel is selected in turn as shown in the channel selection table.

FIGURE 2—I_{IB}, I_{IO}

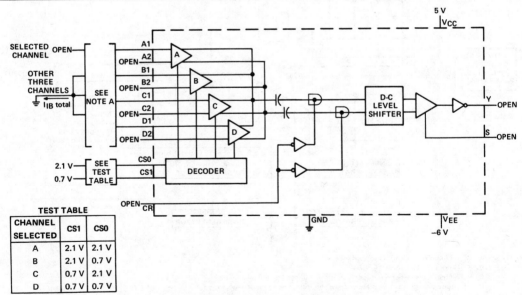

TEST TABLE

CHANNEL SELECTED	CS1	CS0
A	2.1 V	2.1 V
B	2.1 V	0.7 V
C	0.7 V	2.1 V
D	0.7 V	0.7 V

NOTE A: The total bias current I_{IB}, coming from the unselected channels, must be less than 1 μA.

FIGURE 3—V_{IH}, V_{IL}

11

TEXAS INSTRUMENTS
INCORPORATED
POST OFFICE BOX 5012 • DALLAS, TEXAS 75222

9

PARAMETER MEASUREMENT INFORMATION

switching waveforms

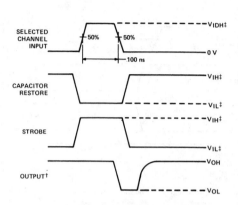

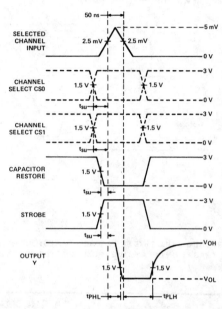

‡ **TABLE OF INPUT LEVELS**

INPUT	TESTING V_T			TESTING V_{OH}, V_{OL}		
	V_{IDH}	V_{IH}	V_{IL}	V_{IDH}	V_{IH}	V_{IL}
Selected Channel	V_T			10 mV		
Capacitor Restore		3 V	0 V		2 V	0.8 V
Strobe		3 V	0 V		2 V	0.8 V

†Output waveform is for latch output (see Figure 1) when testing V_T, otherwise for Y output.

FIGURE 4—V_T, V_{IH}, V_{IL}, V_{OH}, V_{OL}

FIGURE 5—SETUP TIMES OF CHANNEL SELECT CS0, CHANNEL SELECT CS1, CAPACITOR RESTORE, AND STROBE; AND PROPAGATION DELAY TIMES FROM SELECTED CHANNEL

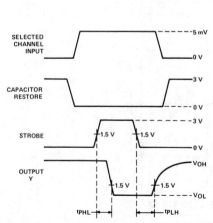

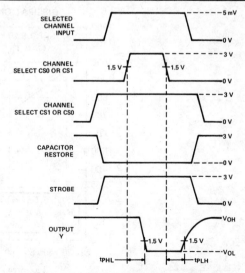

FIGURE 6—PROPAGATION DELAY TIMES FROM STROBE

FIGURE 7—PROPAGATION DELAY TIME FROM CHANNEL SELECT CS0 OR CHANNEL SELECT CS1

11

TYPES SN55244, SN75244
A-C-COUPLED FOUR-CHANNEL SENSE AMPLIFIERS

PARAMETER MEASUREMENT INFORMATION

switching waveforms (continued)

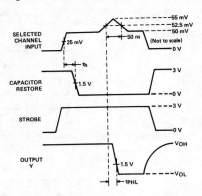

FIGURE 8—HOLD TIME FOR CAPACITOR RESTORE HIGH,
PROPAGATION DELAY TIME FROM SELECTED CHANNEL

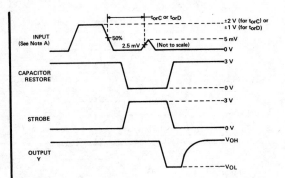

NOTE A: Although the large initial pulse is shown as a positive pulse, it may be either a positive or a negative common-mode or differential-mode input pulse. The triangular 5-mV input pulse is a differential-mode pulse.

FIGURE 9—COMMON-MODE AND DIFFERENTIAL-MODE
RECOVERY TIMES

THERMAL INFORMATION

DISSIPATION DERATING CURVE

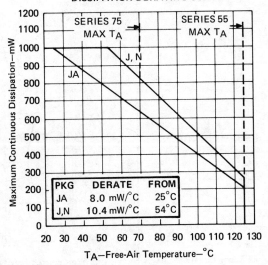

PKG	DERATE	FROM
JA	8.0 mW/°C	25°C
J,N	10.4 mW/°C	54°C

FIGURE 10

TEXAS INSTRUMENTS
INCORPORATED
POST OFFICE BOX 5012 • DALLAS, TEXAS 75222

TYPICAL CHARACTERISTICS†

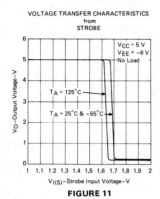

VOLTAGE TRANSFER CHARACTERISTICS
from
STROBE

FIGURE 11

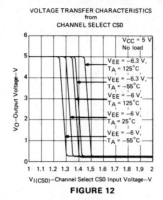

VOLTAGE TRANSFER CHARACTERISTICS
from
CHANNEL SELECT CS0

FIGURE 12

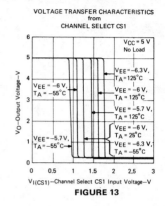

VOLTAGE TRANSFER CHARACTERISTICS
from
CHANNEL SELECT CS1

FIGURE 13

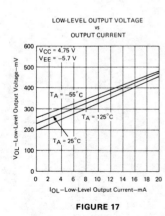

THRESHOLD VOLTAGE
vs
FREE-AIR TEMPERATURE

FIGURE 14

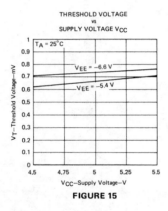

THRESHOLD VOLTAGE
vs
SUPPLY VOLTAGE V_{CC}

FIGURE 15

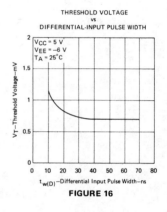

THRESHOLD VOLTAGE
vs
DIFFERENTIAL-INPUT PULSE WIDTH

FIGURE 16

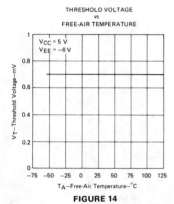

LOW-LEVEL OUTPUT VOLTAGE
vs
OUTPUT CURRENT

FIGURE 17

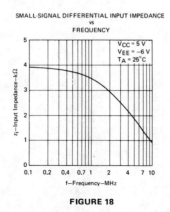

SMALL-SIGNAL DIFFERENTIAL INPUT IMPEDANCE
vs
FREQUENCY

FIGURE 18

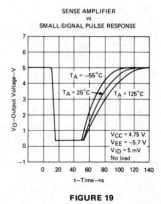

SENSE AMPLIFIER
vs
SMALL-SIGNAL PULSE RESPONSE

FIGURE 19

†Data for temperatures below 0°C and above 70°C are applicable for SN55244 only.

11

TEXAS INSTRUMENTS
INCORPORATED
POST OFFICE BOX 5012 • DALLAS, TEXAS 75222

38510/MACH IV
High Reliability Microelectronics Procurement Specifications
MIL-STD-883

12

TEXAS INSTRUMENTS
INCORPORATED
POST OFFICE BOX 5012 • DALLAS, TEXAS 75222

1.0 INTRODUCTION

High-reliability linear integrated circuits are processed per Texas Instruments MACH IV Procurement Specification in accordance with MIL-M-38510. This program was initiated by TI to ensure that quality and reliability are built into, not tested into, integrated circuits.

For ease of selection, a complete listing is included giving device, package, and process level for all stocked devices. Other combinations are available on special request.

Section 3.0 gives the different process levels available in the TI MACH IV Procurement Specification. This includes 100% processing, Group A lot acceptance, Group B and C periodic qualification tests, and manufacturing qualification procedure. Also included in this section is a copy of the TI Group B and C periodic data plan. With this plan, Group B and Group C data is generated quarterly on each generic family of devices.

Section 4.0 covers JAN ICs and provides a table of recommended usage and cross-reference from 38510 slash sheet to TI type number.

2.0 38510/MACH IV DEVICE LIST

The products listed in this section are those most often used in military applications. These devices are offered with both 883-Class C (SNM) and 883-Class B (SNC) processing. 883-Class A (SNH) processing is also available on most device types and can be supplied on special request. (Contact a TI sales office for further information.)

OPERATIONAL AMPLIFIERS

CIRCUIT TYPE	PROCESS FLOW										DESCRIPTION	BURN-IN CIRCUIT FIGURE NO.	DATA SHEET PAGE NO.
	SNM					SNC							
	PACKAGE TYPE					PACKAGE TYPE							
	FA	J	JA	JP	L	FA	J	JA	JP	L			
52L022				X	X				X	X	Dual Low Power, Internal Compensation	1	4-3
52L044			X					X			Quad Low Power, Internal Compensation	2	4-7
52101A	X		X	X	X	X		X	X	X	High Performance, External Compensation	3	4-19
52107	X		X	X	X	X		X	X	X	High Performance, Internal Compensation	3	4-23
52108	X		X	X	X	X		X	X	X	High Performance, External Compensation	3	4-27
52108A	X		X	X	X	X		X	X	X	High Performance, External Compensation	3	4-27
52110	X		X	X	X	X		X	X	X	Wide Band, Voltage Follower	3	4-32
52558			X	X				X	X		Dual General Purpose	4	4-43
52702	X			X	X				X		General Purpose, Wide Band	5	4-51
52709	X		X	X	X	X		X	X	X	General Purpose, External Compensation	3	4-60
52741	X		X	X	X	X		X	X	X	General Purpose, Internal Compensation	3	4-67
52747	X		X		X	X		X		X	Dual General Purpose	6	4-72
52748	X		X	X	X	X		X	X	X	General Purpose, External Compensation	3	4-76
52770	X		X	X	X	X		X	X	X	High Performance, External Compensation	3	4-80
52771	X		X	X	X	X		X	X	X	High Performance, Internal Compensation	3	4-86

12

TEXAS INSTRUMENTS
INCORPORATED
POST OFFICE BOX 5012 • DALLAS, TEXAS 75222

38510/MACH IV PROCUREMENT SPECIFICATION

VOLTAGE REGULATORS

CIRCUIT TYPE	SNM PACKAGE TYPE					SNC PACKAGE TYPE					DESCRIPTION	BURN-IN CIRCUIT FIGURE NO.	DATA SHEET PAGE NO.
	FA	J	JP	L	LA	FA	J	JP	L	LA			
52104		JA		X			JA		X		Negative-Voltage Regulator	7	5-2
52105			X	X				X	X		Positive-Voltage Regulator	8	5-6
52109				X						X	5-Volt Regulator	9	5-11
52723	X	J		X		X	J		X		Precision Voltage Regulator	10	5-15

VOLTAGE COMPARATORS

CIRCUIT TYPE	SNM PACKAGE TYPE				SNC PACKAGE TYPE				DESCRIPTION	BURN-IN CIRCUIT FIGURE NO.	DATA SHEET PAGE NO.
	FA	J	JP	L	FA	J	JP	L			
52106	X	X	X	X	X	X	X	X	Single with Strobe	11	6-2
52111	X	X	X	X	X	X	X	X	Single, High-Impedance Inputs	12	6-9
52506	X	X			X	X			Dual with Strobes	13	6-18
52510	X	X	X	X	X	X	X	X	Single with Strobe	14	6-25
52514		X				X			Dual with Strobes	15	6-31
52710	X	X	X	X	X	X	X	X	Single	14	6-33
52711	X	X		X	X	X		X	Dual Channel with Strobes	16	6-37
52810	X	X	X	X	X	X	X	X	Single	14	6-44
52811	X	X		X	X	X		X	Dual Channel with Strobes	16	6-50
52820		X			X				Dual	15	6-56

VIDEO AMPLIFIERS

CIRCUIT TYPE	SNM PACKAGE TYPE				SNC PACKAGE TYPE				DESCRIPTION	BURN-IN CIRCUIT FIGURE NO.	DATA SHEET PAGE NO.
	FA	J	JP	L	FA	J	JP	L			
5510	X		X	X	X		X	X	40 MHz	17	7-2
5511	X			X	X			X	100 MHz	17	7-16
5512				X				X	80 MHz, Offset-Voltage Null Capability	17	7-22
5514			X	X			X	X	80 MHz	17	7-22
52733	X	X		X	X	X		X	200 MHz, Gain Select	18	7-28

SPECIAL FUNCTIONS

CIRCUIT TYPE	SMC PACKAGE TYPE			SNC PACKAGE TYPE			DESCRIPTION	BURN-IN CIRCUIT FIGURE NO.	DATA SHEET PAGE NO.
	J	JP	L	J	JP	L			
52555		X	X		X	X	Precision Timer	19	7-53
56502	X			X			Logarithmic Amplifier	20	7-40
56514	X		X	X		X	Balanced Mixer	21	7-47

TEXAS INSTRUMENTS
INCORPORATED
POST OFFICE BOX 5012 • DALLAS, TEXAS 75222

LINE DRIVERS

CIRCUIT TYPE	PROCESS FLOW				DESCRIPTION	BURN-IN CIRCUIT FIGURE NO.	DATA SHEET PAGE NO.
	SNM		SNC				
	PACKAGE TYPE		PACKAGE TYPE				
	J	SB	J	SB			
55109	X		X		Dual, Party Line (Differential)	22	8-6
55110	X		X		Dual, Party Line (Differnetial)	22	8-6
55113	X	X	X	X	Dual, 3-State Outputs (Differential)	23	8-26
55114	X	X	X	X	Dual, Differential, Single 5-V Supply	24	8-26
55121	X		X		Dual, 75-mA Output (Single-Ended)	25	8-44
55138	X		X		Quad Transceiver, Single-Ended, Single 5-V Supply	26	8-56
55183	X		X		Dual, Differential, Single 5-V Supply	27	8-84

LINE RECEIVERS

CIRCUIT TYPE	PROCESS FLOW						DESCRIPTION	BURN-IN CIRCUIT FIGURE NO.	DATA SHEET PAGE NO.
	SNM			SNC					
	PACKAGE TYPE			PACKAGE TYPE					
	J	L	SB	J	L	SB			
55107A	X			X			Dual, Party Line (Differential)	28	8-25
55108A	X			X			Dual, Party Line (Differential)	28	8-25
55115	X		X	X		X	Dual, Differential	29	8-26
55122	X			X			Triple, Built-In Hysteresis	30	8-44
55138	X			X			Quad Tranceiver, Single-Ended, Single 5-V Supply	26	8-56
55180		X			X		Dual, Level Converter	31	9-2
55182	X			X			Dual, Differential, Single 5-V Supply	32	8-84

MEMORY DRIVERS

CIRCUIT TYPE	PROCESS FLOW						DESCRIPTION	BURN-IN CIRCUIT FIGURE NO.	DATA SHEET PAGE NO.
	SMC			SNC					
	PACKAGE TYPE			PACKAGE TYPE					
	J	JB	SB	J	JB	SB			
55325†	X	X	X	X	X	X	Dual Sink/Source, 600 mA	33	10-21
55326†	X	X	X	X	X	X	Quad Sink, 600 mA	34	10-36
55327†	X	X	X	X	X	X	Quad Source, 600 mA	35	10-36
55329*							Eight-Channel Core Driver, ±350 mA	36	3-13

†Precap visual inspection as defined by TI (Paragraph 6.1.2 of Bulletin CB-149 entitled ''38510/MACH IV High Reliability Microelectronics Procurement Specifications MIL-STD-883).

*This device is to be announced in custom 24-pin flat package designated RA.

12

PERIPHERAL DRIVERS

CIRCUIT TYPE	PROCESS FLOW								DESCRIPTION	BURN-IN CIRCUIT FIGURE NO.	DATA SHEET PAGE NO.
	SNM				SNC						
	PACKAGE TYPE				PACKAGE TYPE						
	J	JB	JP	L	J	JB	JP	L			
55450B	X	X			X	X			Dual	37	10-42
55451B			X	X			X	X	Dual Positive-AND	38	10-42
55452B			X	X			X	X	Dual Positive-NAND	39	10-42
55453B			X	X			X	X	Dual Positive-OR	38	10-42
55454B			X	X			X	X	Dual Positive-NOR	39	10-42
55460	X	X			X	X			Dual	37	10-67
55461			X	X			X	X	Dual Positive-AND	38	10-67
55462			X	X			X	X	Dual Positive-NAND	39	10-67
55463			X	X			X	X	Dual Positive-OR	38	10-67
55464			X	X			X	X	Dual Positive-NOR	39	10-67

SENSE AMPLIFIERS

CIRCUIT TYPE	PROCESS FLOW						DESCRIPTION	BURN-IN CIRCUIT FIGURE NO.	DATA SHEET PAGE NO.
	SNM			SNC					
	PACKAGE TYPE			PACKAGE TYPE					
	J	JA	SB	J	JA	SB			
5524		X			X		Dual Sense Amplifier, ±4 mV	40	11-3
55232		X			X		Dual Sense Amplifier, ±4 mV	40	11-3
55234		X			X		Dual Sense Amplifier, ±4 mV	40	11-3
55236			X			X	Dual Sense Amplifier/Data Register, ±2 mV	41	11-59
55237			X			X	Dual Sense Amplifier/Data Register, ±4 mV	41	11-59

TEXAS INSTRUMENTS
INCORPORATED
POST OFFICE BOX 5012 • DALLAS, TEXAS 75222

3.0 38510/MACH IV PROGRAM

The Texas Instruments 38510/MACH IV Program includes a complete procurement document encompassing general specification MIL-M-38510 and MIL-STD-883. The 38510/MACH IV Program is a realistic cost-effective supplement to JAN, offering 38510/883 screening for those device types not yet covered by JAN specifications or those JAN circuits without adequate availability. The 38510/MACH IV Program device types may be cross-referenced to JAN circuit types, class, package and finish codes on page 12-23. The 38510/MACH IV Program places major emphasis or designing and building quality and reliability into the device, realizing that no specification or screening procedure can substitute for inherent reliability. It is realized that irrespective of lot quality, there will always be some small percentage of devices that are subject to early failure ("infant mortality"). The 38510/MACH IV screening will eliminate these early failures and serve to demonstrate with a high degree of statistical confidence that the required levels of quality and reliability have in fact been built into the device. The program is backed up by factory and distributor stocking programs on standard 38510/MACH IV Class B (SNC) devices, allowing quick delivery on most popular device types.

3.1 38510/MACH IV PROCESS FLOWS (1)

MIL-STD 883		CLASS C	TI	CLASS B	CLASS A
TEST	METHOD	SNM	SNA	SNC	SNH
Pre-cap visual	2010.1	Cond B	TI defined	Cond B	Cond A
Stabilization bake	1008	24 h/150°C	24 h/150°C	24 h/150°C	24 h/150°C
Thermal shock	1011	—	—	—	15 cycles
Temperature cycle	1010	10 cycles	10 cycles	10 cycles	10 cycles
Mechanical shock	2002	—	—	—	Y_1
Centrifuge	2001	COND E; Y_1	COND E; Y_1	COND E; Y_1	COND E; Y_2, Y_1
Fine leak	1014	5×10^{-8}	5×10^{-8}	5×10^{-8}	5×10^{-8}
Gross leak	1014	Cond C	Cond C	Cond C	Cond C
Electrical test	Data sheet	—	100%	100%	100%
Burn-in at 125°C	Sect. 3.8	—	168 h	168 h	240 h
Electrical test	Data sheet	100%	100%	100%	100%
Group A-lot acceptance	Data sheet	Sect. 3.3	Sect 3.3	Sect.3.3	Sect. 3.3
Radiographic inspection	2012	—	—	—	100%
External visual	2009	3X-20X	3X-20X	3X-20X	3X-20X
Pack & ship	2009	STD	STD	STD	STD

1. Refer to TI Bulletin CB-149 for description of TEST METHODS AND CONDITIONS.

3.2 38510/MACH IV RECOMMENDED USAGE

MIL-M-38510 provides for three reliability levels of processing and screening of integrated circuits, as defined in MIL-STD-883. Class A provides for the tightest level of processing and is intended for critical applications in missiles and manned spacecraft. Class B is provided for Hi-Rel avionics applications, while Class C is intended for less critical military applications. The reliability level required is determined by the System application, as shown in the following table.

RECOMMENDED USE	TYPICAL SYSTEM APPLICATIONS	MIL-STD-883 MIL-M-38510 CLASS	38510/MACH IV CLASS
Where repair or replacement is readily accomplished and "down time" is not critical	Prototype, noncritical ground systems	Class C	SNM52XXX or SNM55XXX
Where repair or replacement is difficult or impossible and reliability is vital	Complex industrial Nonmilitary avionics (Cost effective)	–	SNA52XXX or SNA55XXX
Where repair or replacement is difficult or impossible and reliability is vital	Avionics systems space satellite	Class B	SNC52XXX or SNC55XXX
Where repair or replacement is difficult or impossible and reliability is imperative	Manned Space Program- NASA	Class A	SNH52XXX or SNH55XXX

For more information on processing levels, refer to TI Bulletin CB-149.

3.3 GROUP A CONFORMANCE

Group A conformance shall consist of the electrical parameters in the manufacturer's data sheet. If an inspection lot is made up of a collection of sublots, each sublot shall conform to Group A, as specified.

SUBGROUP	LEVEL I 38510C	LTPD (%) LEVEL II	LEVEL III 38510B	LEVEL IV 38510A
Subgroup 1 25°C, dc	5	7	5	5
Subgroup 2 High Temperature, dc	10	10	7	5
Subgroup 3 Low Temperature, dc	10	10	7	5
Subgroup 4 Dynamic and Switching Tests @ 25°C,	10	10	7	5

NOTE: Functional tests included in D.C. tests.

TEXAS INSTRUMENTS
INCORPORATED
POST OFFICE BOX 5012 • DALLAS, TEXAS 75222

3.4 CERTIFICATION

The manufacturer shall include a certificate of compliance with each shipment of parts if requested on the purchase order. This certificate shall indicate that all specified tests and requirements of this specification have been made or met, and that the lot of devices (identified by lot and/or batch number) are acceptable. The certificate shall bear the name and signature of the manufacturer's Quality Control representative, the date of acceptance or signing, and any pertinent notes as applicable.

3.5

TABLE I
MANUFACTURERS QUALIFICATION PROCEDURE

TEST	MIL-STD-883 METHOD	CONDITIONS	LTPD
Subgroup 1			
Physical Dimensions Visual and Mechanical	2008	Condition A & B	15
Subgroup 2[1]			
Solderability	2003		15
Subgroup 3[2]			
Thermal Shock	1011	Condition B	
Temperature Cycling	1010	Condition C	
Moisture Resistance	1004	Omit step 7B and Initial Conditioning	
Critical Electrical Parameters	5004	25°C, DC ·	15
Subgroup 4[2]			
Mechanical Shock	2002	Condition B	
Vibration Variable Freq.	2007	Condition A	
Constant Acceleration	2001	Condition E	
Critical Electrical Parameters	5004	25°C, DC ·	15
Subgroup 5[1]			
Lead Fatigue	2004	Condition B2	
Fine Leak	1014	Condition A, Per Para. 4.3.7 Herein	
Gross Leak	1014	Condition C, Per Para. 4.3.7 Herein	15
Subgroup 6[1]			
Salt Atmosphere	1009	Condition A, Omit Initial Conditioning	15
Subgroup 7[2]			
Storage Life	1008	150°C, 1000 Hrs. Minimum	
Critical Electrical Parameters	5004	25°C, DC ·	10
Subgroup 8[2]			
Operating Life	1005	125°C, 1000 Hrs. Minimum Return to 25°C without bias	
Critical Electrical Parameters	5004	25°C, DC ·	10
Subgroup 9[1]			
Bond Strength			10 devices not greater than 1% defective
a. Thermocompressions	2011	Condition B, D	
b. Ultrasonic	2011	Condition B, D	

1. Visual and/or hermetic end points hence electrical or visual rejects may be used. Reference MIL-STD-883, Method 5005, Para. 3.4.

2. Electrical end points only.

12

3.6

TABLE II
LOT ACCEPTANCE/PERIODIC QUALIFICATION TESTS
(GROUP B/GROUP C)

GROUP B

TEST	MIL-STD-883 METHOD	CONDITIONS	LEVEL IV 38510A	LTPD LEVEL III 38510B	LEVEL I[1] 38510C
Subgroup 1					
Physical Dimensions Visual and Mechanical	2008	Condition A	10	15	20
Subgroup 2					
Marking Permanency	2008	Condition B, para. 3.2.1			
Visual and Mechanical	2008	Condition B per applicable detail specification			
Bond Strength 3[2]	2011	Condition B or D 2 grams for Au bonds 1 gram for Al bonds	10	15	20
Subgroup 3[3]					
Solderability	2003		10	15	15
Subgroup 4[3]					
Lead Fatigue	2004	Conditions B2			
Fine Leak	1014	Conditions A or B, per para. 4.3.7 of this spec.			
Gross Leak	1014	Condition C, per para. 4.3.8 of this spec.	10	15	15

GROUP C

Subgroup 1[4]					
Thermal Shock	1011	Condition B			
Temp. Cycle	1010	Condition C			
Moisture Resistance	1004	Omit Initial Cond. & step 7B			
Critical Electrical Parameters	5004	25°C, DC	10	15	15
Subgroup 2[4]					
Mechanical Shock	2002	Condition B			
Vibration Variable Freq.	2007	Condition A			
Constant Acceleration	2001	Condition E			
Critical Electrical Parameters	5004	25°C, DC	10	15	15
Subgroup 3					
Salt Atmosphere	1009	Condition A Omit Initial Conditioning	10	15	15
Subgroup 4[4]					
High Temp. Storage	1008	150°C, 1000 Hrs.			
Critical Electrical Parameters	5004	25°C, DC	7	7	7
Subgroup 5[4]					
Operating Life Test	1005	125°C, 1000 Hrs. Minimum			
Critical Electrical Parameters		25°C, DC	5	5	5

1. Also applicable for Level II.

2. Bond strength test may be performed on samples randomly selected immediately following internal visual prior to sealing

3. See footnote 1 in Table I

4. See footnote 2 in Table I

TEXAS INSTRUMENTS
INCORPORATED
POST OFFICE BOX 5012 • DALLAS, TEXAS 75222

3.7 GROUP B/GROUP C PERIODIC DATA PLAN

All linear devices listed in section 2.0, after passing the 100% processing required by section 3.0, are then required to pass periodic Group B/Group C test as outlined in Section 3.6. Each quarter, devices are selected from each Generic family per the schedule shown below. After completion of all testing a report is complied for each family showing all tests results. These reports are available for shipment with parts when funded on purchase order. Please contact a TI Field Sales Office for pricing.

GROUP B/GROUP C SCHEDULE

GENERIC FAMILY	1Q	2Q	3Q	4Q
Op Amps	—	—	—	—
Comparators	—	—	—	—
Regulators	—	—	—	—
Memory Drivers	—	—	—	—
Sense Amps	—	—	—	—
Line Drivers	—	—	—	—
Line Receivers	—	—	—	—
Video Amps	—	—	—	—

38510/MACH IV PROCUREMENT SPECIFICATION

3.8 BURN-IN CIRCUIT GUIDE

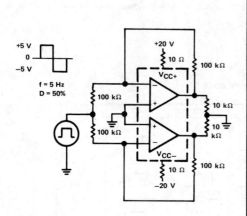

MIL-STD 883, METHOD 1015, CONDITION D
SN52L022

FIGURE 1

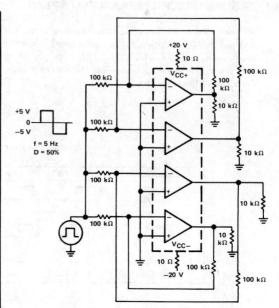

MIL-STD 883, METHOD 1015, CONDITION D
SN52L044

FIGURE 2

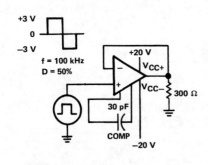

MIL-STD 883, METHOD 1015, CONDITION D

SN52101A	*SN52108A	SN52741
SN52197	SN52110	SN52748
SN52108	SN52709	SN52770
		SN52771

*For this device replace 300 Ω resistor with 1500 Ω resistor

FIGURE 3

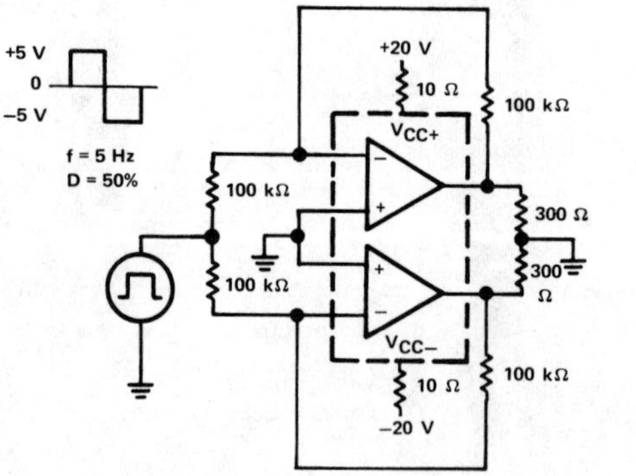

MIL-STD 883, METHOD 1015, CONDITION D
SN52558

FIGURE 4

TEXAS INSTRUMENTS
INCORPORATED
POST OFFICE BOX 5012 • DALLAS, TEXAS 75222

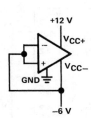

MIL-STD 883, METHOD 1015, CONDITION A
SN52702

FIGURE 5

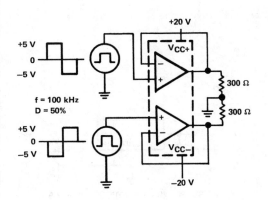

MIL-STD 883, METHOD 1015, CONDITION D
SN52747

FIGURE 6

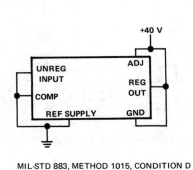

MIL-STD 883, METHOD 1015, CONDITION D
SN52104

FIGURE 7

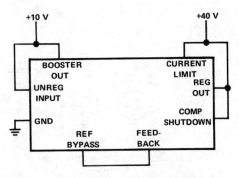

MIL-STD 883, METHOD 1015, CONDITION B
SN52105

FIGURE 8

12

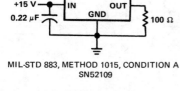

MIL-STD 883, METHOD 1015, CONDITION A
SN52109

FIGURE 9

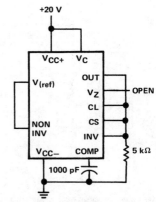

MIL-STD 883, METHOD 1015, CONDITION A
SN52723

FIGURE 10

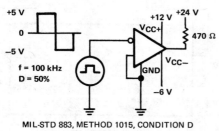

MIL-STD 883, METHOD 1015, CONDITION D
SN52106

FIGURE 11

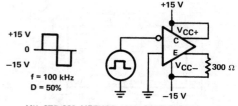

MIL-STD 883, METHOD 1015, CONDITION D
SN52111

FIGURE 12

TEXAS INSTRUMENTS
INCORPORATED
POST OFFICE BOX 5012 • DALLAS, TEXAS 75222

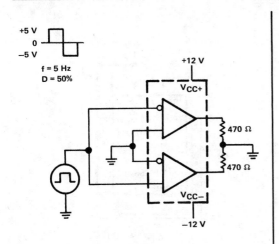

MIL-STD 883, METHOD 1015, CONDITION D
SN52506

FIGURE 13

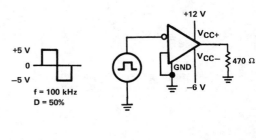

MIL-STD 883, METHOD 1015, CONDITION D
SN52510
SN52710
SN52810
FIGURE 14

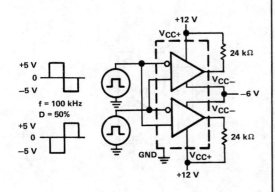

MIL-STD 883, METHOD 1015, CONDITION D
SN52514
SN52820

FIGURE 15

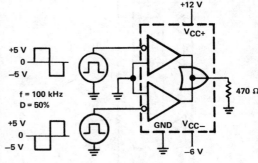

MIL—STD 883, METHOD 1015, CONDITION D
SN52711
SN52811

FIGURE 16

12

38510/MACH IV PROCUREMENT SPECIFICATION

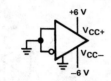

MIL-STD 883, METHOD 1015, CONDITION A
SN5510
SN5511
SN5512
SN5514

FIGURE 17

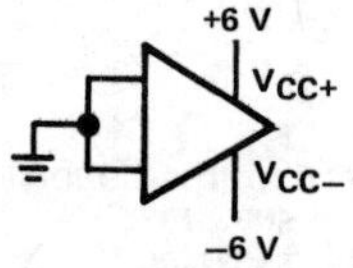

MIL-STD 883, METHOD 1015, CONDITION A
SN52733

FIGURE 18

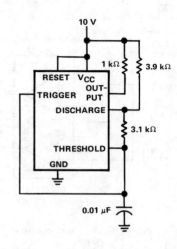

MIL-STD 883, METHOD 1015, CONDITION D
SN52555

FIGURE 19

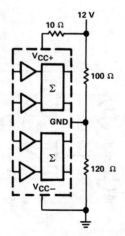

MIL-STD 883, METHOD 1015, CONDITION B
SN56502

FIGURE 20

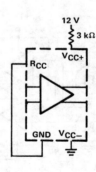

MIL-STD 883, METHOD 1015, CONDITION B
SN56514

FIGURE 21

TEXAS INSTRUMENTS
INCORPORATED
POST OFFICE BOX 5012 • DALLAS, TEXAS 75222

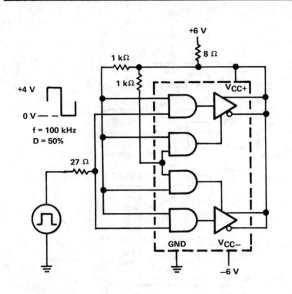

MIL-STD 883, METHOD 1015, CONDITION D
SN55109   SN55110

FIGURE 22

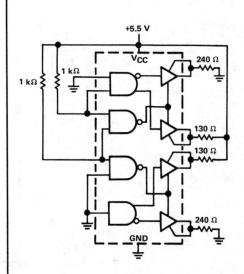

MIL-STD 883, METHOD 1015, CONDITION A
SN55113

FIGURE 23

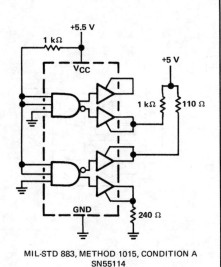

MIL-STD 883, METHOD 1015, CONDITION A
SN55114

FIGURE 24

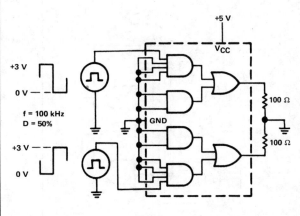

MIL-STD 883, METHOD 1015, CONDITION D
SN55121

FIGURE 25

12

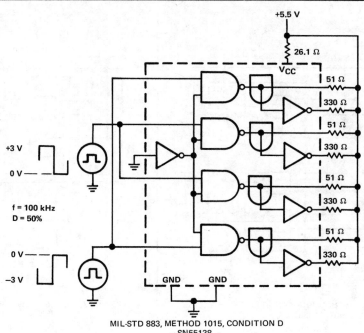

MIL-STD 883, METHOD 1015, CONDITION D
SN55138

FIGURE 26

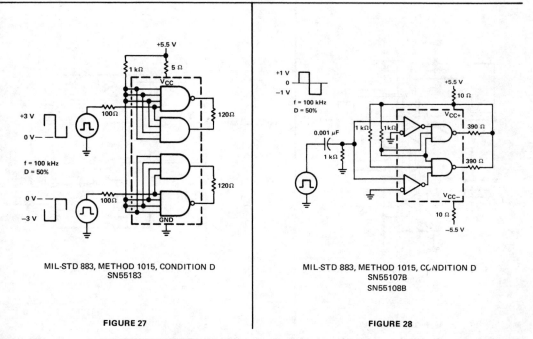

MIL-STD 883, METHOD 1015, CONDITION D
SN55183

FIGURE 27

MIL-STD 883, METHOD 1015, CONDITION D
SN55107B
SN55108B

FIGURE 28

TEXAS INSTRUMENTS
INCORPORATED
POST OFFICE BOX 5012 • DALLAS, TEXAS 75222

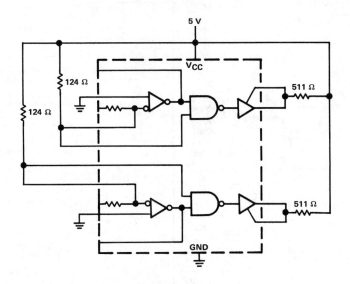

MIL-STD 883, METHOD 1015, CONDITION A
SN55115

FIGURE 29

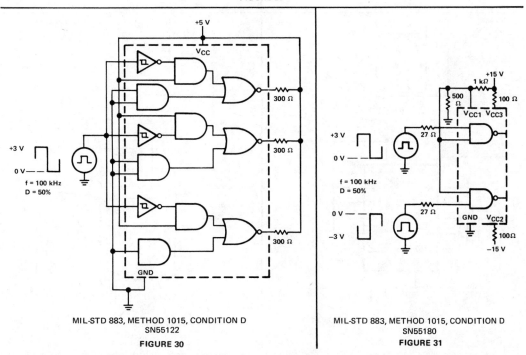

MIL-STD 883, METHOD 1015, CONDITION D
SN55122

FIGURE 30

MIL-STD 883, METHOD 1015, CONDITION D
SN55180

FIGURE 31

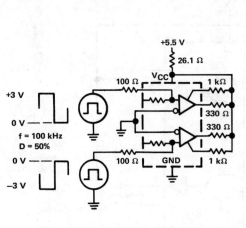

MIL-STD 883, METHOD 1015, CONDITION D
SN55182

FIGURE 32

SEQ	INPUT			
	a	b	c	d
1	H	L	L	L
2	L	H	L	L
3	L	L	H	L
4	L	L	L	H

H = 3 V, L = 0 V
Pulses applied sequentially at the rate of
100,000 pps, D = 10%.

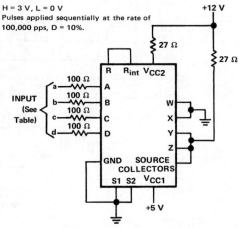

MIL-STD 883, METHOD 1015, CONDITION D
SN55325

FIGURE 33

SEQ	INPUT			
	a	b	c	d
1	H	L	L	L
2	L	H	L	L
3	L	L	H	L
4	L	L	L	H

H = 3 V, L = 0 V
Pulses applied sequentially at the rate of
100,000 pps, D = 10%.

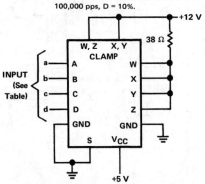

MIL-STD 883, METHOD 1015, CONDITION D
SN55326

FIGURE 34

SEQ	INPUT			
	a	b	c	d
1	H	L	L	L
2	L	H	L	L
3	L	L	H	L
4	L	L	L	H

H = 3 V, L = 0 V
Pulses applied sequentially at the rate of
100,000 pps, D = 10%.

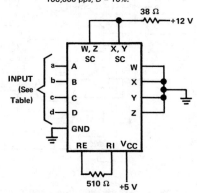

MIL-STD 883, METHOD 1015, CONDITION D
SN55327

FIGURE 35

12

TEXAS INSTRUMENTS
INCORPORATED
POST OFFICE BOX 5012 • DALLAS, TEXAS 75222

SEQ	INPUT						SEQ	INPUT				
	a	b	c	d	e		(cont.)	a	b	c	d	e
1	L	L	L	L	L		17	L	L	L	H	L
2	L	L	L	L	H		18	L	L	L	H	H
3	H	L	L	L	L		19	H	L	L	H	L
4	H	L	L	L	H		20	H	L	L	H	H
5	L	H	L	L	L		21	L	H	L	H	L
6	L	H	L	L	H		22	L	H	L	H	H
7	H	H	L	L	L		23	H	H	L	H	L
8	H	H	L	L	H		24	H	H	L	H	H
9	L	L	H	L	L		25	L	L	H	H	L
10	L	L	H	L	H		26	L	L	H	H	H
11	H	L	H	L	L		27	H	L	H	H	L
12	H	L	H	L	H		28	H	L	H	H	H
13	L	H	H	L	L		29	L	H	H	H	L
14	L	H	H	L	H		30	L	H	H	H	H
15	H	H	H	L	L		31	H	H	H	H	L
16	H	H	H	L	H		32	H	H	H	H	H

H = 3 V, L = 0 V

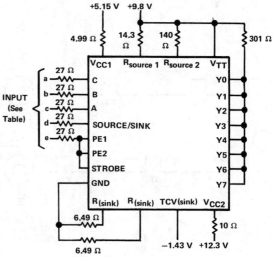

MIL-STD 883, METHOD 1015, CONDITION D
SN55329

FIGURE 36

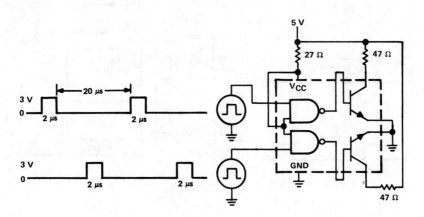

MIL-STD 883, METHOD 1015, CONDITION D
SN55450B
SN55460

FIGURE 37

12

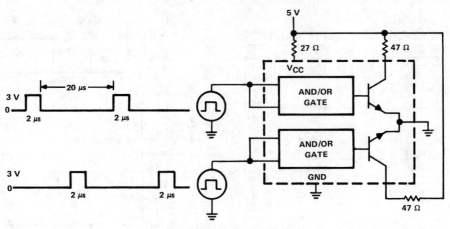

MIL-STD 883, METHOD 1015, CONDITION D

SN55451B	SN55453B
SN55461	SN55463

FIGURE 38

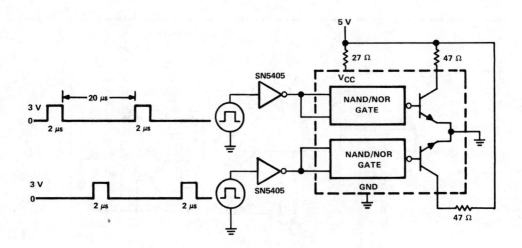

MIL-STD 883, METHOD 1015, CONDITION D

SN55452B	SN55454B
SN55462	SN55464

FIGURE 39

12

TEXAS INSTRUMENTS
INCORPORATED
POST OFFICE BOX 5012 • DALLAS, TEXAS 75222

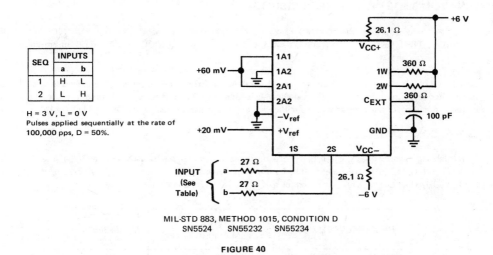

SEQ	INPUTS	
	a	b
1	H	L
2	L	H

H = 3 V, L = 0 V
Pulses applied sequentially at the rate of
100,000 pps, D = 50%.

MIL-STD 883, METHOD 1015, CONDITION D
SN5524   SN55232   SN55234

FIGURE 40

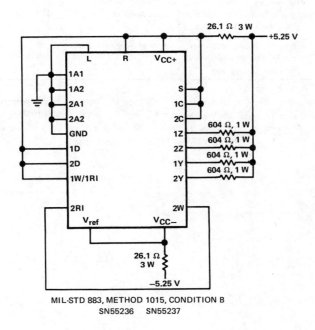

MIL-STD 883, METHOD 1015, CONDITION B
SN55236   SN55237

FIGURE 41

12

38510/MACH IV PROCUREMENT SPECIFICATION

4.0 JAN MIL-M-38510 INTEGRATED CIRCUITS

The Texas Instruments JAN MIL-M-38510 Program provides production capability for Hi-Rel JAN IC's. MIL-M-38510 and MIL-STD-883 have been fully implemented to provide JAN MICROCIRCUITS for both military original equipment and logistic requirements.

Section 4.2 provides a convenient cross reference from the JAN part number to the corresponding standard catalog part number for ease in locating the commercial equivalent. Contact a TI Field Sales Office for information on JAN types currently qualified, or planned for future qualification by Texas Instruments in both Class B and Class C.

4.1 JAN RECOMMENDED USAGE

The following table defines the reliability classifications of MIL-M-38510 JAN IC's, and the intended areas of application. MIL-M-38510 recommends that for original equipment complements the device class appropriate to the need be used, while Class B is recommended for spare parts for logistic support.

RECOMMENDED USE	TYPICAL SYSTEM APPLICATIONS	MIL-STD-883 MIL-M-38510 CLASS
Where repair or replacement is readily accomplished and "down time" is not critical	Prototype, noncritical ground systems	Class C
Where repair or replacement is difficult or impossible and reliability is vital	Avionics systems, space satellite	Class B
Where repair or replacement is difficult or impossible and reliability is imperative	Manned Space Program- NASA	Class A

When system designs utilize IC's not listed on the QPL or for which no slash sheets exist, the TI 38510/MACH IV Program may be used as the detail procurement specification. The 38510/MACH IV Progarm implements the processing and screening requirements of MIL-M-38510 and MIL-STD-883, and is intended as a supplement to the JAN slash sheets. For more information on the 38510/MACH IV Procurement Specification, refer to TI Bulletin CB-149.

TEXAS INSTRUMENTS
INCORPORATED
POST OFFICE BOX 5012 • DALLAS, TEXAS 75222

4.2 JAN INTEGRATED CIRCUITS AND TI CIRCUIT TYPE

JAN NO	CIRCUIT TYPE	JAN NO	CIRCUIT TYPE
38510/101-01BGC	38510/SNC52741L	38510/103-04BGC	38510/SNC52111L
38510/101-01CGC	38510/SNM52741L	38510/103-04CGC	38510/SNM52111L
38510/101-01BHC	38510/SNC52741FA	38510/103-04BHC	38510/SNC52111FA
38510/101-01CHC	38510/SNM52741FA	38510/103-04CHC	38510/SNM52111FA
38510/101-01BCB	38510/SNC52741JA		
38510/101-01CCB	38510/SNM52741JA	38510/104-01BAC	No equivalent
		38510/104-01CAC	No equivalent
38510/101-02BIC	38510/SNC52747L	38510/104-01BCB	38510/SNC55107AJ
38510/101-02CIC	38510/SNM52747L	38510/104-01CCB	38510/SNM55107AJ
38510/101-02BAC	38510/SNC52747FA		
38510/101-02CAC	38510/SNM52747FA	38510/104-02BAC	38510/SNC55108AFA
38510/101-02BCB	38510/SNC52747JA	38510/104-02CAC	38510/SNM55108AFA
38510/101-02CCB	38510/SNM52747JA	38510/104-02BCB	38510/SNC55108AJ
		38510/104-02CCB	38510/SNM55108AJ
38510/101-03BGC	38510/SNC52101AL		
38510/101-03CGC	38510/SNM52101AL	38510/104-03BFC	38510/SNC55114SB
38510/101-03BHC	38510/SNC52101AFA	38510/104-03CFC	38510/SNM55114SB
38510/101-03CHC	38510/SNM52101AFA	38510/104-03BEB	38510/SNC55114J
38510/101-03BCB	38510/SNC52101AJA	38510/104-03CEB	38510/SNM55114J
38510/101-03CCB	38510/SNM52101AJA		
		38510/104-04BFC	38510/SNC55115SB
38510/101-04BGC	38510/SNC52108AL	38510/104-04CFC	38510/SNM55115SB
38510/101-04CGC	38510/SNM52108AL	38510/104-04BEB	38510/SNC55115J
38510/101-04BHC	38510/SNC52108AFA	38510/104-04CEB	38510/SNM55114J
38510/101-04CHC	38510/SNM52108AFA		
38510/101-04BCB	38510/SNC52108AJA	38510/104-05BFC	38510/SNC55113SB
38510/101-04CCB	38510/SNM52108AJA	38510/104-05CFC	38510/SNM55113SB
		38510/104-05BEB	38510/SNC55113J
38510/102-01BIC	38510/SNC52723L	38510/104-05CEB	38510/SNM55113J
38510/102-01CIC	38510/SNM52723L		
38510/102-01BHC	38510/SNC52723FA	38510/105-01BIC	38510/SNC52733L
38510/102-01CHC	38510/SNM52723FA	38510/105-01CIC	38510/SNM52733L
38510/102-01BCB	38510/SNC52723J	38510/105-01BHC	38510/SNC52733FA
38510/102-01CCB	38510/SNM52723J	38510/105-01CHC	38510/SNM52733FA
		38510/105-01BCB	38510/SNC52733J
38510/103-01BGC	38510/SNC52710L	38510/105-01CCB	38510/SNM52733J
38510/103-01CGC	38510/SNM52710L		
38510/103-01BHC	38510/SNC52710FA	38510/106-01BGC	No equivalent
38510/103-01CHC	38510/SNM52710FA	38510/106-01CGC	No equivalent
38510/103-01BCB	38510/SNC52710J	38510/106-01BHC	No equivalent
38510/103-01CCB	38510/SNM52710J	38510/106-01CHC	No equivalent
		38510/106-01BCB	No equivalent
38510/103-02BIC	38510/SNC52711L	38510/106-01CCB	No equivalent
38510/103-02CIC	38510/SNM52711L		
38510/103-02BHC	38510/SNC52711FA	38510/107-01BXC	38510/SNC52109LA
38510/103-02CHC	38510/SNM52711FA	38510/107-01CXC	38510/SNM52109LA
38510/103-02BCB	38510/SNC52711J	38510/107-01BYC	No equivalent
38510/103-02CCB	38510/SNM52711J	38510/107-01CYC	No equivalent
38510/103-03BGC	38510/SNC52106L		
38510/103-03CGC	38510/SNM52106L		
38510/103-03BAC	38510/SNC52106FA		
38510/103-03CAC	38510/SNM52106FA		

12

IC Sockets
and
Interconnection Panels

13

IC SOCKETS AND INTERCONNECTION PANELS

Texas Instruments lines of off-the-shelf interconnection products are designed specifically to meet the performance needs of volume commercial applications. They provide both the economy of a standard product line and performance features developed after many year's experience with custom designs. Foremost among these is our ability to selectively bond a wrought gold stripe at the contact point. No waste. Reduced cost. Reliable contacts.

Wrought Gold Contact

Plate a contact with gold and you get a better contact. More reliable, longer lasting. Increase the gold, you improve the contact. But gold is precious, so improved performance has to be costly — right? Wrong. Because now you can get the gold only where it is needed — at the point of contact.

How? With selective metallurgical bonding; a gold stripe inlay. Not porous plating, but durable wrought gold bonded to the contact by the same technology used to produce clad coins and thermostat metals.

Texas Instruments, Attleboro, Massachusetts, is the world's largest producer of these multimetal systems. We also know our way around electronics. The result? A full line of reliable, low cost, interconnection systems featuring an extra measure of gold where it's needed. Premium performance at no premium in price.

IC Sockets

Texas Instruments family of IC sockets includes every type and size in common use today, and as wide a choice of contact materials as you'll find anywhere. Choose from open or closed entry *wire-wrapped*[†] sockets, standard or low profile solder tail sockets, cable plugs, and component platforms. Sizes from 8 to 40 pins.

IC Panels

To match the industry's broadest line of IC sockets TI offers one of the industry's widest selections of off-the-shelf pin and socket panel products. Logic panels. Logic cards. Accessories. Add TI's custom design capability and wire wrapping for full service.

Additional information including pricing and delivery quotations may be obtained from your nearest TI Distributor, TI Representative, or:

> Texas Instruments Incorporated
> Connector Product Marketing
> MS 11-1
> Attleboro, Massachusetts 02703
> Telephone: (617) 22-2800
>
> TELEX: ABORA927708

[†] Registered trademark of Gardner-Denver

LOW PROFILE SOCKETS

SOLDER TAIL
C-93 SERIES GOLD CLAD CONTACTS

- Universal mounting and packaging
- Mylar anti-wicking wafer
- Stand-off tabs on base for solder flush
- Redundant contact points for low contact resistance, high reliability and repetitive insertion
- Closed entry construction

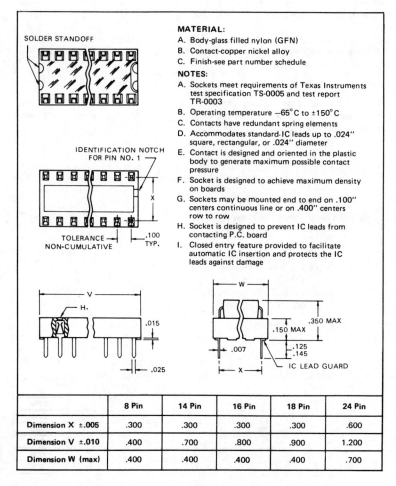

SOLDER STANDOFF

IDENTIFICATION NOTCH FOR PIN NO. 1

TOLERANCE NON-CUMULATIVE

.100 TYP.

X

V

H.

.015

.025

W

.350 MAX
.150 MAX
.007
.125
.145

X

IC LEAD GUARD

MATERIAL:
A. Body-glass filled nylon (GFN)
B. Contact-copper nickel alloy
C. Finish-see part number schedule

NOTES:
A. Sockets meet requirements of Texas Instruments test specification TS-0005 and test report TR-0003
B. Operating temperature −65°C to ±150°C
C. Contacts have redundant spring elements
D. Accommodates standard IC leads up to .024" square, rectangular, or .024" diameter
E. Contact is designed and oriented in the plastic body to generate maximum possible contact pressure
F. Socket is designed to achieve maximum density on boards
G. Sockets may be mounted end to end on .100" centers continuous line or on .400" centers row to row
H. Socket is designed to prevent IC leads from contacting P.C. board
I. Closed entry feature provided to facilitate automatic IC insertion and protects the IC leads against damage

	8 Pin	14 Pin	16 Pin	18 Pin	24 Pin
Dimension X ±.005	.300	.300	.300	.300	.600
Dimension V ±.010	.400	.700	.800	.900	1.200
Dimension W (max)	.400	.400	.400	.400	.700

PART NO. SCHEDULE

BLACK BODY	
Pins	
8	C930802
14	C931402
16	C931602
18	C931802
24	C932402

WHITE BODY	
Pins	
8	C930803
14	C931403
16	C931603
18	C931803
24	C932403

CONTACT FINISH
100 microinch min. gold stripe inlay

13

STANDARD PROFILE SOCKET

WIRE WRAP
C-82 SERIES PLATED CONTACTS • C-92 SERIES GOLD CLAD CONTACTS

SOLDER TAIL
C-81 SERIES PLATED CONTACTS • C-91 SERIES GOLD CLAD CONTACTS

- Designed for low cost, reliable, high density production packaging
- Universal mounting and packaging capabilities
- 8 to 40 pin lead configurations
- Contacts accommodate .015" through .024" rectangular or round dual-in-line leads
- Wire wrap posts held to true position of .015" providing a true position of .020" on boards for efficient automatic wire wrapping

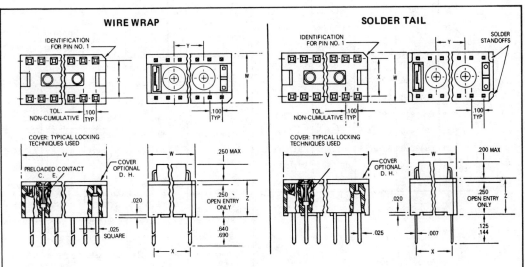

MATERIAL:

A. Body-glass filled nylon (GFN)

B. Contact-phosphor bronze per QQ-B-750 (C-81) copper nickel alloy (C-91)

C. Finish-see part number schedule

NOTES:

A. Sockets meet requirements of Texas Instruments test specification TS-0003 and test report TR-0001

B. Contacts are replaceable

C. Contacts have redundant spring elements

D. Cover is removeable

E. Contact is designed and oriented in the plastic body to generate maximum possible contact pressure

F. Operating temperature −65°C to +150°C

G. Sockets are designed to achieve maximum density on boards and may be mounted .400" row to row centers

H. Closed entry cover is provided to facilitate automatic insertion and protect IC leads against damage

I. Accommodates standard IC leads up to .024" square, rectangular or .024" dia.

J. Contact retention − 7 lbs. min.

K. Sockets are capable of being automatically or semiautomatically wire wrapped

	8 Pin	14 Pin	16 Pin	18 Pin	24 Pin	28 Pin	36 Pin	40 Pin
Dimension V ±.010	.465	.765	.865	.965	1.280	1.480	1.845	2.045
Dimension W (max)	.400	.400	.400	.400	.700	.700	.700	.700
Dimension X ±.005	.300	.300	.300	.300	.600	.600	.600	.600
Dimension Y ±.010	NA	.400	.400	.400	.500	.500	.800	1.000
Dimension Z ±.005	.280	.280	.280	.280	.280	:280	.325	.325

13

WIRE WRAP

Contact Finish	Pins	OPEN ENTRY Black Body	OPEN ENTRY White Body	CLOSED ENTRY Black Cover	CLOSED ENTRY White Cover
Series **C-81** 200-400 microinch min tin per MIL-T-10727	8	C810854	C810855	C810804	C810805
	14	C811454	C811455	C811404	C811405
	16	C811654	C811655	C811604	C811605
	18	C811854	C811855	C811804	C811805
	24	C812454	C812455	C812404	C812405
	28	C812854	C812855	C812804	C812805
	36			C813604	C813605
	40			C814004	C814005
Series **C-91** 50 microinch min gold stripe inlay	8	C910850	C910851	C910800	C910801
	14	C911450	C911451	C911400	C911401
	16	C911650	C911651	C911600	C911601
	18	C911850	C911851	C911800	C911801
	24	C912450	C912451	C912400	C912401
	28	C912850	C912851	C912800	C912801
	36			C913600	C913601
	40			C914000	C914001

SOLDER TAIL

Contact Finish	Pins	OPEN ENTRY Black Body	OPEN ENTRY White Body	CLOSED ENTRY Black Cover	CLOSED ENTRY White Cover
Series **C-82** 30 microinch min gold per MIL-G-45204 *over* 50 microinch min nickel per QQ-N-290	8	C820850	C820851	C820800	C820801
	14	C821450	C821451	C821400	C821401
	16	C821650	C821651	C821600	C821601
	18	C821850	C821851	C821800	C821801
	24	C822450	C822451	C822400	C822401
	28	C822850	C822851	C822800	C822801
	36			C823600	C823601
	40			C824000	C824001
Series **C-82** 50 microinch min gold per MIL-G-45204 *over* 100 microinch min nickel per QQ-N-290	8	C820852	C820851	C820802	C820803
	14	C821452	C821453	C821402	C821403
	16	C821652	C821653	C821602	C821603
	18	C821852	C821853	C821802	C821803
	24	C822452	C822453	C822402	C822403
	28	C822852	C822853	C822802	C822803
	36			C823602	C823603
	40			C824002	C824003
Series **C-82** 200-400 microinch min tin per MIL-T-10727	8	C820854	C820855	C820804	C820805
	14	C821454	C821455	C821404	C821405
	16	C821654	C821655	C821604	C821605
	18	C821854	C821855	C821804	C821805
	24	C822454	C822455	C822404	C822405
	28	C822854	C822855	C822804	C822805
	36			C823604	C823605
	40			C824004	C824005
Series **C-92** 100 microinch min gold stripe inlay	8	C920850	C920851	C920800	C920801
	14	C921450	C921451	C921400	C921401
	16	C921650	C921651	C921600	C921601
	18	C921850	C921851	C921800	C921801
	24	C922450	C922451	C922400	C922401
	28	C922850	C922851	C922800	C922801
	36			C923600	C923601
	40			C924000	C924001

13

SOCKET PANELS

STANDARD
D4 SERIES

- 180 position panel or multiples of 30 position with 14 or 16 position socket pattern
- I/O – 4 rows with 13 pins per row or 3 - 14 pin sockets
- Low cost standard hardware
- Available in 98 standard series
- Off-the-shelf availability

SELECT-A-WRAP
D1 SERIES

- 180 position panel or multiples of 30 position with 14 or 16 position socket pattern
- I/O – 2 rows with 23 pins per row or 3 - 14 pin sockets
- Low cost standard hardware – no tooling
- Available in 98 standard series
- Off-the-shelf availability
- Uncommitted ground and power pin for custom design

MULTIPURPOSE
Z3 SERIES / SELECT-A-WRAP

- Assemble your own custom panel with off-the-shelf hardware and sockets or Texas Instruments will assemble to your prints
- Holes on continuous .100 centers within rows .300 centers between rows
- Accepts 8, 14, 16, 18, 24, 28, 36, and 40 pin dual-in-line sockets, discrete component platforms and interfacing plugs
- Any pin may be soldered to power and ground with solder preform and bridging tabs

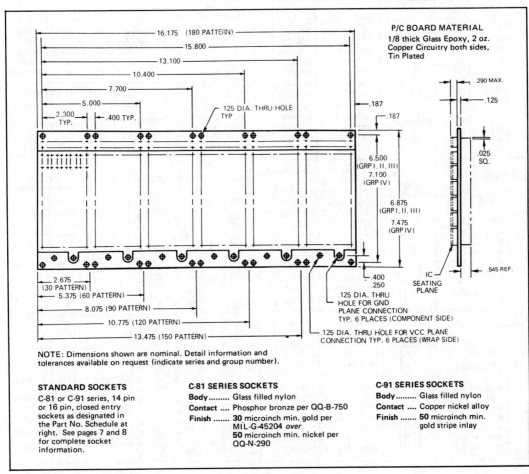

NOTE: Dimensions shown are nominal. Detail information and tolerances available on request (indicate series and group number).

STANDARD SOCKETS
C-81 or C-91 series, 14 pin or 16 pin, closed entry sockets as designated in the Part No. Schedule at right. See pages 7 and 8 for complete socket information.

C-81 SERIES SOCKETS
Body .... Glass filled nylon
Contact .... Phosphor bronze per QQ-B-750
Finish .... 30 microinch min. gold per MIL-G-45204 *over* 50 microinch min. nickel per QQ-N-290

C-91 SERIES SOCKETS
Body .... Glass filled nylon
Contact .... Copper nickel alloy
Finish .... 50 microinch min. gold stripe inlay

13

STANDARD PANEL PART NO. SCHEDULE –D4 Series

Group No.	I/O Option	Sockets Per Panel	C-81 Sockets	C-91 Sockets
Group I 14 Pin PIN 14 .... VCC PIN 7 ...... GRD	SOCKETS	30	D411211	D411231
		60	D411212	D411232
		90	D411213	D411233
		120	D411214	D411234
		150	D411215	D411235
		180	D411216	D411236
	FEED-THRU PINS	30	D411411	D411431
		60	D411412	D411432
		90	D411413	D411433
		120	D411414	D411434
		150	D411415	D411435
		180	D411416	D411436
Group II 14 Pin PIN V ...... VCC PIN G ...... GRD	SOCKETS	30	D434211	D434231
		60	D434212	D434232
		90	D434213	D434233
		120	D434214	D434234
		150	D434215	D434235
		180	D434216	D434236
	FEED-THRU PINS	30	D434411	D434431
		60	D434412	D434432
		90	D434413	D434433
		120	D434414	D434434
		150	D434415	D434435
		180	D434416	D434436.
Group III 16 Pin PIN 16 .... VCC PIN 8 ...... GRD	SOCKETS	30	D423211	D423231
		60	D423212	D423232
		90	D423213	D423233
		120	D423214	D423234
		150	D423215	D423235
		180	D423216	D423236
	FEED-THRU PINS	30	D423411	D423431
		60	D423412	D423432
		90	D423413	D423433
		120	D423414	D423434
		150	D423415	D423435
		180	D423416	D423436
Group IV 16 Pin PIN V ...... VCC PIN G ...... GRD	SOCKETS	30	D444211	D444231
		60	D444212	D444232
		90	D444213	D444233
		120	D444214	D444234
		150	D444215	D444235
		180	D444216	D444236
	FEED-THRU PINS	30	D444411	D444431
		60	D444412	D444432
		90	D444413	D444433
		120	D444414	D444434
		150	D444415	D444435
		180	D444416	D444436

SELECT-A-WRAP PANEL PART NO. SCHEDULE –D1 Series

Group No.	I/O Option	Sockets Per Panel	C-81 Sockets	C-91 Sockets
Group II 14 Pin VCC and GRD Uncommitted	SOCKETS	30	D114211	D114231
		60	D114212	D114232
		90	D114213	D114233
		120	D114214	D114234
		150	D114215	D114235
		180	D114216	D114236
	FEED-THRU PINS	30	D114311	D114331
		60	D114312	D114332
		90	D114313	D114333
		120	D114314	D114334
		150	D114315	D114335
		180	D114316	D114336
Group IV 16 Pin VCC and GRD Uncommitted	SOCKETS	30	D124211	D124231
		60	D124212	D124232
		90	D124213	D124233
		120	D124214	D124234
		150	D124215	D124235
		180	D124216	D124236
	FEED-THRU PINS	30	D124311	D124331
		60	D124312	D124332
		90	D124313	D124333
		120	D124314	D124334
		150	D124315	D124335
		180	D124316	D124336

MULTIPURPOSE PANEL PART NO. SCHEDULE –Z3 Series

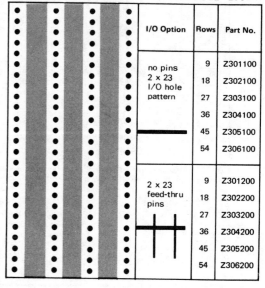

I/O Option	Rows	Part No.
no pins 2 x 23 I/O hole pattern	9	Z301100
	18	Z302100
	27	Z303100
	36	Z304100
	45	Z305100
	54	Z306100
2 x 23 feed-thru pins	9	Z301200
	18	Z302200
	27	Z303200
	36	Z304200
	45	Z305200
	54	Z306200

13

PIN PANELS

STANDARD
D7 SERIES

- Low profile — high density
- Immediate delivery
- Modular construction—1-6 modules per panel—30 patterns per module 14 or 16 pin patterns
- 4 lb minimum strip force
- 10 lb minimum pin push-out force
- Optional I/O interface

SELECT-A-WRAP
D2 SERIES

- Low cost — no tooling — standard hardware — off-the-shelf availability
- Uncommitted ground and power pin for custom design
- Optional feed-thru pins or pin-in-board terminal for I/O interface
- 4 lb minimum strip force
- 10 lb minimum push-out force

UNIVERSAL
D3 SERIES

- Prototype/production
- Meets automatic wire wrapping tolerances
- Modular construction — up to 6 modules — 9 rows per module
- Accepts 8, 14, 16, 18, 24, 28, 36, and 40 pin dual-in-line packages, discrete component platforms and interfacing plugs

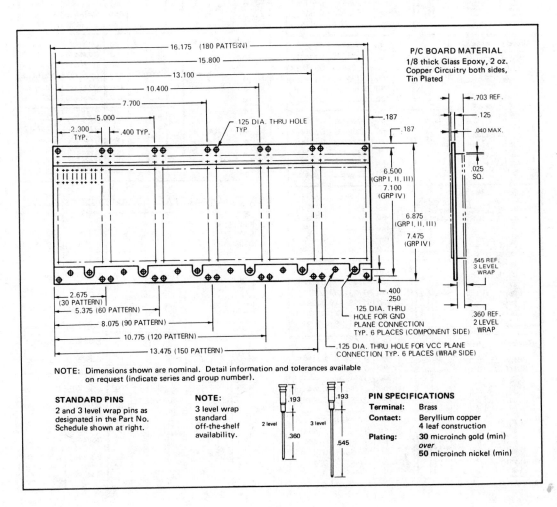

NOTE: Dimensions shown are nominal. Detail information and tolerances available on request (indicate series and group number).

STANDARD PINS
2 and 3 level wrap pins as designated in the Part No. Schedule shown at right.

NOTE:
3 level wrap standard off-the-shelf availability.

PIN SPECIFICATIONS

Terminal:	Brass
Contact:	Beryllium copper 4 leaf construction
Plating:	30 microinch gold (min) *over* 50 microinch nickel (min)

13

STANDARD PANEL PART NO. SCHEDULE —D7 Series

Group No.	I/O Option	Pos. Per Panel	2 Level Wrap	3 Level Wrap
Group I 14 Pin PIN 14 .... VCC PIN 7 ...... GRD	PINS	30	D711521	D711511
		60	D711522	D711512
		90	D711523	D711513
		120	D711524	D711514
		150	D711525	D711515
		180	D711526	D711516
	FEED-THRU PINS	30	D711421	D711411
		60	D711422	D711412
		90	D711423	D711413
		120	D711424	D711414
		150	D711425	D711415
		180	D711426	D711416
Group II 14 Pin PIN V ...... VCC PIN G ...... GRD	PINS	30	D734521	D734511
		60	D734522	D734512
		90	D734523	D734513
		120	D734524	D734514
		150	D734525	D734515
		180	D734526	D734516
	FEED-THRU PINS	30	D734421	D734411
		60	D734422	D734412
		90	D734423	D734413
		120	D734424	D734414
		150	D734425	D734415
		180	D734426	D734416
Group III 16 Pin PIN 16 .... VCC PIN 8 ...... GRD	PINS	30	D723521	D723511
		60	D723522	D723512
		90	D723523	D723513
		120	D723524	D723514
		150	D723525	D723515
		180	D723526	D723516
	FEED-THRU PINS	30	D723421	D723411
		60	D723422	D723412
		90	D723423	D723413
		120	D723424	D723414
		150	D723425	D723415
		180	D723426	D723416
Group IV 16 Pin PIN V ...... VCC PIN G ...... GRD	PINS	30	D744521	D744511
		60	D744522	D744512
		90	D744523	D744513
		120	D744524	D744514
		150	D744525	D744515
		180	D744526	D744516
	FEED-THRU PINS	30	D744421	D744411
		60	D744422	D744412
		90	D744423	D744413
		120	D744424	D744414
		150	D744425	D744415
		180	D744426	D744416

SELECT-A-WRAP PANEL PART NO. SCHEDULE —D2 Series

Group No.	I/O Option	Pos. Per Panel	2 Level Wrap	3 Level Wrap
Group II 14 Pin VCC and GRD Uncommitted	PINS	30	D214421	D214411
		60	D214422	D214412
		90	D214423	D214413
		120	D214424	D214414
		150	D214425	D214415
		180	D214426	D214416
	FEED-THRU PINS	30	D214321	D214311
		60	D214322	D214312
		90	D214323	D214313
		120	D214324	D214314
		150	D214325	D214315
		180	D214326	D214316
Group IV 16 Pin VCC and GRD Uncommitted	PINS	30	D224421	D224411
		60	D224422	D224412
		90	D224423	D224413
		120	D224424	D224414
		150	D224425	D224415
		180	D224426	D224416
	FEED-THRU PINS	30	D224321	D224311
		60	D224322	D224312
		90	D224323	D224313
		120	D224324	D224314
		150	D224325	D224315
		180	D224326	D224316

UNIVERSAL PANEL PART NO. SCHEDULE —D3 Series

PATTERN LAYOUT Double sided board with power and ground planes connected to additional wire wrap terminations outside of contact row.	I/O Option	Rows	2 Level Wrap	3 Level Wrap
	no pins 2 x 23 I/O hole pattern	9	D381501	D381500
		18	D382501	D382500
		27	D383501	D383500
		36	D384501	D384500
		45	D385501	D385500
		54	D386501	D386500
50 contacts on .100 centers	2 x 23 feed-thru pins	9	D381401	D381400
		18	D382401	D382400
		27	D383401	D383400
		36	D384401	D384400
		45	D385401	D385400
		54	D386401	D386400

13

SOCKET CARDS

STANDARD
DO2 SERIES

- Low Cost
- 14 - 16 pin socket pattern — 60 position
- Standard ground and power pin commitment
- 8 standard designs
- Mates with dual 60 position edge connector

MULTIPURPOSE
DO SERIES/SELECT-A-WRAP

- Assemble your own custom logic cards with off-the-shelf hardware and sockets or Texas Instruments will assemble to your prints
- Accepts 8, 14, 16, 18, 24, 28, 36, and 40 pin dual-in-line packages, discrete component platforms and I/O plugs
- 60 position

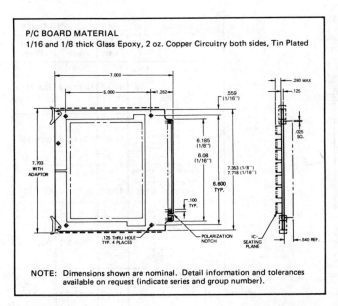

P/C BOARD MATERIAL
1/16 and 1/8 thick Glass Epoxy, 2 oz. Copper Circuitry both sides, Tin Plated

NOTE: Dimensions shown are nominal. Detail information and tolerances available on request (indicate series and group number).

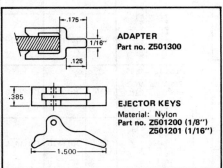

ADAPTER
Part no. Z501300

EJECTOR KEYS
Material: Nylon
Part no. Z501200 (1/8")
        Z501201 (1/16")

DO Series
MULTIPURPOSE CARD PART NO. SCHEDULE

I/O	
Board Thk.	Part No.
1/16"	Z012510
1/8"	Z011510

DO2 Series
STANDARD CARD PART NO. SCHEDULE

Group No.	Board Thk.	C-81 Sockets	C-91 Sockets
Group I 14 Pin PIN 14 .... VCC PIN 7 ..... GRD	1/16"	D022110	D022130
	1/8"	D021110	D021130
Group II 14 Pin PIN V ..... VCC PIN G ..... GRD	1/16"	D022310	D022330
	1/8"	D021310	D021330
Group III 16 Pin PIN 16 .... VCC PIN 8 ..... GRD	1/16"	D022210	D022230
	1/8"	D021210	D021230
Group IV 16 Pin PIN V ..... VCC PIN G ..... GRD	1/16"	D022410	D022430
	1/8"	D021410	D021430

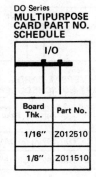

13

PIN CARDS

STANDARD
DO1 SERIES

- Low profile — high density
- 14 - 16 pin pattern — 60 position
- 2 sided P/C board with ground and voltage connected to each pattern
- 4 lb minimum strip force
- 10 lb minimum pin push-out force
- Available on 1/16" or 1/8" P/C board

UNIVERSAL
DO1 SERIES

- Universal pattern accepts wide choice of dual-in-line packages
- 20 rows of 50 contacts per row on .100 X .300 grid
- Meets all requirements for automatic wire wrapping
- Available on 1/16" or 1/8" P/C board

High retention 4-leaf beryllium copper spring contacts

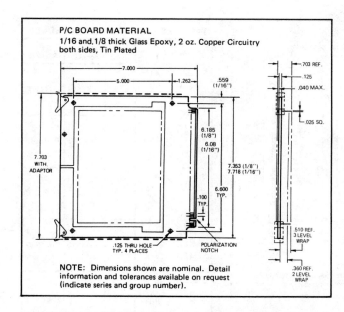

P/C BOARD MATERIAL
1/16 and 1/8 thick Glass Epoxy, 2 oz. Copper Circuitry both sides, Tin Plated

NOTE: Dimensions shown are nominal. Detail information and tolerances available on request (indicate series and group number).

UNIVERSAL PATTERN LAYOUT

Double sided board with power and ground planes connected to additional wire wrap terminations outside of contact row.

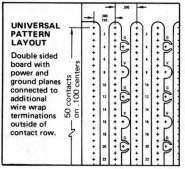

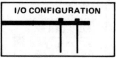

I/O CONFIGURATION

DO1 Series
UNIVERSAL CARD PART NO. SCHEDULE

Board Thk.	2 Level Wrap	3 Level Wrap
1/16"	D012520	D012510
1/8"	D011520	D011510

DO1 Series
STANDARD CARD PART NO. SCHEDULE

Group No.	Board Thk.	2 Level Wrap	3 Level Wrap
Group 1 14 Pin PIN 14 .... VCC PIN 7 ..... GRD	1/16"	D012120	D012110
	1/8"	D011120	D011110
Group II 14 Pin PIN V ..... VCC PIN G ..... GRD	1/16"	D012320	D012310
	1/8"	D011320	D011310
Group III 16 Pin PIN 16 .... VCC PIN 8 ..... GRD	1/16"	D012220	D012210
	1/8"	D011220	D011210
Group IV 16 Pin PIN V ..... VCC PIN G ..... GRD	1/16"	D012420	D012410
	1/8"	D011420	D011410

13